MW01092228

Composite Materials for Aircraft Structures

Second Edition

Composite Materials for Aircraft Structures

Second Edition

Alan Baker
Cooperative Research Centre for Advanced Composite Structures, and Defence Science and Technology Organisation, Department of Defence, Australia

Stuart Dutton
Cooperative Research Centre for Advanced Composite Structures

Donald Kelly
University of New South Wales

EDUCATION SERIES
Joseph A. Schetz
Series Editor-in-Chief
Virginia Polytechnic Institute and State University
Blacksburg, Virginia

Published by
American Institute of Aeronautics and Astronautics, Inc.
1801 Alexander Bell Drive, Reston, VA 20191-4344

American Institute of Aeronautics and Astronautics, Inc., Reston, Virginia

Baker, A. A. (Alan A.)
  Composite materials for aircraft structures / Alan Baker, Stuart
  Dutton, and Donald Kelly— 2nd ed.
    p. cm. — (Education series)
  Rev. ed. of: Composite materials for aircraft structures / edited
  by B. C. Hoskin and A. A. Baker.
  ISBN 1-56347-540-5
  1. Airplanes–Materials. 2. Compsite materials.   I. Durron,
Stuart. II. Kelly, Donald, Donald (Donald W.) III. Title. IV. Series: AIAA
education series.

  TL699.C57B35 2004
  629.134—dc22   200401219

Data and information appearing in this book are for informational purposes only. AIAA is
not responsible for any injury or damage resulting from use or reliance, nor does AIAA
warrant that use or reliance will be free from privately owned rights.

Foreword

This Second Edition of *Composite Materials for Aircraft Structures* edited by Alan Baker, Stuart Dutton and Donald Kelly is an updated, comprehensive treatment of a stimulating and challenging subject in the aerospace field with ever increasing importance. The First Edition has proven to be a valuable part of the AIAA Education Book Series, and we are delighted to welcome this new edition to the series. The lead editor of the First Edition, Brian Hoskin, has since passed away, but the new editorial team has done an admirable job of maintaining the high standards of the earlier book. The Second Edition features considerable new and updated material, and there are now 16 chapters and an appendix. The evolution of this edition is traced in the Preface.

The AIAA Education Series aims to cover a very broad range of topics in the general aerospace field, including basic theory, applications and design. A complete list of titles published in the series can be found on the last pages in this volume. The philosophy of the series is to develop textbooks that can be used in a college or university setting, instructional materials for intensive continuing education and professional development courses, and also books that can serve as the basis for independent self study for working professionals in the aerospace field. We are constantly striving to expand and upgrade the scope and content of the series, so suggestions for new topics and authors are always welcome.

JOSEPH A. SCHETZ
Editor-in-Chief
AIAA Education Series

Foreword to first edition

Composite Materials for Aircraft Structures, edited by B. C. Hoskin and A. A. Baker, is the latest addition to the AIAA Education Series inaugurated in 1984. The series represents AIAA's response to the need for textbooks and monographs in highly specialized disciplines of aeronautics and astronautics. *Composite Materials for Aircraft Structures*, just such a case in point, should prove particularly timely because the field has surged in composite applications.

Composite Materials for Aircraft Structures provides a broad introduction to virtually all aspects of the technology of composite materials for aircraft structural applications: the basic theory of fiber reinforcements; material characteristics of the commonly used fibers, resins, and composite systems; components form and manufacture; structural mechanics of composite laminates; composite joints; environmental effects; durability and damage tolerance; nondestructive inspection (NDI) and repair procedures; aircraft applications; and airworthiness considerations.

This text, expanded and updated, has been prepared from notes used in a series of lectures given at the Aeronautical Research Laboratories (ARL), Melbourne, Victoria, Australia. All lecturers were officers in either the Structures or Aircraft Materials Divisions of ARL. The table of contents gives the names of the lecturers, together with their topics.

The lectures originated with a request to ARL from the Australian Department of Aviation's Airworthiness Branch. The Director of the Aeronautical Research Laboratories, Department of Defense, Australia, has authorized publication of the expanded and updated text by AIAA.

J. S. PRZEMIENIECKI
Editor-in-Chief
AIAA Education Series

Preface

This book is a revised and extended edition to the original 1986 book *Composite Materials for Aircraft Structures*, edited by Brian Hoskin and Alan Baker of the then Aeronautical Research Laboratories in Melbourne, Australia. In 1997, staff responsible for the AIAA Education Series invited Brian and Alan to produce a sequel, but sadly Brian had passed away some years ago. However, Alan was still working full-time as Research Leader of Aerospace Composite Structures at the Australian Defence Science and Technology Organisation (DSTO) and actively engaged in the research activities of the Cooperative Research Center for Advanced Composite Structures Limited (CRC-ACS), which had been established in 1991. This was fortuitous, as Alan was able to call upon the support of a relatively large team of experts working in the CRC-ACS and its member organizations, to undertake the requested revision.

The work on the revised edition began in 1998, as a CRC-ACS education program task led by Alan and supported by the then Director, Dr Gordon Long. The task progressed slowly as most of the contributors were heavily committed, however it continued to be supported by the new CRC-ACS Chief Executive Officer (CEO), Dr Ian Mair. In order to assist Alan in what seemed to be an ever-increasing task, two co-editors joined him: Mr Stuart Dutton, Deputy CEO of the CRC-ACS, and Prof. Don Kelly, Professor at the University of New South Wales. Stuart and Don are widely respected in the Australian composites research community for their contributions to the advancement of the design and manufacture of advanced composite structures.

Whilst much has changed in composites technology since the original book was written, some topics (at the level required) have not changed that much, so they are incorporated into this book more or less unchanged. In particular, the material in the chapter on Structural Analysis by Brian Hoskin has been retained, essentially unchanged. Also, the chapter on Basic Principles, although renamed, is much the same as in the original edition. The remainder of the book is significantly different from the original, except that some of the figures have been recycled. There are now 16 chapters and an appendix, which together provide an outstanding overview and, in many areas, a very detailed exposé of the most important aspects of composite materials for aircraft structures.

Whilst this book has been produced with the support of the CRC-ACS, the efforts of each of the contributors from the CRC-ACS and its members, such as DSTO and Hawker de Havilland, are gratefully acknowledged. Finally, I wish to congratulate the three co-editors for their commitment to this task over the last few years and their success in completing this valuable text book.

MURRAY L. SCOTT
Chief Executive Officer
Cooperative Research Centre for Advanced Composite Structures
Melbourne, Australia

Contents

Contributors

Chapter	Contributors
1. **Introduction and Overview**	A. A. Baker*
2. **Basic Principles of Fiber Composite Materials**	A. A. Baker A. Rachinger*
3. **Fibers for Polymer-Matrix Composites**	A. A. Baker K. H. Leong*
4. **Polymeric Matrix Materials**	A. A. Baker J. Hodgkin[‡] M. Hou[†]
5. **Component Form and Manufacture**	A. A. Baker R. Paton[†] T. Kruckenburg[†] P. Falzon[†] I. Crouch[†] S. Dutton[†] M. Hou[†] X. Liu[†] W. Hillier[†]
6. **Structural Analysis**	B. Hoskin* D. Kelly[§] R. Li[§]
7. **Mechanical Property Measurement**	M. Bannister[†] A. A. Baker A. Garg[•] A. A. Kharibi** Y. W. Mai**

Affiliations at the time of drafting:
*DSTO, Dept of Defence, Commonwealth of Australia
[†]CRC-ACS Ltd.
[‡]Department of Molecular Science, CSIRO
[§]University of New South Wales
[•]Hawker De Havilland Aerospace Ltd.
**University of Sydney

8. **Properties of Composite Systems** — A. A. Baker, A. Mouritz[††], R. Chester[*], M. Bannister

9. **Joining of Composite Structures** — A. A. Baker, D. Kelly

10. **Repair Technology** — A. A. Baker

11. **Quality Assurance** — A. A. Baker, A. Crosky[§], R. Vodicka[*], C. Howe[¶]

12. **Aircraft Applications and Design Issues** — S. Dutton, A. A. Baker

13. **Airworthiness Considerations For Airframe Structures** — B. C. Hoskin, A. A. Baker, S. Dutton, D. Bond[‡‡], P. Callus[*]

14. **Three-Dimensionally Reinforced Preforms and Composites** — A. A. Baker, K. H. Leong, M. Bannister

15. **Smart Structures** — A. A. Baker, S. Galea[*]

16. **Knowledge-Based Engineering, Computer-Aided Design, and Finite Element Analysis** — D. Kelly, K. Wang[§]

Affiliations at the time of drafting:
[*]DSTO, Dept of Defence, Commonwealth of Australia
[†]CRC-ACS Ltd.
[‡]Department of Molecular Science, CSIRO
[§]University of New South Wales
[¶]Hawker De Havilland Aerospace Ltd.
[**]University of Sydney
[††]Royal Melbourne Institute of Technology
[‡‡]Royal Australian Air Force

1
Introduction and Overview

1.1 General

Since the first edition of this textbook[1] in 1986, the use of high-performance polymer-matrix fiber composites in aircraft structures has grown steadily, although not as dramatically as predicted at that time. This is despite the significant weight-saving and other advantages that these composites can provide.

The main reason for the slower-than-anticipated take-up is the high cost of aircraft components made of composites compared with similar structures made from metal, mainly aluminum, alloys. Other factors include the high cost of certification of new components and their relatively low resistance to mechanical damage, low through-thickness strength, and (compared with titanium alloys) temperature limitations. Thus, metals will continue to be favored for many airframe applications.

The most important polymer-matrix fiber material and the main subject of this and the previous book, Composite Materials for Aircraft Structures, is carbon fiber–reinforced epoxy (carbon/epoxy). Although the raw material costs of this and similar composites will continue to be relatively high, with continuing developments in materials, design, and manufacturing technology, their advantages over metals are increasing.

However, competition will be fierce with continuing developments in structural metals. In aluminum alloys developments include improved toughness and corrosion resistance in conventional alloys; new lightweight alloys (such as aluminum lithium); low-cost aerospace-grade castings; mechanical alloying (high-temperature alloys); and super-plastic forming. For titanium, they include use of powder preforms, casting, and super-plastic-forming/diffusion bonding.

Advanced joining techniques such as laser and friction welding, automated riveting techniques, and high-speed (numerically controlled) machining also make metallic structures more affordable.

The growth in the use of composites in the airframes in selected aircraft is illustrated in Figure 1.1. However, despite this growth, the reality is, as illustrated in Figure 1.2 for the U.S. Navy F-18 fighter, that airframes (and engines) will continue to be a mix of materials. These will include composites of various types and a range of metal alloys, the balance depending on structural and economic factors.

1

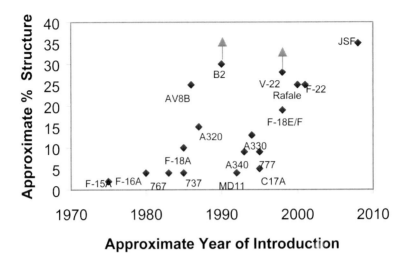

Fig. 1.1   Growth of use of advanced composites in airframe structures.

In this introductory chapter, the incentives or drivers for developing improved materials for aircraft applications are discussed. This is followed by a brief overview of fiber composites, including polymer, metal, and ceramic-matrix composites as well as hybrid metal/composite laminates. Other than polymer-matrix composites, these composites are not considered elsewhere in this book and so are discussed in this chapter for completeness.

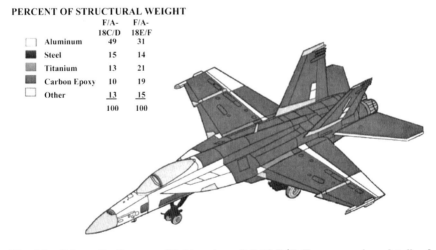

Fig. 1.2   Schematic diagram of fighter aircraft F-18 E/F. For comparison details of the structure of the earlier C/D model are also provided in the inset table.

1.2   Drivers for Improved Airframe Materials

Weight saving through increased specific strength or stiffness is a major driver for the development of materials for airframes.[2] However, as listed in Table 1.1, there are many other incentives for the introduction of a new material.

A crucial issue in changing to a new material, even when there are clear performance benefits such as weight saving to be gained, is affordability. This includes procurement (up front) cost (currently the main criterion) and through-life support cost (i.e., cost of ownership, including maintenance and repair). Thus the benefits of weight savings must be balanced against the cost. Approximate values that may be placed on saving 1 kilogram of weight on a range of aircraft types are listed in Table 1.2.

In choosing new materials for airframe applications, it is essential to ensure that there are no compromises in the levels of safety achievable with conventional alloys. Retention of high levels of residual strength in the presence of typical damage for the particular material (damage tolerance) is a critical issue. Durability, the resistance to cyclic stress or environmental degradation and damage, through the service life is also a major factor in determining through-life support costs. The rate of damage growth and tolerance to damage determine the frequency and cost of inspections and the need for repairs throughout the life of the structure.

1.3   High-Performance Fiber Composite Concepts

The fiber composite approach can provide significant improvements in specific (property/density) strength and stiffness over conventional metal alloys. As summarized in Table 1.3, the approach is to use strong, stiff fibers to reinforce a relatively weaker, less stiff matrix. Both the fiber and matrix can be a polymer, a metal, or a ceramic.

Table 1.1   Drivers for Improved Material for Aerospace Applications

• Weight Reduction	• Improved Performance
– increased range	– smoother, more aerodynamic form
– reduced fuel cost	– special aeroelastic properties
– higher pay load	– increased temperature capability
– increased maneuverability	– improved damage tolerance
	– reduced detectability
• Reduced Acquisition Cost	
– reduced fabrication cost	• Reduced Through-Life Support Cost
– improved "fly-to-buy" ratio	– resistance to fatigue and corrosion
– reduced assembly costs	– resistance to mechanical damage

Table 1.2   Approximate Actual (US$/kg) Values of Saving One Unit of Weight: Costing Based on Some Late 1980s Estimates

• small civil $80	• advanced fighter $500
• civil helicopter $80–$200	• VTOL $800
• military helicopter $400	• SST $1500
• large transport $300	• Space Shuttle $45,000
• large commercial $500	

Chapter 2 describes the basic principles (micromechanics) of fiber composite materials. As an example, to a good first approximation, the stiffness under loading in the fiber direction (unidirectional fibers) may be determined by the simple law of mixtures. This is simply a sum of the volume (or area) fraction of the fibers and the matrix multiplied by the elastic modulus. The strength estimation is similar (for a reasonably high fiber-volume fraction) but with each elastic modulus multiplied by the breaking strain of the first-failing component. In the case of carbon fiber/epoxy composites, this is generally the fiber-breaking strain. If, however, the lowest failure strain is that of the matrix, the first failure event may be the development of extensive matrix cracking, rather than total fracture. This damage may or may not be defined as failure of the composite.

However, toughness is usually much more than the sum of the toughness of each of the components because it depends also on the properties of the fiber/matrix interface. Therefore, brittle materials such as glass fibers and polyester resin, when combined, produce a tough, strong composite, most familiarly known as fiberglass, used in a wide range of structural applications.

Control of the strength of the fiber/matrix interface is of paramount importance for toughness, particularly when both the fiber and the matrix are brittle. If the interface is too strong, a crack in the matrix can propagate directly through fibers in its path. Thus it is important that the interface is able to disbond

Table 1.3   Summary of the Approach for Development of a High-Performance Fiber Composite

• Fibers	• Polymer Matrix	• Composite
– stiff/strong/brittle/low density	– low stiffness and strength ductile or brittle	– toughness through synergistic action (woodlike)
– high temperature capability	– can be polymer, metal, or ceramic	– high strength and stiffness in fiber direction, weak at angles to fiber axis
– able to carry major load as reinforcement	– transmits load to and from fiber	
– usually continuous	– forms shape and protects fiber	– tailor fiber directions to optimize properties
– oriented for principal stresses		

at a modest stress level, deflecting the crack and thereby avoiding fiber failure. However, if the interface is too weak, the composite will have unacceptably low transverse properties. As discussed in more detail in Chapter 2, several other mechanisms contribute to energy absorbed in fracture and thus to toughness, including fiber disbonding and pullout, matrix deformation, and bridging of the cracked region by unbroken fibers.

The composite structure is arranged (tailored) during manufacture of the component with the fibers orientated in various directions in sufficient concentrations to provide the required strength and stiffness (Chapter 12). For in-plane loading, this is usually achieved using a laminated or plywood type of construction consisting of layers or plies of unidirectional or bi-directional orientated fibers. This concept is illustrated in Figure 1.3 for an aircraft wing. Alternatively, the fibers may be arranged by a variety of advanced textile techniques, such as weaving, braiding, or filament winding.

Thus to obtain the desired mechanical properties, the fiber layers or plies in a laminate are arranged at angles from $0°$ to $90°$ relative to the $0°$ primary loading direction. However, certain sequence and symmetry rules must be obeyed to avoid distortion of the component after cure or under service loading (as described in Chapters 6 and 12). For simplicity the plies are most often based on combinations of $0°$, $\pm 45°$, and $90°$ orientations. The laminate is stiffest and strongest (in-plane) in the direction with the highest concentration of $0°$ fibers,

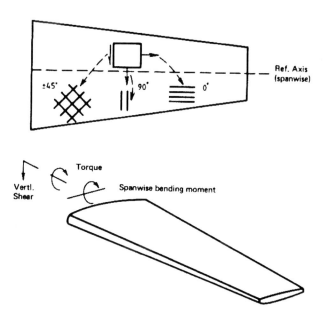

Fig. 1.3   Tailoring of fiber directions for the applied loads in a composite wing skin. Taken from Ref. 1.

but it will have much reduced strength and stiffness in other directions—the laminate is then said to be orthotropic.

When the ply configuration is made of equal numbers of plies at $0°$, $\pm 45°$, and $90°$ the in-plane mechanical properties do not vary with loading direction and the composite is then said to be quasi-isotropic. A similar situation arises with a $0° \pm 60°$ ply configuration. The quasi-isotropic ply configuration is used when in-plane loading is bi-directional. Because the quasi-isotropic configuration has a stress concentration factor (similar to that of an isotropic material), it is also used where local stresses are high, such as in a mechanical joint. However, for most cases, the quasi-isotropic configuration is an inefficient use of the composite material.

1.4   Fiber Reinforcements

As described in Chapter 3, continuous strong, stiff fibers can be made from the light elements; carbon and boron, and the compounds silicone oxide (silica and silica-based glasses), silicon carbide, and silicon nitride. Fibers can also be made from organic materials based on long-chain molecules of carbon, hydrogen, and nitrogen. Such fibers include aramid (Kevlar) fibers. Fibers may be available in the form of single large-diameter filaments or as tows (or rovings) consisting of many thousands of filaments. For example, boron fibers formed by chemical vapor deposition (CVD) are produced as single filaments with a diameter of over 100 μm. Carbon fibers, formed by pyrolysis of a polymer precursor (polyacrylonitrile; PAN), are produced as a filament diameter of about 8 μm and supplied in a tow (bundle of filaments) with up to 2.5×10^4 filaments.

Chemical Vapor deposition and other techniques can make short ultra-strong and stiff fibers called whiskers. These are filamentary single crystals having diameters in the range $1-10$ μm and length-to-diameter ratios up to 10,000. With the correct deposition techniques, whiskers can have strengths approaching the theoretical maximum of one tenth of the Young's modulus. This high level of strength results from the perfection of the crystal structure and freedom from cracklike flaws. Whiskers can be made from various materials, including SiC, Al_2O_3, C, and B_4C.

In the early 1990s, a new form of carbon called carbon nanotubes was discovered.[3] These are essentially sheets of hexagonal graphite basal plane rolled up into a tube, with a morphology determined by the way in which the sheet is rolled up. The tube wall may be made of single or double layers; typically, length varies from 10 nm to several micrometers, and even greater lengths are possible. They can be produced by a variety of processes, including arc-discharge and CVD. As may be expected, carbon in this form has exceptionally high strength and stiffness. Elastic moduli of over 1000 GPa (1 TPa) and strengths over 100 GPa are quoted, although the minute dimensions and wall geometry of the tubes makes measurement extremely difficult.

Whiskers (with some exceptions) are expensive and difficult to incorporate into composites with high degrees of orientation and alignment. So, despite their early discovery, they have not been exploited in any practical composites. Although nanotubes are also expensive and similarly difficult to process into composites, they have such attractive mechanical properties and potential for relatively cheap manufacture that many R&D programs are focused on their exploitation. However, significant technological developments will be required to make composites based on these materials practically and economically feasible.

Textile technology has been developed to produce special reinforcing fabrics from continuous fibers, mainly glass, carbon, or aramid. Small-diameter fiber tows may be woven to produce a wide range of fabrics; simple examples are plain weave or satin weave cloths. Fabrics can also be woven from two or more types of fiber, for example, with carbon fibers in the $0°$ or warp direction (the roll direction) and glass or aramid in the $90°$ weft direction.

To avoid fiber crimping (waviness) associated with weaving, a textile approach can be used in which the fibers are held in place by a knitting yarn. The resulting materials are called non-crimp fabrics, and these can contain fibers orientated at $0°$, $90°$, and $\pm 45°$ in any specified proportions. Because of the elimination of fiber waviness, composites based on non-crimp fabric show a significant improvement in compression strength compared with those based on woven materials. Stiffness in both tension and compression is also improved by around 10%.

Fiber preforms ready for matrix impregnation to form the component can be produced by several techniques including weaving, braiding, and knitting. Advanced weaving and braiding techniques are used to produce preforms with 3-D reinforcement, as described in Chapter 14. Three-dimensional weaving is extensively employed for the manufacture of carbon/carbon composites, described later.

1.5 Matrices

The matrix, which may be a polymer, metal, or ceramic, forms the shape of the component and serves the following additional functions: 1) transfers load into and out of the fibers, 2) separates the fibers to prevent failure of adjacent fibers when one fails, and 3) protects the fiber from the environment. The strength of the fiber/matrix interfacial bond is crucial in determining toughness of the composite. The interface, known as the interphase, is regarded as the third phase in the composite because the matrix structure is modified close to the fiber surface. The interface is even more complex in some fibers, notably glass fibers, which are pre-coated with a sizing agent to improve bond strength, to improve environmental durability, or simply to reduce handling damage.

Properties of the composite that are significantly affected by the properties of the matrix (matrix-dominated properties) include: 1) temperature and environmental resistance, 2) longitudinal compression strength, 3) transverse tensile strength, and 4) shear strength.

The matrix may be brittle or tough. Figure 1.4 shows the inherent toughness of some candidate materials.

Economic production requires that the techniques used for matrix introduction allow simple low-cost formation of the composite without damaging or misaligning the fibers. The simplest method is to infiltrate an aligned fiber bed with a low-viscosity liquid that is then converted by chemical reaction or by cooling to form a continuous solid matrix with the desired properties. Alternatively, single fibers, tows of fibers, or sheets of aligned fibers may be coated or intermingled with solid matrix or matrix precursor and the continuous matrix formed by flowing the coatings together (and curing if required) under heat and pressure.

1.5.1 Polymers

Chapter 4 discusses the thermosetting or thermoplastic polymers that are used for the matrix of polymer composites. Thermosetting polymers are long-chain molecules that cure by cross-linking to form a fully three-dimensional network and cannot be melted and reformed. They have the great advantage that they allow fabrication of composites at relatively low temperatures and pressures since they pass through a low-viscosity stage before polymerization and cross-

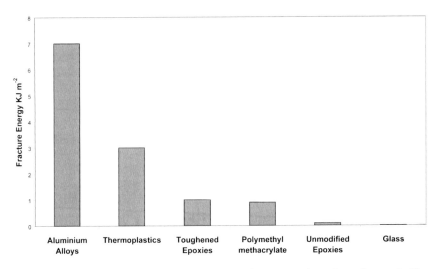

Fig. 1.4 Toughness of some materials used as matrices in advanced fiber composites.

linking. The processes used to manufacture components from thermosetting polymer composites are described in detail in Chapter 5 and include:

- Impregnating a fiber preform with liquid resin, which is then cured (resin-transfer molding; RTM). This process requires the resin to transition through a period of low viscosity (similar to light oil).
- Infusing a melted resin film into a fiber preform under pressure and then curing (resin-film infusion; RFI).
- Pre-impregnating fiber sheet bundles or tows with a "staged" liquid resin (pre-preg) for subsequent arrangement (stacking) followed by consolidation and cure under temperature and pressure.

Epoxies have excellent mechanical properties, low shrinkage and form adequate bonds to the fibers. Importantly, they pass through a low-viscosity stage during the cure, so allow the use of liquid resin-forming techniques such as RTM. Epoxy systems curing at $120\,°C$ and $180\,°C$ have respectively upper service temperatures of $100\,°C$ and $130-150\,°C$.

Bismaleimide resins (BMIs) have excellent formability and mechanical properties similar to epoxies and can operate at higher temperatures; however, they are more costly. BMI systems curing at about $200\,°C$ have upper service temperatures above $180\,°C$.

High-temperature thermosetting polymers such as polyimides, curing at around $270\,°C$, allow increases up to $300\,°C$. However, they are even more expensive and much more difficult to process.

Thermosetting materials generally have relatively low failure strains. This results in poor resistance to through-thickness stresses and mechanical impact damage that can cause delaminations (ply separations) in laminated composites. They also absorb atmospheric moisture, resulting in reduced matrix-dominated properties in the composite, such as elevated temperature shear and compressive strength. Recent developments have resulted in much tougher thermoset systems, some with improved moisture resistance, through modifications in resin chemistry or alloying with tougher polymeric systems, including rubbers and thermoplastics.

Thermoplastic polymers, linear (none-cross-linked) polymers that can be melted and reformed, are also suitable for use as matrices. High-performance thermoplastics suitable for aircraft applications include polymers such as polyetheretherketone (PEEK), application approximately to $120\,°C$; polyether-ketone (PEK), to $145\,°C$; and polyimide (thermoplastic type), to $270\,°C$. Thermoplastic polymers have much higher strains to failure because they can undergo extensive plastic deformations resulting in significantly improved impact resistance.

Because these polymers are already polymerized, they form very high viscosity liquids when melted. Thus fabrication techniques are based on processes such as resin-film (or resin-fiber) infusion and pre-preg techniques. The main approach is to coat the fibers with the resin (from a solvent solution) and then consolidate the part under high temperature and pressure. Alternatively, sheets of thermoplastic film can be layered between sheets of dry fiber or fibers of thermoplastic can be woven through the fibers and the composite consolidated by hot pressing.

Because thermoplastics absorb little moisture, they have better hot/wet property retention than thermosetting composites. However, they are generally more expensive and are more costly to fabricate because they require elevated-temperature processing. In addition, with improvements in thermosets, even the toughness advantage is being eroded. There is little doubt that thermoplastics will be used extensively in the future for aircraft structures, particularly in areas subject to mechanical damage.

1.5.2 Metals

The light metals, magnesium, aluminum, and titanium alloys (including titanium aluminides), are used to form high-performance metal-matrix composites.[4] These materials offer the possibility of higher temperature service capabilities—approximately 150 °C, 300 °C, 500 °C, and >700 °C, respectively—and have several other advantages, as discussed later, over polymer-matrix composites. However, these advantages are offset by more costly, complex, and limited fabrication techniques.

Metals often react chemically with and weaken fibers during manufacture or in service at elevated temperatures, so translation of fiber properties is often poor. The tendency for a metal to react with the fiber is termed *fiber/matrix compatibility*. Generally, because of compatibility problems, ceramic fibers such SiC, Al_2O_3, and Borsic (boron fibers coated with silicon carbide) are most suited for reinforcing metals. However, carbon fibers may be used with aluminum or magnesium matrices, provided that exposure to high temperature is minimized.

Methods based on infiltration liquid metal have many advantages for aluminum, provided damaging chemical interaction between the metal and fibers does not occur and the metal is able (or is forced under pressure) to wet the fibers. The process of squeeze casting is attractive because time in contact with liquid metal is limited, minimizing chemical interaction, and the high pressure overcomes wetting difficulties. Another major advantage of this process is that alloys other than casting alloys can be employed. If the fiber does not react readily with molten metal but is easily wetted, for example, silicon carbide fibers in aluminum, more conventional casting techniques such as investment casting may be used. Conventional casting has the major advantage that the size of the component that can be formed is much less limited and requires only simple equipment. Even carbon fibers can be used if the casting process is very rapid, particularly if the fibers are coated with a barrier layer such as silicon carbide, thus minimizing reaction with the molten metal.

Table 1.4   Comparison of Carbon/Epoxy with Table 1.1 and Conventional Aluminum Alloys for Airframe Applications

• Weight Reduction	• Acquisition Cost
– saving 15–20% compared with aluminum alloys	– *material cost increase*
– cost of reduction $60–$100 per kg	– reduction due to high conversion rate (low fly-to-buy ratio)
– reduction in number of joints	– reduction due to reduction in joints
	– *fabrication cost generally increases*
• Performance	• Repair Costs
– smoother, more aerodynamic form	– fatigue resistant, reduction
– improved aeroelastic properties	– corrosion immune, reduction
– more resistant to accoustic environment	– fretting resistant, reduction
– more resistant to service environment	– *impact sensitive, increase*
– improved fire containment	– *prone to delamination, increase*
– improved crash resistance	
– improved stealth properties	

Diffusion bonding can be employed to produce metal-matrix composites. Fibers are melt-coated, plasma is sprayed or interleaved with metal foil and then hot pressed. However, other than for the larger-diameter fibers such as boron and silicon carbide, excessive fiber breakage resulting from the high mechanical pressures used is a major problem with this approach. Additionally, if high temperatures are required to encourage metal flow, weakening of the fibers by solid-state chemical interactions is difficult to avoid.

Fibers can be coated by electrodeposition or CVD to provide a continuous reinforced matrix without the need for subsequent consolidation (pressure). These approaches are much less severe than liquid metal or diffusion bonding and may be attractive for some applications. However, the range of alloys that can be produced by this route is limited, and the high-temperature properties of the matrix may be poor.

The formation of a metal-matrix composite by hot pressing coated fibers is illustrated clearly in Figure 1.5, which shows an early metal-matrix composite silica fiber–reinforced aluminum, developed in the mid-1960s by Rolls Royce.[5] The fibers are first individually coated with aluminum and then the coated fibers are hot pressed at a temperature of around $500\,°C$ and a pressure of 60 MPa. In the example shown for illustrative purposes, only half of the sample has been consolidated.

1.5.3   Ceramics

For much higher temperatures than can be achieved with polymer or metal matrices, the options are to employ a silica-based glass; a ceramic such as silicon

 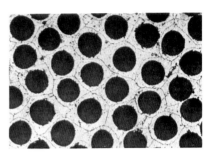

Fig. 1.5   Photograph of a (half) hot-pressed silica fiber/aluminum matrix composite, and (*right*) microstructure of consolidated side showing fibers, aluminum matrix, and boundary between original fiber coatings. Taken from Ref. 5.

carbide, silicon nitride, or alumina;[6] or a carbon matrix. These are called ceramic-matrix composites (CMCs).

In the case of the high-modulus ceramic matrices, the fibers provide little stiffening; their purpose is to increase toughness. This is achieved mainly by blunting and deflecting cracks in the matrix and contributing to increased fracture energy through the various energy-absorbing mechanisms, such as crack bridging and fiber pull-out.

Several techniques are used to form composites with ceramic matrices. These include infiltration of aligned fibers by 1) CVD, 2) impregnation of fibers with a fine powder and consolidating, and 3) impregnation of fibers with a liquid ceramic precursor, generally a polymer, and converting to ceramic at elevated temperature. The powders may be added to the aligned fibers or fiber preforms by injection molding or by sol-gel techniques. Densification of powder coatings may be achieved by hot-pressing, sintering, hot isostatic pressing, or superplastic forging. In most respects, the precursor route is the most promising for ceramics because dense matrices can be produced at low temperatures without causing fiber damage, and complex components can be formed directly.

Glass and glass-ceramic matrices are readily formed by consolidation of fiber preforms impregnated with fine powders applied from a dispersion or gel. The glass melts easily and flows between the fibers to form a continuous pore-free matrix. The procedure is similar to that adopted for thermoplastic matrix composites. In glass-ceramic matrices, the matrix may subsequently be crystallized by heat treatment, greatly enhancing performance at elevated temperatures.

Carbon matrices may also be formed by CVD of carbon from high-carbon content gases, such as methane, propane, and benzene into a fiber preform. They can also be formed by liquid phase impregnation of fibers followed by pyrolytic decomposition of a precursor with a high carbon content. Suitable precursors include phenolic resin, pitch, and tar-based materials, all of which can have over 40% yield of carbon on pyrolysis. The fibers are generally carbon and the composite called carbon/carbon. Silicon carbide fibers are also used in some applications as an alternative to carbon, particularly where improved resistance to oxidation is required.

With the resin-based route, standard polymer-matrix composite manufacturing processes, such as filament winding or braiding, can be used before pyrolysis.

The precursor route is the most efficient for making carbon matrix composites; however, multiple impregnations and pyrolysis steps are required to produce a matrix with an acceptably low porosity level. This is a slow process resulting in high component costs. The CVD process is even slower, therefore it is mainly used to fill-in fine interconnected near-surface voids in composites produced by pyrolysis. The CVD is, however, suited to manufacture of thin-wall components.

PMCs are extensively used in aerospace structures; however, carbon/epoxy is by far the most exploited so is the main focus of this book. Some current airframe applications are described in Chapter 12. Based on the drivers set out in Table 1.1, a comparison of carbon/epoxy with conventional aluminium alloys is provided in Table 1.4.

1.6   Polymer Matrix Composites

The nomenclature used in the U.S. identifies the composite in the format fiber/matrix. For example, the main composites discussed in this book are carbon fibers in an epoxy resin matrix and are referred to as carbon/epoxy or graphite/epoxy (also c/ep and gr/ep). Other common composite systems are carbon/BMI, carbon/polyimide, glass/epoxy, aramid/epoxy, and boron/epoxy. This notation can readily be expanded to specific composite systems; for example, a well-known commercial composite system, Hercules AS fibers in a 3501-6 epoxy resin matrix, is AS/3501-6. In the U.K. the terminology for carbon/epoxy is carbon fiber reinforced epoxy, or more usually, carbon fiber reinforced plastic (CFRP).

1.7   Non-polymeric Composite Systems

In this section, some of the important non-polymeric composite systems are briefly discussed.

1.7.1   Metal-Matrix Composites

Metal-matrix composites (MMCs),[4,7,8] with continuous or discontinuous fiber reinforcement have been under development for well over 30 years, but have yet to be widely exploited.

The main MMCs based on continuous fibers, and their advantages and disadvantages compared with PMCs, are listed in Table 1.5. Potential aircraft

Table 1.5   Candidate Continuous Fiber MMCs Compared with PMCs

---

- Promising Systems
- boron/aluminium alloy; silicon carbide/aluminum; alumina/aluminum
- silicon carbide/titanium; silicon carbide/titanium aluminide
- carbon/aluminum; carbon/magnesium (only for space applications)

- Advantages
- higher temperature capability, particularly titanium and titanium aluminide
- higher through-thickness strength, impact damage resistant
- higher compressive strength
- resistant to impact damage
- high electrical and thermal conductivity

- Disadvantages
- limited and costly fabrication technology
- difficult and inefficient joining technology
- limited in temperature capability by fiber/matrix chemical incompatibility
- prone to thermal fatigue: fiber/matrix expansion mismatch problem
- prone to corrosion, particularly with conducting fibers

---

applications of the MMCs include engine components, such as fan and compressor blades, shafts, and possibly discs, airframe components, such as spars and skins, and undercarriage components, such as tubes and struts.

Carbon/aluminum alloy and carbon/magnesium alloy composites are particularly attractive for satellite applications, including aerials and general structures. These MMCs combine the high specific properties and low, thermal expansion coefficients exhibited by the PMCs together with the advantages indicated in Table 1.5. For example, high conductivity serves to minimize thermal gradients, and therefore distortion, when a space structure is subjected to directional solar heating.

However, MMCs based on carbon fibers, although potentially low-cost, suffer several drawbacks for non-space applications. These include oxidation of carbon fibers from their exposed ends at elevated temperature and corrosion of the metal-matrix in wet environments due to galvanic action with exposed fibers. Other potential non-structural applications of carbon/metal composites include 1) carbon/lead and carbon/copper-tin alloys for bearings, 2) carbon/copper for high-strength conductors and marine applications, and 3) carbon/lead for battery electrodes.

The earliest developed and probably still the most exploited aluminum matrix MMC is boron/aluminum, based on CVD boron filaments. This MMC is used in the tubular structure in the Space Shuttle. In the future, boron/aluminum may be superseded by CVD silicon carbide/aluminum (or silicon carbide coated boron), which has the advantage of much greater resistance to attack by liquid aluminum. The increased resistance simplifies composite fabrication and improves fiber/matrix compatibility at elevated temperature.

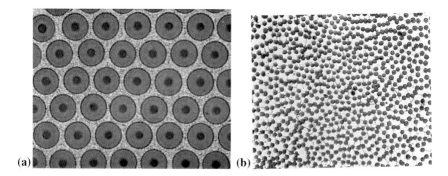

(a) (b)

Fig. 1.6 *a*) **Boron-fiber/aluminum composite, showing boron fibers around 125 μm in diameter (see Chapter 3 for fiber details);** *b*) **carbon-fiber/aluminum composite produced from aluminum-coated carbon fibers (fibers around 8 μm in diameter).**

A typical microstructure of a boron/aluminum composite is shown in Figure 1.6a, whereas, for comparison, Figure 1.6b shows the microstructure of a typical carbon/aluminum composite.

Current aluminum matrix MMCs do not offer a significant increased temperature capability over PMCs based on high-temperature matrices such as BMIs and polyimides. Thus, unless some other properties are required, such as thermal conductivity, aluminum MMCs generally have no major advantage over PMCs and are far more expensive.

In contrast, titanium alloy and titanium aluminide MMCs, based on CVD silicon-carbide-fiber reinforcement, have a large margin on temperature capability over PMCs. They also have excellent mechanical properties compared with conventional titanium alloys (100% increase in stiffness and 50% increase in strength); however, they cannot match PMCs in terms of moderate temperature properties and are much more expensive.

Titanium-based MMCs are damage tolerant, and so in addition to high-temperature applications in high-speed transport and gas-turbine engines, they are also being evaluated as a replacement for steel undercarriage components where they could prove to be cost-effective. Titanium MMCs lend themselves very well to selective reinforcement (where reinforcement is applied only in high-stress areas), as titanium is readily diffusion bonded. For example, layers of titanium/silicon carbide can be used to reinforce a high-temperature compressor disk[9] with a 70% weight saving. The large weight saving results from the elimination of much of the inner material of the disk. The resulting construction is a titanium MMC–reinforced ring. If the disk has integral blades, it is called a bling. Blings provide marked improvements in the performance of military gas-turbine engines. Titanium MMCs can also be used to reinforce titanium-skinned fan blades or for the face skins of a sandwich panel with a super-plastically formed core.

MMCs capable of operation to temperatures over 800 °C are also keenly sought for gas-turbine applications. Unfortunately, the use of available high-performance carbon or ceramic fibers is not feasible with high-temperature alloy matrices because of severe compatibility problems. Attempts to use barrier layers on fibers, such as metal oxides or carbides, to prevent chemical reaction have been unsuccessful. In addition, due to the high temperatures and mismatch in coefficients of thermal expansion, thermal fatigue would be a serious problem with these composites. A practical, but not very attractive solution because of the poor specific properties, is the use of refractory metal wire as the reinforcement. This approach has the potential to produce turbine blade materials with an additional 100 °C capability over conventional superalloys. A promising composite is based on tungsten alloy wires (W-1% ThO_2 or W-Hf-C type) in an iron-based (Fe-Cr-Al-Y) matrix. This alloy has relatively high ductility and excellent oxidation resistance requiring no protective coating. However, a coating such as TiC or TiN may be needed on the fibers to avoid attack by the matrix.

Costs of the continuous fiber MMCs are (and almost certainly will continue to be) very high compared with PMCs, and the range of sizes and shapes that can be produced is much more limited. As mentioned previously, MMCs based on aluminum alloy matrices will be strongly challenged for most elevated temperature applications by current and emerging PMCs.

An alternative to the use of "artificial" fiber reinforcement to produce high-temperature MMCs is to use directionally solidified eutectics. Here the reinforcing phase, produced by eutectic (or eutectoid) decomposition, is in the form of aligned platelets or fibers. These "natural" composites have a great advantage in that the matrix and reinforcement are in chemical equilibrium. However, surface energetics can cause the fibers or laminates to form spherical particles over long periods at elevated temperature, destroying the reinforcing effect. In addition, thermal fatigue can cause internal cracking as well as accelerating spheroidizing of the microstructure. Promising systems studied in the past include Co-Ta-C and Ni-Ta-C.

1.7.2 Particulate MMCs

Particulate MMCs should be mentioned in this overview because they may have extensive aerospace applications[10] as structural materials. In these composites, aluminum or titanium alloy-matrices are reinforced with ceramic particles, generally silicon carbide or alumina in the micron range. Because reinforcement is not directional as with fiber-reinforced MMCs, properties are essentially isotropic. The specific stiffness of aluminum silicon-carbide particulate MMCs (Al/SiC_p, where the subcript p refers to particulate) can exceed conventional aluminum alloys by around 50% at a 20% particle volume fraction. For comparison, an MMC with inclusion of silicon-carbide fibers at a similar volume fraction will increase its specific stiffness increased by around 100%.

The primary fabrication techniques are rapid-liquid-metal processes such as squeeze casting or solid-state powder processes based on hot-pressing. Particulate MMCs also have the considerable cost advantage of being formable by conventional metal-working techniques and possibly super-plastic forming and diffusion bonding in the case of titanium-matrix systems. However, because of their high wear resistance, special tools such as diamond-coated drills and diamond-impregnated grinding wheels are required for machining.

When fabricated using clean high-grade particles with low porosity and moderate particulate volume fraction, particulate MMCs have high strength, acceptable fracture toughness, and good resistance to fatigue crack propagation.

The MMCs also have high stiffness and wear resistance compared with conventional alloys. They are therefore suited to small components requiring high stiffness combined with fatigue and wear resistance.

1.7.3 Ceramic-Matrix Composites

Ceramic-matrix composites (CMCs)[6] summarized in Table 1.6, offer the main long-term promise for high-temperature applications in gas turbine engines and for high-temperature airframe structures, although there are formidable problems to be overcome. The main requirement is for lightweight blades able to operate uncooled in environments around 1400 °C.

The main limitation is the unavailability of fibers with high-elastic moduli and strength, chemical stability, and oxidation resistance at elevated temperatures. For suitable reinforcement of ceramic matrices (such as alumina and silicon carbide or silicon nitride), the fiber must have high oxidation resistance at high

Table 1.6   Candidate Matrix Composites—Advantages and Disadvantages Compared with PMCs

- Systems
- silicon carbide/glass; silicon carbide silicon nitride
- carbon/carbon; carbon/glass
- alumina/glass

- Advantages
- high to very high temperature capability (500–1500 °C)
- resistant to moisture problems
- low conductivity
- low thermal expansion
- resistant to aggressive environments

- Disadvantages
- fabrication can be costly and difficult
- joining difficult
- relatively low toughness
- matrix microcracks at low strain levels

temperature because microcracking of the ceramic allows contact between the fibers and the external environment. The fiber must also be chemically compatible with the matrix and must closely match it in its coefficient of thermal expansion. Thus, the use of similar materials for both components appears to offer the most promise, for example, silicon-carbide-fibers/silicon-carbide-matrix or alumina fibers/alumina matrix.[11] Unfortunately, available fibers either do not maintain strength at high enough temperatures or (in the case of carbon fibers, for example) have adequate oxidation resistance to provide anywhere near the full exploitation of the potential benefits.

CMCs are sometimes based on three-dimentional fiber architectures because in many (but not all) applications, the fibers are required to provide toughness, including through-thickness toughness, rather than stiffness as required in other classes of composites. Thus, for some CMCs, the relatively low fiber volume fraction resulting from this form of construction is not a major limitation.

Glass and glass-ceramic matrices are promising for applications at temperatures around 500 °C because of their excellent mechanical properties and relative ease of fabrication. In contrast to CMCs based on conventional ceramics, such as silicon carbide, the low modulus matrix can be effectively stiffened by suitable fibers and relatively high toughness achieved (typically, an increase of over 30 times the matrix glass alone). Because the matrix does not microcrack at relatively modest strain levels and temperatures, carbon fibers can be used. However, for higher-temperature applications more oxidation resistant fibers such as silicon carbide fibers must be used.

Carbon/carbon composites[12] have no significant chemical or thermal expansion compatibility problems. However, unless protected, they are also prone to rapid attack at elevated temperature in an oxidizing environment. Even where oxidation is a problem, the composites can be used where short exposures to severe applications at temperatures over 2000 °C are experienced, for example, in rocket nose-cones, nozzles, and leading edges on hypersonic wings. In the presence of reducing conditions, for example with a hypersonic engine running slightly rich on hydrogen fuel, operations for prolonged periods can be maintained. Carbon/carbon composites could be used for prolonged periods at elevated temperature, above 1600 °C, if effective oxidation-preventative barrier coatings were available. This is a topic of considerable research interest because this composite has the best structural capability of any material at the highest operation temperatures when compared on a specific strength, creep-resistance, or stiffness basis.

Some oxidation barriers include silicon carbide or silicon nitride coatings, which provide an oxidation-resistant outer layer over an inner glass layer; the glass can flow into cracks to seal the coating against oxygen penetration. This approach is called *self-healing*. An inner oxidation-resistant layer may also be used under the glass layer. The refractory layers are applied by CVD or by dip coating, from a liquid or sol-gel precursor. This coating is applied after producing, in the case of the inner layer, a thin tie (coating anchor) layer on the surface of the composite by reaction with, for example, boron or silicon.

A more sophisticated approach to self-healing is to use glass-forming silicon- and boron-based particulate materials in the carbon matrix, which reacts with oxygen to form a glass. The glass flows into cracks, sealing them off from oxygen penetration. More sophisticated approaches involve the inclusion of organic compounds in the matrix precursor materials to inhibit oxidation. If successful barrier layers could be developed, carbon/carbon could be used extensively in gas turbines and in the airframes of future hypersonic aircraft.

Finally, carbon/carbon is widely used for aircraft brake disk pads, where its combination of low weight, high-temperature capability, thermal conductivity, and excellent wear resistance results in considerable weight savings.

1.8 Hybrid Metal/PMC Composites

Structural metals, such as aluminum alloys and composites, including carbon/ epoxy, have a variety of advantages and disadvantages for airframe applications. For example, metals are prone to fatigue cracking but PMCs are not; PMCs are easily damaged by low-energy mechanical impacts but metals are not. Thus, the potential exists to combine these materials in such a way as to get the best of both materials.

One such approach is the aluminum/fiber composite hybrid laminate,[13] which consists of thin sheets of aluminum alloy bonded with a fiber-reinforced adhesive. When a crack grows through the metal, the fibers, which are highly resistant to fatigue damage, are left spanning or bridging the crack in its wake (Fig. 1.7). The result is a reduction in crack growth rate by approximately one order of magnitude and an insensitivity to crack length. However, the fibers have little influence on crack initiation and, indeed, because the hybrid composite has relatively low modulus, the increased strain in the aluminum alloy can encourage earlier crack initiation. The fibers also significantly increase the post-yield strength compared with unreinforced aluminum alloy, and the composite has a much higher damping capacity.

Disadvantages of these materials include sensitivity to blunt notches due to the inability of the fibers to withstand very high strain levels. Thus, the notch insensitivity of metals is not retained in the hybrid. Also, depending on the reinforcement used, the elastic modulus of the hybrid is generally lower than aluminum alloys, however, this is compensated for by a reduction of specific gravity of between 10–15%. Another problem is cost, which is typically 7–10 times that of standard aerospace-grade aluminum alloys.

The aluminum alloy is generally either 2024 T3 or 7475 T761, 0.2–0.4 mm thick. The composite is aramid (Kevlar) or glass fibers in an epoxy nitrile adhesive, around 0.2 mm thick for unidirectional reinforcement, or 0.25–0.35 mm thick for (glass reinforcement only) cross-ply. With aramid reinforcement, the laminate is called ARALL (aramid reinforced aluminum laminate), and with glass fiber, GLARE. Because of the sensitivity of aramid fibers to compressive

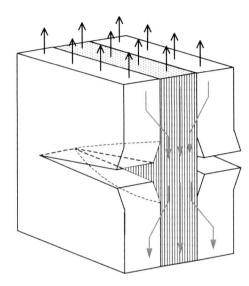

Fig. 1.7   Schematic diagram of hybrid consisting of thin (∼0.4 mm) aluminum alloy sheets bonded with an epoxy film adhesive reinforced with glass or aramid fibers. The fibers are left spanning or bridging fatigue cracks if they develop in the aluminum sheets, vastly reducing the rate of crack growth. Taken from Ref. 13.

stresses and the favorable residual strength that is produced, ARALL may be pre-stretched. This also overcomes, at a cost, the adverse residual stresses arising from the differences in thermal expansion coefficient between aramid, or glass, and aluminum. GLARE does not require pre-stretching as the high-strain glass fiber used is less susceptible to compressive stresses. Consequently, the glass fibers can be cross-plied to give crack growth resistance in two orthogonal directions as may be required for a fuselage structure. Although GLARE has a lower modulus than conventional aluminum alloys, with a reduction of around 20% (particularly with cross-plied fibers), it has the best resistance to fatigue crack growth.

Significant weight savings—20% or so—can be achieved in fatigue-prone regions such as pressurized fuselage skins and stiffeners and lower wing skins by the use of these materials. The hybrid composites are also suited to high-impact regions such as leading edges and inboard flaps and to components subject to mishandling, such as doors.

For applications requiring higher stiffness and strength, as well as a higher temperature, capability studies have been conducted[13] on hybrid laminates made of thin sheets of titanium alloy (Ti-6Al-4V) and a low-modulus carbon fiber composite. The matrix for the composite and adhesive is a thermoplastic (PEEK). This laminate is reported to have excellent resistance to fatigue crack growth as well as good blunt-notch strength.

References

[1]Hoskin, B. C., and Baker, A. A. (eds.), *Composite Materials for Aircraft Structure*, AIAA Education Series, AIAA, New York, 1986.

[2]Baker, A. A., "Development and Potential of Advanced Fibre Composites for Aerospace Applications" *Materials Forum*, Vol. 11, 1988, pp. 217–231.

[3]Thostenson, E. T., Ren, Z., and Chou, T.-W., "Advances in the Science and Technology of Carbon Nanotubes and Their Composites: A Review," *Composites Science and Technology (UK)*, Vol. 61, No. 13, Oct. 2001, pp. 1899–1912.

[4]Cline, T. W., and P. J. Withers, An Introduction to Metal-Matrix Composites, Cambridge, England, UK, 1993.

[5]Cratchley, D., Baker, A. A., and Jackson, P. W., "Mechanical Behaviour of a Fibre Reinforced Metal and Its Effect Upon Engineering Applications" *Metal-Matrix Composites*, American Society for Testing Materials STP, 1967, p. 438.

[6]Richerson, D. W., "Ceramic Matrix Composites," *Composite Materials Handbook*, edited by P. K. Mallick, Marcel Dekker, 1997.

[7]Rawal, S., "Metal-Matrix Composites for Space Application," *Journal of Metal*, Vol. 53, 2001, pp. 14–17.

[8]Baker, A. A., "Carbon Fibre Reinforced Metals—A Review of the Current Technology," *Materials Science and Engineering*, Vol. 17, 1975, pp. 177–208.

[9]Leyens, C., Kocian. F., Hausman, J., and Kaysser, W. A., "Materials and Design Concepts for High-Performance Compressor Components," *Aerospace Science and Technology*, Vol. 7, 2003, pp. 201–210.

[10]Lloyd, D. J., "Particle Reinforced Aluminum and Magnesium Matrix Composites." *International Materials Reviews*, Vol. 39, 1994, p. 1.

[11]Parlier, M., and Ritti, M. H., "State of the Art and Perspectives for Oxide/Oxide Composites," *Aerospace Technology*, Vol. 7, 2003, pp. 211–221.

[12]Buckley J. D., and Edie, D. D. (eds.), *Carbon-Carbon Materials and Composites*, Noyes, Park Ridge, NJ, 1993.

[13]Volt, A., and Willem, J. (eds.), *Fibre Metal Laminates: An Introduction*, Kluwer Academic Publishers, 2001.

Bibliography

Chawla, K. K., *Composite Materials Science and Engineering*, Springer-Verlag, New York.

Kelly, A., and Zweben, C. (eds.), *Comprehensive Composite Materials*, Elsevier, 2000.

Mallick, P. K., (ed.), *Composite Materials Handbook*, Marcel Dekker, New York, 1997.

Middleton, D. H. (ed.), *Composite Materials in Aircraft Structures*, Longmans, UK, 1990.

Niu, M. C. Y., *Composite Airframe Structures*, Comilit Press, Hong Kong, 1992.

Peel, C. J., "Advances in Materials for Aerospace," *Aeronautical Journal*, Vol. 100, 1996, pp. 487–506.

2
Basic Principles of
Fiber Composite Materials

2.1 Introduction to Fiber Composite Systems

A fiber composite material consists of a filamentary phase embedded in a continuous matrix phase. The aspect ratio (i.e., ratio of length to diameter) of the filaments may vary from about 10 to infinity (for continuous fibers). Their scale, in relation to the bulk material, may range from microscopic (e.g., 8-μm diameter carbon fibers in an epoxy matrix) to gross macroscopic (e.g., 25-mm diameter steel bars in concrete).

Composite constituents (fibers and matrices) can be conveniently classified according to their elastic moduli E and ductility. Within the composite, the fibers may, in general, be in the form of continuous fibers, discontinuous fibers, or whiskers (very fine single crystals with lengths of the order 100–1000 μm and diameters of the order 1–10 μm) and may be aligned to varying degrees or randomly orientated. This classification is depicted in Figure 2.1 for a number of common fibers and matrices; also listed are examples of composites formed from these materials.

2.2 MIcromechanical Versus Macromechanical View of Composites

Fiber composites can be studied from two points of view: micromechanics and macromechanics. Micromechanical analyses are aimed at providing an understanding of the behavior of composites, usually those with unidirectional fiber reinforcement, in terms of the properties of the fibers and matrices. Models of varying degrees of sophistication are used to simulate the microstructure of the composite and hence predict its properties (such as strength and stiffness) in terms of the properties and behavior of the constituents.

Macromechanics is the approach used to predict[1] the strength and stiffness of composite structures, as well as other properties such as distortion, on the basis of the "average" properties of the unidirectional material; namely, the longitudinal modulus E_1, transverse modulus E_2, major Poisson's ratio v_{21} and the in-plane shear modulus G_{12}, as well as the appropriate strength values. A full analysis also

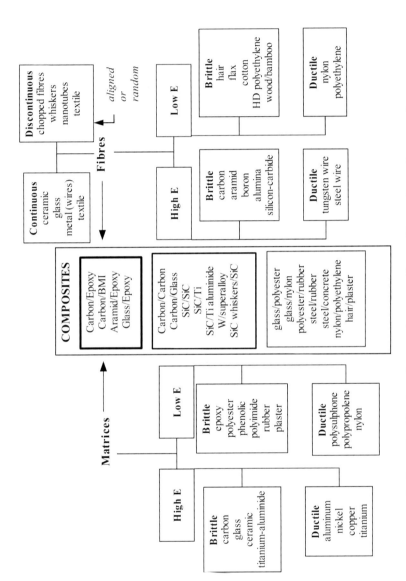

Fig. 2.1   Classification of composites according to fiber and matrix properties.

requires data on the thermal expansion coefficients of the plies in the longitudinal and transverse directions, α_1 and α_2, respectively.

Composite structural components used in aircraft are most often based on plies (sheets of unidirectional fibers or bi-directionally aligned woven fibers in a matrix) laminated together with the fibers at various orientations, as outlined in Chapter 1. Thus the properties required in the analysis are for a single ply of the composite, as described in Chapter 6. Although this analysis draws largely on data for the plies obtained from physical and mechanical testing of unidirectional composites, estimates of these properties provided by the micromechanical approach can provide useful approximate values of these properties when test data are unavailable.

2.3   Micromechanics

As already mentioned, micromechanics utilizes microscopic models of composites, in which the fibers and the matrix are separately modelled. In most simple models, the fibers are assumed to be homogeneous, linearly elastic, isotropic, regularly spaced, perfectly aligned, and of uniform length. The matrix is assumed to be homogeneous, linearly elastic, and isotropic. The fiber/matrix interface is assumed to be perfect, with no voids or disbonds.

More complex models, representing more realistic situations, may include voids, disbonds, flawed fibers (including statistical variations in flaw severity), wavy fibers, non-uniform fiber dispersions, fiber length variations, and residual stresses.

Micromechanics[2] can, itself, be approached in three ways:

(1) The *mechanics of materials* approach, which attempts to predict the behavior of simplified models of the composite material.
(2) The *theory of elasticity* approach, which is often aimed at producing upper and lower bound exact analytical or numerical solutions.
(3) The *finite-element* (F-E) approach based on two-dimensional or three-dimensional models of varying degrees of sophistication.

The most difficult aspect of the composite to model is the fiber/matrix interface, also known as the interphase, which can have a profound effect on strength and toughness. In view of this and other complexities, the F-E micromechanics approach offers by far the best prospect of success to predict strength behavior. Indeed, failure theories, described in Chapter 6, require local modelling at the micromechanical level for predicting the strength of actual components.

A common aim of both approaches is to determine the elastic constants and strengths of composites in terms of their constituent properties. As previously stated, the main elastic constants for unidirectional fiber composites are:

$$E_1 = \text{longitudinal modulus (i.e., modulus in fiber direction)}$$
$$E_2 = \text{transverse modulus}$$

v_{12} = major Poisson's ratio (i.e., ratio of contraction in the
transverse direction consequent on an extension in the
fiber direction)
G_{12} = in-plane shear modulus
α_1 = longitudinal thermal expansion coefficient
α_2 = transverse expansion coefficient

The main strength values required are:

σ_1^u = longitudinal strength (both tensile and compressive)
σ_2^u = transverse strength (both tensile and compressive)
τ_{12}^u = shear strength

where the superscript u refers to ultimate strength.

2.4 Elastic Constants

2.4.1 Mechanics of Materials Approach

The simple model used in the following analyses is a single, unidirectional
ply, or *lamina*, as depicted in Figure 2.2. Note that the representative volume
element shown, is the full thickness of the single ply and that the simplified "two-
dimensional" element is used in the following analyses. The key assumptions
used in connection with this model are indicated in Figure 2.3.

2.4.1.1 E_1 Longitudinal Modulus. The representative volume element under
an applied stress is shown in Figure 2.3a. The resultant strain ε is assumed to be
common to both the fiber and matrix. The stresses felt by the fiber, matrix, and
composite are, respectively, σ_f, σ_m, and σ_1. Taking E_f and E_m as the fiber and matrix
moduli, respectively, then:

$$\sigma_f = E_f \varepsilon_1, \quad \sigma_m = E_m \varepsilon_1, \quad \sigma_1 = E_1 \varepsilon_1 \tag{2.1}$$

The applied stress acts over a cross-sectional area A consisting of A_f, the fiber cross-
section, and A_m, the matrix cross-section. Because the fibers and matrix are acting in
parallel to carry the load:

$$\sigma_1 A = \sigma_f A_f + \sigma_m A_m \quad \text{or} \quad \sigma_1 = \sigma_f V_f + \sigma_m V_m \tag{2.2}$$

where $V_f = A_f/A$ = fiber volume fraction and $V_m = A_m/A = 1 - V_f$ = matrix
volume fraction.
Substituting equation (2.1) into equation (2.2) gives:

$$E_1 = E_f V_f + E_m V_m \tag{2.3}$$

Equation (2.3) is a "rule-of-mixtures" type of relationship that relates the
composite property to the weighted sum of the constituent properties.

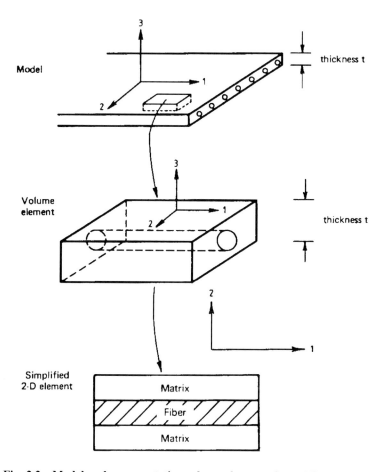

Fig. 2.2   Model and representative volume element of a unidirectional ply.

Experimental verification of equation (2.3) has been obtained for many fiber/resin systems; examples of the variation of E_1 with V_f for two glass/polyester resin systems are shown in Figure 2.4.

2.4.1.2 E_2 Transverse Modulus.   As shown in Figure 2.3b, the fiber and matrix are assumed to act in series, both carrying the same applied stress σ_2. The transverse strains for the fiber, matrix, and composite are thus, respectively:

$$> \varepsilon_f = \frac{\sigma_2}{E_f'}, \quad \varepsilon_m = \frac{\sigma_2}{E_m}, \quad \varepsilon_2 = \frac{\sigma_2}{E_2} \qquad (2.4)$$

where E_f' is the effective transverse modulus of the fiber.

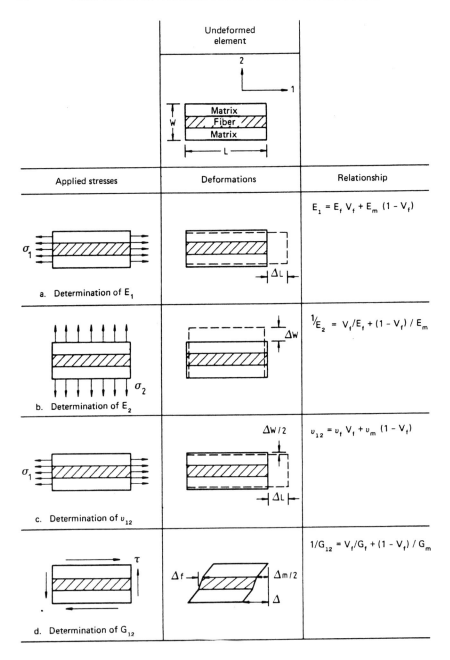

Fig. 2.3   Models for the determination of elastic constants by the "mechanics of materials" approach.

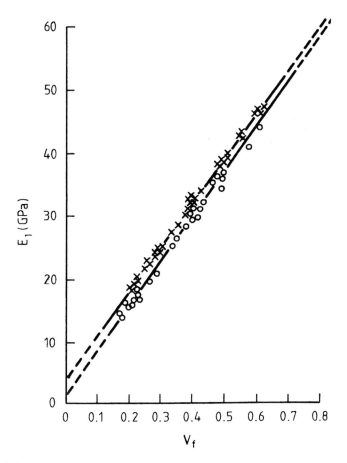

Fig. 2.4 E_1 versus fiber volume fraction V_f for two glass/polyester systems.

Deformations are additive over the width W, so that:

$$\Delta W = \Delta W_f + \Delta W_m$$

or

$$\varepsilon_2 W = \varepsilon_f(V_f W) + \varepsilon_m(V_m W) \tag{2.5}$$

Substitution of equation (2.4) into equation (2.5) yields:

$$\frac{1}{E_2} = \frac{V_f}{E'_f} + \frac{V_m}{E_m} \tag{2.6}$$

Experimental results are in reasonable agreement with equation (2.6) as shown, for example, in Figure 2.5, for a glass/polyester composite.

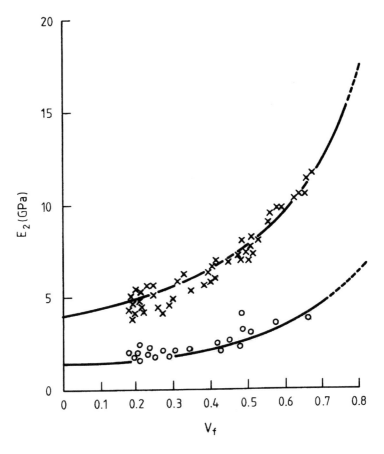

Fig. 2.5 E_2 versus V_f for two glass/polyester systems, solid lines are based on Eq. 2.6.

In contrast to glass fibers, which are isotropic, with an E_f around 72 GPa, carbon fibers are highly anisotropic (stiffness varies with direction), having E_f around 200 GPa and E_f' around 7 GPa.

Several interesting features emerge from equations (2.3) and (2.6). In high-performance composites, the fiber moduli are much greater than the resin moduli, so that, in the typical fiber/volume fraction range of 50–60%, the matrix has only a small effect upon E_1 while the fibers have only a small effect on E_2. In other words,

$$E_1 \approx E_f V_f, \quad E_2 \approx \frac{E_m}{V_m}$$

2.4.1.3 *Major Poisson's Ratio* v_{12}.   The major Poisson's ratio is defined by:

$$v_{12} = -\frac{\varepsilon_2}{\varepsilon_1} \qquad (2.7)$$

where the only applied stress is σ_1 (Fig. 2.3c).

The transverse deformation is given by

$$\Delta W = \Delta W_f + \Delta W_m$$

or

$$\varepsilon_2 W = -v_f \varepsilon_1 (V_f W) - v_m \varepsilon_1 (V_m W) \qquad (2.8)$$

Substituting for ε_2 from equation (2.7) into equation (2.8) gives the result

$$v_{12} = v_f V_f + v_m V_m \qquad (2.9)$$

which is another rule-of-mixtures expression.

2.4.1.4 G_{12} *In-Plane Shear Modulus.*   The applied shear stresses and result-ant deformations of the representative volume element are shown in Figure 2.3d. The shear stresses felt by the fiber and matrix are assumed to be equal, and the composite is assumed to behave linearly in shear (which is, in fact, not true for many systems).

The total shear deformation is given by:

$$\Delta = \gamma W$$

where γ is the shear strain of the composite. The deformation Δ consists of two additive components, so that:

$$\gamma W = \gamma_f (V_f W) + \gamma_m (V_m W) \qquad (2.10)$$

Because equal shear stresses are assumed:

$$\gamma_f = \frac{\tau}{G_f}, \quad \gamma_m = \frac{\tau}{G_m}, \quad \gamma = \tau/G_{12} \qquad (2.11)$$

substitution of equation (2.11) into equation (2.10) yields:

$$\frac{1}{G_{12}} = \frac{V_f}{G_f} + \frac{V_m}{G_m} \qquad (2.12)$$

Because G_m is much smaller than G_f, the value of G_m has the major effect on G_{12} for typical 50–60% V_f values; the situation is analogous to that for the transverse modulus E_2.

2.4.2 Refinements to Mechanics of Materials Approach for E_1 and E_2

2.4.2.1 Prediction of E_1. Equation (2.3) is considered to provide a good estimate of the longitudinal modulus E_1; however it does not allow for the triaxial stress condition in the matrix resulting from the constraint caused by the fibers. Ekvall[3] has produced a modified version of the equation to allow for this effect

$$E_1 = E_f V_f + E'_m V_m \tag{2.13}$$

where

$$E'_m = \frac{E_m}{(1 - 2v_m^2)}$$

and v_m is Poisson's ratio for the matrix material. However, the modification is not large for values of v_m of approximately 0.3.

2.4.2.2 Prediction of E_2. Equation (2.6) is considered to provide only an approximate estimate of the transverse modulus E_2. This is because, for loading in the transverse direction, biaxial effects resulting from differences in contraction in the longitudinal (fiber) direction between the fiber and the matrix become significant. The contraction difference arises because the two phases experience different strains, and this is even more marked if there is a difference in their Poisson's ratios.

The modified version of equation (2.6) produced by Ekvall[3] is

$$\frac{1}{E_2} = \frac{V_f}{E_f} + \frac{V_m}{E_m} - \frac{V_f}{E_f} \frac{[(E_f v_m/E_m) - v_f]^2}{[(V_f E_f/V_m E_m) + 1]} \tag{2.14}$$

2.4.3 Theory of Elasticity Approach to the Elastic Constants

The theory of elasticity approach to the determination of the elastic constants for composites is based on a wide variety of models and energy balance treatments. A detailed discussion of these approaches is beyond the scope of this chapter; however, some aspects are outlined here.

2.4.3.1 Energy Approach. Bounding (or variational) derivations use energy balance considerations to produce upper and lower bounds on the elastic constants. The usefulness of the results, of course, depends upon the closeness of the bounds, as demonstrated in the following example.

Considering the stressed element shown in Figure 2.3a, it can be shown[4] that the lower bound on the longitudinal modulus E_1 is given by:

$$\frac{1}{E_1} \leq \frac{V_m}{E_m} + \frac{V_f}{E_f} \tag{2.15}$$

Compare with equation (2.6), while the upper bound is given by:

$$E_1 \leq \frac{1 - v_f - 4v_f v_{12} + 2v_{12}^2}{1 - v_f - 2v_f^2} E_f V_f$$

$$+ \frac{1 - v_m - 4v_m v_{12} + 2v_{12}^2}{1 - v_m - 2v_m^2} E_m V_m \qquad (2.16)$$

where

$$v_{12} = \frac{(1 - v_m - 2v_m^2)v_f E_f V_f + (1 - v_f - 2v_f^2)v_m E_m V_m}{(1 - v_m - 2v_m^2)E_f V_f + (1 - v_f - 2v_f^2)E_m V_m}$$

It is of interest to note that if $v_{12} = v_f = v_m$, the upper bound solution becomes:

$$E_1 \leq E_f V_f + E_m V_m$$

which is the same result as equation (2.3), which implies an equality of v_f and v_m in the mechanics of materials approach.

In this example, the bounding solutions are not very useful because the bounds are too far apart, the lower bound being the transverse modulus as predicted by the mechanics of materials approach.

2.4.3.2 Direct Approaches. Here, various representative models of elastic inclusions in an elastic matrix are employed to obtain exact solutions for the stiffness properties. Typical volume elements assumed for a hexagonal and a square fiber distribution are shown in Figure 2.6. In many cases, the solutions are highly complex and of limited practical use. Regular fiber distributions do not occur in practical composites. Rather, the array is random and the analysis for regular arrays must be modified to allow for the extent of contact between fibers. This is called the *degree of contiguity* [5] and is measured by a coefficient c, which can vary from $c = 0$ for isolated fibers to $c = 1$ for contacting fibers. This situation is illustrated in Figure 2.7. The effective value of c may be determined experimentally. The degree of contiguity has more effect on E_2 and G_{12} than on E_1. These matters, and other simplifying approaches, such as the Halpin-Tsai equations, are discussed more fully in Ref. 5.

2.4.4 Expansion Constants α_1 and α_2

The coefficients of thermal expansion α_1 and α_2 for the unidirectional ply are required, for example, in the thermomechanical analysis of multidirectional laminates.

The actual values of the two constants derive from the expansion coefficients of the fibers α_f and matrix α_m, and their orientation. Differences between α_f and

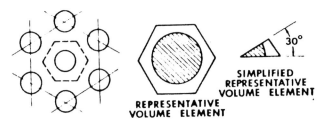

Hexagonal array and representative volume elements.

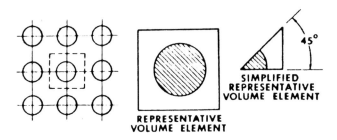

Fig. 2.6   Typical models of composites for exact elasticity solutions.

α_m give rise to internal stresses and possibly distortion when cooling laminates after manufacture and during subsequent service.

2.4.4.1 Longitudinal Expansion Coefficient α_1.

A simple estimate of α_1 can be made based on the model in Figure 2.3 used to estimate E_1. We have that:

$$\varepsilon_1 = \varepsilon_f = \varepsilon_m = \frac{\sigma_f}{E_f} + \alpha_f \Delta T = \frac{\sigma_m}{E_m} + \alpha_m \Delta T$$

where ΔT = temperature change.

Also, since there are no external stresses:

$$\sigma_f V_f = -\sigma_m(1 - V_f)$$

This leads to:

$$\alpha_1 = \frac{E_f \alpha_f V_f + E_m \alpha_m (1 - V_f)}{E_f V_f + E_m (1 - V_f)} \tag{2.17}$$

Because, in many composites, $\alpha_f \ll \alpha_m$ the α_f term can be ignored in the equation.

2.4.4.2 Transverse Expansion Coefficient α_2.

A simple rule-of-mixtures estimate of α_2 is obtained assuming the series model used in Figure 2.3. To

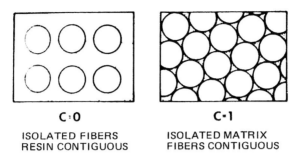

C:0   C-1

ISOLATED FIBERS   ISOLATED MATRIX
RESIN CONTIGUOUS   FIBERS CONTIGUOUS

Extremes of fiber contiguity.

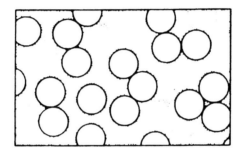

Schematic diagram of actual fiber arrangement

Fig. 2.7   Concept of contiguity used for semi-empirical-elasticity solutions.

estimate E_2 we have that

$$\alpha_2 = \alpha'_f V_f + \alpha_m(1 - V_f) \qquad (2.18)$$

where α'_f is the transverse expansion coefficient for the fiber, which often differs significantly from the longitudinal value α_f. Carbon fibers represent an extreme case of variation because the fiber is highly anisotropic. Thus, although α_f is around 0, the α'_f is around $10^{-6}°C^{-1}$. For the epoxy resin $\alpha_m = 55 \times 10^{-6}°C^{-1}$

However, this model does not account for any interaction between the fiber and matrix, due in part to ignoring differences in Poisson's ratio, and leads to the conclusion that there are no thermally induced stresses between the fiber and matrix.

If interaction is included, it can be shown[2] that:

$$\alpha_2 = \alpha'_f V_f + \alpha_m(1 - V_f) + \left(\frac{E'_f v_m - E_m v_m}{E_1}\right)(\alpha_m - \alpha_f)(1 - V_f)V_f \qquad (2.19)$$

2.5 Micromechanics Approach to Strength

2.5.1 Simple Estimate of Tensile Strength

The simplest analysis of longitudinal tensile strength assumes that all fibers break at the same stress level, at the same time, and in the same plane. Although this assumption is grossly unrealistic, it provides a useful starting point for more realistic analysis.

As with the model used to determine E_1, the fibers and matrix are assumed to experience equal strains. In advanced epoxy/matrix composites, the strain-to-failure capability of the stiff fibers ε_f^u is markedly less than that of the matrix ε_m^u, as shown in Figure 2.8a. The fibers will thus fail first, and the total load will be transferred to the matrix. Two composite failure modes can be envisaged depending on the fiber volume fraction V_f. At high V_f, the matrix alone is not capable of bearing the full load and fractures immediately after fiber fracture. The composite strength is thus given by

$$\sigma_1^u = \sigma_f^u V_f + \sigma_m' V_m \qquad (2.20)$$

where σ_f^u is the fiber failure stress and σ_m' is defined in Figure 2.8a as the stress carried by the matrix material at the fiber breaking strain. At low V_f, there is enough matrix material to carry the full load after the fibers fracture; the composite strength is then given by

$$\sigma_1^u = \sigma_m^u V_m$$

σ_1^u is plotted as a function of V_f in Figure 2.8b, where it can be readily seen that the value of V_f corresponding to a change in the failure mode is given by:

$$V_f' = \frac{(\sigma_m^u - \sigma_m')}{(\sigma_f^u + \sigma_m^u - \sigma_m')} \qquad (2.21)$$

Note also that there is a minimum volume fraction V_{min} below which composite strength is actually less than the inherent matrix strength.

$$V_{min} = \frac{(\sigma_m^u - \sigma_m')}{(\sigma_f^u - \sigma_m')} \qquad (2.22)$$

For high-strength, high-modulus fibers in relatively weak, low-modulus epoxy matrices, σ_m', V_f' and V_{min} will be quite small.

Analogous treatments can be applied to systems in which the matrix fails first, but obviously the physical characteristics and consequences of the fracture modes will be quite different. With composites having a metal matrix, consideration must be given to yielding of the matrix. Ref. 6 discusses this issue with respect to strength and other relevant mechanical properties.

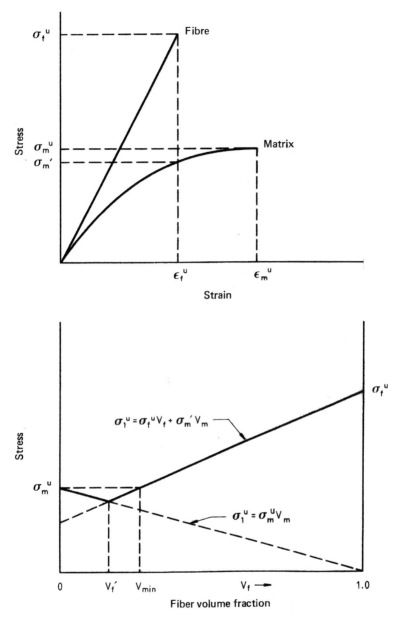

Fig. 2.8   Rule of mixtures prediction of σ_1^u for $\varepsilon_f^u < \varepsilon_m^u$.

2.5.2 Statistical Analysis of Tensile Strength

The foregoing analysis of tensile strength assumed simultaneous fracture of equal-strength fibers in one plane. In reality, the situation is much more complex because of the brittle (flaw-sensitive) nature of the fibers and the fiber/matrix interaction. These two features are discussed below.

Brittle fibers contain surface flaws or imperfections that produce "weak spots" along the fiber length. Fiber fractures will occur at these flaws at more or less random positions throughout the composite. Therefore, fracture will not occur in a single plane. In the simplest case, in which the imperfect fibers all have the same strength and the matrix is unable to grip the broken fibers, the strength of the composite would be calculated as in the previous subsection.

For brittle fibers, however, flaws vary not only in position, but also in severity. The way in which the fiber strength changes as a result of this variation in the flaw severity is shown in Figure 2.9 for a typical case. Therefore, it would be expected that fiber fractures would occur throughout a range of stress levels, up to ultimate composite failure. This is indeed the case, as shown in Figure 2.10.

Another important characteristic of composite fracture is the fiber/matrix interaction in the vicinity of a fiber fracture. Rather than becoming ineffective, a broken fiber can still contribute to composite strength because the matrix is able to transfer stress back into the fiber from the broken end, as shown in Figure 2.11. High shear stresses develop in the matrix and then decay a short distance from the break; at the same time, the tensile stress carried by the fiber increases from zero at the broken end to the full stress carried by unbroken fibers. The characteristic length over which this stress build up occurs is known as the ineffective length δ (See Fig. 2.11). Often, the term *critical transfer length* is used in this context, the critical transfer length being twice the ineffective length.

The ineffective length δ can be determined experimentally by measuring the stress required to pull fibers of various lengths from a matrix.[7]

If the fiber/matrix bond strength is low, the high shear stresses will cause fiber/matrix debonding, as shown in Figure 2.12a. It is also possible that the stress elevation felt by fibers adjacent to the fractured fiber (Figure 2.11) is sufficient to cause further fiber fractures and crack propagation through the matrix in the brittle fashion shown in Figure 2.12b. In addition to the stress concentration felt by fibers resulting from the ineffectiveness of adjacent fractured fibers near the broken ends, there is also a stress concentration associated with the crack in the matrix surrounding the fiber fracture.

If fiber/matrix debonding, crack propagation, and fiber fracture propagation are not the dominant failure mechanisms, the composite will accumulate damage under increasing stress and failure will occur by the cumulative damage mechanism outlined below and shown in Figure 2.12c.

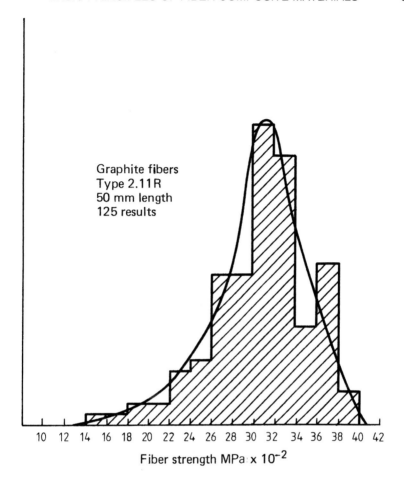

Fiber strength MPa x 10^{-2}

Fig. 2.9   Plot of number of observations versus strength for carbon fibers, showing typical strength distribution.

2.5.3   Rosen's Model of Cumulative Damage

The strength of individual fibers is dependent on the probability of finding a flaw and, therefore, is dependent on the fiber length. It has been shown that the strength/length relationship takes the form of a Weibull distribution of the form:

$$f(\sigma) = L\alpha\beta\sigma^{\beta-1}\exp(-L\alpha\sigma^{\beta})$$

where $f(\sigma)$ is the probability density function for fiber strength σ, L is the fiber length, and α and β are the material constants.

Constant α determines the position of the Weibull distribution, while constant β determines its shape. Both α and β are experimentally accessible quantities and

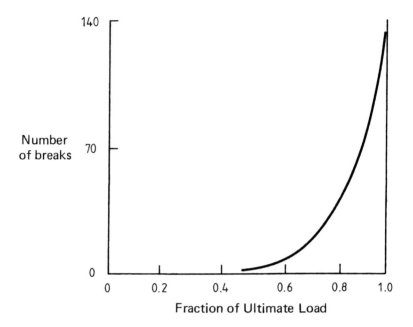

Fig. 2.10   Number of fiber fractures versus fraction of ultimate composite strength.

can be determined, for example, from a log–log plot of mean fiber strength for fibers of given lengths versus fiber length.

Daniels[8] showed that the strength of a bundle of N fibers having such a Weibull distribution can be described by a normal distribution where the mean value $\bar{\sigma}_{BL}$ is a function of fiber length:

$$\bar{\sigma}_{BL} = (L\alpha\beta)^{-1/\beta}\exp\left(\frac{-1}{\beta}\right) \tag{2.23}$$

and whose standard deviation is proportional to $N^{-1/2}$. Thus, for very large N, all of the bundles tend toward the same strength value σ_{BL}.

Rosen[9] models the composite as a chain of bundles (Figure 2.13), the length of each bundle (or chain link) being the ineffective length δ. For very large N, the strength of each bundle or chain link will be the same, and the strength of the whole chain (or composite) will be equal to the link strength, which is given by:

$$\bar{\sigma}_{B\delta} = (\delta\alpha\beta)^{-1/\beta}\exp\left(\frac{-1}{\beta}\right) \tag{2.24}$$

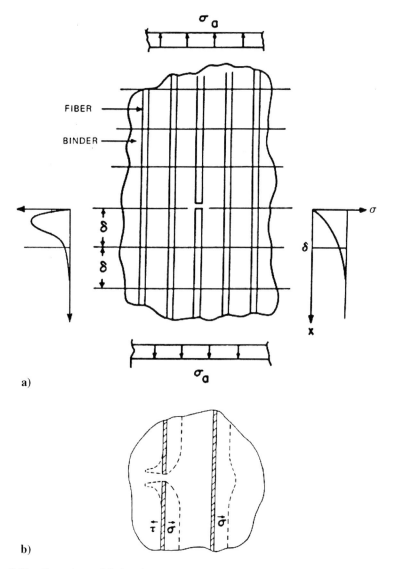

Fig. 2.11   Rosen's model showing *a)* **ineffective length at break and** *b)* **perturbation of stress in adjacent fiber.**

Thus, it is possible to compare the strengths of a bundle of "dry" fibers of length L and a composite with ineffective length δ as follows:

$$\frac{\bar{\sigma}_{B\delta}}{\bar{\sigma}_{BL}} = \left(\frac{L}{\delta}\right)^{1/\beta} \tag{2.25}$$

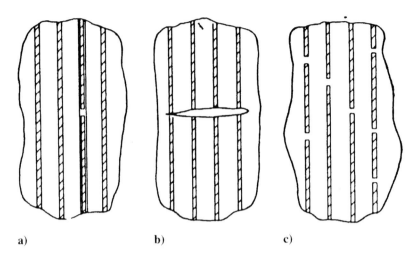

a)   b)   c)

Fig. 2.12 Possible composite tensile failure modes: *a*) **fiber bundle;** *b*) **crack;** *c*) **statistical.**

For carbon fibers in an epoxy matrix, $\beta \cong 10$ and $\delta = 10^{-2}$ mm (about a fiber diameter), so if $L = 100$ mm, then:

$$\frac{\bar{\sigma}_{B\delta}}{\bar{\sigma}_{BL}} = \left(\frac{100}{10^{-2}}\right)^{1/10} \cong 2.5$$

This is the strengthening obtained by composite action.

2.6 Simple Estimate of Compressive Strength

The previously introduced equations relating to tensile failure do not apply to compressive strength because fibers do not fail in simple compression. Rather, they fail by local buckling. The actual behavior is complicated because the stresses are influenced by residual strains in the matrix. It has been shown, for example, that glass fibers in an epoxy matrix can buckle simply after cooling down from the resin cure temperature. As may be expected, when it is assumed that the fibers act as circular columns on an elastic foundation, the wavelength of the buckling increases with the fiber diameter.

Two pure buckling modes can be envisaged (See Fig. 2.14): 1) the shear mode in which the fibers buckle in-phase and the matrix is sheared or 2) the extensional mode, in which the matrix is stretched and compressed in an out-of-phase manner. The most likely mode is that producing the lowest energy in the system. While mixed modes are possible, they require more energy than do either of the pure modes.

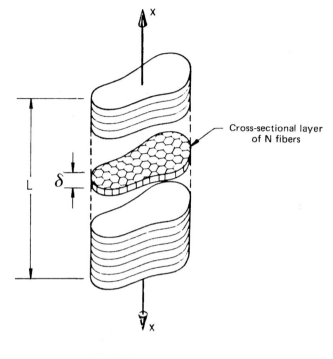

Cylindrical specimen of
n layers (n = L/δ)

Fig. 2.13   Rosen's model showing chain of fiber bundles.

Analysis of the buckling[1] is based on the energy method in which the change in strain energy of the fibers ΔU_f and of the matrix ΔU_m is equated to the work done ΔW by the external loads as the composite changes from the compressed but unbuckled state to the buckled state.

$$\Delta U_f + \Delta U_m = \Delta W \qquad (2.26)$$

In the model, the composite is considered two-dimensional, the fibers are treated as plates normal to the plane of Figure 2.15 (rather than rods), and the buckling pattern is assumed to be sinusoidal. The resulting buckling stress for the extensional mode is:

$$\sigma_{c\,\text{max}} \cong 2V_f \left[\frac{V_f E_m E_f}{3(1 - V_f)} \right]^{1/2} \qquad (2.27)$$

and for the shear mode:

$$\sigma_{c\,\text{max}} = \frac{G_m}{(1 - V_f)} \qquad (2.28)$$

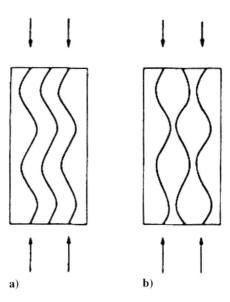

Fig. 2.14   Two pure buckling modes for unidirectional composites in compression:
a) **shear or in-phase mode;** *b*) **extension or out-of-phase mode.**

As V_f tends to zero, $\sigma_{c\,max}$ for the extensional mode tends to zero; but, as V_f tends to unity, $\sigma_{c\,max}$ for the extensional mode becomes very large compared with $\sigma_{c\,max}$ for the shear mode. Thus, the extensional mode would be expected to apply for only small V_f. Assuming $E_f \gg E_m$ and $v_m = 1/3$, with $G_m = E_m/2(1 + v_m)$, then the transition occurs at $(E_m/10E_f)^{1/3}$, or at $V_f = 10\%$ for $E_f/E_m = 100$, and at $V_f = 22\%$ for $E_f/E_m = 10$.

It has been found that these equations overpredict the compressive strength considerably. In the case of boron/epoxy, the actual compressive strength is about 63% lower than that predicted, while for other material combinations the prediction can be worse. Generally the problem is that the predicted failure strains are much higher than the matrix yield strain. As an approximation to the inelastic behavior, the theory was expanded (Ref. 10) using a gradually reducing matrix shear modulus. This gives more reasonable agreement with experimental results.

A very simple approach that appears to predict the experimental behavior in some cases is obtained by assuming failure occurs when the matrix reaches its yield stress σ_m^y. Thus, at failure:

$$\sigma_{c\,max} = \sigma_f V_f + \sigma_m^y V_m \tag{2.29}$$

where the fiber stress is given by strain compatibility as:

$$\sigma_f = \frac{\sigma_m^y E_f}{E_m} = \varepsilon_m^y E_f \tag{2.30}$$

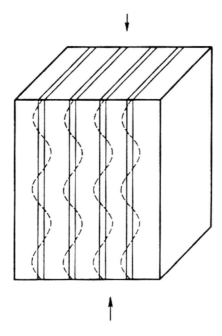

Fig. 2.15   Model for buckling fibers in a unidirectional composite.

taking ε_m^y for an epoxy resin as 0.02 and $E_f = 70$ GPa for glass fibers, then

$$\sigma_f = 0.02 \times 70\,\text{GPa} = 1.4\,\text{GPa}$$

and so:

$$\sigma_c{}^u = \sigma_f V_f = 1.4 \times 0.6 = 0.84\,\text{GPa}$$

(ignoring the small contribution from the matrix).

This result is in more reasonable agreement with typically observed values.

2.7   Off-Axis Strength in Tension

The failure of an orientated, but still unidirectional composite can be envisaged as occurring in any of three modes:

(1) Failure normal to the fibers (as occurs with straight tension in the fiber direction)
(2) Failure parallel to the fibers by matrix rupture or fiber/matrix interface tensile failure

(3) Failure by shear of the matrix or fiber/matrix interfaceIf the fibers make an angle ϕ with the direction of applied tensile stress σ, then, as shown in Figure 2.16, the stresses can be resolved as follows:

Tensile stress parallel to fibers $\quad \sigma_1 = \sigma\cos^2\phi$

Tensile stress normal to fibers $\quad \sigma_2 = \sigma\sin^2\phi$

Shear stress parallel to fibers $\quad \tau_{12} = \tfrac{1}{2}\sigma\sin 2\phi$

If σ_1^u, σ_2^u and τ^u represent the composite strengths in direct tension ($\phi = 0°$), transverse tension ($\phi = 90°$), and shear ($\phi = 45°$), respectively, then the failure stress for each mode can be expressed as:

$$\text{Mode 1:} \quad \sigma = \frac{\sigma_1^u}{\cos^2\phi}$$

$$\text{Mode 2:} \quad \sigma = \frac{\sigma_2^u}{\sin^2\phi} \tag{2.31}$$

$$\text{Mode 3:} \quad \sigma = \frac{2\tau_u}{\sin 2\phi}$$

Thus, the failure mode changes with ϕ as shown in Figure 2.17. Although these results are obeyed quite well for many systems and the observed fracture modes

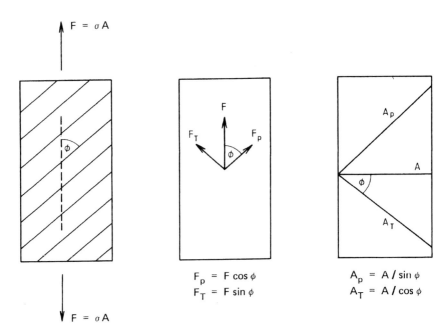

$$F = \sigma A$$

$$F_p = F\cos\phi$$
$$F_T = F\sin\phi$$

$$A_p = A/\sin\phi$$
$$A_T = A/\cos\phi$$

Fig. 2.16   Resolution of forces and areas in off-axis tension.

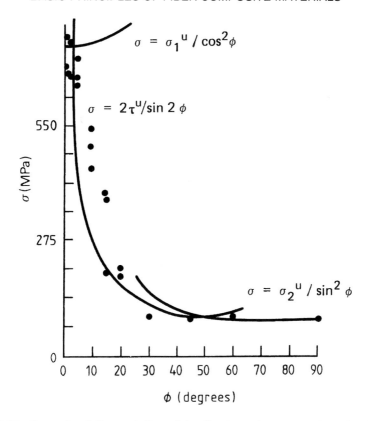

Fig. 2.17   Example of the variation of tensile strength versus orientation for a unidirectional composite.

are as predicted, the interaction of stresses and the occurrence of mixed-mode fractures are not accounted for. Ref. 1 presents a more detailed analysis that accounts for the complex stress states.

Figure 2.17 shows that strength falls rapidly with increasing ϕ. However, if the plies are placed at $+\phi$ and $-\phi$, the rate of fall-off is very much less, even to values of ϕ as high as 30°. The reasons for this are intuitively obvious because the plies reinforce each other against mode 1 or mode 2 failure.

2.8   Fracture Toughness of Unidirectional Composites

2.8.1   Fracture Surface Energy

A measure of the toughness, or the resistance of a material to crack propagation, is its fracture surface energy γ. This is defined as the minimum amount of energy required to create a unit area of free surface (crack) and is usually given in units of kJ m^{-2}. Because two free surfaces are produced, R (for crack resistance) equal to 2γ is the term often employed in fracture calculations.

It is a matter of considerable importance that, for crack propagation normal to the fibers (Fig. 2.18a), the fracture energy of a composite consisting of brittle fibers in a brittle matrix is usually much greater than is predicted by a simple rule-of-mixtures relationship. In general, $R_1 \gg V_f R_f + V_m R_m$. For example, in the case of a typical carbon/epoxy composite, $R_m \approx 1$ kJ m^{-2} for the bulk epoxy resin and $R_f \approx 0.1$ kJ m^{-2} for the carbon fiber. However, the fracture surface

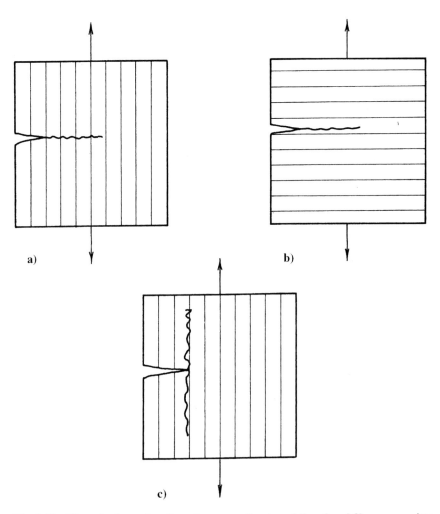

Fig. 2.18   **Three basic modes of crack propagation in unidirectional fiber composites subject to simple tensile loading: *a*) normal to the fibers; *b*) parallel to the fibers; and *c*) crack deflection along the fibers, or splitting. Modes *a* and *b* are self-similar modes of propagation.**

energy of a unidirectional composite R_c (if the crack is forced to propagate normal to the fibers) is typically $25-50$ kJ m^{-2}.

In contrast, for crack propagation parallel to the fibers (Fig. 2.18b), the fracture surface energy R_2 is of the order of R_m if the crack propagates solely through the matrix; however R_m will be lower if the crack propagates partially through the weaker fiber/matrix interface. Because $R_2 \ll R_1$, crack propagation parallel to the fibers, or splitting (Fig. 2.18c), will generally result even when the starting crack is normal to the fibers.

Considering crack propagation normal to the fibers (Fig. 2.18a), the total work of fracture can be attributed to a number of sources[11,12] as shown in Figure 2.19 and Table 2.1 taken from Ref. 11. In the case of the brittle fiber/brittle matrix composite (Fig. 2.19a), crack growth proceeds by pulling fibers out of the matrix behind the crack front and by fracturing fibers ahead of the crack tip. Energy is absorbed during *pull-out* if the shear stress at the fiber/matrix interface is maintained while the fracture surface is separating. If the fiber/matrix interface is relatively weak, local stresses will cause the fibers to be *debonded* from the matrix, with a resultant loss of stored strain energy. Stored strain energy is also lost by *stress relaxation* over the transfer length when the fiber fractures. Finally, strain energy is also lost from the fiber by crack bridging if the fiber spans the opening crack before fracture.

If the matrix is ductile, as in a metal-matrix composite, energy is also absorbed by *matrix plastic deformation*. This situation is illustrated in Figure 2.19b for the case in which the fiber is strongly bonded to the matrix so that little fiber *pull-out* occurs.

The work of the fracture contribution for *pull-out* in Table 2.1 refers to short constant-strength fibers. The expression would have to be modified for a statistical flaw distribution in continuous fibers. The contribution due to creation of new surfaces of fibers and matrix can be ignored in brittle systems, as can contributions from the matrix yield.

2.8.2 *Fracture Mechanics*

The energetic requirement for crack propagation is that the energy-release rate (equal to the "fixed grips" strain energy release rate) G must equal the fracture surface energy R. At the critical condition,

$$G = G_c = R \tag{2.32}$$

In many cases, it is more convenient to work in terms of the stress intensity factor K. For an isotropic material in the crack opening mode, K_I, is related to G through the equation $K_I^2 = EG$ and $K_{Ic}^2 = EG_c$ at failure.

In the simple case of a small centre crack in a sheet under tension:

$$K_I = \sigma(\pi a)^{1/2} \tag{2.33}$$

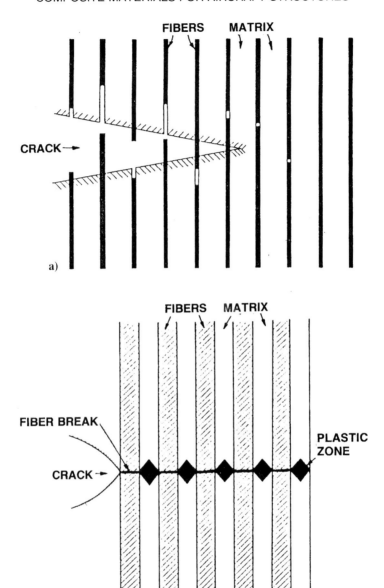

Fig. 2.19   Fracture behavior during failure of *a*) a brittle fiber/brittle matrix composite and *b*) a brittle fiber/ductile matrix composite where the fibers are assumed to be strongly bonded to the matrix.

Table 2.1   Models for Contributions to Work of Fracture for a Discontinuous Fiber Composite, Taken from Ref. 11

Model	γ
Pull-out (short fibers of length L)	$\dfrac{V_f \sigma_f^u \delta^2}{3L} (L > 2\delta)$
	$\dfrac{V_f \sigma_f^u L^2}{24\delta} (L < 2\delta)$
Debonding	$\dfrac{V_f (\sigma_f^u)^2 y}{4E_f}$
Stress relaxation	$\leq \dfrac{V_f (\sigma_f^u)^2 \delta}{3E_f}$
Crack bridging	$\dfrac{2V_f r (\sigma_f^u)^3}{\tau_i E_f} \times \dfrac{(1 - v_f)(1 - 2v_f)}{12(1 - v_f)}$
Matrix plastic deformation	$\dfrac{(1 - V_f)^2}{V_f} \times \dfrac{\sigma_m^u r}{\tau_m} \times U$

where σ is the applied stress and 2a the crack length. Thus, the stress σ_F at failure is given by

$$\sigma_F = \left(\frac{ER}{\pi a}\right)^{1/2} \tag{2.34}$$

which is the familiar Griffith equation.[13]

A relationship between G and K can also be obtained for a fiber composite material by modelling it as a continuous linear orthotropic material with the crack propagating on one of the planes of symmetry. Using the analysis for such materials given in Ref. 14,

$$G = K_I^2 \left(\frac{a_{11} a_{22}}{2}\right)^{1/2} \left[\left(\frac{a_{22}}{a_{11}}\right)^{1/2} + \left(\frac{a_{66} + 2a_{12}}{2a_{11}}\right)\right]^{1/2} \tag{2.35}$$

Here the a_{ij} terms are the coefficients of the stresses in the stress-strain law defined using a coordinate system based not on the fiber direction, but on the crack in the "1 direction" and the load in the "2 direction". This seems to be conventional in fracture mechanics treatments of this type. The factor involving the a terms can be considered as the reciprocal of the effective modulus E' of the composite. For the simple case illustrated in Figure 2.18a, where the crack is perpendicular to the fiber direction:

$$a_{22} = \frac{1}{E_{11}}, \quad a_{11} = \frac{1}{E_{22}}, \quad a_{66} = \frac{1}{G_{12}}$$

$$a_{12} = -\frac{v_{12}}{E_{11}} = -\frac{v_{21}}{E_{22}}$$

taking as values typical of a carbon/epoxy composite, $E_{11} = 140$ GPa, $E_{22} = 12$ GPa, $G_{12} = 6$ GPa, $v_{12} = 0.25$, and $v_{21} = 0.0213$, then $E' \approx 0.4E_{11}$. If, alternatively, the crack is considered to lie parallel to the fibers (Fig. 2.18b), then $E' \approx 2E_{22}$ where E' substitutes for the a terms in equation (2.35).

As long as crack propagation occurs on a plane of symmetry, the relationship between K_1, σ, and a for the linear orthotropic material remains the same as that for the isotropic material. Thus, referring back to the unidirectional composite, for a given crack length α and normal stress σ, a crack parallel to the fibers produces a larger G than one normal to the fibers. This results from the lower compliance of the composite when stressed in the fiber direction.

In the fiber composite material, the orientation dependence of R must also be taken into consideration. In general, a composite is notch-sensitive to cracks running parallel to the fibers (Fig. 2.18b) and the fracture mechanics principles described above may be directly employed. However, the composite may not be notch-sensitive in the situation shown in Figure 2.18a. In some cases,[7] the composite may become notch-sensitive when $a \gg \delta$, the ineffective length, because the strain concentration in the matrix may then lead to fiber fractures at the crack tip. The crack would then become more effective with increasing a, as required in fracture mechanics considerations. However, in other cases, gross failure of the fiber/matrix interface may occur, resulting in the splitting mode of failure illustrated in Figure 2.18c. This situation, which occurs in more weakly bonded composites, results in complete notch-insensitivity (failure at the net section strength). Both of these situations are illustrated in some experimental work on carbon/epoxy composites in Figure 2.20, taken from Ref. 11.

The conditions for crack turning or splitting can be approached from energy considerations.[15] For the cracking illustrated in Figure 2.18c to occur in a unidirectional composite, it is necessary that:

$$\frac{G_1}{G_2} < \frac{R_1}{R_2} \tag{2.36}$$

where G_1 is the energy release rate for self-similar propagation and G_2 the release rate for splitting. Typically, for carbon/epoxy R_1/R_2 is in the range 25–50 and G_1/G_2 is about 20, so splitting is generally predicted.

As mentioned earlier, most advanced composite structures are made of laminates in the form of unidirectional plies laminated together at various orientations. The fracture behavior of these materials is considered in Chapter 6 and 8. In laminates, toughness is highly dependent on the degree of ply splitting and inter-ply disbonding (delamination), resulting in high-energy absorption and crack deflection.

An approach similar to that just described can be taken for this highly complex situation.[16] The direction of crack growth is based on the R_1/R_2 ratio for each ply and the G_1/G_2 ratio for the laminate. The energy release rates are calculated by finite element procedures and recalculated after each increment of crack growth until the point of catastrophic failure.

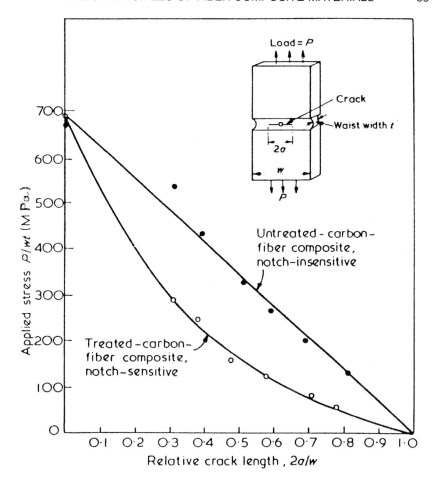

Fig. 2.20   Nominal applied stress versus relative crack size for a carbon-fiber/ epoxy-composite showing notch-sensitive and notch-insensitive behavior. Taken from Ref. 11.

References

[1]Jones, R. M., *Mechanics of Composite Materials*, Scripta Book, Washington, DC, 1975.

[2]Hyer, M. W., and Waas, A. M., "Micromechanics of Composite Materials," *Comprehensive Composite Materials*, edited by A. Kelly and C. Zwebin, Vol. 1, Elsevier Science Ltd, 2000.

[3]Ekvall, J. C. "Structural Behaviour of Monofilament Composites" AIAA 6th Structures and Materials Conference, April 1965.

[4]Fung, Y. C., *Foundations of Solid Mechanics 1965*, Prentice-Hall, Englewood Cliffs, NJ, 1965.

[5]Tsai, S. W., and Halpin, H. T., *Introduction to Composite Materials*, Technomic Publishing, Lancaster, PA, 1980.

[6]Kelly, A., and Davis, G. J., "The Principles of the Fibre Reinforcement of Metals," *Metallurgical Reviews*, Vol. 10, 1965, p. 1.

[7]Kelly, A., *Strong Solids*, 3rd ed., Clarendon Press, Oxford, UK, 1986.

[8]Daniels, H. E., "The Statistical Theory of the Strength of Bundles of Threads," *Proceedings of the Royal Society of London*, Vol. A183, 1945, p. 405.

[9]Rosen, B. W., "Tensile Failure of Fibrous Composites," *AIAA Journal*, Vol. 2 1964, pp. 1985–1991.

[10]Dow, N. F., Rosen, B.W., "Evaluations of Filament-Reinforced Composites for Aerospace Applications," NASA CR-207, April 1965.

[11]Philips, D. C., and Tetleman, A. S., "The Fracture Toughness of Fibre Composites," *Composites*, Vol. 3, 1972, pp. 216–223.

[12]Argon, A. S., "Fracture Strength and Toughness Mechanisms," Cambridge, MA, Comprehensive Composite Materials, edited by A. Kelly and C. Zwebin, Vol. 1, Elsevier Science, 2000.

[13]Lawn, B. R., and Wilshaw, T. R., *Fracture of Brittle Solids*, Cambridge University Press, Cambridge, England, UK, 1975.

[14]Sih, G., Paris, P. C., and Irwin, G. R., "On Cracks in Rectilinearly Anisotropic Bodies," *International Journal of Fracture Mechanics*, Vol. 1, 1965, p. 189.

[15]Harrison, N. L., "Splitting of Fibre-Reinforced Materials," *Fibre Science and Technology*, Vol. 6, 1973, p. 25.

[16]Griffith, W. I., Kanninen, M. F., and Rybicki, E. F., *A Fracture Mechanics Approach to the Analysis of Carbon/Epoxy Laminated Precracked Tension Panels*, ASTM STP 1979, p. 696.

3
Fibers for Polymer-Matrix Composites

3.1 Overview

As a result of their strong directional interatomic bonds, elements of low atomic number, including C, B, Al, and Si, can be formed into stiff, low-density materials. These materials may be made entirely from the elements themselves (e.g., C or B), or from their compounds (e.g., SiC), or with oxygen or nitrogen, (e.g., Al_2O_3, SiO_2 or Si_3N_4).

The strong bonding[1] also inhibits plastic flow, at least at temperatures below around half the melting temperature. Because these materials are unable to relieve stress concentrations by plastic flow, they are markedly weakened by sub-microscopic flaws, particularly those open to the surface. Thus, it is generally only when made in the form of fibers that the inherent very high strength of these materials can be realized.[2,3] There are several reasons for this, including the following:

- The probability of a flaw being present (per unit length) in a sample is an inverse function of volume of the material, as described by Weibull statistics.[4] Hence a fiber having a very low volume (per unit length) is much stronger on average than the bulk material. However, the bulk material, having a much higher content of weakening flaws, exhibits a much lower variability in strength, as shown in Figure 3.1. It follows similarly that the smaller the fiber diameter and the shorter the length, the higher the average and maximum strength, but the greater the variability.
- Flaws can be minimized by appropriate fiber manufacturing and coating procedures to minimize surface damage. Also, the precursor materials used in fiber making must be of a high purity, including freedom from inclusions. The effect of flaws on strength can be estimated from thermodynamic (energy balance) and elasticity considerations.
- Fiber manufacturing processes that involve drawing or spinning can impose very high strains in the direction of the fiber axis, thus producing a more favorable orientation of the crystal or atomic structure.
- Some fiber manufacturing processes involve a very high cooling rate or rapid molecular deposition to produce metastable, often ultra-fine grained structures, having properties not achievable in the bulk material.

55

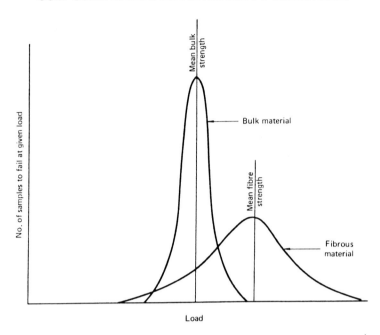

Fig. 3.1   Effect of sample cross-section on distribution of strength.[4]

Polymeric materials, based on a suitable carbon backbone structure, can also form strong, stiff fibers. Some of these materials rely on a very high drawing ratio to orientate the polymer chains, as well as high purity to develop their stiffness and strength.

Finally, some polymeric fiber materials can be used as precursors for producing inorganic fibers, through a process of controlled pyrolysis.

Thus, commercially available continuous fibers used in structural polymer-matrix composites (PMCs) for aerospace applications can be loosely classed as ceramic or as polymeric. Ceramic fibers, for the purposes of this discussion, include silica, carbon, and boron, although strictly these last two are not classed as ceramics. True ceramic fibers include silicon carbide and alumina, whereas polymeric fibers include aramid and high-density polyethylene.

Ceramic fibers, including glass, are typically flaw-sensitive and fail in an elastic brittle fashion from surface or internal flaws and inclusions.

Polymer fibers exhibit a complex fibrous type of fracture, as they essentially are made of a bundle of relatively weakly bonded sub-filaments or fibrils. As a result these fibers, compared with the ceramic fibers, are relatively insensitive to flaws. However, under compression loading they can defibrillate, resulting in poor compression properties.

Figure 3.2 summarizes the specific properties of several fiber types and includes, for comparison, structural metals. As a result of fiber volume fraction and other limitations, maximum properties for a PMC with unidirectional fibers are around 60% of the values shown. It is apparent from this plot that significant improvements in specific stiffness compared with the metals are achieved only by using some of the more advanced fibers, including carbon and boron. More details on fiber properties are provided in Table 3.1.

3.2. Glass Fibers

3.2.1 Manufacture

Glass fibers,[5] based on silica (SiO_2) melted with oxides, are the mainstay of PMCs because of their high strength and low cost. High-strength glass fibers have been used in demanding structural applications such as pressure vessels and rocket casings since the early 1960s. Structural applications in airframes are limited because glass fibers have a relatively low specific stiffness, as shown in Table 3.1 Nevertheless, they are widely exploited for airframes of gliders and other aircraft, where their low specific stiffness is not a design limitation, and in secondary structures such as fairings, with which relatively low cost (compared with the high-performance fibers) is attractive. Because of the suitability of their

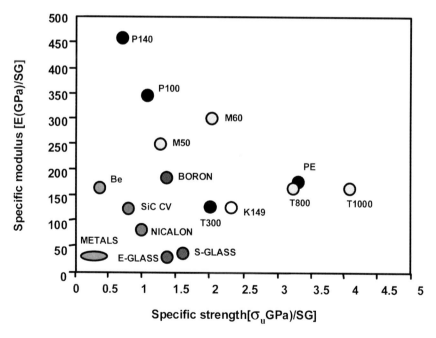

Fig. 3.2   Plot of specific fibers versus specific strength; the zone in which structural metals fall is shown for comparison. SG, specific gravity.

Table 3.1   Details of the Mechanical Properties of Various Fiber Types (the Temperature Column is the Nominal Maximum Operating Temperature in an Inert Environment)

Fiber	Fiber diameter (μm)	Specific gravity	Stiffness (GPa)	Specific stiffness	Ultimate strain (%)	Strength (GPa)	Specific strength	Coefficient of thermal expansion ($\times 10^{-6}$ m/m/°C)	Maximum use temperature (°C)	Commercial name
Glass										
E-Electrical	5–20	2.6	73	1.1	3.5	3.5	11.2	5.0	350	
S-High strength	8–14	2.5	87	1.3	4.5	4.6	15.3	5.6		
Carbon PAN based										*Toray*
High strength*	8	1.76	230	4.9	1.5	3.5	16.6	−0.4		T300
Intermediate modulus	5	1.80	294	6.1	2.4	5.9	32.9	−1.0	>2000	T800
High modulus	8	1.90	490	9.7	0.5	2.5	11.0	−1.0		M-50
High modulus	6	1.94	588	14.3	0.7	3.9	16.8	−1.2		M-60
Carbon pitch based										*Amoco*
High modulus	10	2.03	520	9.6	0.4	2.1	8.6	−1.4		P-75
High modulus	10	2.15	725	12.7	0.3	2.2	8.5	−1.4	>2000	P-100
High modulus	10	2.18	830	14.3	0.3	2.2	8.4	−1.4		P-120
Boron CVD	140	2.50	400		0.7	2.8	9.3	4.9	1500	*Textron*
Silicon carbide										
Monofilament	140	2.50	430	6.5	0.8	3.4	11.3	—	1400	Textron SCS8
Multifilament	15	2.60	200	2.9	1.5	2.8	9.0	3.1	1200	Nippon Carbon Nicalon

Alumina										*Du Pont*
Monofilament	20	3.90	380	3.7	0.5	1.8	3.8	5.7	1000	FP
										Sumitomo
Multifilament	17	3.30	210	2.4	0.7	2.1	5.3	4.0	1100	Alumina
Aramid										*Du Pont*
Ballistic	12	1.43	80	2.1	3.6	2.9	9.7	16.9	250	Kevlar 29
Structural	12	1.45	120	3.1	2.8	2.9	9.7	17.1		Kevlar 49
High modulus	12	1.47	185	4.7	1.5	2.3	7.7	17.3		Kevlar 149
Polyethylene										*DSC*
	10–12	0.97	87	3.4	3.5	2.7	9.0	23.2	120	Dyneema
										Allied Signal
	38	0.97	117	4.5	3.5	2.6	8.7	22.3	100	Spectra 900
	28	0.97	172	6.7	2.7	3.0	10.0	25.8		Spectra 1000

N.B. The specific stiffness and strength is normalized to aluminum alloy 2024 T3; strength is based on stress at nominal yield.

dielectric properties, glass-fiber PMCs are also widely used in applications in which transparency to electromagnetic radiation is required, including radomes and aerial covers.

Glass is an amorphous solid produced by cooling a viscous liquid at a sufficiently high rate to prevent the formation of ordered or crystalline regions. Compounds that make up the glass in glass fibers can include (in addition to silica) oxides of aluminum, boron, calcium, magnesium, sodium, and potassium. Additives are used to lower the melting point of silica so that the required viscosity is obtained at a lower temperature. In addition, they facilitate the removal of gas bubbles and have a significant effect on the mechanical and chemical properties of the final product.

Glass fibers are manufactured by a viscous drawing process depicted in Figure 3.3 in which glass, melted in a furnace at temperatures of about 1400 °C, flows into an electrically heated platinum-rhodium alloy bushing or spinneret, containing a large number (400–8000) of holes in its base. The emerging glass drops are drawn into fibers by pulling at speeds of up to 50 m s.$^{-1}$ They are then cooled by a fine water spray and coated with a size by contact with a rotating applicator. Finally, the fibers are combined into a strand as they are wound onto a take-up spool.

The fiber diameter, typically around 5–20 μm, is a function of the size of the holes in the bushing, the viscosity of the melt (which is dependent on the composition of the glass and the temperature), the head of glass in the furnace, and the rate of winding. Depending on the number of holes in the bushing, the strand typically consists of 52, 102, or 204 fibers.

The cooling rate experienced by the fibers is very high, $> 10,000$ °C s^{-1}. A parameter[5] called the *fictive temperature* is the apparent temperature at which

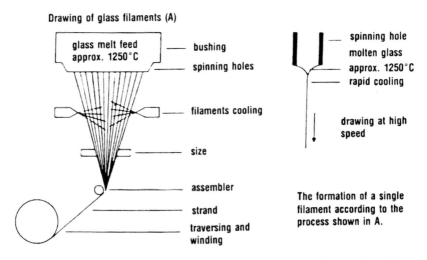

Fig. 3.3   Schematic illustration of the process used to manufacture glass fibers.

the glass is frozen, generally found to be 200–300 °C above the liquidus. As a result, the fiber structure is somewhat different from that of bulk glass, resulting in a higher tensile strength but lower elastic modulus and chemical resistance.

3.2.2 Effect of Flaws

Glass fibers, being essentially monolithic, linearly elastic brittle materials, depend for their high strength on the absence of flaws and defects. These take the form of sub-microscopic inclusions and cracks The inclusions can often be seen with a scanning electron microscope, but "cracks" sufficient to reduce strength significantly can be very difficult to find because they are of nanometre dimensions. The origin of flaws is, however, generally obvious when examining the fracture surface because growth starts from the region of the flaw as a flat (mirror) surface and transforms to hackles radiating from this region as growth accelerates.

Commercial glass fibers are particularly prone to the formation of flaws by abrasion against other fibers, resulting in a reduction in strength of the order of 20% compared with pristine fibers made under laboratory conditions.

The tensile strength is probably significantly dependent on the composition, structure, and internal stresses in the surface layer, all of which differ significantly from those in the internal structure due in part to the high cooling rate. Although this layer is only of the order of a nanometer thick, it is of the order of the size of the flaws that control the strength of high strength fibers >2 GPa. Generally, surface flaws have a similar strength-reducing effect compared with internal flaws of twice the length.

Humid environments reduce the strength of glass fibers under sustained loading, as the moisture adsorbed onto the surface of the flaw reduces the surface energy, thus facilitating slow growth to critical size. This phenomenon in glass is called *static fatigue*.

The strength of the glass fibers is reduced by about a further 50% when they are formed into a polymer-matrix composite. However, because of the bundle effect described in Chapter 2, this reduction is not noticeable. Essentially, the gauge length for a bundle of fibers is the length of the bundle, whereas, due to load transfer from the matrix, for a composite it is only of the order of 1 mm, depending on fiber diameter and fiber/matrix bond strength. Further reductions in strength can occur if the composite is exposed to wet conditions because components leached out of the polymer can cause acidic or basic conditions to develop at the fiber surface.

3.2.3 Types of Glass Fiber

The compositions of glass made into fibers for PMCs are listed in Table 3.2 There are two types of glass fiber used for structural applications: "E," a calcium alumino-borosilicate glass, and "S," a magnesium alumino-silicate glass. *E* stands for electrical grade, because compared with other standard forms of glass, its electrical resistivity is high and its dielectric constant low. These are by far the most widely exploited in structural applications, particularly in the non-aerospace area, because of their relatively low cost and high strength. A modified (low boron and fluorine) version of E glass fiber, ECR (E glass chemically resistant), is used where improved chemical properties are required. *S* stands for high-strength grade, although stiffness is also somewhat increased. These fibers can also withstand significantly higher temperatures than E glass fibers. Thus S glass fibers are used in more demanding structural applications. However, this marginal increase in stiffness is obtained at a relatively high cost. Where high specific strength and stiffness are required (with good dielectric properties) aramid fibers, described later, may be more attractive. More recently, a boron-free E glass has been developed that has markedly improved resistance to corrosive environments, but with no loss in mechanical properties.

3.2.4 Glass Fiber Coatings

As mentioned earlier, glass fibers are highly sensitive to surface damage. Because the coefficient of friction between glass fibers is around unity, mechanical damage sufficient to cause a significant loss in strength can result from fiber-to-fiber abrasion during the forming process. To prevent contact damage, within milliseconds of solidifying, the fibers are coated with a protective size that also serves to minimize losses in strength due to atmospheric moisture absorption. For example, the tensile strength of as-drawn fibers can be reduced by over 20% after contact with air during drawing under normal ambient conditions. It seems likely that the atmospheric moisture is absorbed into microscopic flaws, reducing fracture energy because time would be too limited chemical attack. In any case, the tensile strength of the glass fibers drops significantly during the manufacturing process, from as high as 5 GPa immediately after drawing to typically around 2–3 GPa postproduction.

The size consists of several components. The simplest is a lubricant, such as a light mineral oil for protection and to aid further processing such as weaving, filament winding, and pultrusion. Binders such as starch and polyvinyl alcohol

Table 3.2   Chemical Composition of the Two Main Glass Fiber Types

Glass type	Si	Al_2O_3	CaO	B_2O_3	MgO	$Na_2O\ K_2O$
E-Electrical	53	14	18	10	5	< 1
S-High strength	65	25	—	—	10	—

(PVA) are included in the size to bond or hold the filaments together into strands and tows. Finishes, also called primers, are used in the size to improve the adhesive bonding between the fiber and the polymer matrix. Primers may be added to the size or applied later after removal of the size components by heat treatment.

The finish is often based on a coupling agent that for most polymer-matrix resins is an organo-silane compound. Organo-silanes effectively have dual functionality, with their organo portion interacting with the organic resins or adhesives and the silane portion interacting with the inorganic fibers. Thus, these compounds are used to improve the interfacial (resin/fiber) properties of PMCs. Briefly, the silane molecule on hydration in water can be represented by the following simplified formula:

$$R \cdots Si(OH)_3$$

The $Si(OH)_3$ bonds with the oxide film at the surface of the inorganic fiber-glass in this case, while the organic functional group R is incorporated into the organic matrix during its cure. R must therefore be a group that is chemically compatible with the matrix resin. For example, for an epoxy resin, an epoxy silane may be used. The following lists some of the coupling agents used as finishes for various resins:

• Vinyl silane (methacrylate silane), suitable for polyester resins
• Volan (methacrylate chromic chloride), suitable for polyester and epoxy resins
• Amino silane, suitable for epoxy, phenolic, or melamine resins
• Epoxy silane, suitable for epoxy and phenolic resins

3.3 Carbon Fibers

3.3.1 Manufacture

Carbon fibers are widely used for airframes and engines and other aerospace applications. High modulus (HM, Type I), high strength (HS, Type II) and intermediate modulus (IM, Type III) form the three broad categories of carbon fibers available commercially, shown in Table 3.3

The name *graphite* for these fibers is sometimes used interchangeably with carbon, but this is actually incorrect. Graphite is a form of carbon in which strong covalently bonded hexagonal basal planes are aligned in a three-dimentional lattice. The weak dispersive atomic Van der Waals' bonding allows easy slip between the basal planes, the basis for the lubricating properties of graphite. As discussed later, the atomic structure of carbon fibers differs in that the basal planes have only a two-dimensional order, which inhibits slip.

Table 3.3   Typical Properties for the Major Types of Commercial Carbon Fibers

Property	HM Type I	HS Type II	IM Type III
Specific gravity	1.9	1.8	1.8
Tensile modulus (GPa)	276–380	228–241	296
Tensile strength (MPa)	2415–2555	3105–4555	4800
Ultimate strain (%)	0.6–0.7	1.3–1.8	2.0
Coefficient of thermal expansion ($\times 10^{-6}$ mm^{-1} K^{-1})	-0.7	-0.5	N/A
Thermal conductivity (Wm^{-1} K^{-1})	64–70	8.1–9.3	N/A
Electrical resistivity ($\mu\Omega$ m)	9–10	15–18	N/A

Carbon fibers are made from organic precursor materials by a process of carbonization. The bulk of carbon fibers used in aerospace and other structural applications, are made from polyacrylonitrile (PAN) fibers.[6] Carbon fibers are also made from various forms of pitch.[7] Early carbon fibers were manufactured from rayon, however, these fibers have been gradually phased out due to their low carbon yield (20–25%) and their generally poorer mechanical properties compared to PAN and pitch-based carbon fibers.

3.3.2 PAN-Based fibers

PAN is an acrylic textile fiber produced by wet or dry spinning of the basic polymer or copolymer. Dry spinning produces round smooth fibers whereas wet spinning (extrusion into a coagulating bath) produces a variety of cross-sections, including dog-bone, elliptical, and kidney-shaped. There are some advantages in the non-circular cross-sections; for example, the larger relative surface area improves effective bonding. The fibers are stretched during the spinning process. The greater the stretch, the smaller the fiber diameter and the higher the preferred orientation of the molecular chain along the fiber axis, resulting in a stiffer carbon fiber when processed. PAN fiber tows typically contain around 10^4 fibers, although much larger or smaller tows are also produced. The finished carbon fibers are between 5–10 μm in diameter.

Figure 3.4 schematically illustrates the process of conversion of the PAN fibers into carbon fibers. The PAN is first stabilized in air at around 250 °C by oxidation to form a thermally stable ladder polymer, having a high glass transition temperature (T_g), which is resistant to melting at the higher temperatures. The cyclic groups in the ladder polymer are rather similar in molecular structure to the carbon basal plane, except that they also contain nitrogen and hydrogen atoms. The fibers are maintained under tension to prevent them from contracting during oxidation and, through the resulting deformation, to align further the ladder structure with the fiber axis.

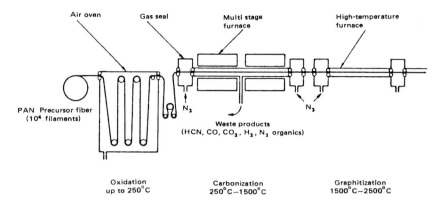

Fig. 3.4   Schematic illustration of the process used to make carbon fibers from PAN.

The next step in the process is carbonization in the temperature range of 1200–1600 °C in an inert nitrogen atmosphere. This removes the nitrogen, oxygen, and hydrogen from the ladder.

As the heat treatment proceeds, benzene aromatic rings link to form polynuclear aromatic fragments, with the basal planes aligned along the fiber axis. Gradually the aromatic network transforms to mainly carbon atoms and becomes denser through cross-linking with the evolution of N_2 through open pores in the fiber. At 120 °C the transformation to carbon is almost complete and closed pores remain in the fiber. Finally, at around 1500–1600 °C the strength of the fiber reaches its peak.

Although the basal planes in carbon fibers are aligned (with varying degrees of perfection) parallel to the axis of the fibers, ordering of the planes is largely two-dimensional, having extended two-dimensional ribbons of basal carbon. Crystalline order in the third dimension, Figure 2.5, is very limited, as the alignment of one ribbon with another is generally very low. This structure is referred to in the literature as turbostratic carbon.

The strength and stiffness of carbon fibers are a function of the degree of perfection of the structure and the alignment of the ribbons of basal planes with the fiber axis. These depend on several processing factors, including the heat treatment temperature as well the nature and content of weakening voids and flaws—determined to a large degree by the purity and freedom from inclusions in the PAN precursor. Of course there is a high cost penalty if ultra-high-purity PAN is required, which sets a high baseline cost for high-performance carbon fibers.

After heat treatment at 1500–1600 °C the strain capability of the fibers is then over 1.5% with an intermediate value of the Young's modulus of around 240 GPa, Table 2.3.

If higher modulus is required, which will be at the expense of strength and strain capability, the fibers undergo a final graphitisation stage of heat treatment up to 2500 °C. This treatment is generally carried out in a clean and more inert atmosphere, such as argon, to prevent the formation of flaws through chemical reactions and/or local graphitisation. During this process, the aromatic carbon basal layer planes grow, by further coalescence of adjacent layers, resulting in an increase in preferred orientation along the fiber axis and thus in elastic modulus. As indicated in Table 2.1, strain capacity is then reduced to around 0.7% and the Young's modulus up to 380 GPa.

3.3.3 Pitch-Based Fibers

Pitch is a relatively cheap precursor material for the manufacture of carbon fibers.[7] However, although low cost fibers can be produced from isotropic pitch, they have rather poor mechanical properties. Pitch can also be used as a precursor for ultra high-stiffness fibers, however these involve much more elaborate processing, so are very expensive.

Commercial pitch, made of mixtures of organic compounds, is subjected to prolonged heating to form a liquid crystal phase known as mesophase (MP) prior to spinning into precursor fibers. Heat is applied at approximately 400-450 °C in an inert atmosphere for an extended period in order to transform isotropic pitch to mesophase pitch. This is then melt-spun into filamentary form. The draw ratio employed during spinning determines the degree as well as uniformity of molecular orientation of the fiber. To reduce relaxation of the orientated structure, the pitch fibers are cross-linked by heat-treating at 300 °C for a short period in an atmosphere containing oxygen. Pre-carbonisation at 1000 °C to reduce the rate of gas evolution (and hence the creation of surface flaws), precedes carbonisation and graphitisation at temperatures ranging between 1200–3000 °C.

The main advantage of this process over the PAN processing route, is that no tension is required to develop or maintain the molecular orientation required to achieve high modulus and strength. Owing to the anisotropic liquid crystal nature of the pitch, molecular orientation is achieved in the spinning process and is enhanced, or at least preserved, throughout processing without the need to use tension.

The main advantage of this process over the PAN processing route is that no tension is required to develop or maintain the molecular orientation required to achieve high modulus and strength. Owing to the anisotropic liquid crystal nature of the pitch, molecular orientation is achieved in the spinning process and is enhanced, or at least preserved, throughout processing without the need to use tension.

MP-based fibers in general exhibit higher tensile modulus than their PAN-based counterparts. This is due to the more highly graphitizable character of the former precursor. However, this results in relatively lower compression and shear properties. The structure of MP-based fibers is also more porous, leading to lower

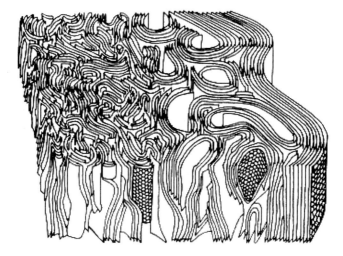

Fig. 3.5 Schematic illustration of the structure of carbon fiber.[4]

achievable strengths. Their carbon content is much higher, however, being around 80% compared with 50% for PAN precursors.

Very high values of Young's modulus and thermal and electrical conductivities can be obtained from pitch fibers as shown in Table 3.1. Therefore, they are widely used in space-based applications where ultra-high stiffness and conductivity are highly advantageous.

The other main continuous inorganic fibers[8] in production are boron and various types of silicon carbide. Continuous alumina fibers are also manufactured, but are not discussed here, although some properties are included in Table 3.1 for completeness. These fibers are of interest for the development of metal-matrix and ceramic-matrix composites, as discussed in Chapter 1. For these applications, retention of high static and creep strength and resistance to attack by the matrix material are important requirements. Ideally, they should also match the matrix in thermal expansion properties to minimize residual stresses—this is only feasible with ceramic-matrices.

Their low electrical and thermal conductivity make them preferred options to carbon fibers for some applications.

3.4 Boron Fibers

Boron fibers[9] are large monofilaments around 125–140 μm in diameter, compared with around 10 μm for carbon. Because boron is almost as hard as diamond, PMCs based on this fiber are difficult to drill and machine. Therefore, carbon fibers which are much cheaper as well as being more machinable and formable, have largely replaced boron fibers for aerospace PMC applications.

However, several recent U.S. aircraft such as the F-14, F-15, and B-1 contain a number of important boron/epoxy components. Boron is also used to reinforce aluminium metal-matrix composites (Chapter 1).

Boron fibers are made by chemical vapor deposition (CVD) of boron onto a fine incandescent tungsten or a pitch-based carbon fiber, around 10 μm in diameter. The carbon fiber is coated with a thin layer of pyrolytic graphite to alleviate internal stresses by promoting relative movement.

Deposition is usually achieved through hydrogen reduction of a boron trichloride gas at a temperature of above 1000 °C at atmospheric pressure in a glass reactor; alternatively, boron bromide, iodide, or fluoride can be used. The process, illustrated in Figure 3.6, involves gradual growth of the boron deposit, which is quite slow, around 3—4 μm min^{-1}, and therefore very expensive.

Because tungsten has a high density and is also expensive, the boron monofilament must have a large diameter to minimize fiber density and cost. Even if a carbon fiber substrate is used, the economics dictate the formation of large-diameter fibers. For some reason, the use of carbon precursor fibers is not common, although carbon is used for the core in the CVD of silicon carbide fiber, described next.

The traverse speeds for producing the fibers are critical. At relatively low temperatures, around 1200 °C, the desired near-amorphous form of boron is deposited. Above this temperature, at slow traverse speeds, some crystalline boron is formed, which has an adverse effect on mechanical properties. The final fiber has a distinctive corncob appearance, typical of solids made by CVD, resulting from multiple nucleation of boron and growth from the substrate. The properties of boron fibers are listed in Table 3.1.

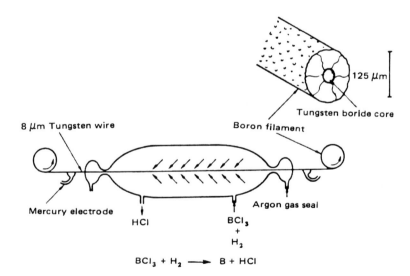

Fig. 3.6   Schematic illustration of the process used to make boron fibers.

Detailed X-ray studies show that the preferred form of the boron is actually not amorphous but a microcrystalline b-rhombohedral, with a crystal size of around 2 nm. In the reaction process with tungsten wires, the boron diffuses into and reacts with the tungsten core to produce various tungsten boride compounds, including WB_4 and W_2B_5. These have a greater volume than the tungsten fiber and so produce quite severe internal tensile stresses that can lead to internal cracking. However, the CVD process apparently leaves compressive stresses on the fiber surface that should reduce sensitivity to surface flaws.

Strength is reduced by the presence of flaws such as microscopic dust particles enveloped during fiber manufacture, or localized growth of coarse crystals caused by undesirable temperature fluctuations during manufacture. Strength can be enhanced by smoothing the surface, using chemical etching, or dissolving the fiber core. However, these processes are not used industrially because of the cost. Boron fibers made by deposition onto a carbon fiber substrate are much smoother, which may be a result of the smoothness of the carbon fiber or an increase in the number of nucleation sites.

Boron fibers undergo significant anelastic deformation (apparent creep) under prolonged loading at elevated temperature that is recovered upon unloading.

Because boron was the first fiber capable of reinforcing metals, considerable effort was made to use this fibers in this application. To improve chemical compatibility with aluminum and titanium matrices, the use of a nitride or silicon carbide coating was developed. The silicon carbide coated fiber was called "Borsic" and offered some improvement over the uncoated fibers. However, the inherent temperature limitations of the core boron fiber resulted in the focus for development of metal-matrix composites moving to silicon carbide fibers.

3.5   Silicon Carbide

Silicon carbide fibers are produced by a CVD process similar to boron or by a polymeric precursor route. The highest strength and chemical stabile fibers are produced by CVD, which produces fibers suitable for reinforcing aluminum and titanium alloys. CVD silicon carbide fibers are also highly suited for reinforcing ceramics, as mentioned in Chapter 1, notably silicon carbide, silicon nitride, or glass.

3.5.1   CVD-Based Silicon Carbide Fibers

CVD fibers are produced by the reaction of hydrogen with a mixture of chlorinated alkyl silanes (such as methyltrichlorosilane) at the surface of a resistivity-heated substrate fiber. In this case, the substrate fiber is a spun carbon monofilament, around 30 μm in diameter, coated with a thin layer of pyrolytic graphite. The resulting fiber is polycrystalline β-SiC, having a fairly coarse grain compared with the microcrystalline boron. Internal stresses in CVD silicon carbide fibers are fairly low, in contrast to the high stresses found in boron fibers.

Since the cost of carbon core is much lower than tungsten and the deposition rate is significantly greater, the potential cost of the silicon carbide fibers is about one third that of boron. Properties of CVD SiC fibers are listed in Table 1

The fibers retain most of their room temperature strength up to about 900 °C then maintain a strength of around 1 GPa up to 1300 °C. Also ambient temperature strength is recovered on cooling after exposure at temperatures up to 1400 °C. Above this temperature, coarsening of the SiC crystal structure occurs, resulting in permanent weakening. The fibers undergo creep deformation at temperatures below 1400 °C, this is attributed to grain boundary sliding due to the presence of free silicon between the grains. Heat treatment above 1400 °C improves creep resistance at the cost of reduced strength by coarsening of the β-SiC grains and possibly by disrupting the weak layers between the grains.

The key issue in the use of fibers to reinforce metals in MMCs, is chemical compatibility and the need to form a strong stable surface bond (See Chapter 1). To achieve this, three types of CVD fibers are produced, each having a carbon-rich zone of several microns close to the surface. For example, SCS-6 is designed for reinforcing aluminium alloys, while SCS-8 is designed for reinforcing titanium. The carbon-rich layer at the grain boundaries in these versions of the SiC CVD fiber, improves creep-resistance by reducing grain-boundary-sliding and also inhibiting grain growth.

3.5.2   Silicon Carbide Fibers Based On A Polymeric Precursor

The polymer-precursor textile route to the manufacture of silicon carbide fibers[10] is based on a high molecular weight polymer (made by polymerisation of dichorodimethylsilane) containing silicon and carbon. A similar polymer precursor/textile route can be used to make a range of multi-filament ceramic fibers, including alumina and silicon nitride.

The polycarbonsilane polymer is melt spun to form a multi-filament tow and then pyrolised in two temperature stages; 550 °C to stabilise the precursor to be infusible and 850 °C to form an impure form of silicon carbide, containing a non-stoichiometric form of SiC, SiO_2 and free carbon.

Table 1 lists typical properties for Nicalon (trade name, see Table 1), which is the most well-known and used version of these fibers. As a result of the low fiber diameter and tow size, the fiber can be produced in a wide variety of textile forms and allows similar flexibility in manufacture to PAN-based carbon fibers.

Due to the impurities and the crystalline form of SiC produced, the elastic modulus of the fiber is lower than monolithic SiC; 220 GPa compared with 450 GPa. It also tends to decompose at temperatures above 1200 °C and has low retained strength above 1400 °C. The fibers are also prone to oxidise at temperatures above around 1000 °C to form surface SiO_2. As may be expected, the presence of SiO_2 at the grain boundaries has a negative impact on creep properties. Creep resistance is also a function SiC grain size, and improves as the grain size increases.

Some of the disadvantages of Nicalon have been overcome in a version called Hi-Nicalon, which is produced from the same precursor material, but cured by electron-beam radiation. The improvement results from the lower oxygen content leading to a reduced level of SiO_2, but the non-stoichiometric form of SiC and excess carbon, remain. Further improvements were made by heat-treating the fiber at a high temperature to produce a near-stoichiometric form of SiC with coarser grains, without significant loss of strength. Hi-Nicalon retains a high level of strength even after exposure at 1600 °C and has significantly improved creep properties. Presumably, this version of the fiber would also have improved compatibility with aluminum and/or titanium, so, is more suited to formation of metal-matrix composites.

Silicon carbide is a semiconductor; in the case of the fibers resistivity depends on impurity content and crystal structure. The resistivity of Nicalon fibers can be controlled in the range $10 - 10^6 \ \Omega \ mm^{-1}$ according to the heat treatment.

Finally, although Nicalon fibers exhibit significant creep at elevated temperatures and do not have the required high chemical compatibility with metals of CVD SiC, they are substantially cheaper than the CVD fiber and are suitable for some modest temperature applications in metals and ceramics.

3.6 Aramid Fibers

Aramid fibers,[11] trade name Kevlar (Du Pont), were the first organic fibers with sufficient stiffness and strength for use in PMCs suitable for airframe applications. Table 3.1 lists the important physical and mechanical properties of three types of Kevlar. This shows that Kevlar aramid fibers significantly exceed the specific strength and stiffness of glass fibers. PMCs based on aramid fibers have attractive tensile properties for temperatures of over 400 °C; however, they have poor compression strength. This is a major limitation for applications subject to significant compression loading, including those requiring high bearing strength.

A major advantage of aramid fibers is their ability to absorb large amounts of energy during fracture, which results from their high strain-to-failure, their ability to undergo plastic deformation in compression, and their ability to defibrillate during tensile fracture. The fibers exhibit plastic behavior at around 0.3% compression strain, and deformation is linear up to failure at strains greater than 2% in tension. Hence aramid PMCs are used for ballistic protection and also for engine containment rings. The most common use of aramid PMCs in aerospace has been in fairings, but it is also used as the skins or face sheets for honeycomb panels. Aramid PMCs are also used in radomes and other applications requiring structural efficiency and suitable dielectric properties.

Kevlar fibers are based on an aromatic polyamide (poly para-phenylene terphalamide; PPD-T) polymer chain. Nylon is a generic name for textile fibers based on a linear form of polyamide. In PPD-T, the aromatic rings contribute high thermal stability and result in a crystalline rigid, rodlike polymer. The strong covalent bonds in the polymer chain and the weak hydrogen bonding between these chains result in highly anisotropic properties; the polymer structure is depicted in Figure 3.7. The polymer rods, as in mesophase pitch, aggregate in solution to form liquid crystals.

When PPD-T, as a 20% solution in concentrated sulphuric acid, is extruded through a spinneret at around 100 °C the liquid crystal zones or domains align in the direction of the flow. The fiber precipitates in a short air gap after emerging from the spinneret and then coagulates by passing through a cold water bath that removes the acid. Some rotation of domains occurs during the spinning process. The fiber structure thus consists of highly crystalline, aligned polymer chains separated, on a larger scale, into distinct zones or fibrils. The fiber structure is essentially made up of a bundle of these fibrils that are relatively weakly bonded together.

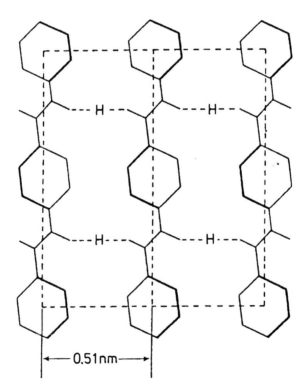

Fig. 3.7   The polymeric structure of aramid fibers. Note the hydrogen bonding between the polymer chains. Taken from Ref. 3.

Under tensile loading, failure occurs by a defibrillation process (due to the presence of weak interfaces) that reduces flaw sensitivity in individual fibrils and is therefore highly effective for energy absorption. The strength of aramid fiber falls to around 80% of room temperature strength at 180 °C, followed by a more rapid decline above this temperature. However, as mentioned earlier, under compression loading, aramid fibers exhibit pronounced non-linear behavior. This is caused by the formation of kink bands resulting from in-phase compressive buckling of the fibrils. As a result, compression strain-to-failure is only about 25% of the tensile value.

Aramid fibers have a high tendency to absorb moisture. For Kevlar 49, moisture absorption is around 4% at 60% relative humidity, while for Kevlar 149, it is around 1.5%, but the effect on tensile strength at ambient temperatures does not appear to be significant.

Aramid fibers are prone to significant short-term creep even at modest temperatures, however, long-term creep is negligible. The fibers are also prone to stress rupture under prolonged loading but are much less sensitive to this mode of failure than are glass fibers.

Finally, aramid fibers are degraded in strength by prolonged exposure to ultraviolet radiation but, although this can be a serious concern with cables having exposed fibers, it is not a significant problem for aramid PMCs because the fibers are protected by the resin matrix.

3.7   Orientated Polyethylene Fibers

High modulus polyethylene fibers[12] can be produced with a specific gravity below that of water (Table 3.1). Two types of fiber are currently commercially available—Spectra by Allied Signal and Dyneema by DSM. Polyethylene fibers are produced by the drawing of melt-crystallized polyethylene to very high draw ratios. Other routes to manufacturing these fibers include solution and gel spinning of very high molecular weight polyethylenes.

In common with aramid fibers, polyethylene fibers exhibit low compression strength and fail under compression by a process involving the formation of kink bands. On a specific basis, polyethylene fibers have tensile properties that exceed those of most other fibers including aramid (Table 3.1). However, the fibers are prone to creep deformation and creep rupture under long-term loading, particularly at modest temperature, which limits their use in applications involving high, prolonged static loading. Creep occurs in part because the fibers cannot be drawn to their full extent in commercial production; however, sliding of the polymer chains encouraged by the weak inter-chain bonding also makes a significant contribution.

Polyethylene fibers are limited to temperature applications under 100 °C; Spectra, for example, melts at 150 °C. Nevertheless, they have exceptional chemical resistance and low moisture absorption characteristics. It is difficult for the resin matrix to form strong adhesive bonds to the fibers as a result of their non-polar nature; however, bonding can be improved by various pre-bonding etching techniques, including corona discharge.

As with PMCs based on aramid fibers, high toughness is a very attractive feature of PMCs based on polyethylene fibers. Thus, the fibers are being developed for use in PMCs with applications requiring ballistic protection or very high impact resistance.

3.8   Dry Fiber Forms

Continuous carbon, glass, aramid, and other multi-filament fibers are produced in various dry forms[13] (no matrix precursor added) for subsequent processing into high-performance PMCs using pre-impregnation (pre-preg), resin film, or liquid resin injection techniques. The forms include continuous rovings, woven rovings, yarns, and woven cloth (see Fig 3.8). The various types of resin pre-impregnated fiber forms are mentioned briefly here, and a more detailed discussion of the subject is given in Chapter 5. The monofilament CVD fibers are available in the dry form either as a single-fiber spool or as a tape or cloth, which is held in place by polymeric fibers and sometimes attached by a light resin coating to a very fine glass fiber cloth.

3.8.1   Rovings and Tows

Rovings, a term generally used in association with glass fibers, consist of an untwisted bundle of strands that in turn consist of a collection of more than one continuous glass filament. Rovings are made by collating ends from several primary strand creels and then, using a precision winder, winding them onto a cylindrical package.

In the case of carbon, the bundle of fibers is called a *tow* and results directly from processing the PAN precursor. Typically, a carbon fiber tow contains between 1000 and 48,000 individual filaments.

It is very important that the strands in the roving or tow are maintained under even tension because uneven tension markedly affects later processing. Uneven tension in processes such as filament winding and pultrusion can result in strands sagging and becoming entangled. Importantly, fiber tension in the finished component will vary significantly, reducing the reinforcing efficiency.

3.8.2   Yarns

Yarns are made by twisting a collection of strands (usually smaller than rovings) or filaments as they are pulled off the creel under tension. The twist, approximately one turn per centimeter, holds the fibers in place and maintains even tension during subsequent processes such as weaving and filament winding.

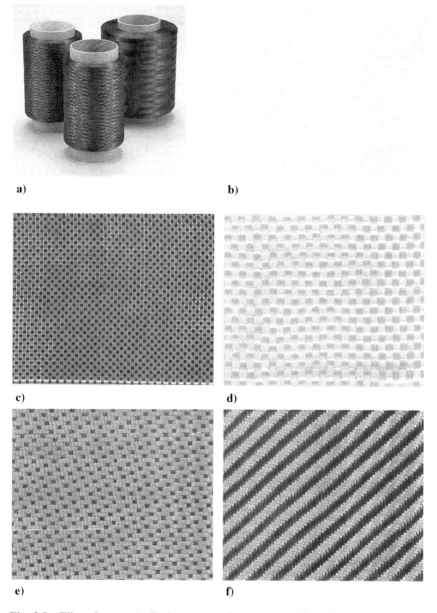

Fig. 3.8   Fiber forms: *a*) Carbon tows of various weights (Torayca brochure); *b*) non-wovens (CSM); *c*) plain woven; *d*) 4 × 4 basket woven; *e*) five-harness satin woven; *f*) 4 × 4 twill woven.

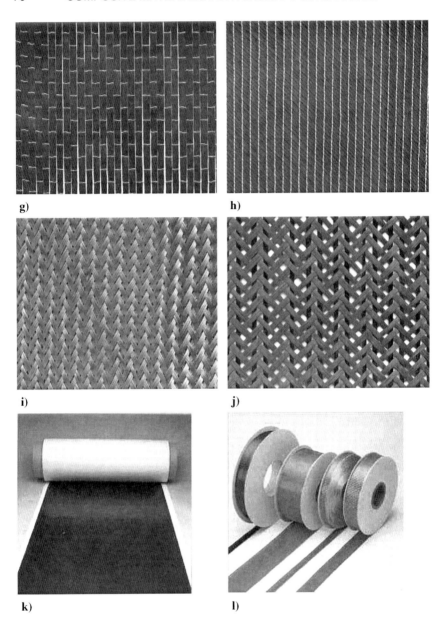

Fig. 3.8   (*continued*) Fiber forms: *g*) uniweave; *h*) non-crimp; *i*) biaxial braided; *j*) triaxial braided; *k*) pre-pregs (Torayca brochure); *l*) narrow fabrics/tapes (Torayca brochure).

Where heavier yarns are required, two or more stands may be twisted together and then plied by re-twisting several twisted yarns together in the opposite direction of the strand twist. The directions of the twist are denoted by S- or Z-type twist. Hence two or more strands with an S-twist are plied with a Z-twist to maintain balance.

3.8.3 Non-woven Fabrics

Mats are non-woven fabrics that provide near isotropic properties and come in either chopped or continuous strand form. The former consists of fibers cut to lengths typically up to 50 mm and randomly deposited onto a moving belt. Continuous strand mats, on the other hand, are manufactured by swirling continuous strands of fibers onto a moving belt. The reinforcements, usually glass, in both forms of mat are held together with a polymeric binder. Stitch-bonded and needle felt fabrics are two other kinds of non-wovens.

3.8.4 Woven Fabrics

A wide variety of textile cloths are made using conventional textile weaving looms. The type of weave influences the formability/drapability and reinforcing efficiency of the fibers. The weave is made up of warp fibers that run in the direction of the loom and the weft (or fill) fibers that are normal to the direction of the warp.

The main styles of woven fabric reinforcement are plain, twill, satin, and basket weaves (Fig. 3.9). In the plain weave, each warp yarn alternately crosses over and under each weft yarn (i.e., 1×1). This is by far the most common structure used and affords relatively good fabric stability. Twill (e.g., 2×2 and 4×4) and satin (e.g., 5-harness and 8-harness) weaves are woven such that yarns go over and under multiple warp yarns. Twill weaves involve warp and weft interlacing in a programmed sequence so that a pattern of diagonal lines is obtained on the fabric. Satin weaves, on the other hand, offer a reduced amount of

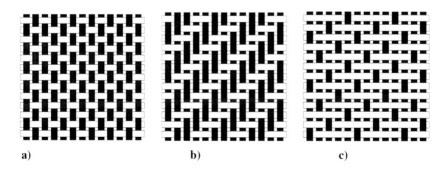

a)   b)   c)

Fig. 3.9   Various commonly used weave architectures: *a*) plain; *b*) twill; *c*) satin.

interlacing, whereby the weft yarns pass over several (4 in the case of 5-harness satin and 7 in the case of 8-harness satin) warp yarns. Twill and satin weaves have lower degrees of fiber crimp than plain weave and hence are heavier fabrics due to better packing density. They also have better drapability, formability, and in-plane properties. As a result of the lower degree of interlacing, these fabrics are also less stable and can create some difficulty during handling. Basket weaves have two or more warp yarns interlacing with two or more weft yarns. In some cases, the woven fabric has a highly biased fiber content in the warp direction, whereby the warp yarns are held by sparingly introduced weft yarns that are also normally much thinner than the warp yarns. These are referred to as *uni-weaves.*

Woven fabrics are also available in a number of hybrid (mixed-fiber) forms. For example, a cloth could be made in any of the forms previously discussed, having carbon fibers in the warp direction and glass or aramid in the weft direction. Alternatively, carbon and one or more of the other fiber types may alternate in the warp or weft direction. Hybridization may be desirable for either property or cost reasons.

Woven fabrics can be produced from rovings (and hence they are called *woven rovings*), or from finer yarns. Woven fabrics come in either wide or narrow forms; the latter is convenient for localized, selective reinforcement.

Woven fabrics may also be produced in a form in which the main fibers are mixed (comingled) with thermoplastic polymer fibers. During consolidation of the fabric, the thermoplastic fiber melts and flows to form a thermoplastic matrix.

Weaving causes a periodic out-of-plane undulation of the fibers, resulting in a significant loss of reinforcing efficiency because the optimum reinforcing efficiency is obtained only when the fibers are absolutely straight and in plane. Compression strength is particularly compromised with undulating fibers. However, as may be expected, through-thickness strength including delamination resistance is improved.

3.8.5 Braided Fabrics

Braids are generally more expensive than woven fabrics due to the more complex manufacturing process. However, they also usually offer greater strength per fabric weight. Produced in either the flat or tubular forms, braided fabrics can have at least one axial yarn that is not crimped, thereby allowing $[0, \pm \theta]$ orientations to be achieved. Due to limitations imposed by the size of braiding machines, the widths of these fabrics are normally much narrower than those of woven fabrics and are only suitable for selective reinforcement and production of components with small cross-sections, such as poles and tubes. Chapter 14 provides information on braided composites.

3.8.6 Non-crimp Fabrics

Also known as multiaxial, multilayer warp-knit fabrics, non-crimp fabrics consist of fibers that are held straight and in plane by a stitched or knitted thermoplastic polymer (typically nylon or polyester) fiber or a flexible high-performance fiber such as glass or aramid. The material is not crimped as in the case of woven material, and as such, the fibers are arranged in a more optimal fashion. These important fabrics are further discussed in Chapter 14.

3.8.7 Tapes

Tapes are essentially narrow dry fiber fabrics having widths of less than 100 mm. The tape may be a woven cloth or it may contain mainly warp, unidirectional fibers with a light cross weave or knit of polymer fibers to hold the tows in place. Another alternative is to bond the fibers onto thin supporting fiber mat or cloth, using a low-volume fraction of a thermoplastic polymer or uncured thermoset that is later absorbed into the matrix. Monofilament tapes are often made this way. If the tape is held together by woven or knitted fibers, it usually has a stitched or reinforced edge to keep it from falling apart. This is generally trimmed off after the composite has been cured.

3.8.8 Three-dimensional Textiles Preforms

Three-dimensional textiles preforms are dry fiber forms in which the complete reinforcement is manufactured as a single product. The finished component then requires only the addition of resin and curing. Three-dimensional preforms can be woven, braided, or knitted. All these textile techniques are capable, within limits, of producing fully-fashioned or net-shaped preforms with improved formability/ drapability and can potentially reduce production times, particularly for complex-shaped components. These processes are also discussed in Chapter 14.

References

[1] Kelly, A., *Strong Solids*, 3rd ed., Clarendon Press, Oxford, UK, 1986.

[2] Watt, W., and Perlov, B. V., (eds.), *Handbook of Composites: Volume 1 Fibers*, 1985, edited by A. Kelly, and Y. N. Rabotnov, Series Ed. North Holland,

[3] Chawla, K. K., "Fibers," *Composite Materials: Science and Engineering*, Spinger-Verlag, 1987, Chap. 2.

[4] Weibull, W., *Journal of Applied Mechanics*, Vol. 18, 1951, pp. 293–297.

[5] Dwight, D. W., "Glass Fiber Reinforcement," *Comprehensive Composite Materials*, edited by A. Kelly and C. Zweben, Vol. 1, Elsevier, Cambridge 2000.

[6] Shindo, A., "Polyacrylonitrile (PAN)-Based Carbon Fibers," *Comprehensive Composite Materials*, edited by A. Kelly and C. Zweben, Vol. 1, Elsevier, 2000.

[7] Diefendorfe, R. J., "Pitch Precursor Carbon Fibers," *Comprehensive Composite Materials*, edited by A. Kelly and C. Zweben, Vol. 1, Elsevier, Cambridge 2000.

[8] Pagliacampi, J. J., "Inorganic Fibers" *Engineered Material Handbook*, Vol. 1, ASM International, 1987.

[9]Wawner, F. E., "Boron and Silicon Carbide CVD Fibers," *Comprehensive Composite Materials*, edited by A. Kelly and C. Zweben, Vol. 1, Elsevier, 2000.

[10]Ichikawa H., and Ishikawa, T., "Silicon Carbide Fibers (Organometallic Pyrolysis)," *Comprehensive Composite Materials*, edited by A. Kelly and C. Zweden, Elsevier, Cambridge 2000.

[11]Yang, H. H., *Kevlar Aramid Fiber*, John Wiley and Sons, Chichester, West Sussex, England, UK, 1993.

[12]Peus, T., Jacobs, M. J., and Lemstra, P. L., "High Performance Polythene Fibers," *Comprehensive Composite Materials*, edited by A. Kelly and C. Zweben, Vol. 1, Elsevier, 2000.

[13]Kumar S., and Wang, Y., "Fibers, Fabrics and Fillers," *Composite Engineering Handbook*, edited by P. K. Mallick, Marcel Dekker, 1997, Chapter 2.

[14]Bennett S. C., and Johnson D. J., "Strength-Structure Relationships in Pall-Based Carbon Fibers," *Journal of Materials Science*, Vol. 18, No. 11, Nov. 1983.

4
Polymeric Matrix Materials

4.1 Introduction

The matrix, as discussed in the Chapter 1, serves the following functions: 1) transfers load into and out from the fibers, 2) separates the fibers to prevent failure of adjacent fibers when one fails, 3) protects the fiber from environmental damage, supports the fibers in the shape of the component.

The mechanical properties of the composite that are significantly affected by the properties of the polymeric matrix (and fiber/matrix bond strength) include 1) longitudinal compression strength, 2) transverse tensile strength, and 3) interlaminar shear strength. These are generally called *matrix-dominated properties*.

To be suitable as matrices, polymers must also have resistance to aircraft solvents such as fuel, hydraulic fluid, and paint stripper and to service temperatures typically up to around $80\,°C$ for civil and $150\,°C$ for military applications; however, a capability to over $200\,°C$ may be required in some applications.

In the production of advanced composites suitable for aerospace applications, it is important that the method of matrix incorporation does not damage the reinforcement fibers or inadvertently change their orientation. One suitable method is to infiltrate an aligned fiber bed with a low-viscosity liquid that is then converted, by chemical reaction or simply by cooling, to form a continuous solid matrix with the desired properties.

4.1.1 Background on Polymeric Materials

Polymers consist of very long chain molecules,[1] generally with a backbone consisting of covalently bonded carbon atoms. In the simplest type of polymer, each carbon atom is joined to two others to form a linear polymer. The other two available bonds not used in the chain are linked to side groups (Fig. 4.1). If, however, the carbon atoms link with carbon atoms that are not in simple groups, then a three-dimensional network or cross-linked polymer results.

Figure 4.2 is a highly simplified schematic[2] comparing the polymer backbones of linear and cross-linked polymer chain configurations. There are, however, several intermediate forms, including branched and ladder polymers, shown in

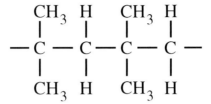

Fig. 4.1   Example of the polymer chain arrangement of a simple linear polymer.

Figure 4.2. Polymer branching can occur with linear or cross-linked polymers; ladder polymers are made of two linear polymers joined by regular linkages. As may be expected, ladder polymers are more rigid than simple linear polymers.

Linear molecules can be characterized in terms of the molecular weight, which is an indication of the average length of the molecular chain; however, this has no meaning for cross-linked polymers because these do not form as discrete molecules. The formula for a linear polymer is $(M)_n$ where M is the repeating unit and n the degree of polymerization. For example, in a sample of the polymer with an average n of 5000, the range will typically be in the range 1000–10,000.

If there is only one type of repeating unit, the polymer is called a homopolymer. When, however, there are two types of repeating unit based on two types of monomer, the resulting polymer is called a copolymer. In a block copolymer, each repeating unit has a regular distribution of long sequences. If, however, the sequence is random, the resulting polymer is called a regular or random copolymer. If there is a chain of one type of polymer with branches of another type, the resulting polymer is called a graft copolymer.

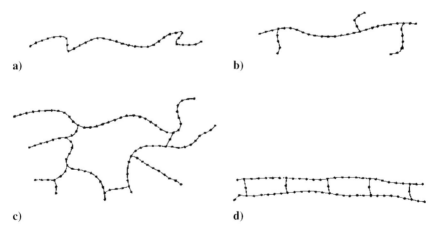

a)

b)

c)

d)

Fig. 4.2   Schematic illustration of the molecular configuration of *a*) linear, *b*) branched, *c*) cross-linked, and *d*) ladder polymers.

The process of polymerization generally involves the linking of carbon atoms in short-chain organic compounds called monomers, through reaction or by catalysis. The two principal types of polymerization are called condensation polymerization and addition polymerization.

In condensation polymerization, the monomers link together (or cure) producing water or other small molecules as a by-product, while in addition polymerization, the monomers link without producing any by-product. The production of small volatile molecules during matrix formation is highly undesirable, as it can lead to extensive voiding. However, voiding can be minimized in these systems if polymerization occurs under high-pressure conditions.

Polymers with a three-dimensional network structure are called thermosetting polymers, and the process of network formation is called curing. The precursor materials used to form the network are monomer or oligomer (several monomers joined together) mixtures called resins. These, depending on formulation and temperature, can range in viscosity from free-flowing liquids, similar to a light oil (< 1000 centipoise) or highly viscous semi-solids (> 100,000 centipoise). Curing is brought about by the reaction of the resin with a curing agent (which may be another resin) or a catalyst, often at elevated temperature. Thermosets, once cured, become solids that cannot be melted and reformed. Thermoplastics are higher molecular weight linear polymers that undergo no permanent chemical change on heating (below the decomposition temperature). They flow upon heating so that they can be reformed.

Finally, a common chemical theme among polymeric materials used for aerospace matrices is that they contain rigid rings (aromatic rings) in their structure. This provides the required chemical resistance and mechanical properties at elevated temperature.

4.1.2 Structure and Mechanical Properties

Thermosetting and thermoplastic polymers differ in many respects. One important difference is that some degree of crystallinity is possible with thermoplastics, whereas thermosets are amorphous. The degree of crystallinity in thermoplastic polymers depends on many parameters, particularly those that allow or inhibit easy alignment of the polymer chains, for example the size and regularity of the side groups. Depending on the temperature, the molecular chains are in a constant state of motion relative to one another. At modest temperatures, depending on the polymer chain, islands of crystallinity exist in an amorphous matrix.

The crystalline regions consist of regions of aligned chains, generally produced by folding of a single chain (Fig. 4.3). In some cases, order is further increased by groups of crystals forming ordered regions known as spherulites because of their spherical geometry. The important point is that the density of the polymer is much higher in the crystalline regions, but its random molecular

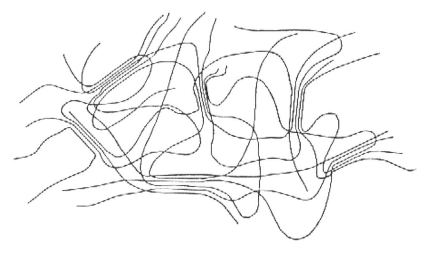

Fig. 4.3   Schematic representation of a linear polymer showing amorphous and local areas of crystallization where the polymer chains are aligned.

motion is reduced, resulting in increases in mechanical properties such as stiffness and chemical properties such as solvent resistance. This degree of order is changed at elevated temperature as the crystalline order is reduced, resulting in a marked but gradual change in, for example, stiffness. Unlike simple solids where a definite transition from a crystal to a liquid occurs at a specific temperature T_m, in polymers T_m is a range and melting results in an amorphous semi-solid material (Fig. 4.4). In contrast, since there are no regions of crystallinity, thermosets and amorphous thermoplastics show no sharp melting point, but a gradual reduction in stiffness over a range of temperatures.

At low temperatures, thermoplastics form a solid that may be partially crystalline and partially amorphous. The degree of crystallinity depends on the polymer structure and the cooling rate. With rapid cooling or with polymers having bulky side chains, the structure could be largely amorphous.

Below a certain temperature called the glass-transition temperature T_g, the random molecular motion drops to a very low level, which is particularly marked in the amorphous regions. The chains thus become set in their random patterns, and the material becomes rigid and glass-like. Above T_g, polymers exhibit a low stiffness and rubbery behavior. This behavior above and below T_g also occurs for similar reasons in thermosets, but is not so marked as the movement of the polymer chains is restricted by the cross-links.

Figure 4.5 schematically illustrates this behavior for 1) a crystalline thermoplastic, 2) an amorphous thermoplastic, 3) a thermoset, and 4) a rubber. Because the crystalline regions inhibit slippage of the polymer chains even above T_g, the drop in stiffness is dramatic when crystalline melting occurs.

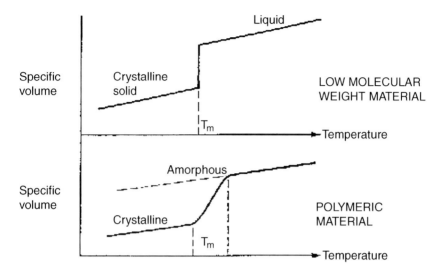

Fig. 4.4 Schematic plot of the variation of specific volume with temperature for a low molecular weight material, such as a metal, and for a linear polymeric material.

The temperature determined for T_g is generally a function of the method of measurement. Most practical determinations of T_g involve stressing the sample and determining the effect of temperature. The speed of application of the stress and the rate of change of temperature has a pronounced effect on the observed temperature of the glass transition. Modern dynamic mechanical (thermal) analysis equipment is able to simultaneously carry out such stress testing at a

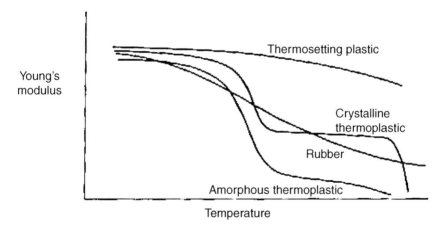

Fig. 4.5 Schematic plot of variation of Young's modulus with temperature for various types of polymer.

range of frequencies. The mechanical failure mode of particular composite items made with these resins could therefore be different at different temperatures as well as under different testing regimens. Many rubbery materials will fail in a "glassy manner" if tested at a high enough speed.

4.2 Thermoset and Thermoplastic Polymer Matrix Materials

As discussed earlier, polymers fall into the two major categories: thermosetting and thermoplastic. Thermosets have the great advantage that they allow fabrication of composites at relatively low temperatures and pressures because they go through a low-viscosity stage (sometimes very low) before polymerization and cross-linking.

Based on Ref. 3, the relative properties of thermosets and thermoplastics, and their advantages and disadvantages, are summarized in Table 4.1.

Table 4.1   Thermoset Matrices and Thermoplastic Matrices

Thermoset	Thermoplastic
Main Characteristics	
• Undergoes chemical change when cured	• Non-reacting, no cure required
• Low strain to failure	• High strain to failure
• Low fracture energy	• High fracture energy
• Processing is irreversible	• Very high viscosity
• Very low viscosity possible	• Processing is reversible
• Absorbs moisture	• Absorbs little moisture
• Highly resistant to solvents	• Limited resistance to organic solvents, in some cases
Advantages	
• Relatively low processing temperature	• Short processing times possible
• Good fiber wetting	• Reusable scrap
• Formable into complex shapes	• Post-formable can be reprocessed
• Liquid-resin manufacturing feasible	• Rapid processing
• Resistant to creep	• Unlimited shelf life without refrigeration
	• High delamination resistance
Disadvantages	
• Long processing time	• Lower resistance to solvents
• Long ($\sim 1-2$ h) cure	• Requires high temperature (300– 400° C) and pressure processing
• Restricted storage life (requires refrigeration)	• Can be prone to creep
	• Very poor drapability and tack

Of all thermosetting resins, epoxy resins are the most widely used in aircraft structures. Epoxies have excellent chemical and mechanical properties, have low shrinkage, and adhere adequately to most types of fiber. Importantly, they go through a low-viscosity stage during cure and so allow for the use of liquid resin–forming techniques such as resin-transfer molding (RTM). In general, the glass transition temperature T_g of epoxy resins increases with increasing temperature of cure. Thereby, epoxy systems cured at 120 °C and 180 °C have upper (dry) service temperatures of 100–130 °C and 150 °C, respectively (note a significant margin on T_g is mandated in designs; see Chapter 12). It is important to note that T_g is reduced significantly by absorbed moisture, as discussed later.

Bismaleimide resins (BMIs) have similar excellent processability and comparable mechanical properties to epoxies. Importantly, they can operate at higher temperatures; however, as with epoxies, T_g is markedly reduced by absorbed moisture. Generally, BMI resins cured at around 200 °C have upper service temperatures above 180 °C. The higher cost of BMI resins limits their use to applications where the operating temperatures exceed the capability of epoxies.

If even higher operating temperatures are required, composites based on polyimide resin matrices may be the only option. These high-temperature thermosetting resins typically cure around 270 °C and allow operating temperatures of up to 300 °C. However, there are penalties of a higher cost than BMIs and much more difficult processing.

Thermosetting resins have relatively low fracture strains and fracture toughness as inelastic deformation is limited by the highly cross-linked structure. This translates into poor fracture resistance in the composite. These systems also absorb atmospheric moisture, in some cases over 3%, resulting in reduced matrix-dominated properties in the composite, such as elevated temperature shear and compressive strength.

Thermoplastics suitable for use as matrices for high-performance composites include polymers such as polyetheretherketone (PEEK), for applications up to approximately 120 °C; polyetherketone (PEK) for up to 145 °C; and polyimide (thermoplastic type) for up to 270 °C. Fabrication of thermoplastic composites involves melting and forming steps.[4] Because these materials are already fully polymerized, their viscosity, even when melted, is generally much higher than that of most thermosetting resins. They are thus not well suited to conventional liquid resin techniques such as RTM. Fabrication techniques based on resin-film infusion (RFI) or pre-preging (pre-coating the fibers by dissolving the polymer in an appropriate solvent) and then hot-pressing are more appropriate (See Chapter 5).

An advantage of thermoplastic composites is their higher retained hot/wet properties as they absorb less moisture (typically around 0.2%) than thermosetting resin composites. These polymers also have a much higher strain to failure because they can undergo plastic deformation, resulting in significantly improved impact resistance.

Aerospace-grade thermoplastics are generally more expensive than thermo-sets and are more costly to fabricate, due to the high temperatures and pressures involved. In addition, with continual research and development improvements in thermosets, even the toughness advantage of thermoplastic composites is being eroded. There is little doubt that thermoplastics will be used extensively in the future—especially in niche areas in which high resistance to impact or edge damage (for example, in the case of doors) justifies the higher cost.

The comparative physical properties of the standard matrix resins are discussed in Ref. 5 and 6, and Ref. 7 provides a good overview of the chemistry of the various systems.

The following sections provide more details on the various polymer matrix materials.

4.3   Thermosetting Resin Systems

Table 4.2 and 4.3 list some of the relevant attributes of some of the thermosetting thermoplastic matrices, and Table 4.4 provides details on some of the important properties, including fracture energy.

4.3.1   Epoxy Resins

Epoxy resins[8] are a class of compounds containing two or more epoxide groups per molecule. Figure 4.6 depicts the structures of the major epoxy systems used in aerospace composite matrices. The epoxide is the three-membered ring formed by the oxygen and the two carbons. It is also called an oxirane ring, or the glycidyl group.

Epoxies are formed by reacting polyphenols or other active hydrogen compounds with epichlorohydrin under basic conditions. The most common phenol used is bisphenol A (Diphenylolpropane). It provides the basis of a whole family of aerospace epoxy resins having the general structure shown in Figure 4.6a. These are usually complex mixtures of molecules with various values of n. The lower the value of n or the more complex the mixture, the lower the resin viscosity but the more brittle the final cured resin. Trade names of these resins include such materials as Epikote or Epon 828, Dow DER 331, and Araldite F.

There are many other epoxy resins manufactured for special purposes, but of particular importance in advanced aerospace materials are the tetraglycidyl derivative of diaminodiphenylmethane (TGDDM) (Fig. 4.6b) and the triglycidyl derivative of p-aminophenol (TGAP) (Fig. 4.6c). The high functionality of these materials makes for higher resin reactivity and greater cross-linking, which translates into higher composite stiffness and glass transition temperatures. In contrast, use is often made of small amounts of reactive diluent epoxy resins such as the bis epoxy from butane diol (Fig. 4.6d) to improve the flow

Table 4.2 Some Details on Selected Thermosetting Matrix Materials Used in Aerospace Composites

Matrix	Examples	~Cure °C/KPa	Max (wet) Capability °C	Comments on Performance as Matrix
Epoxy	Hexcel 920	120/700	80+	Best properties all around.
Epoxy	Hercules 3501–6 Fiberite 934 Narmco 5208	180/700	100+	Excellent adhesion to fibers. Easy to process, wide viscosity range, good wetting, and large process window. Not prone to voiding, low volatile emission. Excellent water and other chemical resistance. Large database for aerospace application. Fairly low toughness, composites sensitive to impact damage. Limited temperature capability. Absorbs moisture, reducing elevated temperature. Mechanical properties. Sensitive to UV exposure.
Epoxy Toughened	Hercules 3502 Fiberite 977–2	180/700	100+	All of the above, plus: Improved tolerance to damage. Increased moisture sensitivity.
BMI	Hexcel F560	180/700 + postcure 200	230	Exceeds epoxy temperature capability. Relatively easy to process. Even less tough than epoxies. Undergoes shrinkage during cure. Prone to microcrack with thermal cycling.
BMI Toughened	Cytec 5250–4	180/700	180	All of the characteristics listed for BMI, plus: More damage resistant. Lower temperature capability than untoughhned.
Polyimide Condensation	PMR-15	300/4100	320	Resistant to oxidation. Similar properties to epoxy—matrix composites possible but overextended temperature range. Low toughness. Prone to severe voiding. Difficult to process.

(Continued)

Table 4.3 Some Details on Selected Thermoplastic Matrix Materials Used in Aerospace Composites (continued)

Polymer	Examples	Process Temp~°C	T_g °C	Comments on Performance as a Matrix
PEEK, Polyether-etherketone	Victrex	400	145	Excellent mechanical properties, including toughness. For application at temperatures up to 120°C. Highly resistant to damage by aircraft fluid. Excellent fire resistance. Most widely used for high-performance composites.
PPS, Polyphenylene-sulfide	Ryton	340	90	Good strength, stiffness, and temperature capability. Some grades have low viscosity, aiding composite manufacture. Resistant to most aircraft fluids, but attacked by some solvents, including paint stripper. Good fire resistance. Low impact resistance.
PSF, Polysulfone	Udel	400	190	
PAS, Polyarylsulfone	Radel	400	220	
PES, Polyether-sulfone	Vitrex	400	230	
PI, Polyimide	Kapton	390	320	Selected for highest-temperature applications. Highly viscous. Difficult to process.
PEI, Polyetherimide	Ultem	370	215	Selected for high-temperature applications. Lower cost than PI.

Table 4.4 Approximate Properties of Selected Polymer Matrix Materials

Matrix Material Details	G_{1C} (J/m^2)	E (GPa)	ε (%)	T_g (°C) Dry	Wet $\sim$
920 Hexcel	541	3.8	8.4	107	85
RTM6 Resin transfer molding resin	168	2.9	3.4	183	167
F584 First generation pre-preg epoxy	175	4.1	1.8	171	121
914 First generation pre-preg epoxy	103	3.9	1.5	190	N/A
F593 Pre-preg epoxy	420	3.0	2	172	131
977-3 Pre-preg epoxy	217	N/A	N/A	218	178
977-2 Toughened version of 977-3	478	3.5	N/A	212	N/A
6376 Toughened pre-preg epoxy	432	3.0	3.1	N/A	N/A
8552 Toughened pre-preg epoxy	N/A	4.0	4	195	154
524C Modified BMI resin	67	3.3	2.9	220	–
PMR 15 Polyimide	280	4.0	1.1	340	–
Udel Polysulfone	3200	2.7	50	190	–
Radel Polyarylsulfone	5500	2.8	60	220	–
PES Polyether sulfone	2600	2.9	40	220	–
Ultem Polyetherimide	3700	4.0	60	220	–
Torlon Polyamideimide	3400	4.9	15	275	–
PEEK Polyetheretherketone	4400	3.6	30	145	–

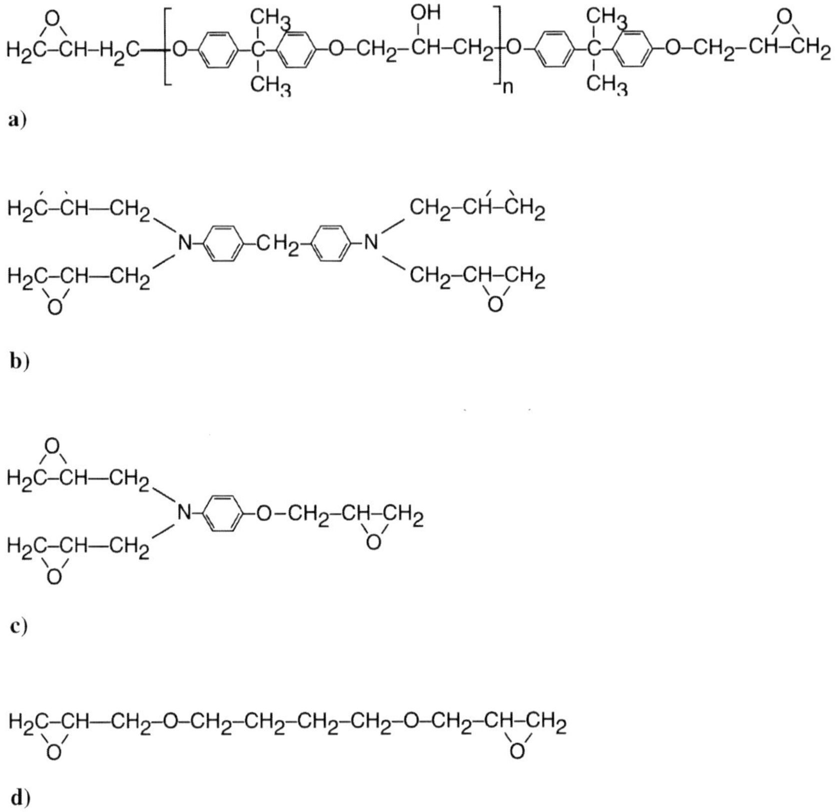

a)

b)

c)

d)

Fig. 4.6   Major epoxy resins used in aerospace composite matrices: *a*) **bisphenol A-epichorohydrin (DGEBA) resins;** *b*) **tetraglycidyl derivative of diamino diphenyl methane (TGGM);** *c*) **triglycidyl derivative of p-aminophenol (TGAP);** *d*) **reactive diluent epoxy resin such as the bis epoxy from butane diol.**

characteristics of epoxy formulations before cure. This does, however, result in some loss in final high-temperature properties.

4.3.1.1 Curing of Epoxy Resins.   The epoxide group has unfavorable bonding angles, which makes it chemically reactive with a variety of substances that can easily open the ring to form a highly cross-linked structure. The cross linking may occur through the epoxy groups or the resulting hydroxy groups.

While epoxy resins can be self-polymerized using suitable catalysts, the majority of applications make use of curing agents—often called hardeners. The major classes of curing agents include aliphatic amines, which give cold-curing systems and aromatic amines and polyanhydrides, which give heat-curing

systems. Aromatic amines form the bulk of the curing agents in the advanced
aerospace composites as they produce matrix materials and hence composites
with high glass-transition temperatures.

An epoxy resin cure is the result of a complex series of individual chemical
reactions that have different rates, even at the same temperature. An example is
the reaction of an amino group in a hardener with an epoxy group in the resin, as
shown in Figure 4.7. Reaction 1 is usually much faster than 2, which is in turn
faster than 3 (epoxy self-polymerization), but this sequence can change with
different catalysts and as the viscosity changes. The last reaction is often the
major type of reaction that can occur at high viscosities, after gelation or in highly
cross-linked systems. Because of this reaction rate difference, it is very important
to follow an exact cure profile in making a composite part: the incorrect cure
cycle gives different molecular architecture and hence different, possibly inferior,
mechanical and chemical properties. What is also important about this sequence
of individual reactions to form the solid matrix (called a step growth mechanism
of polymerization) is that it requires the correct "stoichiometry," or ratio of
functional groups, and each step required takes time. This contrasts with the
polyester mechanism, described later. Another important point to be considered
with an epoxy resin is that it goes through a number of physical states as it cures.
An initial low-viscosity state is important to get the resin to flow into and wet-out
all the fine crevasses between the fibers in a composite part. The viscosity reaches
a minimum, caused by outside heat or the heat of reaction of the functional
groups, and then increases rapidly due to molecular chain extension. The next
step in the reaction is gelation—when the chains start to cross-link, the resin no
longer flows and most individual reaction rates decrease markedly. The final step
at high cross-linking is called vitrification, at which point-chain motion stops.

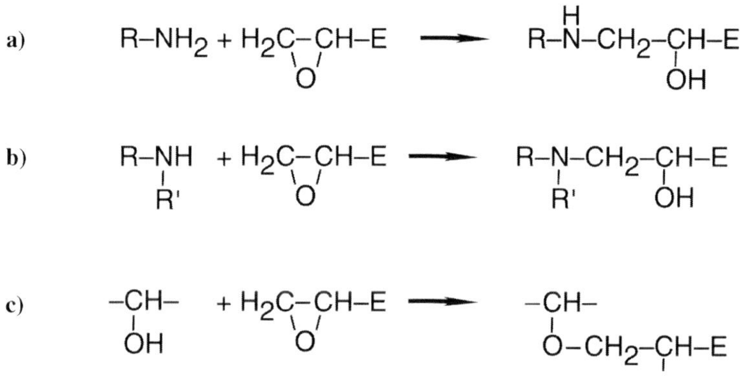

Fig. 4.7   Epoxy cure reactions: *a)* **primary amine-epoxy reaction,** *b)* **secondary
amine-epoxy reaction,** *c)* **hydroxyl group reaction (etherification). R is a general
amine backbone, E is a general epoxy backbone.**

Diffusion of the reacting groups in this glassy phase is very slow, and the normal cure reactions effectively stop at this point.

As mentioned above, the cure of an epoxy resin can be accelerated by the use of suitable catalysts (such as dicyanimide or BF_3-monoethylamine) or heat, but the maximum rate is normally much slower than for polyesters. This is partly because the epoxy/hardener group reaction is strongly exothermic (generates heat), so the use of excessive quantities of catalyst or inappropriately high cure temperatures will result in thermal degradation of the matrix, especially in thick composite sections. In particularly bad cases or where there are large quantities of resin, uncontrollable exothermic decomposition can occur. Use of catalysts also allows the development of resin systems with long pot lives; this is very important for manufacturing processes such as filament winding.

4.3.1.2 Epoxy Matrix Properties.   The occurrence of rubber (gelled) and glassy states is characteristic of amorphous polymers such as epoxy resins. Such polymers become glassy at relatively low temperatures, and at high temperatures they usually become rubbery again. As the normal polymerization mechanism of an epoxy resin stops in the glassy state, it is very difficult to design a system that will be capable of operation at much over the maximum temperature in the cure cycle. Systems cured at room temperature, using aliphatic polyamine curing agents, are not suitable for use at temperatures much higher than $50\,°C$. Systems cured with aromatic polyamines or anhydrides are usually cured at temperatures around $120-180\,°C$ and can often be postcured at $150-220\,°C$. These can have maximum operating temperatures in the range of $100-250\,°C$.

Gillham[9] devised a very helpful diagrammatic representation of the cure properties of various matrix resins (especially epoxy materials). Such a generalized time-temperature-transformation diagram is shown in Figure 4.8.

4.3.1.3 Formulating With Epoxy Resins.   The properties of the final cured matrix are partially defined by the choice of resin and curing agent but may be further modified by a range of additives. As always, the choice of starting materials for a particular purpose depends on a whole series of compromises, not the least of which are cost and availability. For example, the DGEBA materials of structure Figure 4.6a provided the bulk of the epoxy resins previously used in the aerospace industry; more recent formulations have substituted the multifunctional resins TGDDM (Fig. 4.6b) and TGAP (Fig. 4.6c). These improve the thermal stability properties and modulus, with some loss in toughness and an increase in costs.
The choice of resin curing agents or hardeners often includes a compromise on safety, with some of the more active amine hardeners being relatively toxic or unpleasant.

The various additives that can be used to modify resin properties include:

(1) Diluents are added to reduce the viscosity before cure to aid in handling, wet-out, etc. (usually these cause decreases in the maximum operating temperatures, except for low-viscosity aromatic resins like TGAP).

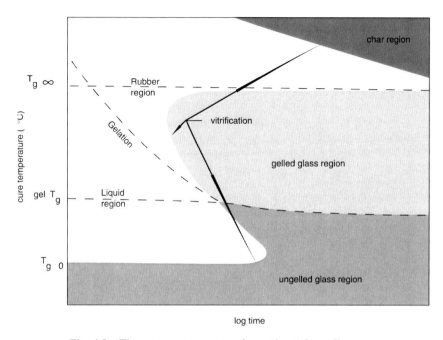

Fig. 4.8   Time-temperature-transformation (phase diagram).

(2) Flexibilizers are added to reduce the elastic modulus and increase the elongation to failure.

(3) Toughening agents that precipitate from the reacting matrix during cure as fine particles, designed to modify the crack propagation properties in a cured matrix. In the past, most of these were reactive rubbers, but much more interest is now centered on engineering thermoplastic additives because they have fewer detrimental effects on the high-temperature properties of a matrix resin. Toughening mechanisms are discussed in the following section.

(4) Inert fillers, including hollow spheres, are added to alter density, resin flow, cost, and effective modulus.

4.3.1.4 Toughening Epoxy Resins.   Epoxies, though they generally have relatively high strength and stiffness and many other desirable properties, are too brittle to be used in their unmodified form as structural adhesives. Thus, various approaches are used to provide toughening, including the formation of a solid solution with a more ductile polymer, precipitation of a elastomeric second phase, and development of interpenetrating polymer networks.

By far, the most explored and practically exploited approach to the toughening of epoxy resins is the formation of a finely distributed elastomeric second phase. There are two ways of achieving this microstructure. The main way is by the addition of an elastomer in the unreacted form to the base resin. It is important that the elastomer molecules employed react with the resin matrix (by copolymerization) and that they then precipitate out by phase separation to form a dispersed second phase, without leaving excessive amounts of the elastomer completely dissolved in the matrix. Significant amounts of dissolved elastomer would result in an unacceptable reduction in T_g. The main elastomer used is a carboxy-terminated butadiene nitrile rubber (CTBN) that can be used in concentrations of up to about 18% in the uncured epoxy. Figure 4.9 shows a typical relationship between CTBN and measured fracture toughness.

Another approach is to add the elastomer as a very fine powder to form a dispersion. However, this is generally used in addition to the precipitation approach to increase the total amount of dispersed phase.

A number of processes result in the toughening observed with elastomer modification.[10] Firstly, it is thought that the hydrostatic tensile stresses at the crack tip are relieved by dilation and fracture of the elastomer particles, allowing increased ductility at the crack tip. Secondly, the local stress concentrations associated with the elastomeric particles are considered to encourage shear yielding of the epoxy matrix around the crack tip, which is both more extensive and at more sites. Thirdly (and probably least important), some rubber particles actually bridge the growing crack, increasing the fracture energy by the work required to elongate and rupture them; for this mechanism to operate, a strong bond between the elastomer particles and the matrix is essential.

4.3.1.5 Moisture Sensitivity in Epoxy Resins and Other Thermosets.   Each type of epoxy matrix has a moisture sensitivity that depends largely on the polarity

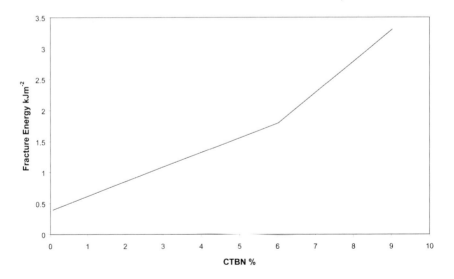

Fig. 4.9   Fracture energy of epoxy resin system as a function of the carboxyl-terminated butadiene acrylonitrile (CTBN) content.

of the molecular structure. For example, for the relatively non-polar but high-shrinkage polyester and vinylester resins, the moisture absorption problems tend to be between the fiber surface and the resin. However, for the highly polar epoxy resins, which have been most heavily studied, the major moisture problems occur because of changes to the bulk resin.

Depending on their individual molecular structures as well as their degree of cure, epoxy resins have a tendency to absorb considerable amounts of moisture, especially in very humid environments. A typical aerospace TGDDM cured resin may absorb between 4.5% and 7% by weight of water at equilibrium, and this may reduce the glass transition temperature by $70-100\,^\circ C$, which will have a major effect on composite properties. The sorption of water may also cause irreversible damage to the material as a result of the formation of microcracks through repeated absorption/desorption cycles. Of course the rate of absorption of water in an epoxy matrix composite will depend on the thickness of the composite and the type and architecture of the fiber. However, there is usually a fast early absorption peak followed by a long, slow absorption plateau before equilibrium is reached.

To explain some of the anomalies in the behavior of epoxy resins, it has been postulated that the absorbed water is made up of at least two different species. One species forms a molecular solution, hydrogen bonded to polar groups in the molecule (such as the hydroxyl or amine groups), and another species is confined to areas of abnormally large free volume often called holes or microvoids. There has been considerable spectroscopic evidence obtained from Fourier transform infrared spectra (FTIR) mainly mid IR and near IR as well as nuclear magnetic resonance (NMR), supporting this view, but not everyone agrees. The absorbed moisture that is present in the polymer matrix is believed to act as a plasticizer, especially at elevated temperatures. However, as only the bound water should have this effect, it is important to understand the ratio of bound to unbound water. The environmental effects that appear to be especially damaging are sudden large temperature changes, referred to as "thermal spikes," and these are encountered, for example, by aircraft flying at supersonic speeds. There is considerable experimental evidence that these thermal spikes can significantly and permanently alter both the moisture absorption levels and the mechanical properties of a composite material over time. Both long-term ageing studies (with commercially important materials) and attempts at theoretical predictions from fundamental chemical structures have been carried out (and are ongoing) to try to quantify the problems that these moisture effects cause in aircraft composite parts.

4.3.1.6 Improved Flame and Thermal Resistance.
The flame resistance[6] of epoxy and other themoset polymers, such as polyesters, can be improved by using flame retardants such as aluminum oxide trihydrate, halogenated compounds in combination with antimony oxide, and phosphorous and phosphorous-halogen compounds. Although the use of aromatic bromine

compounds with antimony oxide has wide commercial applications, when charring, these systems produce highly toxic and corrosive compounds during combustion. Finally, epoxy resins incorporating cyclic phosphine oxide and tetra-oxirane ring in the polymer backbone have good thermal stability and high char yield.

4.3.1.7 Advantages and Disadvantages of Epoxy Resins. The main advantages of epoxy resins are 1) the ability to formulate for optimum properties for a particular application; 2) the control of fracture toughness; 3) the convenience and safety of use due to low volatiles. Other advantages include low shrinkage, which helps give high bond strengths and adhesion to fibers, as well as good chemical resistance and good dimensional and thermal stability.

The main disadvantages are 1) relatively high cost compared with polyesters (especially the advanced aerospace epoxies); 2) moisture sensitivity; 3) less convenience than polyesters due to relatively slow cure and high viscosity; 4) limited resistance to some organic materials (particularly organic acids and phenols); and (5) a limited high-temperature performance even with the most advanced epoxy formulations.

4.3.2 Polyester Resins

The thermoset unsaturated polyester resins used in composite matrix resins are very different in character from the polyesters used in paints (alkyds) and thermoplastics (polyethylene-terepthalate), although they contain many of the same functional groups.

The polyesters used as matrices in composites are produced by first forming a low molecular weight (poly-) unsaturated polyester intermediate from a mixture of dibasic acids (including an unsaturated acid or anhydride such as maleic anhydride) and dihydric alcohols (glycols) or dihydric phenols as in Figure 4.10. These materials are usually viscous oils of molecular weight of 2000–4000 and are diluted with a reactive solvent such as styrene (35%) to improve flow properties and reactivity. When a source of free radicals is added (the initiator), and often a catalyst (the accelerator) as well, the styrene starts to polymerize. The polymerizing styrene radicals react with the unsaturated polyester sites to form a three-dimensional cross-linked network as shown in Figure 4.11. Higher

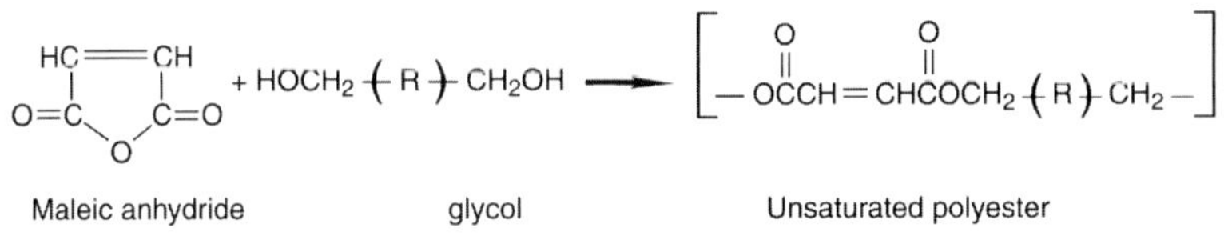

| Maleic anhydride | glycol | Unsaturated polyester |

Fig. 4.10   Formation of unsaturated polyester resin.

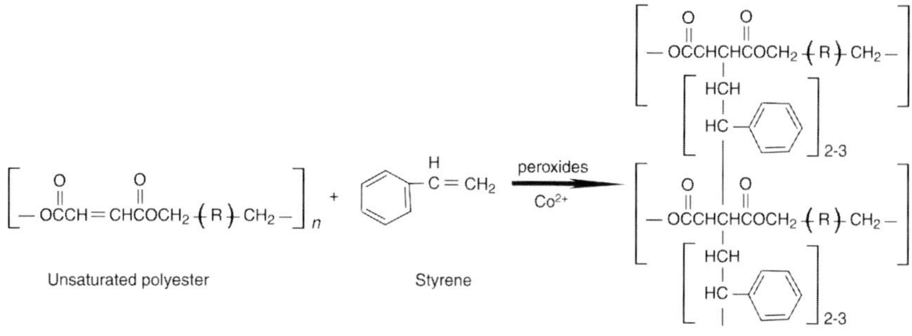

Fig. 4.11 Cure of polyester resin.

percentages of styrene lower the initial resin viscosity and increase reactivity but also increase the volatiles and the resin shrinkage.

4.3.2.1 Types of Polyester. The major commercial variations of polyester are based on modifications of the polyester component by partial replacement of the standard saturated phthalic acid or the glycol by alternative materials. For example, resins of improved strength and durability are obtained by replacing the normal (and lower cost) orthophthalic acid by isophthalic acid (isophthalic polyesters) or by the use of diphenylol propane in place of some of the glycol monomers (DPP resins). Another common variation is the use of adipic acid, which improves flexibility and increases the failure strain in the cured matrix. Halogenated anhydrides, such as tetrachlorophthalic anhydride, can be used in fire retardant formulations.

4.3.2.2 Curing of Polyesters. In contrast to the step growth cure of epoxy resins, polyester resins are cured by a free radical polymerization of unsaturated groups in a chain growth mechanism of polymer formation. This means that quite small quantities (0.5–3% of the resin) of an active initiator are used to start the reaction of a long "chain" of monomer double bonds. The speed of the polyester polymerization may be controlled over a wide range by adjustment of the quantities of this initiator and any accelerators that need to be added. However, the polymerization is strongly exothermic, and the use of high levels of initiator and accelerator will cause severe thermal damage in thick sections. The use of massive molds and the incorporation of fillers will reduce the exotherm by increasing the system thermal mass.

Although the free radical mechanism of cure means that the stoichiometric ratio of monomers is not important (so it is possible to obtain matrix materials with a wide range of properties), it is easy to kill the free radicals with impurities or oxygen. In fact, the resins are stabilized by quinone stabilizers that do just this and use up significant quantities of the initiators in the early stages of the cure. This means that unless precautions are taken, cure may be incomplete at free surfaces. Also, almost all free radical initiators are very sensitive, unpredictable, and dangerous chemicals that have to be handled with care, especially in a concentrated form.

The most commonly used initiator for the ambient temperature cure of polyester resins is methylethyl ketone peroxide (MEKP), usually supplied as a solution in dimethylphthalate. Metal salts such as cobalt naphthenate, supplied as a solution in naphtha, are used as accelerators with MEKP. MEKP is an extremely hazardous material that can cause permanent eye damage, skin burns, etc. and can also lead to serious fires and explosions if used incorrectly. Of particular importance is the admixture of the initiator and accelerator, which will spontaneously inflame and may explode if not properly diluted by the bulk resin. This can occur if the two materials are accidentally added successively to the resin without intermediate stirring.

Another common initiator is benzoyl peroxide (BzP), which is sold as a paste in dimethylphthalate. The appropriate accelerator for BzP is a tertiary amine. It should be noted that the accelerators for MEKP and BzP are not interchangeable. Systems cured with BzP without an accelerator, or cured with one having a very low accelerator content, are stable at room temperature but can be cured at elevated temperatures. A range of free radical initiators similar to BzP is available that will allow resin cure at a particular limiting temperature; for example, BzP is stable to 70 °C, whereas t-butyl peroxide is stable to 140 °C. Heat-cured polyesters are generally used in matched die molding, where fast cycle times are required.

As with epoxy resin chemistry, the cure of polyesters progresses from the liquid resin through a soft rubbery gel state. Cross-linking proceeds rapidly and establishes the structure of the three-dimensional network in which polymers and monomers are immobile. However, in the intermediate gel state, there is a decrease in the termination rate constant, a net increase in free radical concentration, an exponential jump in copolymer growth, and an increase in heat generated before a rigid plastic forms. This gel effect in free radical polymerization is in contrast to the slow-down effect seen in epoxy polymerization.

4.3.2.3 Advantages and Disadvantages of Polyesters.   The major advantages of polyesters are 1) initial low viscosity that allows easy wet-out of the reinforcement; 2) low cost (all raw materials are readily available and relatively inexpensive with easy long-term storage of starting materials); 3) cure conditions that can be modified easily with little operator experience; 4) easy manufacture in a range of modifications for particular applications; and 5) excellent environmental durability.

The major disadvantages are 1) high exotherm and high shrinkage on cure (both factors lead to a poor fiber/matrix bond strength due to in-built stress and thus poorer mechanical properties than epoxy resins); 2) systems with adequate shear strength tend to be brittle, and toughening additives appear to be ineffective; and 3) poor chemical resistance to even very dilute alkali.

4.3.3 Vinyl-Ester Resins

In many ways, vinyl-ester resins are an intermediate class of materials between epoxy resins and polyesters. The major ester ingredient is the product of the reaction of a standard epoxy resin such as DGEBA and methacrylic acid to give active ester products with structures such as those shown in Figure 4.12.

The unsaturated end groups are very reactive with the styrene diluent but tend to form linear, saturated polymer chains with less cross-linking, so they are tougher and more chemically resistant than polyesters. The resins are cured by the same, low-cost type of free radical reaction process as the polyesters, with many of the same process characteristics. A wide variety of epoxy systems have been used as starting materials for vinyl esters, therefore there is a large commercial range of vinyl esters with different mechanical properties. Examples include resins made from phenolic epoxies for high heat distortion temperatures and rubber-toughened resins.

The major advantages of vinyl esters are 1) they can combine the chemical resistance of epoxies with the easy processing of polyesters; 2) reactive double bonds only on the end of the polymer chains and their high relative reactivities with styrene result in a lower cross-link density and better mechanical properties in the cured polymer; 3) improved bond strength between the fiber and matrix exists. The major disadvantages of vinyl esters include 1) their higher costs when compared to polyesters and 2) higher shrinkage levels than epoxy resins.

4.3.4 Phenolic Resins

When phenol is condensed with formaldehyde under alkaline or strong acid conditions, polymerization occurs. If the system is carefully controlled, polymerization can be stopped while the polymer is still fusible and soluble. This prepolymer, when formed under basic conditions, is termed a *resol*. It will further polymerize under the influence of heat or of acidic or basic catalysts to

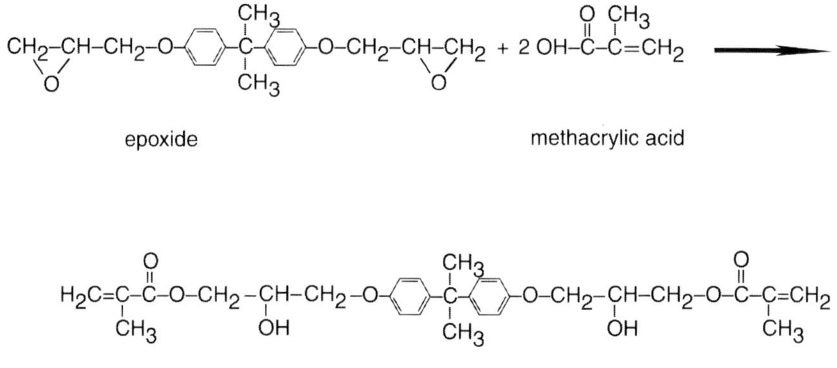

Fig. 4.12 Formation of vinyl ester resin.

give a densely cross-linked material of complex chemical structure (Fig. 4.13). Water and other volatile by-products are formed in this reaction, which requires that the polymerization be carried out under high pressure to avoid the formation of a friable foam. Cured resol-type phenolics usually have a high void content.

If the pre-polymerization is conducted under acidic conditions, a different polymerization path is followed, and a novolak resin is produced. This will not self-polymerize, but can be cross-linked under the influence of a complex amine, usually hexamethylene tetramine, to give structures such as those shown in Figure 4.14. Again, polymerization of the pre-polymer is carried out under pressure as volatile by-products are also formed in this reaction.

The phenolic pre-polymers for use in composites are solids and are usually supplied in solution. Due to the dilution effect, the solutions are stable at room temperature. Fibers, usually in the form of a cloth or mat, may be impregnated with the solution and the solvent evaporated to form a pre-preg. Alternatively, some acid-curing systems can be used in liquid molding processes (see Chapter 5) such as RTM and VARTM as the volatiles emitted during cure are controllable to the extent that excessive voiding (foaming) can be avoided.

4.3.4.1 Advantages and Disadvantages of Phenolic Resins.   The principle advantage of phenolic resins is their excellent resistance to high temperature, especially under oxidizing conditions. The fire-resistance of phenolics is related to their ablation properties, in other words, the speed at which they burn off when directly exposed to flame or other very high level heat fluxes. Under these conditions, phenolics char readily and thus give a high yield of a superficial layer of porous carbon. This protects the underlying composite, while the carbon slowly burns away. Most other resins usually provide a poor char yield and burn

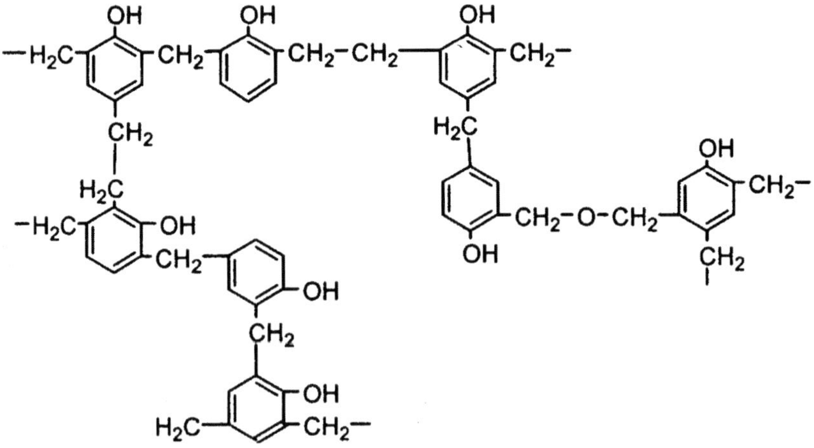

Fig. 4.13   Structure of a cross-linked phenolic resin (resol type).

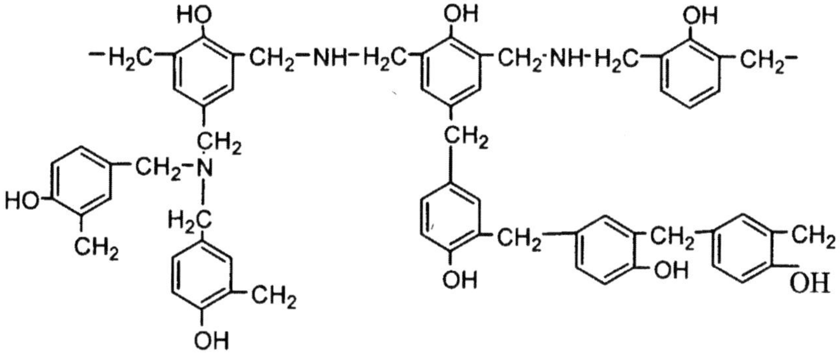

Fig. 4.14   Structure of a cross-linked phenolic resin (novolak type).

away to gaseous products relatively quickly. There are many applications of phenolic composite panels in non-structural internal panels where fire retardancy requirements, including smoke generation, are more critical than the mechanical strength properties. In recent times, some of these applications have been taken over by new thermoplastic matrix resin composites because their higher cost can be offset by their much better mechanical properties and their relative ease of processing by thermoforming.

The disadvantages of phenolics include 1) the difficulties in fabrication caused by the high pressures needed during polymerization; 2) their color (dark brown to black); and 3) the fact that the mechanical properties of derived composites are significantly lower than for those composites based on other resins due to the high content of the voids.

4.3.5 Bismaleimide Resins

Bismaleimide matrix resin formulations (BMIs) are highly cross-linked polymers produced by an addition-type polymerization of monomeric imide units synthesised from aromatic diamines and maleic anhydride. Varying the diamine precursor or the type of diamine mixtures used produces chemically different BMIs that in turn lead to unique matrix formulations. The most widely used building block is 4,4-bismaleimidodiphenylmethane (Fig. 4.15a) because the corresponding diamine precursor (Fig. 4.15b) is relatively available, is not costly, and the intermediate —CH_2— group provides some molecular flexibility in an otherwise very rigid molecule. In recent times there have been questions regarding the long-term health and safety aspects of this diamine and its products.

BMIs are thermoset resins, which are similar to epoxy matrix materials in their processability, although they can have better flow and wet-out properties. Typical glass transition temperatures range from 180–320 °C, and the composites can operate in the range from 175–235 °C for short periods. However, long-term use at temperatures over 150 °C, especially under hot/wet conditions, has been

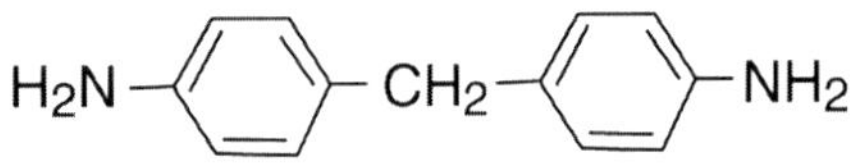

Fig. 4.15 *a*) **4,4-bismaleimidodiphenylmethane;** *b*) **diaminodiphenylmethane precursor.**

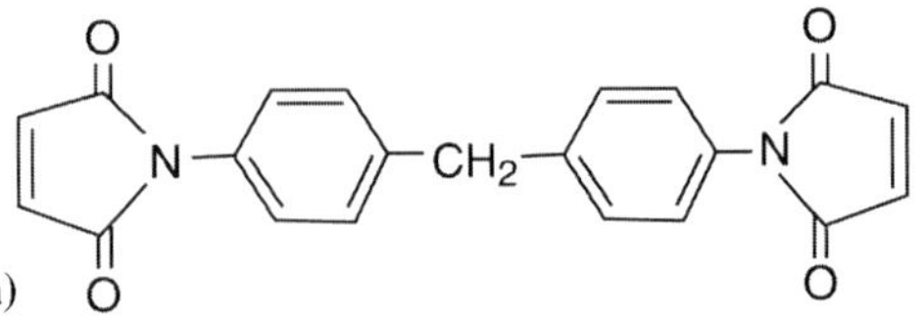

shown to not be advisable due to matrix embrittlement caused by continued cross-linking. The standard BMI generally provide a brittle end product, but the properties can be tailored by polymeric additives to give much higher fracture toughness. This is usually achieved at the expense of some of the high-temperature properties and at higher cost. BMI composites have been extensively used in high-speed military aircraft and other areas where thermal stability requirements exclude the use of epoxy resins. As military aircraft, in particular, have been flying at higher and higher speeds, the requirements for more thermally resistant (thermoset) composites for external structural applications have increased significantly in recent years. Although good aerospace epoxy resin-based composites have T_gs of up to 180°C, they are not suitable for continuous use much above 125°C, especially when combinations of heat and moisture are encountered. The next step up in thermal stability is usually taken by composites made with bismaleimide matrix resin materials and aircraft such as the F-22 contain high proportions of these composites.

In summary, there is a wide variety of BMI resins that can be used as composite matrix materials, but their use is generally restricted to situations in which their good mechanical properties at high temperatures outweigh their relatively high cost.

4.3.6 *Polyimide Resins*

Polyimide resin matrices are unique in that they exhibit extremely high temperature resistance compared with almost all other polymers. These aromatic/heterocyclic systems can have glass transition temperatures between 220–400°C. Extensive research has been carried out on polyimide matrix resins in composite products in recent years, and a large number of different types of materials have been produced. However, relatively few of these are commercially relevant.

There are two classes of polyimide matrices used in advanced composites: those produced by condensation reactions and those produced by addition reactions. Condensation polyimides are generally thermoplastic materials whereas the addition polyimides are considered to be thermoset resins. The former materials are usually produced by reacting aromatic diamines with aromatic dianhydrides, and large volumes of water are evolved. Condensation polyimides include materials such as DuPont's Avimid-N and Kapton, LARC-TPI from NASA, General Electric's Ultem, and Mitsui's Aurum. Apart from their use in thermoplastic composites, they have been applied as toughening additives in some high-temperature epoxy composite formulations.

Addition polyimides are produced by an addition reaction (no release of volatile chemicals) of unsaturated end groups on a previously formed imide-containing unit. BMIs are a subclass of this type but the polymerisable monomeric reactant (PMR) type, originally developed by NASA Lewis Research Center are the major commercially available matrix resin materials of this type. In this case, the reactive end groups are unsaturated cyclic units that are postulated to react by a complex series of addition reactions to give a highly cross-linked polyimide resin system when cured. In practice, the reaction does not proceed wholly as described, and large quantities of volatiles can be liberated unless the composites are fabricated under high pressures and temperatures in a very controlled fabrication program. However, high-quality composite parts can be produced under the correct conditions.

PMR-15 is the most common example of these addition resins types, and quite large structural composite parts have been produced in this material and used in advanced aircraft systems that are subject to high-temperature environments, in for example, engine components, such as casings or in the structure of high-speed military aircraft. Extensive engineering and material science studies have been carried out with both the neat resin and carbon fiber composite parts in an effort to qualify the product for service in extreme conditions including possible use in the new supersonic airliners. However, because PMR-15 composites lose their physical properties in long-term use above 170 °C (due to microcracking and embrittlement), a family of new PMR-type resins has recently been developed from oligoimides with fluorinated groups in the molecule. This includes materials such as Avimid N (DuPont), PMR-II 5O, AFR 700B, and others. All are very expensive, difficult to process, and do not have particularly good mechanical properties except at high temperatures, so their applications are very limited.

Composites based on PMR-15 matrices are generally manufactured by the pre-preg route, which involves hot-pressing layers of fibers pre-impregnated with the uncured polymer, as described in Chapter 5. However, this is a costly method of manufacture, especially with these polymers, because of the high temperature and pressure required to prevent voiding. Thus efforts are being made to develop the use of resin transfer molding (RTM), as described in Chapter 5. To achieve this, methods are being developed to reduce viscosity of PMR-15 type polymers to levels less than 1000 centipoise and to extend their working life to allow sufficient time for impregnation. Most of the PMR-type resins have viscosities around 2×10^5 centipoise. A number of approaches are being attempted including 1) dissolving the resin in a solvent; 2) dissolving the resin in a low-viscosity reactive polymer which subsequently forms part of the cured matrix; and 3) introducing molecular twists into the backbone of the polymer. In the case of 1), the solvent is removed under vacuum before curing the resin; this process is called solvent-assisted RTM.

A final range of addition (thermoset) polyimide resins with very good high-temperature stability properties, as well as good mechanical properties, are the phenylethynyl terminated imide (PETI) materials developed by NASA. These were candidates for structural applications on the previously planned Boeing supersonic airliner. The complex aromatic structure of these materials, combined with their very high processing temperatures ($\sim$370 °C), make these materials extremely expensive, but their advantages include a high T_g ($>$270 °C), long-term thermo-oxidative stability, and excellent mechanical properties. These qualities mean that they have applications in unique situations.

4.3.6.1 Advantages and Disadvantages of Polyimide Resins. The major advantage of polyimide resins (thermosets) is their stability at high temperatures and resistance to most chemicals. They can be formulated to have very good mechanical properties at these temperatures unlike the much cheaper phenolic resins. The major disadvantages of polyimides are their high cost and the difficulty of processing.

4.3.7 Cyanate Resins

Cyanate resins, also known as cyanate esters, cyanic esters, or triazine resins, contain the polymerizable functional group —O—C≡N on an aromatic ring structure. The commercial dicyanate monomers used fit the model compound structure shown in Figure 4.16a and are derived from standard phenolic compounds.

4.3.7.1 Curing Chemistry. It is postulated that the cyanate functionality undergoes cyclotrimerization to form symmetrically substituted triazine structures of the type shown in Figure 4.17. Cure catalysts are normally required to achieve high conversions under practical fabrication conditions (170–250 °C), and generally the process is carried out via partially reacted prepolymers, where the degree of trimerization is between 25–40%. The materials are then tacky semi-solids that have a molecular weight range between 1000–2000 or hard resins, about 4000. Cure advantages of these materials can include fast cure cycles and very low shrinkage problems compared with most thermoset materials. They are very susceptible to moisture at the partially cured stages.

4.3.7.2 Properties of Cyanate Resins. The major advantages of cyanate ester resins are their low dielectric loss and low moisture-absorption properties.

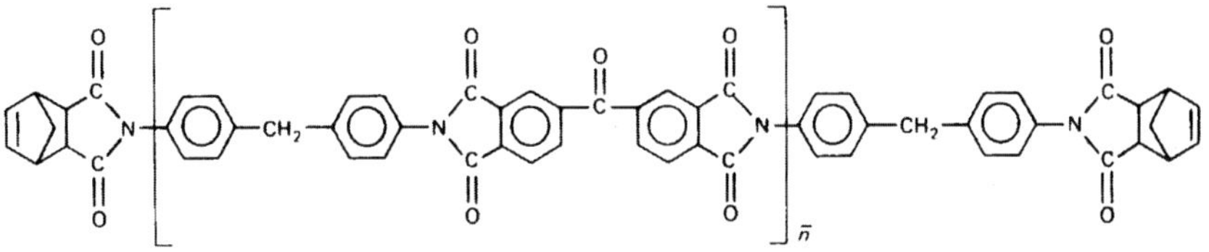

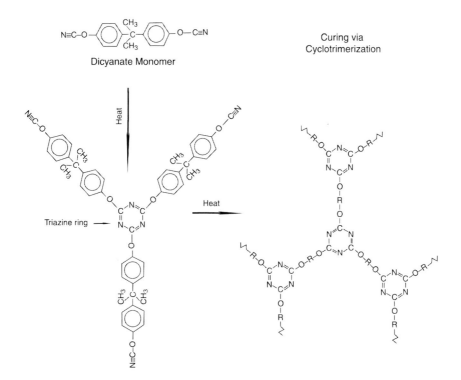

Fig. 4.16 Idealized structure of the PMR-15 polymer.

They have good high temperature strength and toughness values and can be coreacted with epoxy resins or alloyed with a number of engineering thermoplastics for advanced composite applications. They have found extensive use in areas such as printed circuit boards and satellite dishes. While short-term thermal stability is often superior to matrix resins such as bismaleimides, there have been problems with long-term stability in moist conditions, which has troubled the aerospace industry. The problems of composite blistering in these cases may be due to moisture reaction with incompletely reacted monomer groups in the resins.

Dicyanate Monomer

Curing via
Cyclotrimerization

Heat

Triazine ring

Heat

Fig. 4.17 Formation of cyanate ester monomer and its reaction to form cross-linked cyanate ester.

4.4 Thermoplastic Systems

Thermoplastic polymers can be very broadly classified as amorphous or crystalline. Most thermoplastics suitable for use as matrices for high-performance composites exhibit some degree of crystallinity—because this type of structure has better resistance to chemical attack by fuels, hydraulic oil, and paint stripper.

Thermoplastics, compared with thermosetting polymers, absorb much less moisture with less consequential reduction in elevated temperature mechanical properties. Thermoplastics are much tougher than thermosets, therefore they have much better interlaminar strength and resistance to impact. Because no chemical reaction is required, they have very short processing times, although the temperatures and pressures are much greater than those required for thermosetting systems, with a concomitant increase in costs. Another major advantage is that matrix flaws can be healed (at least in principle) and components welded. Table 4.3 provides details on some of the important thermoplastic systems for aerospace composites.[4,11]

4.4.1 Amorphous Thermoplastic

Polymer chains in an amorphous thermoplastic are in a random coil status without any high degree of local order. Because amorphous thermoplastics are often dissolvable in common industrial solvents, the reinforcement can be impregnated with low-viscosity solution, thus avoiding the problem of high-melt viscosity, but, as may be expected, the resultant composite is not solvent-resistant. Because these composites are of particular interest to the aerospace industry, where hydraulic fluid, aviation fuels, and the use of paint stripper are widely encountered, soluble thermoplastics are placed at a severe disadvantage. Amorphous polymers also tend to be more subject to creep deformation and fatigue damage than semi-crystalline polymers. The lack of solvent resistance relegated some of the amorphous materials to non-structural applications, where their good fire, smoke, and toxicity characteristics and toughness could still be exploited. Nevertheless, amorphous thermoplastic composites are being used in various areas in the aerospace industry, especially where high-temperature performance is required, and some solvent susceptibility can be accommodated.

4.4.2 Semi-Crystalline Thermoplastic

In several thermoplastics, polymer chains may, under certain conditions, align themselves into a regular, preferred, low-energy configuration—crystal formation. In reality, it is not possible to achieve complete crystallinity, due to the interference of long molecular chains. Polymers possessing the ability to crystallize are referred to as semi-crystalline. In the solid phase, these locally ordered regions, or crystallites, act as physical cross-links, giving the polymer a good solvent resistance and preventing the dissolution of the entire molecular structure. The crystallinity also improves high-temperature mechanical properties, including creep resistance. The level of crystallinity can be varied by differences in processing history. In addition, rapid cooling from the melt causes low crystallinity, where as very slow cooling, or annealing near the crystalline point may lead to excessive crystallinity. Semi-crystalline polymers shrink more than amorphous polymers upon solidification. The main difficulty in using semi-crystalline polymers is in finding methods for coating the fibers. Because solvents normally cannot be used to dissolve such polymers, coating the fibers with molten thermoplastic is often the only option.

4.4.3 Polyketones

The group of thermoplastic resins known as polyketones are crystalline polymers with exceptionally high temperature resistance. There are numerous aromatic polyketones, such as polyetherketone (PEK), polyetherketoneketone (PEKK), etc., the most common is polyetheretherketone (PEEK); Figure 4.18 depicts the molecular structures. PEEK possesses high mechanical properties, high temperature tolerance, and good solvent resistance. The level of crystallinity achieved in PEEK polymer depends on the processing history. Very rapid cooling can produce an amorphous polymer. This can subsequently be annealed to achieve any desired level of crystallinity. The optimum level of crystallinity for PEEK resin is 25–40%.[3] With respect to resistance to hostile environments, PEEK is generally considered to be outstanding in the field of polymeric resins. PEEK is resistant to non-oxidizing acids (such as hydrochloric acid, alkalies, salts, and solvents). The only common material that will dissolve PEEK is concentrated sulphuric acid.[4] The cost of PEEK is high, but can be justified in composites for high-performance applications in the aerospace and defense industries. Besides continuous fiber reinforced products, PEEK is also available in fiber and film forms.

4.4.4 Polyphenylene Sulfide

Polyphenylene Sulfide (PPS) is a highly crystalline polymer recognized for its unique combination of properties, including thermal stability, chemical

PEEK

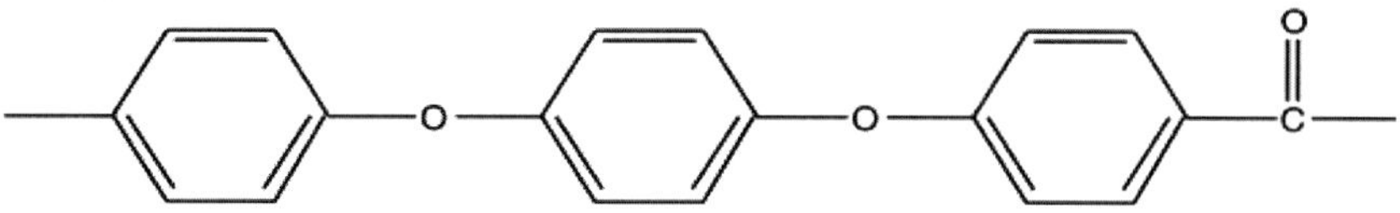

Fig. 4.18   Molecular structure of polyetheretherketone (PEEK).

resistance, and fire resistance. PPS polymer crystallizes very rapidly at temperatures above its T_g and usually has a crystallinity content in the range of 50–60%.[5] PPS exhibits intermediate mechanical properties and temperature tolerance. Its excellent corrosion resistance is attributed to its inertness to organic solvents, inorganic salts, and bases. PPS composites are not affected by aircraft fluids. PPS is soluble in aromatic hydrocarbons and chlorinated aromatic compounds.[6] PPS is inherently flame-resistant, and its composites pass The Ohio State University fire safety test required by the U.S. Federal Aviation Administration (FAA) for materials for use in aircraft interiors. Property retention at elevated temperatures shows that PPS composites exhibit classical deterioration above their T_gs. However, due to crystallinity effects, the loss in strength is gradual; even at temperatures of 200 °C, considerable integrity is retained.

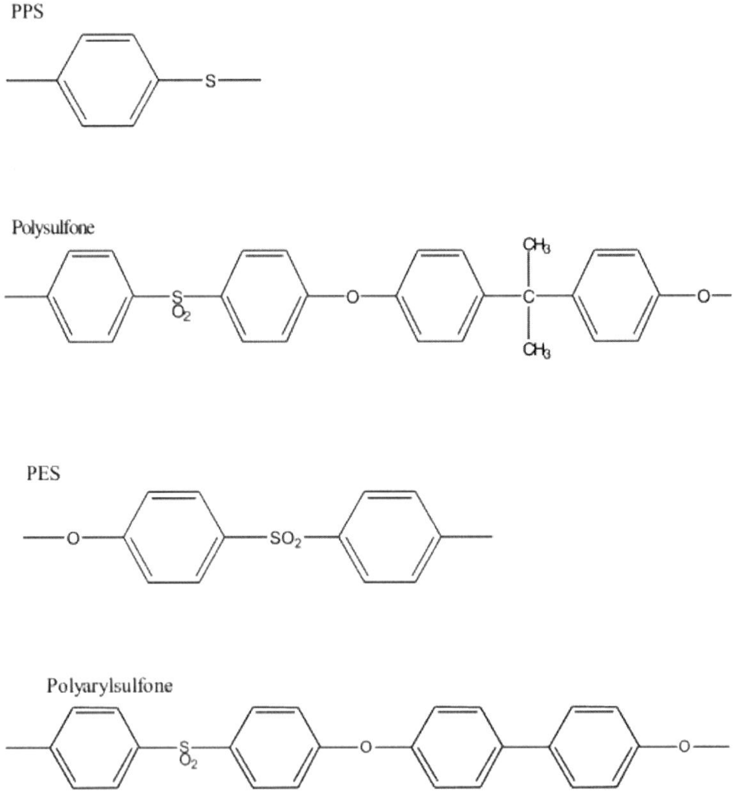

Fig. 4.19   Molecular structure of sulphur-containing thermoplastics.

4.4.5 Polysulfone

Polysulfone (PSU), polyether sulfone (PES), and polyaryl sulfone (PAS) are members of a family of thermoplastics based on sulphone derivatives.[7] They are high-performance amorphous polymers with good tolerance to high temperatures and fire. They are characterized by their high heat-deflection temperature, combined with excellent hydrolytic stability and an ability to retain mechanical properties in hot/wet conditions. They are self-extinguishing and, when they do burn, produce little smoke. Because polysulfones are amorphous, they are not resistant to all solvents, although their resistance to many chemicals is nevertheless very good. Figure 4.19 depicts the molecular structure of some of the relevant sulphur-containing thermoplastics.

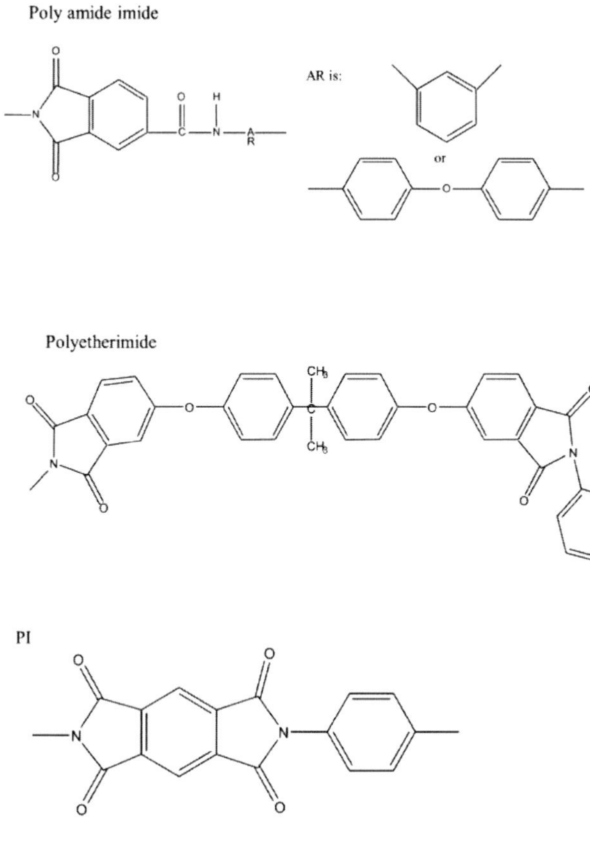

Poly amide imide

Polyetherimide

PI

Fig. 4.20   Molecular structure of polyimide thermoplastics.

4.4.6 Polyetherimide

Polyetherimide (PEI) is an amorphous, high-performance thermoplastic. The amorphous structure of PEI contributes to its dimensional stability, low shrinkage, and highly isotropic mechanical properties compared with most crystalline polymers. The high T_g allows PEI to be used intermittently at $200\,^{\circ}$C. Un-reinforced PEI is one of the strongest engineering amorphous thermoplastics and offers very good mechanical properties but has the forming disadvantage of very high viscosity in the molten state. Despite being amorphous, PEI is very tolerant to solvents and environmental exposure and resists a broad range of chemicals, including most hydrocarbons, non-aromatic alcohols, and fully halogenated solvents. The molecular structure of some of the polyimide resins is depicted in Figure 4.20.

References

[1] Kumar, A., and Gupta, R. K., *Fundamentals of Polymers*, McGraw-Hill, New York, 1998.

[2] Chawla, K. K., *Composite Materials Science and Engineering*, Springer–Verlag; New York, 1987.

[3] Niu, M. C., *Composite Airframe Structures*, "Materials," Conmilit Press, Hong Kong, Chapter 2, 1992.

[4] Muzzy, J. D., "Thermoplastics Properties," *Comprehensive Composite Materials*, edited by A. Kelly and C. Zweben, Vol. 2, Elsevier, Cambridge, 2000.

[5] Brandrup, J., Immergut, E. H., and Grulke, E. A., *Polymer Handbook*, 4, John Wiley & Sons, New York, 1999.

[6] Varma, I. K., and Gupta, V. B., "Thermosetting Resin Properties," *Comprehensive Composite Materials*, edited by A. Kelly, C. Zweben, Vol. 2, Elsevier, Cambridge, 2000.

[7] Green, G. E., "Matrices for Advanced Structural Composites," *Composite Materials in Aircraft Structures*, edited by D. H. Middleton, Longmans, UK, 1997, Chapter 4.

[8] May, C. A. (ed.), *Epoxy Resins, Chemistry and Technology*, 2nd ed., Marcel Dekker, New York, 1988.

[9] Gillham, J. K., "The Formation and Properties of Network Polymeric Materials," *Polymer Engineering & Science*, Vol. 19, 1979, pp. 676–682.

[10] Bascum, W. D., and Hunston, D. L., "The Fracture of Epoxy and Elastomer-Modified Epoxy Polymers," *Treatise on Adhesion and Adhesives*, Vol. 6, edited by R. L. Patrick, Marcel Dekker, New York, 1989, Chapter 4.

[11] Reinhart, T. J., (ed.), *Composite Engineered Materials Handbook*, Vol. 1, American Society for Metals International, 1993, pp. 100–101.

5
Component Form and Manufacture

5.1 Introduction

Because fiber reinforcement is essentially a one-dimensional strengthening process, a major function of the component-forming process is to orientate the fibers in the matrix in the appropriate directions and proportions to obtain the desired two-dimensional or 3-dimensional mechanical properties. The forming process must also produce the shape of the component and develop the required properties of the matrix and the fiber/matrix bond. The forming process must not damage the fibers and must ensure that they are reasonably evenly distributed in a matrix, free from significant voiding or from large areas devoid of fibers.

The simplest method that satisfies these requirements is to infiltrate an appropriately aligned fiber bed with a liquid, which is then converted by chemical reaction (in the case of thermosets) or simply by cooling (in the case of thermoplastics) to form a continuous solid matrix with the desired properties. Techniques based on liquid resin are known as liquid molding, with several subcategories according to various modifications of the process.

Alternatively, sheets of aligned fibers may be pre-coated with matrix precursor and the continuous matrix formed by flowing the coatings together (and curing, if a thermoset matrix) under heat and pressure. In this widely used form, the material is known as pre-preg (pre-impregnated).

There are several methods that can be used to arrange the fibers when forming the composite structure. The main method for the manufacture of aircraft components is laminating woven cloth, or aligned fiber sheets, with the fibers orientated in appropriate directions in each layer.

There are also several methods based on continuous fiber tow or yarn; these include:

(1) filament winding onto a rotating mandrel; (2) braiding onto a rotating mandrel (the process of braiding is covered in detail in Chapter 14); (3) tow placement; and (4) pultrusion.

The main differences between the use of thermosets and thermoplastic matrices are the need for extended times to cure (cross-link) the thermosets and the relatively high viscosities of the thermoplastics melts and the consequential requirement for high processing temperatures and pressures. Table 5.1 lists generic aircraft components made using these manufacturing procedures.

**Table 5.1   Typical Aircraft Fiber Composite Forms Made by the Different
Techniques, as Listed**

Type of Structure	Typical Application
Laminates	
Sheets, thick monolithic	Wing skins
Sheets, integrally stiffened	Tail skins
Sandwich panels	Control surfaces, floor sections
Shells	Fuselage sections
Beams	Spars/ribs
Complex forms	Aerofoils
Filament Wound	
Closed shells	Pressure vessels
Open shells	Radomes
	Rocket motors
Tubes	Drive shafts
Secondary formed tubes	Helicopter blades
Braided	
Tubes	Drive shafts
Complex tubes	Curved pipes
	Truss joints
	Ducts
Closed shells	Pressure vessels
Secondary formed	Fuselage frames
	Aircraft propellers
	Helicopter blades
Tow Placed	
See laminates	See laminates
Complex wraps	Grips
	Shafts
	Ducts
Pultrusion	
Beams	Floor beams
	Stringers
	Spars
	Ribs
	Longerons

Considerable structural and cost efficiency can be obtained by using the
composite in the most highly stressed regions, for example, in the upper and
lower surfaces of components subject to bending or buckling. This is achieved by
using a sandwich construction, as also listed in Table 5.1, with the composite
laminate forming the outer skins, which are bonded to a metallic or polymeric

composite honeycomb or polymeric foam core. The metallic honeycomb is generally an aluminum alloy such as 5052, often with a coating or anodized layer to resist corrosion. The composite honeycomb would generally be glass-reinforced epoxy or phenolic; however, the most usual honeycomb material is Nomex, which is the trade name for a composite based on random meta-aramid fibers in a phenolic matrix. The foam core used for aerospace applications is generally made of PVC, but this material is not generally used in applications exposed to high temperatures. Polyetherimide (PEI) and polymethacrylimide (PMI) polyimide foams are alternative cores for higher-temperature applications.

This chapter deals primarily with pre-preg laminating procedures in some detail because this is the prime method for manufacturing aircraft composite components. Methods based on liquid resin are then considered, followed by details of the various processes, resin transfer and infusion, and filament winding and pultrusion. Finally, the particular processes for manufacturing with thermoplastic resins are covered.

5.2 Outline of General Laminating Procedures

Most reinforced-plastic components based on long fibers are manufactured by some form of laminating procedure.[1] In this process, sheets of reinforcement, pre-coated with resin (pre-preg) or with resin freshly applied, are forced against the surface of a mold under the required conditions of pressure, temperature, and time. Chapter 3 provides details of some of the cloth materials available, and details of the pre-pregging process are provided later in this chapter.

5.2.1 Open Die Molding

Open die molding involves the use of only one mold surface, over which the layers of fiber are placed or "laid-up." If dry cloth is used, the resin may be applied by brushing or spraying. With care and suitable materials, this method (which is still widely used outside the aircraft industry) can produce good-quality parts. However, handling wet resins can be messy and can raise occupational health and safety (OH&S) concerns. In addition, a particular concern with the use of wet lay-up in aircraft-part production is the lack of repeatability of the process, especially the control of resin content and therefore the weight, thickness, and mechanical properties. Some smaller companies, notably in the German Glider Industry, have adopted wet pre-preg dispensing machines, which saturate reinforcement fabric on demand with a controlled amount of liquid resin, normally epoxy, and hardener. This solution is cheap and flexible, and it does not require cold storage.

Various methods are engaged to apply pressure to consolidate the lay-up. In contact molding, which is generally used only for fairly low-stress applications of glass/polyester composites, the pressure is developed by hand-rolling over a sheet of plastic film placed over the surface of the lay-up.

The bag procedure involves the use of a flexible plastic membrane that is formed over the surface of the lay-up to form a vacuum-tight bag. In vacuum bagging, the bag is evacuated and atmospheric pressure used to consolidate the lay-up against the surface of the mold. The vacuum initially removes most of the air and volatile materials. Vacuum bagging is an inexpensive and versatile procedure; however, it can provide only limited consolidation pressure and may produce voided laminates due to the enlargement of the bubbles (formed by any residual gases or volatile material) trapped in the resin in regions where the bag is unable to apply pressure, for example, because of local bridging. To minimize this problem, autoclave procedures, described later, are used to manufacture most of the high-quality laminates used in the aircraft industry.

Alternatively, pressure may be applied to the surface of an open mold by means of a flexible plunger mounted in a press, by gas-bags, or by thermal expansion of an entrapped rubber or metallic insert.

Temperature, generally required to cure the resin, can be applied to the open mold in various ways, including external methods such as hot-air blowers and ovens or internally by electric elements or steam or oil pipes buried in the mold. Temperatures up to 180 °C may be required in aerospace-grade epoxy resin systems.

5.2.2 Compression Molding

Compression or matched-die molding involves the use of matching male and female dies that close to form a cavity of the shape of the component (Fig. 5.1). The dies, generally made of tool steel, can be internally heated, if required, by electric elements or steam, or hot oil pipes. The fiber layers are placed over the lower mold section, and the two halves of the mold are brought together in a press. Lands built into the mold usually control the thickness of the part. Advantages of matched-die molding include excellent dimensional control; high-quality surface finish, produced on both surfaces; high production rates; and good consolidation and high fiber content.

However, the cost of the matching dies (with hardened faces) is very high, and the size of the available hydraulic presses used to apply the closing pressure limits the size of parts that can be produced.

Wet laminating procedures may be used, in which case the dry fiber is laid in the mold and the resin added. High-quality fiber composite components are generally based on the use of pre-pregs or by the use of a solid, but uncured, resin film that is laid on the mold surface, followed by dry fiber layers or a fiber preform.

Alternatively, a liquid resin can be injected into the sealed and evacuated mold cavity, as discussed later.

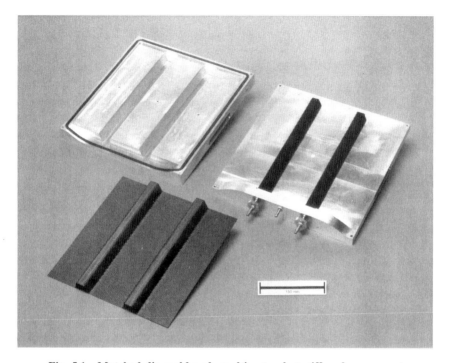

Fig. 5.1   Matched-die mold and resulting top-hat stiffened component.

5.2.3 Wrapping

Wrapping is an alternative procedure to filament winding, described later, for producing tubular components. A pre-preg sheet, either wrap sheet or cloth, is wrapped onto a removable metal mandrel and cured under pressure. Special machines are available to perform the wrapping operations. The pressure during an elevated temperature cure may be applied by the use of shrink film (applied by a tape-winding machine), vacuum bag, or autoclave. Alternatively, a silicon-rubber bladder may be placed over the mandrel before the wrapping of the laminate. Pressure is applied to the laminate through-inflation of the bladder that forces the laminate against an outer mold surface. This technique is often used to make fishing rods, golf clubs, and tennis rackets.

5.3 Laminating Procedures For Aircraft-Grade Composite Components

Major aircraft manufacturers and their subcontractors, especially in the United States, use B-staged epoxy pre-preg as their preferred material form. In this material, the reinforcement is pre-impregnated by a supplier with a resin already containing hardener.[2] This has been partially cured (B-staged) such that the resin does not flow at room temperature, but at the same time it remains tacky (sticky to the touch). B-staged epoxy pre-pregs are normally staged (partially cured) to about 15% of full cure for hand lay-up, and up to 25% for automated lay-up. To protect this material and keep it from sticking to itself, a backing or release film is added to at least one side of the pre-preg before it is rolled up for storage or transport.

5.3.1 Pre-Preg Production

A pre-preg can be made incorporating a variety of reinforcement fabrics and fiber types. Although it can be produced by the component fabricator, it is normally purchased from a materials-supply company. The following material forms are available as carbon/epoxy pre-pregs.

Woven bi-directional cloth pre-preg is most commonly made from plain weave or satin weave fabrics, 0.2–0.4 mm thick and up to 1200 mm wide. One common method of pre-impregnation is to infuse the cloth with matrix resin diluted with solvent to lower its viscosity. The pre-preg then passes through a heating tower to remove the solvent and stage the resin. The newer hot-melt method (See Fig. 5.2) involves first continuously casting a B-staged resin film on a non-stick backing film of coated paper or polymer. A doctor blade is used to control the thickness of the resin film applied (the same method used to make adhesive film). The reinforcement is then sandwiched between two of these films as it passes through a pair of heated rollers. This process has an advantage over the solvent process in that it produces lower volatile emissions.

Unidirectional pre-preg (warp sheet) is made by spreading and collimating many fiber tows (typically around 10^4 fibers in each tow) into a uniform sheet of

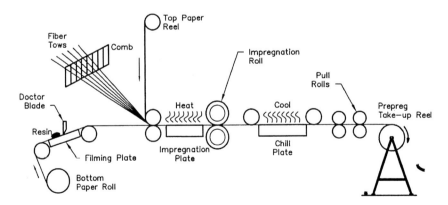

Fig. 5.2   Schematic illustration of hot-melt film pre-pregging process. Adapted from Ref. 2.

parallel fibers typically 0.125–0.25 mm thick and 300 or 600 mm wide. This is immediately pre-impregnated. Unidirectional pre-preg is the cheapest to make, and it provides laminates with the best mechanical properties. However, it may be difficult to lay into double-curved shapes. Other types of reinforcement architecture, such as multi-axial warp knit (also known as non-crimp, knitted, or stitched) fabrics can also be pre-impregnated, but the process becomes increasingly difficult as the fabric becomes thicker.

The pre-preg with its non-stick backing films is then inspected for resin content, which is typically between 34% and 42% by weight for carbon pre-pregs, wound onto a roll, and sealed to prevent the absorption of water vapor. Some pre-pregs have up to 15% more resin than is required to form a laminate with the desired fiber/volume fraction. With these pre-pregs, the resin is required to bleed out of the laminate during curing. Low-bleed or non-bleed pre-pregs with a more viscous resin are now more popular.

The standard pre-preg thickness for unidirectional materials is of the order of 0.125 mm. More recently, to cut costs, much larger tows are being used, resulting in much thicker pre-pregs; however, because it is more difficult to maintain fiber alignment in thick tows, there is some reduction in mechanical properties of the finished composite.

5.3.2 Pre-Preg Transport and Storage

The major disadvantage of pre-preg (apart from the extra cost of creating it from the fiber and resin) is that once the hardener has been added, the resin begins to react. Therefore the material normally only has a limited "shelf" (storage) life and "shop" (usage) life before the resin has reacted sufficiently for the pre-preg to become stiff and intractable for lay-up, or for the quality of the resulting composite to suffer. Most pre-pregs need to be stored in a freezer, typically at around $-20°C$, which halts or at least greatly slows down the curing reaction in the resin. Pre-pregs generally used in aerospace are cured at elevated temperatures, typically 120°C or 180°C for epoxy resins. Because the resin is designed to react at elevated temperature, the supplier can normally guarantee a shelf (freezer) life of 6 months to a year, and a shop life ("out" life at room temperature) of at least 2 weeks.

If the distance from the supplier to the user is long, the pre-preg will need to be shipped in refrigerated shipping containers; or for smaller lots, in insulated packages containing dry ice (frozen carbon dioxide).

5.3.3 Cutting and Kitting

When pre-preg is required for use, it is thawed to room temperature before being removed from its bag to avoid picking up condensation. The pre-preg is then moved into the cutting room, which like the lay-up room is maintained as a "clean room," free of dust and with controlled temperature (around 20°C) and humidity (e.g., between 50–70% RH). The pre-preg is then unrolled onto the cutting table, with its backing paper still in place. Plies of the required size, shape, and fiber orientation are then cut from the roll; as an example, Figure 5.3 shows a ply stack for a wing rib. This can be done by hand-using a template, or with a die in a roller press; in all but the smallest operations, this is usually done by a numerically controlled flat-bed cutter similar to those used in the textile industry. Cutting is usually achieved using an oscillating blade, but sharp "draw knife" blades as well as lasers or water jets are also used. Some cutters can cut multiple layers of fabric. Some flat-bed cutters can also label the plies automatically. The various ply shapes are then labelled, if necessary, and assembled as part of a kit containing all the plies for a component, which may be delivered directly to the lay-up room or sealed and stored in a plastic bag in the freezer for later use.

Abrasive water jet cutting uses a high-pressure water stream, perhaps up to 400 MPa, which is forced through a small sapphire orifice to produce a supersonic jet travelling at speeds up to 900 m s^{-1}, carrying abrasive particles to form a powerful cutting jet. Most materials can be machined with the water jet's ability to revolve with the robotic end effector. The critical process parameters are speed; stand-off distance; impact angle; water-jet pressure; water flow rate; orifice diameter; abrasive particle shape, hardness and size; and nozzle mixing tube geometry and material. Generally, the impact angle can be optimized to produce the maximum removal rate. The work-piece material should be softer than the abrasive compound. Oscillation of the cutting head can also influence the quality of the cut.

Laser cutting can be considered a thermal process as a portion of the beam energy is absorbed by the surface material, and this energy raises the temperature

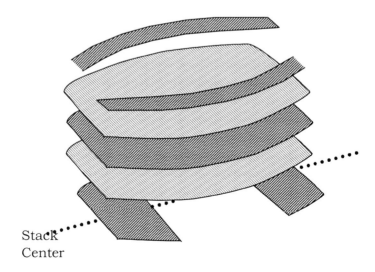

Stack
Center

Fig. 5.3   Schematic diagram of a typical ply stack for a wing rib.

of the material. A sufficient amount of such energy will cause local decomposition of the material. Some compromise is required when focussing the laser beam as minimum spot size (a result of using short focal length lenses) is achieved at the expense of depth of field. The creation of thermal energy during cutting can produce problems in the course of dealing with standard epoxy pre-preg systems producing local cure and toxic vapors.

All methods of cutting for complex geometry flat shapes must be capable of operation with either a standard robot or gantry-type equipment.

5.3.4 Lay-Up

Most aerospace components are still laid-up by skilled labor, although considerable efforts are being made to automate or mechanize the process, as described in the subsequent sections. Hand lay-up is very versatile because human hands make excellent grippers, eyes marvellous sensors, and the brain a powerful process control and quality control unit! Any residual dust or resin from previous use is cleaned off before a thin layer of release agent is applied to the surface, where necessary. The mold will then be moved into the lay-up clean room.

The pre-preg plies are then applied to the mold in the correct position, orientation, and sequence according to a set of instructions sometimes called a ply book; these instructions may be viewed on a computer screen. The ply is located on the surface by reference to markings on the mold or with the aid of a rigid or flexible template. Many companies now have lay-up stations where an overhead projector rapidly scans a low-power laser beam to "draw" the outline of each ply on the mold surface. These machines can also project instructions for ply lay-up onto the mold.

Typically, the lower backing paper is removed by the operator before lay-up, and the upper one after positioning and consolidating using rollers or other simple tools. For larger plies, two or more operators may be required to handle and position the tacky pre-preg. Where the mold surface is doubly-curved, the pre-preg needs to be further distorted, enabling it to fit the surface.

Different types of material may be combined in the same lay-up as long as the materials are compatible. For instance, in sandwich structures, aluminium or Nomex honeycomb and adhesive films will normally be combined with carbon-epoxy pre-preg to form the structure. Different fibers such as glass and carbon may be combined to form hybrid lay-ups, and different reinforcement arrangements such as unidirectional tape and woven fabric may be combined.

5.3.5 Automated Forming of Pre-Preg Stacks

To reduce lay-up times and consequently labor costs, automated or semi-automated methods have recently been introduced to aircraft component production lines.

Instead of shaping and consolidating (laying up) each ply separately by hand, a flat stack can be assembled by manual or mechanical means. This flat stack can then be formed into the required shape using various methods; pressing, stamping, or diaphragm-forming. One version of the diaphragm-forming process is illustrated in Figure 5.4. A flat pre-preg stack is laid up and placed over a male-forming die. A diaphragm is fitted and sealed to the forming box. A vacuum is then applied to the box cavity. Because they are not extensible in the fiber direction, the plies must deform by shear to conform to the shape of the tool. It may be necessary to heat the flat pre-preg stack to a temperature above room temperature to assist forming. An infrared heating source is often used for this purpose.

This process is most attractive for deep draws, and consequently the shear deformation required can be considerable. There are three main modes of deformation: intraply shear (a trellising action in which the fiber tows pivot at the crossover points), slippage between plies, and ply out-of-plane bending. The main problem is to avoid wrinkling of the plies caused by the development of compressive residual stresses. Computer simulation to assist in predicting the optimum conditions for forming is a recent development discussed later in this chapter.

5.3.6 Automated Lay-Up

Lay-up of large components such as wing skins requires automation because, owing to the time required for hand lay-up, materials may be close to their out-life when the task is nearing completion.

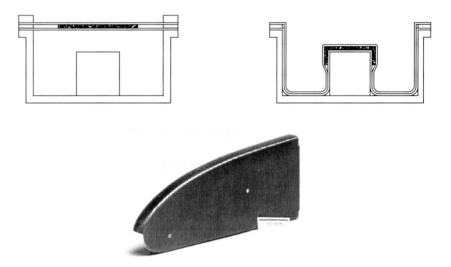

Fig. 5.4 Schematic diagram of the diaphragm-forming process; below, carbon fiber-epoxy rib made using this process.

There are two established approaches to automating the lay-up process: automated tape layers (ATL) and automated tow placement (ATP) machines. ATL machines normally consist of a gantry with a dispensing head that is free to move over the surface of the tool. Generally, unidirectional pre-preg tape is placed onto the surface (Fig. 5.5) according to a programmed routine.

As the tape is placed on the surface, the backing layer is stripped away, and the surface of the tool may be heated to aid tack of the pre-preg. Tape width is typically around 300 mm, and the lay-down rate is of the order of 50 m min^{-1}. Advanced ATLs are capable of laying tape onto a highly contoured surface. However, these machines are very costly and can be justified only where long runs of expensive components, such as tail or wing skins, are to be made.

ATLs are also being developed for use with thermoplastic pre-pregs. In this application, a gas flame or laser is used to heat the tape as it is laid down and a consolidation roller is then used to form the composite layer.

The limitations to the capability of ATL machines to manufacture more complex shapes has led to the development of automatic tow placement (ATP) systems. These machines lay down multiple pre-preg tows and are able to stop, cut, and restart individual fiber tows. A multi-axis manipulator arrays a group of pre-preg tows into a continuous band and compacts them against the surface of the lay-up tool. This allows more complex shapes to be fabricated, including lay-up onto relatively severe and complex curves and the steering of tows into curved trajectories. Heat and pressure are used to ensure proper adhesion and consolidation of the material.

ATPs offer the potential for greater structural optimization by locating fiber where it is most effective. Some systems are combined with a spindle, (Fig. 5.6) to allow lay-up of closed shapes such as ducts, combining the advantages of both filament winding and automated tape lay-up while alleviating some of the problems associated with each. However, these are, so far, even more expensive to purchase and operate and have been limited to use on military aircraft

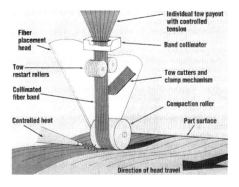

Fig. 5.5 Schematic diagram of an automatic tape-laying process (*left*) and a typical product (*right*).

Fig. 5.6   An automatic tape placement system in use at Bell Helicopter from Automated Dynamics Corporation literature.

programs and in cases where the complexity of shape means that the part cannot be practicably fabricated in any other way.

5.3.7 Bagging

After all plies have been laid-up and inspected, the lay-up is prepared for curing. An autoclave or vacuum bag will be applied over the surface of the lay-up and sealed to the mold, so that a consolidating pressure can be applied during cure by evacuating the space under the bag, and/or by increasing the outside pressure. As illustrated in Figure. 5.7, the bagging process uses a number of different materials. These include:

- Release film—a smooth non-stick film often made from fluro-polymers, placed over the lay-up, which may be perforated to allow passage of gases or resin
- Breather fabric—transmits gases even under pressure and is used to allow gases to flow from all over the part to the vacuum fitting
- Bleeder fabric—used to soak up excess resin, especially in high-bleed pre-pregs
- Vacuum bag film, normally nylon
- Mastic tape—also called tacky tape and often made from butyl rubber; used to seal the edge of the bag to the mold

In addition, for surfaces to be bonded, a peel ply (non-bonding woven cloth, such as nylon) is placed on the surface of the lay-up. During the cure this is incorporated into the surface resin and is subsequently peeled off to create a clean, roughened surface that is ready for adhesive bonding.

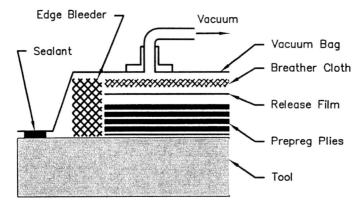

Fig. 5.7 Schematic diagram of a vacuum bag lay-up, indicating the various layers used Taken from Ref. 2.

The bagging must allow an even consolidation pressure to be applied to the part, while at the same time allowing any gases trapped in the lay-up or generated during curing to be removed from the system. The gases include volatiles from solvents left in the resin during the pre-pregging process, water, and air.

The cost of the non-reusable materials described above is considerable; many companies use permanent, shaped vacuum bags made from high-temperature elastomers. Where thermocouples are not embedded in the mold, these may be inserted into the edge of the lay-up through the edge sealant.

Vacuum bags are also applied temporarily during the lay-up process to tack the pre-preg firmly onto the mold, to consolidate previous pre-preg layers, and to allow the removal of air and volatiles. This process is often called debulking and may be required at the introduction of each ply in some complex-shaped parts, especially those with sharp corners.

Where it is critical that both surfaces of a part be smooth and of controlled dimensions, matched (usually metal) tooling can be used, as described previously. In these cases, most of the bagging materials are not required, and even the vacuum bag need not be used if the matched molds include integral seals. Careful control of tool contour, pre-preg resin content and placement, cure pressure, and resin bleed are necessary for successful matched-die molding with pre-pregs.

Alternatively, if a smooth outer surface is required, but control of tolerance is not required to a high level, a caul plate may be used. This is a stiff, free-floating plate or mold of the outer surface which is placed on the lay-up, just above the release film

5.3.8 Curing

The majority of aerospace composite parts with thermosetting matrices are cured at elevated temperatures to ensure that the service temperature of the composite is sufficiently high. As a typical example, a carbon/epoxy composite cured at 180°C for 2 hours might have a glass transition temperature (T_g) of 200°C when dry, but only 160°C when saturated with moisture. This would allow the composite to be used at a maximum service temperature of around 135°C.

As mentioned earlier, composites may be cured in an oven under a vacuum bag, but the best results come from the use of pressure above one atmosphere (compaction pressure), usually generated in an autoclave. The autoclave is basically a very large, internally heated pressure vessel, with internal connections for vacuum hoses and sensors such as thermocouples (Fig. 5.8). The autoclave is usually computer controlled, and often pressurized with nitrogen or carbon dioxide to reduce the risk of an internal fire. A standard machine for epoxy composites will be capable of temperatures over 200°C and pressures over 700 KPa. Autoclaves for processing thermoplastic composites or high-temperature thermoset composites may be capable of 400°C and 1200 KPa or more. The part is normally heated by convection of heat from the fan-forced air circulation, although electrically heated molds are sometimes used. Although more costly, there are several advantages in heating the mold, including more rapid and uniform heating and the ability to use high temperatures as the walls of the autoclave remain cool.

Normally the lay-up will be under vacuum from the time it leaves the lay-up room and while it is loaded into the autoclave, to keep the lay-up in position and help remove air and volatiles. The vacuum and sensor connections will be checked before the autoclave door is closed and the cycle commences. Pressurization and heating will begin immediately, and the target pressure will be reached in less than 30 minutes whereas, in thick parts, the target temperature may not be reached for several hours. After more than 100 KPa (gauge) pressure has been reached in the autoclave, the space under the vacuum bag is vented

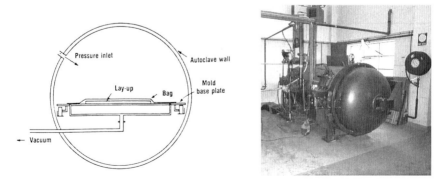

Fig. 5.8   Layout of an autoclave and, *right*, a small typical autoclave.

(connected to the atmosphere) to discourage the growth of existing bubbles and the generation of new bubbles, from entrapped gases and volatiles, in the resin as it is heated. Heat-up and cool-down rates are controlled to ensure even curing throughout the part and to reduce the possibility of residual stresses causing structural deficiencies or distortions.

The viscosity of the resin falls with increasing temperature until the resin begins to chemically cross-link (gel). It is important that full pressure is applied before gelation occurs to allow removal of entrapped gases and removal of excess resin.

Under some circumstances, a dwell is incorporated (isothermal hold), as shown in Figure 5.9, to prolong the time for consolidation and volatile removal. The hold also pre-reacts the resin and reduces the danger of large damaging exothermic reactions that can occur in thick laminates, for example, over 50 plies thick. A hold will also allow the temperature to become more uniform; this is very important in components with large variations in thickness.

The need for complex heating/pressure cycles is important for earlier, less viscous epoxy resins and high-temperature resins because this is necessary to accommodate the requirements of the chemical reactions and to ensure that the resin viscosity is optimum when pressure is increased. Most modern non-bleed epoxy pre-pregs, however, can be processed with a simple "straight-up" cure cycle, provided that the component is not too thick or complex.

If an autoclave is not available, compaction pressure may also be applied by an inflated rubber bladder or by materials with a high coefficient of thermal expansion (CTE) such as silicone rubber, used in conjunction with matched mold tooling. The expansion force generated by these arrangements requires that the

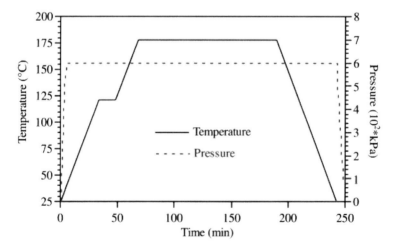

Fig. 5.9   Typical autoclave cycle incorporating a dwell to allow temperature equilibration in thick lay-ups.

tooling be stiff to resist the bending forces applied to the tool. (Bending forces are low in autoclave tooling because the pressure acts on all sides.)

Autoclave molds must be vacuum tight and free of distortions under temperature. Ideally, they should have a low thermal mass to avoid slow heating and cooling and should have a low CTE, similar to that of the laminate.

5.3.9   Cocuring of Complex Components

Complex integrally stiffened components, such as those shown in Figure 5.10, can be manufactured using internal pressurization[3] (Fig. 5.11). There are essentially two methods of applying internal pressure: thermal expansion of a rubber or metallic mandrel, and expansion under autoclave pressure of a rubber bladder. In both cases, the approach is to wrap pre-preg around the internal mandrel, which is inserted into an outer mold containing the outer skins. As shown in Figure 5.10, it may be desirable to arrange for one, usually the top outer skin, to be removable to allow equipment to be installed or for inspection purposes. This can be achieved by introducing a release film between the outer (removable) skin lay-up and the substructure. The outer skin, though cured at the same time as the substructure, can be separated, the release film removed, and the skin mechanically fastened or bonded in a secondary operation.

5.3.10   Processing Problems

The main processing problems encountered in autoclave molding include overheating (caused by excessive exothermic reactions), porosity, resin-rich

Fig. 5.10   Cocured control surface components with integral lower skin and ribs and removable top skin. Courtesy of CRC-ACS.

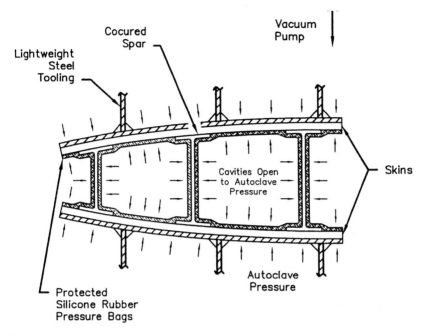

Fig. 5.11 Schematic diagram of the tooling used to make a cocured carbon/epoxy wing structure, using rubber bladder expansion for internal pressurization. Adapted from Ref. 3.

areas, resin-dry areas, poor surface finish, insufficient consolidation, uneven cure, and distortion.

Many of the problems can be resolved by correct timing of application of temperature and pressure and use of pre-preg materials with a wide processing window with (ideally) low exothermic cures.

The formation of voids is generally caused by the entrapment of volatiles, water, and air that have remained after debulking. At the high processing temperatures in the autoclave, more solvents are liberated, and the volume of the solvents and other entrapped gases increases. To avoid the formation of severe porosity, it is necessary that the hydrostatic pressure in the resin before gelation exceeds the partial pressure of the gases, allowing them to be expelled. Once the resin gels no further, void removal or consolidation is possible. Water is often considered to be the main cause of void formation so that the applied pressure needs to exceed the partial pressure of the water.[2]

While a low temperature hold is often used to increase the time at low resin viscosity for the reasons stated above, excessive pressure or over-efficient resin-bleed when the resin viscosity is low may lead to dry spots. Resin-rich areas result when areas in the lay-up have lower resistance to resin-flow and insufficient pressure is applied before gelation.

To reduce surface porosity, a surfacing resin film or fine glass/epoxy scrim ply may be placed on the mold surface before the pre-preg is placed.

The use of honeycomb core in the composite component can result in several problems, of which the most common is core-crushing. The reason for this is illustrated in Figure 5.12, which shows how a lateral force can arise in an autoclave, causing inward collapse of the core.[2] Methods for avoiding this problem include the use of reduced pressure in the autoclave (reduced from 700 to 300 KPa with a concomitant reduction in laminate quality, however) and use of friction grips to prevent the inner pre-preg skin sliding inwards. The gripped skin region must be surplus to the component and must be removed after processing.

Distortion can be a serious problem, and can arise from uneven cure, unbalanced fiber lay-ups, or the expansion differential between the composite

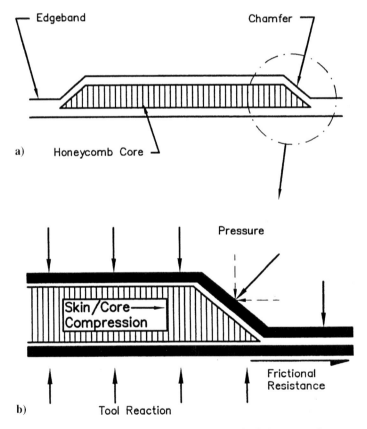

Fig. 5.12 Schematic diagram, showing *a*) a typical honeycomb arrangement incorporating a chamfer and *b*) the origin of lateral crushing forces. Adapted from Ref. 2.

part and the tooling. It will be found that long parts such as spars may appear to have "grown" with respect to the tooling, especially if this is made of a high-CTE material such as steel or aluminum. This phenomenon occurs because the resin is solidified at the curing temperature, and, compared with the tool, the composite shrinks little during cooling. This also can make it difficult to remove some complex components from their mold without damage.

Parts such as "C" sections made on male mandrels may grip the mandrel due to a condition known as *spring-in*, in which composite angles close up slightly (about 1°) during cool-down because of CTE differences between the resin and fiber. Allowance has to be made in the tool design to compensate for this.

5.3.11 Debagging, Finishing, and Painting

The part is normally cooled down to below 60°C before it is removed from the autoclave. The bagging layers are stripped off, and the part is carefully separated from the mold. If the release coating is imperfect or the mold does not have sufficient draught angle for deep parts, this may present processing difficulties.

The part should be smooth on the tool side, but unless matched molds are used, there will be some texture or roughness on the bag side of the part; however, this is minimized if a stiff caul plate is used. Due to slight variations in pre-preg fiber areal weight and resin contents, and in resin-bleed during curing, it is difficult to specify the thickness of a pre-preg part to less than about ± 5%. This becomes a serious concern in thicker parts such as wing skins, where the choice may be between having a smooth outside surface with the correct aerodynamic contour (outer mold line tooling), and controlling the inner surface dimensions (inner mold line tooling) to allow easy assembly to the substructure.

Any surface blemishes may need to be filled with special putty. For epoxy composites, a typical paint scheme is an epoxy primer coat followed by a polyurethane topcoat. Any residue from the release coating applied to the mold may cause problems with poor adhesion of the paint. For this reason, many parts may be abraded lightly on the surface before painting.

Painting may either be carried out by traditional hand-operated methods or with robots. Robotic painting is normally controlled by computer-aided-design-generated off-line process trajectories. Computer modelling and test simulations can verify the programs before production commitment. Paint application robotics can vary the paint thickness applied that would be specified to suit the service environment. Contemporary systems for automatic paint spraying can be applied to a series of small parts through to a working envelope of up to 3 million cubic feet using gantry-mounted robots.

5.3.12 Trimming and Drilling

Increasingly, trimming and drilling processes[4] are also being carried out automatically by robots.[5]

Some of the attractions of applying automation to these kind of applications are inclusion of a vision system for part recognition, elimination of jigs and templates, high speed and accuracy, and flexibility and in-process inspection.

Routing refers to the shaping of apertures or edge-trimming of components in flat and shaped panels. Robotic manipulation of routing heads with the appropriate cutting device can offer a low-cost solution, particularly when the article is of complex geometry. With automatic tool changers, a robot cell can perform a multitude of functions such as drilling holes and inserting bushes.

Trimming of the part can also be carried out using a water-jet cutter. The prime attractions of water-jet cutting of a cured composite are the negligible force on the work-piece (such that tooling is simplified) and elimination of edge delamination.

One of the more time-consuming operations in aerospace manufacture is the drilling of panels and subsequent fastener installation. Use of six-axis robots enables the most complex components such as nacelles to be automatically fastened. All the power supplies associated with any tooling, electrical and pneumatic, are automatically connected via the face-plate at the end of the robot arm. Robot-drilling and combined countersinking can be achieved in a matter of a few seconds for each hole. These systems are the same as those used for metal assemblies; however, drill-bit configuration depends on the material being drilled. Because composite structures are often attached to metal components, the bit has to be chosen such that it satisfactorily drills both materials. This is usually achieved with a carbide-tipped tool.

5.4 Liquid Resin Molding Techniques

5.4.1 Resin Transfer Molding

The resin transfer molding (RTM) process shown in Figure 5.13 involves first placing the dry fabric preform into the cavity of a matched mold and then filling the mold and hence the preform with liquid resin. The mold and resin are typically preheated before injection. After injection, the mold temperature is increased to cure the part. In some cases, the resin is injected into a mold that has been preheated to the cure temperature. The resin preheat, injection time, and mold temperatures are set by the characteristics of the resin being used. If the temperature(s) is too high, the resin will gel before the mold is filled; if too low, then the resin viscosity may be too high to permit flow through the preform.

A vacuum is typically applied at the exit port to evacuate air and any moisture from the mold/preform before injection. Injection pressures of around 700 KPa are usual. The application of a vacuum during injection is useful to prevent void entrapment and also supplements the injection pressure; however, care needs to be taken that the injection temperature is not above the resin boiling point when the resin is under vacuum. This will lead to high and unacceptable porosity.

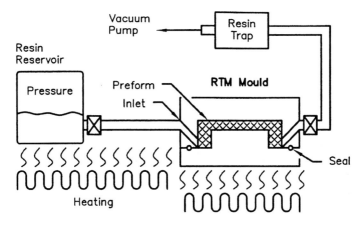

Fig. 5.13   Resin transfer molding (RTM) process.

5.4.2 Materials Systems

A large range of resins can be used for RTM, including polyesters, vinyl esters, epoxies, bismaleimides (BMIs), phenolics, and cyanate esters. Resin systems for RTM are supplied either as one-component (resin already mixed with hardener) or two-component systems.

The selection of a resin will be influenced by the suitability of its viscosity for a particular molding and the required fiber/volume fraction. For low fiber/volume moldings (around 40%), resin viscosities up to 3500 centipoise are suitable; however, for higher fiber/volume fractions, such as are usually required for aerospace structures, the viscosity should be less than 500 centipoise.

To maximize pot-life, the resin injection temperature is usually less than the preheat temperature of the mold. Material suppliers will normally provide isothermal viscosity curves for RTM resins such as those shown in Figure 5.14, allowing the optimum injection and mold temperatures to be selected by the molder.

Preforms may be made up of various reinforcements such as fabrics, braids, and other advanced textiles. Preforms are usually fabricated by using a "tackifier" or binder in the reinforcement at around 2–5% by volume. The shape is formed and consolidated on a mandrel with the application of heat and pressure (usually vacuum pressure) before it is loaded in the mold. The action of closing the mold will increase the compaction and, correspondingly, the final achievable fiber/volume fraction. Fiber/volume fractions up to 70% are achievable with certain "high-nesting" reinforcements.

When high injection pressures are used, the possibility of fiber-wash (i.e., reinforcement distortion) exists. Loose weaves and unidirectional reinforcements will have a greater tendency to fiber-wash than tightly woven performs, such as plain weaves. Additionally, high injection pressures will cause an increase in resin flow speed between tows, without complete fiber wetting, leading to voids

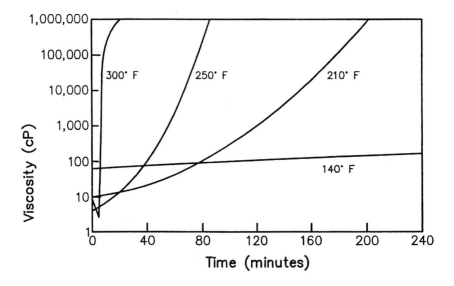

Fig. 5.14   Typical isothermal dynamic viscosity curves for an RTM resin.

within the tow bundles. Alternatively, a pressure that is too low can result in voids between tows.

The flow of the resin through the preform can be simulated using computer models. These help to establish the optimum injection pressures and predict irregular flow fronts that can trap air and cause dry spots. Generally, the highest pressure that can be used without causing significant mold deflections is sought. The models treat the flow through the preform as flow through a porous medium. In such a material, the flow velocity v and the pressure in fluid p are coupled via the generalized Darcy's law:

$$v = -\left(\frac{K}{\eta}\right) \cdot (\Delta p) \tag{5.1}$$

Here η is the resin viscosity and K is the preform permeability.[6]

5.4.3   Tooling Systems

Tooling for RTM is similar to other closed (matched die) molds in many respects. The mold determines both the inside and outside geometry of the part. For most composite components, the outside mold line may not be critical and may be uncontrolled. However, in RTM, the cavity always needs to be controlled, otherwise processing difficulties can be experienced. Too much "pinch" on the preform will affect permeability and hence resin flow and may lead to dry spots. For this reason, all mold surfaces of aerospace RTM tooling must be accurately machined.[7]

Due to the relatively high injection pressures, the mold halves must be securely clamped and reinforced to prevent expansion of the cavity. Alternatively, the mold halves can be held in a press.

Gating refers to the resin distribution system that is used to transfer the resin uniformly into the preform from the resin inlet position(s) to the outlet(s). The aim of the gating is to ensure that a smooth and predictable infusion takes place without the flow front becoming distorted by local variations in permeabilities or by geometric features and without air entrapment. Line gates, point gates, and perimeter gates are all methods employed, each having its advantage under different circumstances (Fig. 5.15).

Race-tracking describes a situation in which the resin tracks the perimeter of the part (between a trimmed preform and the cavity wall), usually in an uncontrolled manner. It can lead to trap-off of air with resulting dry spots in the cured part. This condition needs to be guarded against when the gating is designed. Figure 5.15 shows how dry spots can result from a point gate arrangement and (in the example shown) are eliminated through the use of a line gate. Perimeter inlet gates will typically be combined with one or more outlet point gates. This method provides the quickest means of filling a part as well as eliminating race-tracking concerns because the resin is planned to fill first the perimeter before migrating into the part.

5.4.4 Applications

Advantages of RTM include excellent dimensional control, good surface finish, reproducibility, reduced material cost, reduced labor cost, net or near-net

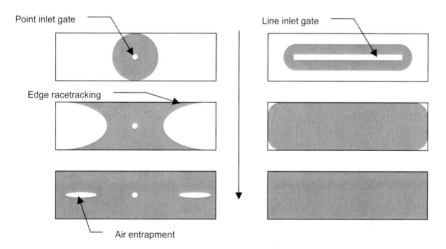

Fig. 5.15 Alternative gating arrangements for the RTM process, showing possible defects.

shape fabrication and elimination of the use of an autoclave. Consequently, the process is often used for smaller parts of complex geometry that requires good dimensional control on both inner and outer surfaces.

Other advantages include the ability to use preforms with through-thickness reinforcement and to mold inserts integrally with the part. A further advantage over pre-preg processing is that the materials need not be limited by shelf-life; however, preforms with some thermosetting binder materials can lose some drapability if excessively exposed to room temperature.

Figure 5.16 shows an example of a component that realizes many of the benefits of RTM. The component is a section of a helicopter door pillar designed as two mating Z-section details that are bonded together to make a hollow section with two flanges or lands for the transparency and door seal. The complex shape of this component would require time-consuming pre-preg hand lay-up. In the RTM process, two dry fabric stacks are draped into each half of the mold before closure over a mandrel. The individual stacks are separated by a film to allow the mold to be opened and the two parts and the mandrel removed after curing. The molding is carried out in a single operation. The two halves mate exactly at the film-line and are bonded together in a secondary operation.

The interest in RTM for larger parts has led to some novel design concepts such as multi-spar flaps and spoilers. These contain no ribs and are made with multiple internal mandrels onto which the dry preforms are laid before loading

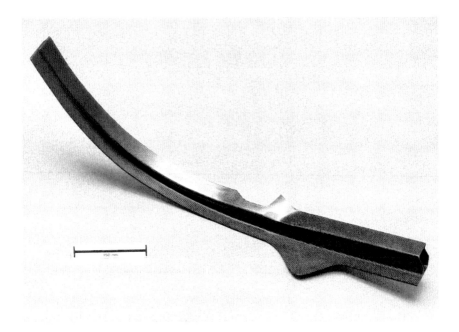

Fig. 5.16   Complex hollow section RTM part. Courtesy of CRC-ACS.

into an outer shell mold set. After resin fill and cure, the mandrels are removed to leave a multi-cell open-ended box structure.

5.4.5 Resin Film Infusion

In the resin film infusion (RFI) process illustrated in Figure 5.17, a film of resin is placed onto a mold either beneath or above the dry reinforcement. A vacuum bag is then placed over the assembly. This is then loaded into an autoclave and subjected to heat and pressure. The temperature is increased to a level such that the resin viscosity reduces and a low-level pressure is applied to force the resin into the reinforcement. Once the infusion has been completed, the pressure and temperature are increased to compact and cure the part. The appropriate viscosity-temperature-time profile must be established for each particular resin system so that complete saturation is obtained.[8]

Two areas are particularly critical to the success of this process: preform design and placement within the tool, and tool design and dimensional control throughout the process.[8]

Higher viscosity resin systems (such as Hexcel 3501-6) can be used for RFI because the resin travel distance is shortened considerably compared with that of a RTM part. The RFI process is ideally suited to the infusion of large relatively flat areas and has been used successfully to manufacture stiffened skins and rib-type structures. In these cases, the majority of the flow is one-dimensional (through the thickness); however, race-tracking around the perimeter of the reinforcement can occur, resulting in additional in-plane flow. If this is controlled (by careful design and trimming of the preform), flow distances can be advantageously increased. Quite large box-section structures have been produced by these means. However, extreme care is required to avoid trap-off and consequent dry spots.

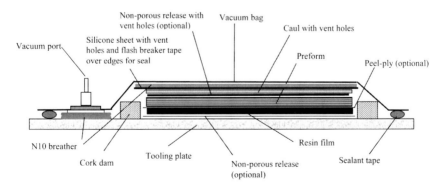

Fig. 5.17 Schematic diagram of the lay-up and tool for the resin film infusion process.

The consistency (tackiness) of the film is similar to that of pre-preg. The film is usually supplied on a roll and is available in several areal weights. In some cases, several plies will be required for thicker parts or the film can be fabricated in sections by casting or pressing the resin to the desired thickness. Resin film made using this technique may be either solid or slightly flexible, depending on the degree of staging.

RFI is more suitable than RTM for large structures (over 3 m) because it becomes difficult to handle the weight of large RTM molds. Additionally, being a single-sided tooling process, tooling costs will be considerably less for an RFI component; however, as there is inevitably some "float" of the mandrels, tool design and set-up are more complicated.

5.4.6 Vacuum-Assisted RTM

The vacuum-assisted RTM (VARTM) process, shown in Figure 5.18, is also a single-sided tooling process. It involves laying a dry fiber preform onto a mold, then placing a permeable membrane on top of the perform, and finally vacuum bagging the assembly. Inlet and exit feed tubes are positioned through the bag, and a vacuum is pulled at the exit to infuse the preform. The resin will quickly flow through the permeable material across the surface, resulting in a combination of in-plane and through-thickness flow and allowing rapid infusion times. The permeable material is usually a large open-area woven cloth or plastic grid. Commercial "shade-cloth" is often used for this purpose.

In foam-cored sandwich structures, the resin can be transported through grooves and holes machined in the core, eliminating the need for other distribution media. However, foam-cored structures are rarely selected for aerospace structures with the exception of some light aircraft and sailplanes.

The VARTM process results in lower fiber/volume fractions than RTM or RFI because the preform is subjected to vacuum compaction only. Reductions in the order of 5% can be expected depending on the form of the reinforcing. Hence, VARTM has in the past generally been used for lower-performance composite structures, such as ship hulls, and superstructures, where the advantages of lower tooling costs and the ability to cure under vacuum without the need of an autoclave outweigh the slightly reduced performance. However, some aerospace companies are overcoming this problem by pre-compacting or stitching the preform before lay-up. Although the infusion is conducted at room temperature in the manufacture of commercial grade parts, VARTM for aerospace structures involves the use of high-temperature resin systems and therefore the process will require a heating oven.

As noted, the advantage of VARTM over RTM is in the reduced tooling costs and compared with RFI or pre-preg processing, the elimination of the need for an autoclave is a significant consideration.

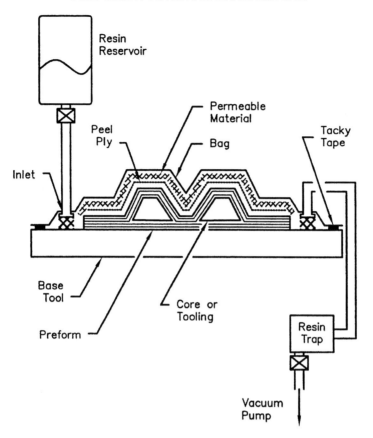

Fig. 5.18 Schematic diagram of the vacuum-assisted resin-transfer molding process.

Example 5.1

Simple calculations can determine the time to fill a rectilinear RTM mold for validation of a flow simulation model. The length of the preform is 0.20 m. The permeability is 3.5×10^{-11} m^2 for a 54% fiber/volume fraction, 8 harness carbon fabric preform. The resin is injected at 200 KPa and room temperature where the viscosity of the resin is 400 centipoise.

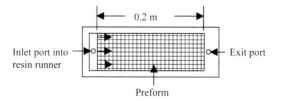

Rectilinear RTM Mold.   The one-dimensional Darcy's law is:

$$Q = -\frac{KA}{\eta}\frac{dP}{dx} \tag{5.2}$$

where Q is the volume flow of resin per unit time.
   Assuming $-(dP/dx)$ constant:

$$Q = vA(1 - V_f) = \frac{KA}{\eta}\frac{P}{x} \tag{5.3}$$

$$\textbf{average velocity:}\quad v = \frac{dx}{dt} = \frac{KP}{\eta(1 - V_f)}\frac{1}{x} \tag{5.4}$$

Solve for time by integrating the equation (5.4), where
K is the permeability
P is the injection pressure
V_f is the fiber/volume fraction
x is the mold length
η is the resin viscosity
t is the time to fill
A is the mold cross-sectional area (width $\times$ thickness)

$$\text{Answer: } t = \frac{\eta(1 - V_f)}{KP}\frac{x^2}{2} = \frac{0.4(1 - 0.54)}{3.5E^{-11} \times 200,000}\frac{(0.2)^2}{2} = 526 \text{ seconds}$$

5.5   Filament Winding

5.5.1   *General*

   Filament winding[9,10] is a composite-material manufacturing process that enables continuous reinforcement to be laid down at high speed and precision in predefined (generally, geodesic) paths. The process basically involves the winding of continuous fiber, impregnated with resin, over a rotating or stationary mandrel. The mandrel, whose geometry cannot include any re-entrant curvature, is subsequently removed after cure. By varying process parameters, such as winding tension, winding angle, and resin content, during the laying of the fiber, the desired part thickness, ply lay-up, and fiber/volume fraction can be achieved.
   Filament winding is considered to be less versatile than other composite manufacturing techniques, particularly for complex shapes with varying thickness and fiber orientation. The process is better suited to parts with simple surfaces of revolution, although developments of the process with the introduction of multi-axis machines and sophisticated control software has enabled more complex-shaped components that are non-axisymmetric to be produced.

5.5.2 Winding Process

The basic filament-winding machine (Fig. 5.19) comprises a mandrel, fiber feed head and carriage, drive systems, and control box. The mandrel is motor driven such that it rotates about its longitudinal axis. As it rotates, it takes up fiber from the feed head. The feed head is attached to a carriage that is located onto a track, enabling the head to traverse back and forth in a direction parallel to the longitudinal axis of the mandrel. The speeds at which the mandrel rotates and the feed carriage traverses determine the orientation of the fiber being laid down. Basic winding machines can be programmed simply by changing the gearing between the mandrel and feed carriage. Ancillary devices are also used to maintain tension in the fiber as it is being taken off supply spools or creels. The tension in the fiber controls the level of compaction in the wound part.

In the wet-winding procedure, the fibers pass through a heated resin bath before reaching the feed head and are then deposited onto the mandrel. In this situation, rollers are used to remove excess resin, to force remaining resin into the fibers and flatten the tows. A variation to this is the controlled wet procedure, in which resin is metered onto the fiber. In the case of pre-preg winding, the resin bath and rollers are not required, the pre-impregnated fiber being fed directly into

Fig. 5.19 Filament winding machine. Courtesy McClean-Anderson, Schofield, Wisconsin.

the feed head from the spools, then laid onto the mandrel. For pre-preg winding, the mandrel is generally heated to promote resin tack and flow. The fully wound part is then cured either at room temperature in an oven or in an autoclave, depending on the resin system.

The design of the mandrels used in filament winding is highly dependent on the winding machine capabilities, the structural requirements of the part, and the processing characteristics. Mandrels are generally constructed of steel or aluminum, and for situations in which the mandrel forms part of the structure or simple extraction of the mandrel is possible, the mandrel is in one piece. Where simple withdrawal is not possible, various types of removable mandrels are required. This may involve segmented metal mandrels, or mandrels constructed of materials that are soluble, fusible, inflatable, or collapsible.

5.5.3 Winding Patterns

There is a range of winding patterns used in filament winding, with the three primary classes being hoop, helical, and polar (See Fig. 5.20). The simplest is *hoop* winding, which comprises a mandrel rotating continuously about its longitudinal axis while the fiber feed carriage advances one fiber bandwidth after each mandrel axis of rotation. Consequently, fibers are deposited almost normal to the longitudinal axis. *Helical* winding, which is most commonly used, is achieved when the mandrel rotates continuously about a horizontal axis while the fiber feed carriage traverses back and forth. Winding angles ranging between $25-80°$ can be achieved with this method. In *polar* winding, the mandrel is rotated perpendicular to its longitudinal axis and remains stationary while the fiber feed arm rotates about the longitudinal axis, inclined at a slight angle. After each revolution of the feed arm, the mandrel is indexed to rotate about its longitudinal axis by one fiber band-width. A variation to polar winding is *whirling* winding, whereby the mandrel is rotated about a vertical longitudinal axis.

The basic winding patterns enable continuous fiber to be laid down onto the mandrel in the hoop, longitudinal, and bias directions. The ability to achieve these patterns is dependent on the type of filament winder being used. Basic filament winding machines have only two axes, thus limiting the patterns and shapes that can be wound. More sophisticated machines, such as robotic CNC filament winders, can have up to 10 axes of movement, which enables a greater range of patterns and more complex-shaped parts to be wound. These CNC machines have computerized servo-controls that allow complex winding procedures to be defined before their automatic execution.

5.5.4 Materials

The fibers used in the filament winding process typically come in two forms. Wet winding uses dry fibers that are impregnated with a low-viscosity resin during the winding process. In some cases, the part may be wound entirely with

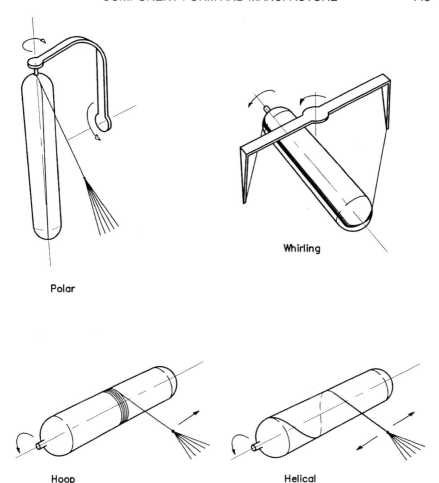

Polar

Whirling

Hoop

Helical

Fig. 5.20 Schematic diagram of the various filament winding machines and patterns. Adapted from Reference 18.

dry fiber then impregnated with resin under pressure. Pre-preg winding utilizes fibers that have been encapsulated within a B-staged resin. The advantages of wet winding are that it uses materials in the lowest cost form having no shelf life limits, and also that it requires fewer compaction cycles during the winding process. Pre-preg systems, on the other hand, can produce parts with higher quality and consistency, reduce winding times, minimize the chance of fiber slippage, and require less consolidating after winding.

Thermosetting resins are most commonly used in filament winding, where consolidation of the material takes place after the winding has been completed. More recently, thermoplastic resins have been used in the form of pre-preg and consolidation takes place as the material is being laid down.

Further discussion of filament winding of thermoplastic composites appears later in this chapter.

5.5.5 Design and Properties

The analysis of filament-wound structures is usually carried out using a netting approximation. This assumes that the fibers are uniformly loaded in tension and provide all the longitudinal stiffness and strength while the resin provides only the shear stiffness. This is a conservative approach; a more realistic procedure is to use techniques such as composite laminate theory (See Chapter 6).

The properties of filament-wound structures are generally inferior to composites made by conventional methods. This can be attributed to the higher void contents that can be as high as 7% for wet-wound material. If the fiber tension is too high, air will be entrapped at crossover points and within the tows that are unable to spread. If the resin viscosity is too high, the entrapped air is also unable to escape. To some extent, excessive voiding may be reduced by control of fiber tension and use of low-viscosity resins, however, autoclave processing with prior vacuum treatment is a more effective method of minimizing voids.

The winding pattern can also contribute to variations in the mechanical properties. Helical winding patterns produce fiber tow crossovers that result in crimping of the fiber and increase stress concentrations at these points. However, interweaving does result in improved interlaminar performance.

One of the most significant problems occurring in filament-wound structures is layer or fiber waviness, which can result in a significant loss of strength and stiffness. The waviness is mainly caused by volumetric changes during resin bleed-out in thick wound structures. It can therefore be avoided by minimizing the amount of resin that needs to be removed and maintaining the correct level filament tension during winding.

5.5.6 Applications

The advantages of the filament winding process are best exploited on components with simple surfaces of revolution. Examples of aerospace parts that have been fabricated using filament winding include rocket-motor cases, pressure vessels, missile launch tubes, and drive shafts. Some of these components, especially rocket-motor cases, can be very large (exceeding 4 m in diameter). Metal end-closures and metal or rubber internal liners are commonly incorporated into the design of filament-wound pressure vessels. These additions are placed onto the mandrel before winding. Filament winding is also commonly used for non-aerospace applications, such as storage and processing tanks, reinforced pipe, crane booms, automotive drive shafts, springs, golf shafts, fishing rods, and paddle shafts.

Filament winding has also been shown to be an ideal method for making geodesic composite structures. These structures utilize reinforcement in an

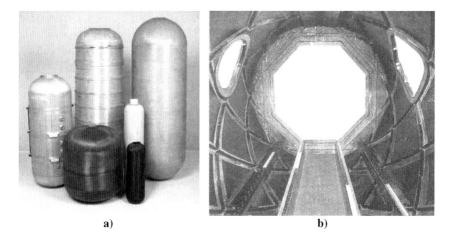

a)   b)

Fig. 5.21   Parts made by filament winding; *a*) pressure vessels, *b*) geodesic structure Reference 18.

efficient manner, achieving ultra-lightweight components with high stiffness and strength. Examples of this include an isogrid helicopter blade and an orthogrid fuselage barrel (Fig. 5.21b).

Filament winding can be combined with a secondary molding process, whereby the winding process is used as a means of rapid and high-precision lay-up. Hollow cylinders are wound up onto mandrels and removed before curing. The uncured lay-up is then loaded into a tool and press-molded. This approach has been used to produce I-beams and helicopters blades. In the case of the latter, inflatable mandrels are used, where the uncured winding is placed into a mold with the deflated mandrel, and the mandrel is then reinflated to apply a consolidation pressure to the lay-up.

5.6 Pultrusion

Pultrusion is a highly automated, continuous, linear process for manufacturing constant cross-sectional profiles of fiber-reinforced polymeric materials. In its simplest form, continuous unidirectional fibers (in the form of tows or rovings) are impregnated with a thermosetting resin and pulled through a heated die to shape and cure the composite into a finished product (Fig. 5.22). As the material progresses through the die, the applied heat triggers the cure reaction, and the resulting solid product is pulled through the die by a set of mechanically or hydraulically driven grippers. Further details are given elsewhere.[11,12]

The aim of the process is to produce a cured part before the product exits the die. The pulling speed is therefore related to the curing kinetics of the resin

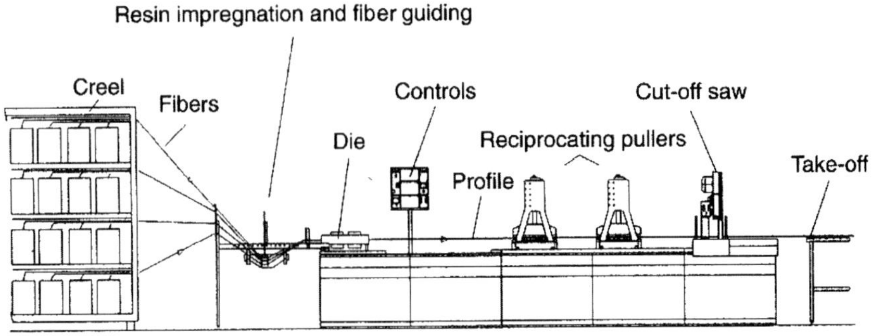

Resin impregnation and fiber guiding

Fig. 5.22   Schematic diagram of basic pultrusion machine (Reference 11).

system being used and the die length. Dies are typically 1 m long and pulling speeds vary between 200 mm min^{-1} for epoxy-based products to 3000 mm min^{-1} for commercial, polyester-based products. With epoxy-based systems, full cure is not normally achieved before the part exits the die, and post-curing operations need to be considered (either on- or off-line).

5.6.1   Reinforcements

Almost all reinforcement material and forms can be processed by the pultrusion technique, including glass, aramid, polyethene (polyethylene), and carbon fibers. One intrinsic requirement of the process is the need for a high percentage of fibers aligned parallel to the pulling direction. With need for off-axis fibers, as is the case for aerospace products, there is a fundamental requirement to have sufficient zero degree fibers to withstand the pulling forces required to draw the array of collimated fibers and fabrics through the die. When off-axis reinforcement is required, such as at $90°$ or $\pm 45°$, stitched non-crimp fabrics (NCF) can be used. However, these fabrics are effectively incompressible and can give rise to rapid pressure rise at the die entrance.

5.6.2   Resins

With transient times of typically 0.5–5.0 minutes in the heated section of the die, it is essential to use a resin system that gels and/or cures very rapidly.

The majority of commercial pultrusions are manufactured with polyester resin. This is because it is inexpensive and is the easiest resin to process. In applications in which the fire resistance is of primary importance, phenolic resin is normally selected. However, there are certain considerations that must be taken into account when pultruding phenolic-based products. First, the compatibility of the phenolic resin with conventional sizing on glass fibers is poor, and second, in some systems? water, in the form of steam, is generated as a by-product of the curing reaction. Without careful management, the water can remain trapped in the product, resulting in a severely voided laminate. The mechanical properties of phenolic laminates are typically lower than those having polyester or vinyl ester resin systems, and the production rates are also slower.

Epoxy resins are selected for applications where the mechanical properties need to be maximized, such as in aggressive environments and military or aerospace applications. However, epoxies are notoriously difficult to process by pultrusion because the curing mechanism of epoxies is significantly different to that of polyesters and vinyl esters. Epoxies cure very slowly and take a long time to reach their gel point; it may not occur until just before the die exit. Also, the degree of cure at the die exit may be as low as 70–80%.

To maximize the transient time, pulling speeds are normally very low when processing epoxy-based products. Epoxies also have very low cure shrinkages and are exceptional adhesives, which in combination can lead to a surface-roughening phenomenon called *micro-sloughing*.

5.6.3 Pultrusion Process

The process can be separated into three key stages:

- Fiber in-feed system—includes fiber-dispensing, impregnation, collimation, and forming
- Forming system—includes external heating, die design, and the curing reaction
- Pulling system—includes pulling mechanism and the cut-off station

5.6.4 In-Feed System

Of the three stages listed above, the in-feed system, an example of which is shown in Figure 5.23, is by far the most important to the smooth and successful operation of the pultrusion process.

The reinforcing fibers are usually used in a combination of rovings and broadgoods. The rovings are traditionally stored on multi-layer racks called creels, and the fabric is slit to the required widths and dispensed from rolls. The fibers and fabrics can be impregnated with resin either collectively, toward the end of the forming process, or individually at intermediate stations, located throughout the in-feed system. Once impregnated, and before final collimation, the fabrics pass through a series of shaped formers that squeeze-off excess resin. This stage also encourages thorough infiltration of the resin and wet-out of all fibers.

5.6.5 Tooling System

The tooling system consists of a pair of closed, matched dies that are about 1 m in length. The die cavity forms the shape of the finished part and, apart from

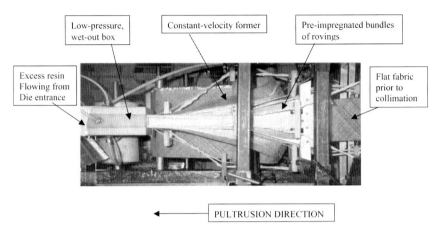

Fig. 5.23   Infeed system for a pultrusion process.

having a bell-mouthed entrance, is normally of constant dimensions along the length of the tool. The dies, which are normally manufactured from tool steel or medium-strength steel with chrome-plated internal surfaces, are then usually placed between a set of heated platens and anchored to the machine.

To achieve thermal equilibrium, additional heaters such as strip heaters can be positioned along the length of the die at strategic locations. Cartridge heaters can be inserted in mandrels, which are otherwise cold because they are isolated from the main external heat source. Heat pipes, which are very efficient thermodynamic devices with extremely high thermal conductivity, can be used to transfer heat from the exit end to the front end. Sometimes when dealing with a reactive resin mix or a complex profile, the mouth of the die is water-cooled to avoid premature gelation. Tooling design is of paramount importance and is normally achieved with the aid of three-dimensional numerical models, such as TOPDIE, which is available from Pultrusion Dynamics Technology Center.[13]

5.6.6   Pulling and Docking Systems

The motive force to draw the solid product from the die is generally supplied by one of two means; either 1) by reciprocating clamps that oscillate in a hand-to-hand motion or 2) by using a pair of caterpillar tracks that continuously clamp and draw the product.

The process is completed when the product reaches the cut-off station where a flying cut-off saw clamps onto the product and cuts the profile to the desired length. The pultrusion process offers the inherent advantage that any transportable length can be produced. This may typically be 6 m for standard construction type profiles (tees, angles, etc.) but may be as long as 2000 m for fiber optic cable core, which is 0.002 m diameter and wound onto a spool mounted at the end of the pultrusion machine.

5.6.7 Aerospace Applications

Starr[11] gives a comprehensive overview of the ever-increasing number of applications of pultrusion from cable-trays and window lineals to full-scale bridge decks and railway bridge constructions.

Within the aerospace market, however, successful examples of the use of structural pultrusions are relatively few. This is due primarily to the limited production runs required for aerospace products; demands are usually too short for the pultrusion process to be viable. Production runs of aircraft are usually measured in hundreds, spread over several years. It is also due in part to the difficulty in reaching the quality of product achievable with other aircraft-molding techniques. This arises both from the unsuitability of most high-performance resins and the difficulty of achieving high-volume fractions when using off-axis reinforcement. Nevertheless, through the development of special resins, high-performance aerospace quality pultrusions with relatively high V_f have been produced, an example of which is shown in Figure 5.24.

5.7 Process Modelling

One of the main barriers to more widespread application of advanced composite structures is their relatively high cost compared with parts made of

Fig. 5.24   Prototype, structural I-beam, produced using carbon fiber tows and NCFs with an epoxy resin system. Courtesy of CRC-ACS Ltd, Australia.

conventional aluminum alloys. The high cost of composite manufacturing is partly due to the trial-and-error philosophies adopted in the manufacturing tooling design and process development. It is therefore very desirable to be able to predict the material and tooling responses during manufacturing through the use of *process modelling* or simulation. Process modelling may help to reduce the manufacturing cost and time on two different scales. First, it is possible to optimize the tooling and process design for a manufacturing process through process modelling if the fundamental response of the materials involved can be characterized relatively accurately. Second, and more broadly, process modelling can be used to predict a desired tooling and process design window within which a reduced number of trials can be conducted.

The processing of advanced composites involves a number of coupled physical and chemical phenomena. These include heat and mass transfer in the two-phase media (reinforcement and matrix), resin cure reactions, and deformation caused by temperature changes, resin cure shrinkage, and applied forces. These phenomena are governed by the well-known conservation rules, such as conservation of energy, conservation of resin mass, and conservation of momentum. Process modelling is used to solve the relevant governing equations under a set of given initial and/or boundary conditions to predict the process variables such as temperature, degree of cure, pressure, flow front positions, and deformation of composite part and tooling. Due to the general complexity of both the process and the part geometry, an analytical solution is usually not possible and therefore a numerical method, such as the finite difference method or the finite element method, has to be used.

5.7.1 Forming of Reinforcement Stacks

Forming a stack of reinforcement layers, whether they be pre-preg plies or "dry" fabric plies for use in RTM, involves transforming a flat stack of reinforcement into a three-dimensional shape. However, the deformation behavior of pre-preg is more complicated than that of the dry reinforcement, making it much more difficult to model.

Two approaches are commonly used to model forming: the kinematic mapping approach and the mechanics approach.

In the mapping or kinematic approach, forming is considered purely as a process of geometrical transformation: the initially flat sheet of material is mapped onto the three-dimensional surface of the forming tool. The material is assumed to be inextensible in the fiber direction and the draping is achieved through shear deformation. Any forces required to shear the fabric are ignored. Consequently, the mapping approach provides only geometrical or strain information on forming, such as fiber orientation in the formed part and the total shear strain experienced by the part. The mapping approach is a good initial tool for investigating forming requirements, and may be all that is required for predicting the formed shape in hand lay-up of single layers of pre-preg or dry fabrics, or preforming of stacks of dry fabric layers with the same orientation. Figure 5.25 shows fiber paths in a woven fabric draped over an aircraft rib shape, predicted by the software Drape from the Technical University of Delft.

The mechanics approach solves equilibrium equations balancing the forces within the material against the applied loads, and the constitutive equations describing how the stress in the material is related to strain and/or strain rate. The transient forming process is modelled by time stepping. Such a model is usually complicated due to the complex deformation modes of composite sheets. It has to be solved by the finite element method and requires large computing power. However, a mechanics model can provide not only more detailed geometrical information, but also the transient strain and stress states in the material, which is needed to predict forming defects. Therefore, much recent development in the modelling of composite sheet forming has used this approach. Figure 5.26 shows the predicted forming behavior of a cross-plied stack of woven pre-preg formed over the same rib shape. The software used is PAMFORM from Engineering Systems International.

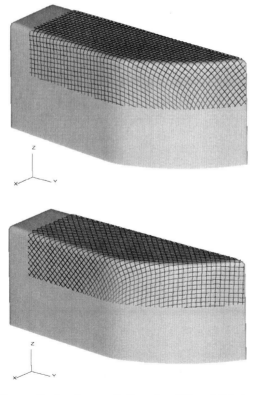

Fig. 5.25   Kinematic draping predictions for different fabric orientations.

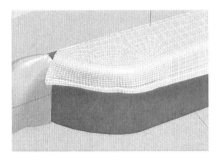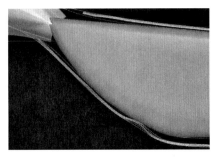

Fig. 5.26   PAM FORM predictions for forming a ply stack over a rib shape.

5.7.2   Heat Transfer and Resin Cure

Advanced composites are usually cured at the relatively high temperature of about 180°C. During a composite curing process, heat transfer and cure in composites are governed by the following equations:

$$\overline{\rho c}_p \frac{\partial T}{\partial t} + V_r \rho_r c_{pr}\left(u_x \frac{\partial T}{\partial x} + u_y \frac{\partial T}{\partial y} + u_z \frac{\partial T}{\partial z}\right)$$

$$= \bar{\kappa}_x \frac{\partial^2 T}{\partial x^2} + \bar{\kappa}_y \frac{\partial^2 T}{\partial y^2} + \bar{\kappa}_z \frac{\partial^2 T}{\partial z^2} + V_r \rho_r H_r R_r \tag{5.5}$$

$$\frac{\partial \alpha}{\partial t} + u_x \frac{\partial \alpha}{\partial x} + u_y \frac{\partial \alpha}{\partial y} + u_z \frac{\partial \alpha}{\partial z} = R_r \tag{5.6}$$

where $\bar{\rho}$ and $\bar{c}_p$, respectively, are density and specific heat of the composites; $\bar{\kappa}_x$, $\bar{\kappa}_y$ and $\bar{\kappa}_z$ are the directional thermal conductivity of the composites; ρ_r, c_{pr}, and κ_r, respectively, are density, specific heat, and conductivity of the resin; V_r is the resin volume fraction; u_x, u_y, and u_z are the components of resin flow velocity; H_r and R_r are the total heat of reaction and the rate of reaction of the resin, respectively; and α is the degree of cure.

For a thermoset resin, the rate of reaction (R_r) at various temperatures can be experimentally determined by differential scanning calorimetry (DSC). The results are then fitted to an equation expressing R_r as a function of temperature T and α. The following Arrhenius-type equation is most frequently used:

$$R_r = \frac{d\alpha}{dt} = K_0 \exp\left(-\frac{E}{RT}\right)\alpha^m (1 - \alpha)^n \tag{5.7}$$

where R is the universal gas constant, K_0, E, m, and n are the parameters to be determined by the fitting.

The existence of resin flow velocity (u_x, u_y, u_z) in equations (5.1) and (5.2) means that modelling of heat transfer and cure in composites is normally coupled with simulation of resin flow. This is often referred to as non-isothermal flow simulation. However, some manufacturing processes, such as autoclave curing and the curing stage of RTM, involve insignificant resin flow. For these processes, the above equations can be simplified by setting the relevant velocity components to zero and can be solved to predict the temperature and curing profiles.

Pultrusion is considered as a special case for which the resin flow relative to the reinforcement can be ignored and hence a coupling with flow simulation is also not needed. However, heat transfer and cure modelling for pultrusion is still somewhat complicated owing to the constant movement of the pultruded part in the pulling direction. The governing equations for a pultrusion process can be written as follows:

$$\overline{\rho c}_p \left(\frac{\partial T}{\partial t} + u \frac{\partial T}{\partial x} \right) = \bar{\kappa}_x \frac{\partial^2 T}{\partial x^2} + \bar{\kappa}_y \frac{\partial^2 T}{\partial y^2} + \bar{\kappa}_z \frac{\partial^2 T}{\partial z^2} + V_r \rho_r H_r R_r \tag{5.8}$$

$$\frac{\partial \alpha}{\partial t} + u \frac{\partial \alpha}{\partial x} = R_r \tag{5.9}$$

where u is the pulling speed.

The above equations can be solved using the finite difference or the finite element method to predict the temperature and curing profiles in pultrusion. Figure 5.27 shows the temperature and curing profiles at the die exit for the pultrusion of a fiberglass-vinyl ester composite I beam, predicted by using the finite element method. Owing to the symmetry in the die, only one quarter of the section need be modelled.

5.7.3 Resin Flow Through Fiber Reinforcement

The flow of resin through fiber reinforcement is considered to obey Darcy's law that states that the velocity of the flow is proportional to the pressure gradient in the resin. Combined with the assumption of resin incompressibility, one can derive the following resin pressure equation:

$$\frac{\partial}{\partial x} \left(\frac{S_x}{\mu} \frac{\partial P}{\partial x} \right) + \frac{\partial}{\partial y} \left(\frac{S_y}{\mu} \frac{\partial P}{\partial y} \right) + \frac{\partial}{\partial z} \left(\frac{S_z}{\mu} \frac{\partial P}{\partial z} \right) = 0 \tag{5.10}$$

where S_x, S_y, and S_z are the directional permeability of the reinforcement and μ is the viscosity of the resin.

The above equation can be solved analytically for the simple cases of isothermal, one-dimensional flow and isothermal radial flow. The solutions have been used to process results of tests to determine the permeability of reinforcement.

To solve these equations for any more complex case, the finite element/control volume method is most frequently used. In this method, the reinforcement is divided into elements/control volumes. A fill factor between 0 and 1 is assigned to each of the control volumes, with 0 indicating an empty volume and 1 for a

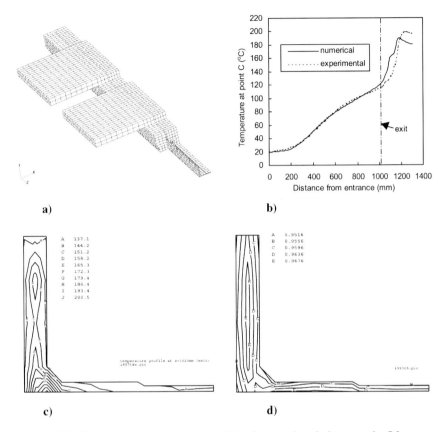

Fig. 5.27   Heat transfer and cure modelling for a pultruded composite I-beam.

resin-saturated one. The flow front is identified as joining those control volumes with fill factors that are neither 0 nor 1. The transient process of resin flow is divided into time steps. Within a step, the pressure equation is first solved by the finite element method. Darcy's law is then used to calculate the net flow into the control volumes at the flow front, and the relevant fill factors and the pressure boundary conditions are updated.

Because the components produced by liquid composite molding are often thin shell structures, the flow model can be simplified as two-dimensional. However, two-dimensional modelling assumes no flow in the through-thickness direction, which may lead to significant errors in the modelling of flow in thick parts, as illustrated in Figure 5.28.

The resin flow in a composite manufacturing process is usually non-isothermal and the viscosity of the resin is affected by its temperature and curing state. To simulate these conditions requires a coupling between flow simulation and heat transfer and cure modelling. Such a non-isothermal flow simulation is

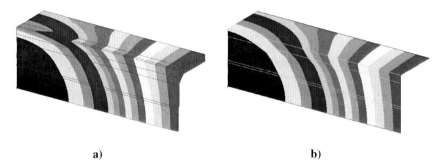

a)   b)

Fig. 5.28   Sequential predicted flow fronts for RTM of a composite I-beam (quarter section). Resin inlet is at lower left. a) Three-dimensional flow simulation; b) two-dimensional flow simulation.

needed for a "fast" liquid molding process such as structural reaction injection molding (SRIM), and high-temperature infusion processes such as resin film infusion during which significant cure reaction occurs simultaneously with resin flow. RTM processes are often operated at a temperature at which the viscosity is lowest and little cure occurs. An isothermal flow simulation can be used for such an operation.

5.7.4   Consolidation of Reinforcement

In general, consolidation can be considered as a phenomenon during which the fiber/volume fraction, and hence the thickness, of the reinforcement stack changes as a result of applied pressure and/or resin flow. This could occur, for example, during compression molding, resin film infusion, or the autoclave processing of thick composites. The change in the fiber/volume fraction presents a number of challenges to process modelling. It results in a moving boundary in the thickness direction. It affects the permeability of the reinforcement significantly, which has a direct impact on flow simulation. Additional models are needed to describe fiber/volume fraction as a function of the fiber compaction stress and to relate the stress to the total applied pressure.

In a consolidation model, it is generally assumed that the applied pressure is balanced by the effective fiber compaction stress p and the resin pressure P:

$$\sigma = p + P \tag{5.11}$$

To account for the compaction of the reinforcement in the thickness direction, the resin pressure equation is modified to:

$$\frac{\partial}{\partial x}\left(\frac{S_x}{\mu}\frac{\partial P}{\partial x}\right) + \frac{\partial}{\partial y}\left(\frac{S_y}{\mu}\frac{\partial P}{\partial y}\right) + \frac{\partial}{\partial z}\left(\frac{S_z}{\mu}\frac{\partial P}{\partial z}\right) = m_v\left(\frac{\partial P}{\partial t} - \frac{\partial \sigma}{\partial t}\right) \tag{5.12}$$

where m_v is the coefficient of volume change, which can be related to the fiber/volume fraction and the fiber compaction stress as follows:

$$m_v = \frac{1}{V_f}\frac{dV_f}{dp} \tag{5.13}$$

The relationship between V_f and p needs to be determined by a compaction test. It is also necessary to experimentally determine the permeability as a function of the fiber/volume fraction. It has been shown that the results of the permeability test can be fitted to the Kozeny-Carman equation:

$$S = \frac{r_f^2}{4K_z}\frac{(1-V_f)^3}{V_f^2} \tag{5.14}$$

where r_f is the fiber radius and K_z the Kozeny constant.

Consolidation modelling has been used for some time to simulate autoclave consolidation of thick pre-preg composites in which the resin flow is predominantly one-dimentional in the thickness direction. More recently, it has been used in other situations such as the simulation of compression RTM and of vacuum bag resin infusion.

5.7.5 Process-Induced Distortion and Residual Stress

Five main factors have been identified as responsible for process-induced part distortion and residual stress in composite structures. These are thermal strains, resin cure shrinkage strains, gradients in temperature and resin degree of cure, resin pressure gradients, and tooling mechanical constraints. To fully model the development of the part distortion and residual stress during a manufacturing process, it is necessary to include the transient temperature, resin flow and cure, and the tooling and part deformation under load. Therefore, modelling of process-induced part distortion and residual stress is one of the most complex process modelling tasks, requiring modelling of heat transfer and cure, flow simulation, and consolidation analysis as sub-models.

Fortunately, aerospace composite structures are often thin panels cured in an autoclave or oven. For these panels, it is reasonable to assume that the gradients in temperature and resin degree of cure are small and can be ignored. Furthermore, the majority of resin cure shrinkage may occur very early in the curing process, when the resin behaves as a viscous fluid or is at least highly viscoelastic. Therefore, the cure shrinkage strains will be relaxed in the subsequent curing and contribute little to the final part distortion. This suggests that the thermal strains caused by the thermal mismatch between different directions/different plies are often the only major source of residual stress. Consequently, prediction of the process-induced distortion and residual stress can often be simplified to a structural analysis of the composite panel loaded thermally by cooling down from the curing temperature. Figure 5.29 illustrates the predicted distortion of a tray-shaped part with a curved flange by considering the thermal loads only.

5.7.6 Experimental Validation

Process modelling should not, and cannot, replace experimentation completely. On the contrary, it should be applied jointly with experimentation for the following two reasons.

First, experimental measurement is needed to obtain various material properties and derive constitutive models to be used in process modelling. Owing to developments in numerical techniques and ever-increasing computing power, there is often little difficulty in solving numerically the macroscopic governing equations for composite manufacturing processes. However, very often process modelling cannot be conducted meaningfully because the required material properties are not available or are not accurate. This is particularly true for modelling of transient processes in which it is often necessary to know the material properties as functions of the process variables, such as temperature, fiber/volume fraction, and pressure.

Second, a process model should always be verified experimentally before it can be confidently used to guide process development. A relatively large amount of process modelling work has been published in the last 20 years. However, comparatively little experimental verification of this modelling has been reported.

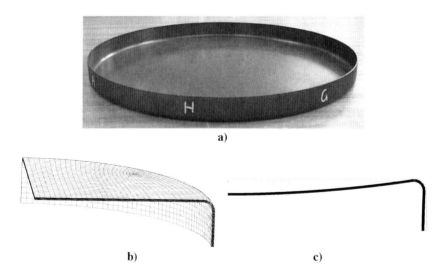

a)

b)   c)

Fig. 5.29   Distortion of a curved composite flange: *a*) manufactured part; *b*) finite element mesh; *c*) distorted shape of cross-section.

5.8 Tooling

The fabrication of composite parts requires tooling that can be described as either closed-mold or open-mold. Closed-mold tooling is used for components produced by the RTM method, and these tools are matched with a cavity whose dimensions are controlled to achieve the specified fiber and resin volume fractions. These tools are usually made from steel due to the high pressures inside the mold required for injection and compaction. Pressure on the mold is usually achieved by a press, but for large parts an autoclave can be used. Small molds can be bolted together and are satisfactory provided that deflections can be minimized. Open-mold tooling is used for manufacture with pre-preg materials, RFI, or vacuum bag resin infusion (VBRI) and consists of a hard tool providing the shape of the required component (or outer mold line; OML) with compaction provided through a flexible bag or bladder. The tooling materials for open-mold tools can be metallic or non-metallic, the choice of which is largely driven by initial cost and the numbers of parts required from the tool. For large production runs, hard metals such as steel, nickel, or invar are preferred. Composite tools are lighter and can be produced by casting from a master shape. Although they are less durable, they can be easily repaired. Wood can also be used for materials with curing temperatures less than 100°C (these materials may require a post-cure that can be undertaken off the tool).

Other factors that need to be considered in the selection of tooling materials are dimensional stability, coefficient of thermal expansion, and specific heat.

Composite tools may be unstable at elevated temperatures if cross-linking has not been sufficiently completed during manufacture. Wooden tools will be unstable if not completely dried. The tendency for uptake of moisture by wooden tools requires they be sealed with an epoxy or similar gel coat.

Carbon fiber composites have very low coefficients of thermal expansion compared with steel and aluminum. Because the part will be cured into shape at an elevated temperature, allowance has to be made for the expansion of the tool at that temperature. Subsequent contraction of the composite part can then usually be neglected, however, care must be taken to ensure that the part does not lock or is cracked due to contraction of the tool on cool-down. This is a particular concern for closed-mold tools.

A high specific heat is desirable to improve the heat-up rate of the tool. This means less energy is required through the curing process and, additionally, cycle times can be reduced.

5.8.1 Metallic Tooling Materials

The most commonly used metallic materials are aluminum alloy, steel, electroformed nickel, and invar.

Aluminum alloy is attractive due to its relatively low cost, ease of machining, and low density. It also has a high specific heat. Unfortunately, because of the low hardness, aluminum tools are easily scratched and damaged. The high CTE (aluminum CTE is twice that of steel) requires considerable compensation be allowed for the dimensions of the tool. This is used to advantage, however, when aluminum is used for internal mandrels where the higher expansion acts to compact the composite against the walls of a steel cavity mold. Cast aluminum tools have proved to have poor vacuum integrity due to the porosity in the casting, and hence they are not usually used.

Steel is a low-cost material, although machining rates are slower than for aluminum, negating the cost advantage. Its specific heat and CTE are half those of aluminum, whereas its density is three times greater. As a consequence, heat-up rates are much slower. The main advantages are its hardness and consequent durability. Steel is usually preferred where high production volumes are expected.

Electroplated or electroformed nickel has a CTE close that of steel, and its specific heat and density are both approximately 10% higher. Electroforming is a rapid electroplating process wherein nickel is deposited from a solution (generally nickel sulphamate) onto a conductive or conductive-coated master. Plating thicknesses up to 6 mm are usual. Because there is no heat generated during the process, the master can be fabricated from materials with low thermal stability such as wax, rubber, or polymer compounds. At the completion of the process the master is removed, leaving a hard, dense shell structure. Vacuum integrity on these tools is very good. They are often used for large surfaces such as wing skins.

Invar is a very dimensionally stable material. It is highly durable and has a CTE very close to carbon fiber composite materials. Thus makes it a very suitable choice for closed-cavity molds. It is however very expensive and cannot be welded.

5.8.2 Composite Tooling Materials

Normally, composite aircraft components are cured in the higher temperature ranges, typically at around 180°C, and in an autoclave under a pressure of up to 700 KPa. Therefore composite tooling, if used, must be able to withstand these conditions and have a glass transition temperature at least 15°C above the curing temperature. The high cross-link densities and high concentrations of polar molecular groups of such polymers result in a cured resin of high brittleness with susceptibility for moisture absorption. Repeated thermal cycling causes micro-cracks leading to eventual loss of vacuum integrity. In extreme cases, blistering occurs from the presence of trapped moisture. With care, however, production runs of over 100 can be achieved, and because they can be produced economically from a master, they are still popular among many manufacturing organizations. Composite tool material suppliers have in some cases developed complete systems for composite tooling that assure good tool durability, an example of which is shown in Figure 5.32. Naturally, there are no concerns from differing CTEs.

Composite tools are taken from a master model that is usually machined from computer-aided design data. Carving or splining by hand were alternative methods used in the past, however these have now largely been discarded. A variety of materials can be used for the master including polyurethane modelling board, hardwood, and medium-density fiberboard (MDF) (Fig. 5.30). The master is a positive of the component shape so that the tool can be cast directly from the surface without a transfer mold. The masters need to be handled and stored carefully because it may be intended to produce replacement tooling at some later date. Contact with moisture must be avoided because these materials are hygroscopic and will not be stable in the presence of moisture.

The tool can be a solid fiber laminate construction that is sometimes reinforced with a backing to increase stiffness. This backing may be in the form of a laminated "egg-crate" or a thick tooling compound sandwiched between the laminations. Cast epoxy can be used for smaller tools where stiffness is not a

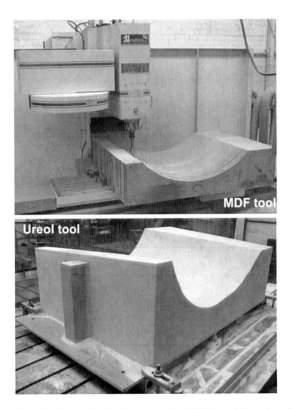

Fig. 5.30   Medium-density fiberboard (MDF) and Ureol tooling.

concern. These are usually filled with aluminum to increase thermal conductivity and modulus.

More recently, tooling pastes have been used whereby the paste is dispensed onto a foam or honeycomb backing structure followed by machining to the desired shape. These are suitable for manufacture of lower-temperature curing materials.

The tools will be surfaced with a high-temperature gel-coat. These sometimes contain fillers such as aluminum, ceramic, or silicone carbide to improve abrasion resistance.

5.8.3 Mandrels

The interest in part integration has led to the concept of cocuring. With this concept, detail laminates are laid-up onto individual mandrels that are loaded together into an assembly mold. An example of this is the Airbus A300 fin box, which is made with pre-preg material and cured in a single autoclave cycle. The key issues for design of the mandrel system are how the mandrels will be removed after cure and how to ensure the correct compaction across all surfaces. Either flexible or rigid mandrels can be used.

Flexible mandrels can be solid or can be inflatable bags that are pressurized internally through a vent to the autoclave chamber. They are usually constructed from a polyacrylic elastomer such as Airpad. This is an uncured non-silcone rubber that can be molded into shape. The sidewalls of inflatable bag mandrels are stiffened with a reinforcing fabric such as woven carbon fiber. This produces a semi-rigid box on which the composite plies can be laid-up (Fig. 5.31). There is sufficient compliance in the mandrel to expand when exposed to internal pressure, forcing the plies against the adjacent surfaces. Removal of the mandrel

Fig. 5.31 Airpad brand inflatable tooling.

after cure can be achieved by applying a partial vacuum whereupon the bag collapses sufficiently for it to be withdrawn.

The durability of the Airpad material is limited, and often a replaceable nylon film is cured onto the surfaces to extend the useful life of the mandrel.

Metal mandrels are an alternative and have an advantage in terms of durability. Aluminum is often used and, in conjunction with a steel mold, provides compaction through differential expansion. Great care has to be taken to control the dimensions such that the correct compaction and hence the correct fiber/volume fraction is achieved. Removal of metal mandrels is less simple and even though an aluminum mandrel will shrink away from the cured part on cool-down, depending on the geometry, this may be insufficient to release it. In these circumstances it is necessary to use a segmented or split mandrel. These segments are joined with an adhesive that holds the mandrel together during lay-up but breaks down at the cure temperature to allow the segments to be removed individually after cure.

For complex geometries when either of the above solutions would still not allow mandrel removal, mandrels made of a soluble plaster are used. These are cast to shape for each part and melted or washed-out under high-pressure water after use. Removal rates of the plaster tend to be low, and the economics of this restrict it to small items or where no other choice is possible.

5.9 Special Thermoplastic Techniques

5.9.1 Intermediate Forms

Because of their very high viscosity at low to moderate temperatures, it is significantly more difficult to impregnate a reinforcement with a thermoplastic

Fig. 5.32   ACG "Toolbrace" tooling.

material than with a thermoset resin. Thermoplastic composites are therefore supplied in a variety of different ready-to-use intermediate forms that may be processed through a number of standard production techniques[14] (Fig. 5.33). Considerable work has gone into developing these intermediates over the past decade. Typically, this has centred on the development of materials that have some form of a "partial impregnation," such as solvent or melt pre-pregs, film stacked pre-pregs, commingled fibers (carbon and thermoplastic fibers in a bundle or woven cloth), and powder-impregnated bundles that can be used in conjunction with contemporary thermoplastic manufacturing technology. The latter two intermediates bring fibers and matrix together in the non-molten state and are arranged such that fibers and matrix are already well mixed before processing. The comingled fibers and powder/sheath fiber bundles can be easily converted to a woven fabric by the standard weaving processes. An advantage of these two intermediates is that they are highly drapable.

5.9.2 Processing Technology of Thermoplastic Composites

The conversion of the intermediate into a final product requires only heat and pressure. No chemical conversion takes place as with thermosetting composites. The economic advantages of thermoplastic composites can be

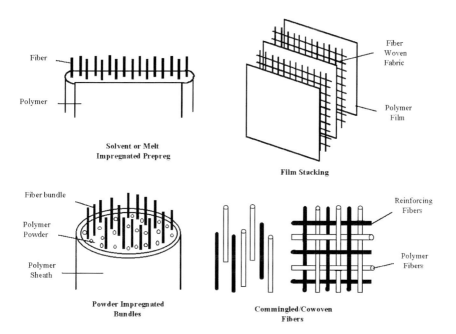

Fig. 5.33 Intermediate material forms for thermoplastic composites.

realized through high-rate, automated, manufacturing technologies that exploit the inherent rapid processibility of the material. The processing methods that are currently being developed for continuous fiber-reinforced thermoplastic composite parts are essentially adapted either from conventional thermoset composite technology or from existing sheet-metal-forming technology. These technologies include roll-forming, filament winding, pultrusion, diaphragm-forming, compression molding, stamping, deep drawing, and folding. Some of these techniques are briefly reviewed in the following subsections. A comprehensive review of various processing operations can be found in Ref. 15 and 16.

5.9.2.1 Roll-Forming.   Figure 5.34 shows a schematic diagram of roll-forming.[17] The method employs consecutive roll stations to progressively deform the pre-consolidated sheet into some desirable shape. The process consists of an infrared preheating station designed to bring the sheet up to the molding temperature, followed by a series of rolling stations to form and consolidate the parts. Normally, several shaping rolls are required. The first one may be heated, but at least the last one must be cool enough to solidify the composite parts. The alignment of the rollers and the tolerance of their spacing are among several critical features that affect the quality of the product.

5.9.2.2 Filament Winding.   The advantage of using a thermoplastic material in the filament winding process is that in situ consolidation can be effected that avoids the lengthy post-winding cure cycle required when using

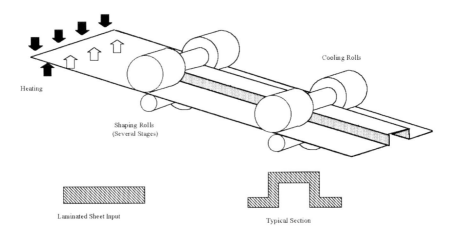

Fig. 5.34   Schematic diagram of roll-forming a thermoplastic composite part.

thermosetting composites. The same basic winding equipment used for thermoset composite systems discussed earlier in this chapter can be used for thermoplastics. Modifications require the addition of a heat source to heat the pre-preg tow above its melting/softening point and a consolidation mechanism to fuse the incoming tape to the face of previously wound material. The key steps are identified as tow preheating, tow guiding, contact point heating, mandrel heating, and post-consolidation. Heating techniques such as ultrasonic, laser beam, focused infrared, conduction, and convection heating have been investigated as methods to introduce localized heating into the process. Tow tension, heated roller, and sliding devices are possible consolidation methods that can be used. Because welding and consolidation take place immediately in the local contact area, composite parts having a re-entrant shape can be made. This is not possible with a filament-wound thermosetting composite.

5.9.2.3 Pultrusion.   Although the pultrusion process is primarily associated with thermoset polymer composites, it is also possible to process continuous fiber-reinforced thermoplastic composites in this way. Pre-impregnated tape or commingled fiber bundles are the most usual intermediate forms that can be used in the pultrusion process. Significantly higher die temperatures are required than are necessary for thermoset pultrusion. Furthermore, while thermosets are allowed to exit the die at high temperatures (because they are chemically cross-linked and cured), thermoplastic pultruded profiles must pass through a cooling die to avoid deconsolidation on exit. The dies for thermoplastic composite pultrusion have tapering die cross-sections from entrance to exit to facilitate consolidation whereas thermoset pultrusion dies have constant cross-sections. In addition, the resin content of the material entering the die is more critical for thermoplastics than thermosets. Thermoset pultrusions enter the die with excess resin, which under these conditions is at a low viscosity, allowing it to be squeezed off at the die entrance. Thermoplastic materials, on the other hand (due to their much higher viscosity), must enter the die with a net resin content. The pultrusion of thermoplastics does not rely on a chemical reaction within the die that is time-dependent. Consequently, pultrusion speeds for thermoplastics will be faster than for thermosets.

5.9.2.4 Diaphragm Forming of Thermoplastic Composites.   Diaphragm forming is also used to form thermoplastic composites, being particularly applicable to the forming of large areas with double curvature. Because the process requires far higher temperatures and pressures than the forming of thermoset pre-pregs described earlier in this chapter, the operation needs to be carried out in an autoclave or in a hydraulic press (Fig. 5.35). In the latter case, a split pressure chamber is mounted between the upper and lower platens. The unconsolidated pre-preg lay-up is sandwiched between two sealed, plastically deformable diaphragms. The diaphragms are clamped to a vacuum ring. After creating a vacuum within the composite lay-up, the entire sandwich is heated

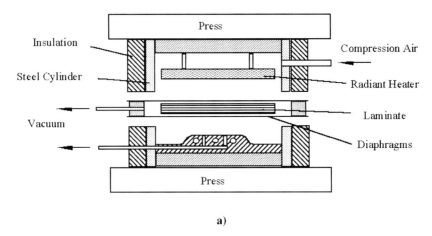

a)

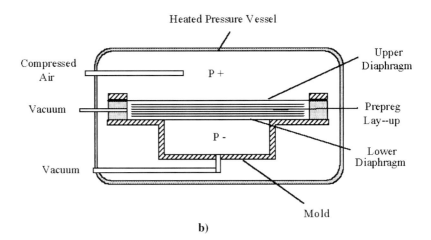

b)

Fig. 5.35   Diaphragm forming a thermoplastic composite part: *a*) in autoclave; *b*) in mold.

above the polymer melting/softening point, and pressure is applied to force the sandwich against the mold. During the processing, the diaphragms undergo a stretching action that supports the pre-preg layers and prevents wrinkling. Once forming is complete, the mold is cooled below the melting temperature of the thermoplastic resin. The diaphragms are then stripped off, and the component can be trimmed and finished. The stiffness of the diaphragm is a critical factor in achieving an optimum process. A typical cycle time of heating, pressurization, forming, and cooling might range from 40 minutes to 2 hours, depending on the tooling, heating, and cooling methods used. The actual time to shape the lay-up is typically 1–5 minutes.

5.9.2.5 Compression Molding. The process of compression molding can be applied to all the various intermediate material forms. Figure 5.36a illustrates the compression molding of a flat panel. The pre-preg lay-up is heated to melt the thermoplastic matrix; pressure is then applied to consolidate the plies together, and the laminate is cooled under pressure. The laminates can either be cooled directly within the molding press or quickly transferred to a cold-press with pressure reapplied. The latter procedure can effectively shorten the cycle time because it eliminates the period required to heat and cool the hot-press during forming. Specific profile shapes instead of flat laminates can also be produced using this technique (Fig. 5.36b). The laminate is supported in a frame or ring that allows the heated laminate to slip between the frame under the drawing forces generated as the mold closes.

5.9.2.6 Stamp-Forming. Stamp-forming is a variation of compression molding, which is similar to the sheet-metal stamp-forming process. This technology is best suited to the forming of simply-folded shapes requiring only a minimum of deformation in the material. In this process, a consolidated flat laminate is heated in an external heater to a temperature above the melting/softening temperature of the thermoplastic matrix. The hot laminate is then quickly transferred into an unheated mold, where it is stamped to conform to the mold geometry and allowed to cool under pressure to a temperature below the melting point of the polymer matrix (Fig. 5.37). The typical cycle time is about 2–3 minutes. Because the heated laminate is exposed to a lower environmental temperature before forming, the use of high closing speeds is important to successfully stamp-form the part. Either mechanical or hydraulic presses can be used.

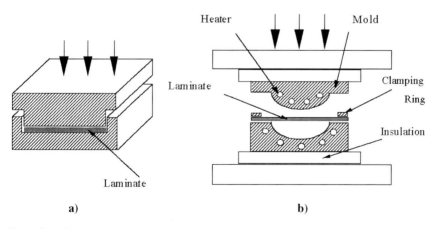

Heater   Mold

Laminate

Clamping

Ring

Insulation

Laminate

a)   b)

Fig. 5.36 Schematic diagram of compression molding of a thermoplastic composite part: a) flat panel molding; b) shaped panel molding.

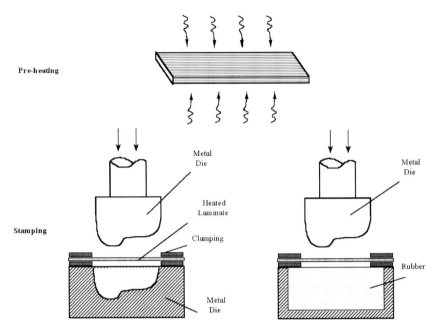

Fig. 5.37   Schematic diagram of stamp-forming a thermoplastic composite part.

The dies can be matched metal or single metal with a conforming rubber block. The use of matched metal dies provides improved dimensional control and surface quality on both sides of the part. Metal dies can apply higher pressures and can also be internally heated, further enhancing the quality of the final product. However, their rigidity creates a non-uniform pressure over the laminate during the forming process that makes it difficult to control wrinkling. Furthermore, it can result in varying fiber/volume fractions through the product and consequently non-uniform mechanical properties. To overcome these disadvantages, one of the metal dies can be replaced with a flexible rubber block. The remaining rigid metal die determines the final shape of the product and gives a good surface quality on the contacting face of the product, and the rubber block generates a homogeneous pressure distribution on the composite material. The flexibility of the rubber will account for any thickness mismatch or thickness variation of the product. To facilitate molding of more complex geometries, the rubber may be contoured to approximately match the shape of the rigid metal mold half. Sometimes it is beneficial to under- or over-shape the rubber die to avoid or create certain high local pressures that can improve the quality of the product. Silicone rubber is usually used as the block material, which allows a relatively high processing temperature range (up to 320°C).

References

[1] Bader, M. G., and Lekakou, C., "Processing for Laminated Structures," *Composites Engineering Handbook*, edited by P. K. Mallick, Marcel Dekker, New York, 1997, pp. 371–480.

[2] Seferis, J. C., Hillermeier, R., and Buehler, F. U., "Pre-Pregging and Autoclaving of Thermoset Composites," *Comprehensive Composite Materials*, edited by A. Kelly and C. Zweben, Vol. 2, Elsevier, 2000.

[3] "Composite Materials in Aircraft Structures," Longman Scientific and Technical Publishers, UK, 1990.

[4] Abrate, S., "Machining of Composite Materials," *Composites Engineering Handbook*, edited by P. K. Mallick, Marcel Dekker, New York, 1997, p. 777.

[5] Wilson, M., "Robots in the Aerospace Industry," *Aircraft Engineering and Aerospace Technology*, Vol. 6, No. 3, 1994.

[6] Advani, S. G., and Simácek, P., "Modelling and Simulation of Flow, Heat Transfer and Cure," *Resin Transfer Moulding for Aerospace Structures*, edited by T. Kruckenberg and R. Paton, Kluwer Academic, Dordrecht, The Netherlands, 1998, p. 229.

[7] Wadsworth, M., "Tooling Fundamentals for Resin Transfer Moulding," *Resin Transfer Moulding for Aerospace Structures*, edited by T. Kruckenberg and R. Paton, Kluwer Academic, Dordecht, The Netherlands, 1998, p. 282.

[8] Beckwith, S. W., and Hyland, C. R., "Resin Transfer Moulding: A Decade of Technology Advances," *SAMPE Journal*, Vol. 34, 1998, p. 14.

[9] Peters, S. T., and Tarnopolskii, Y. M., "Filament Winding," *Composites Engineering Handbook*, edited by P. K. Mallick, Marcel Dekker, New York, 1997, pp. 515–548.

[10] Peters, S. T., and Humphrey, W. D., *Filament Winding, Engineered Materials Handbook*, ASM International, 1987, Vol. 1, pp. 503–518.

[11] Starr, T., *Pultrusion for Engineers*, Woodhead Publishing, 2000.

[12] Martin, J. D., and Sumerak, J. E., "Pultrusion," *Engineered Materials Handbook*, Vol. 1, ASM International, 1993.

[13] Sumerak, J. E., TOPDIE™ Pultrusion Die Thermal Optimization Service, Pultrusion Dynamics Technology Center, Oakwood Village, OH,

[14] Manson, J. A. E., "Processing of Thermoplastic-Based Advanced Composites," *Advanced Thermoplastic Composites: Characterization and Processing*, edited by H. H. Kausch, and R. Legras, Hanser Verlag, New York, 1993, pp. 273–301.

[15] Astrom, B. T., "Thermoplastic Composite Sheet Forming: Materials and Manufacturing Techniques," *Composite Sheet Forming*, edited by D. Bhattacharyya, Composite Materials Series, Elsevier, Amsterdam, 1997, Chapter 2.

[16] Cogswell, F. N., Thermoplastic Aromatic Polymer Composites, Butterworth-Heinemann 1992, pp. 107–150.

[17] Pritchard, G., Developments in Reinforced Plastics—Processing and Fabrication, Elsevier Applied Science Publishers, London and New York, 1984.

[18] Niu, M. C., *Composite Airframe Structures* Comilit Press, Hong Kong, 1992.

6
Structural Analysis

6.1 Overview

In this chapter, the basic theory needed for the determination of the stresses, strains, and deformations in fiber composite structures is outlined. Attention is concentrated on structures made in the form of laminates because that is the way composite materials are generally used.

From the viewpoint of structural mechanics, the novel features of composites (compared with conventional structural materials such as metals) are their marked anisotropy and, when used as laminates, their macroscopically heterogeneous nature.

There is a close analogy between the steps in developing laminate theory and the steps in fabricating a laminate. The building block both for theory and fabrication is the *single ply*, also referred to as the *lamina*. This is a thin layer of the material (typical thickness around 0.125 mm for unidirectional carbon/epoxy "tape" and 0.25 mm for a cross-ply fabric or "cloth") in which all of the fibers are aligned parallel to one another or in an orthogonal mesh. The starting point for the theory is the stress-strain law for the single ply referred to its axes of material symmetry, defined here as the 0–1, 2, 3 material axes. In constructing a laminate, each ply is laid-up so that its fibers make some prescribed angle with a reference axis fixed in the laminate. Here the laminate axes will be defined as the x-, y-, and z-axes.

All later calculations are made using axes fixed in the structure (the structural axes). In a finite element model, the material properties are usually entered in the material axes. The lay-up of the laminate is defined in the laminate axes. The laminate theory described in this chapter will indicate how the properties of the laminate are derived. The transformation from the laminate axes to the global structural axes is then completed during the solution process. Because the designer can select his own lay-up pattern (because the laminate stress-strain law will depend on that pattern), it follows that the designer can design the material (as well as the structure).

For more detailed discussions of the topics covered in this chapter, see Refs. 1–7. For background material on the theory of anisotropic elasticity, see Refs. 8–10.

6.2 Laminate Theory

Classical laminate theory defines the response of a laminate with the following assumptions:

- For two-dimensional plane stress analysis, the strain is constant through the thickness.
- For bending, the strain varies linearly through the thickness.
- The laminate is thin compared with its in-plane dimensions.
- Each layer is quasi-homogeneous and orthotropic.
- Displacements are small compared with the thickness.
- The behavior remains linear.

With these assumptions satisfied, the laminate theory allows the response of a laminate to be calculated, engineering constants to be determined to substitute into standard formulas for stresses and deflections, and material properties of the laminate to be defined for substitution into finite element analysis as described in Chapter 16.

6.2.1 Stress-Strain Law for a Single Ply in the Material Axes: Unidirectional Laminates

Consider a rectangular element of a single ply with the sides of the element parallel and perpendicular to the fiber direction (Fig. 6.1). Clearly, the direction of the fibers defines a preferred direction in the material; it is thus natural to introduce a cartesian set of material axes 0–1, 2, 3 with the 1-axis in the fiber direction, the 2-axis perpendicular to the fibers of the ply plane, and the 3-axis perpendicular to the plane of the ply. Here, interest is in the behavior of the ply when subjected to stresses acting in its plane, in other words, under plane stress conditions. These stresses (also referred to the material axes) will be denoted by σ_1, σ_2, τ_{12} and the associated strains by ε_1, ε_2, and γ_{12}. (Note that in composite mechanics, it is standard practice to work with "engineering" rather than "tensor" shear strains.) Although a single ply is highly anisotropic, it is intuitively evident that the coordinate planes $012, 023$, and 031 are those of material symmetry, there being a mirror image symmetry about these planes.

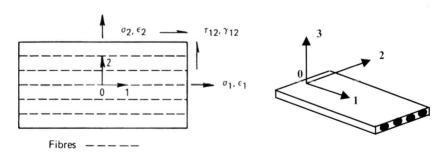

Fig. 6.1   Material axes for a single ply.

A material having three mutually orthogonal planes of symmetry is known as *orthotropic*. The stress-strain law for an orthotropic material under plane stress conditions, referred to the material axes, necessarily has the following form:

$$
\begin{bmatrix} \varepsilon_1 \\ \varepsilon_2 \\ \gamma_{12} \end{bmatrix} =
\begin{bmatrix}
\dfrac{1}{E_1} & \dfrac{-v_{21}}{E_2} & 0 \\[2mm]
\dfrac{-v_{12}}{E_1} & \dfrac{1}{E_2} & 0 \\[2mm]
0 & 0 & \dfrac{1}{G_{12}}
\end{bmatrix}
\begin{bmatrix} \sigma_1 \\ \sigma_2 \\ \tau_{12} \end{bmatrix}
\tag{6.1}
$$

where: E_1, E_2 = Young's moduli in the *1* and *2* directions, respectively; v_{12} = Poisson's ratio governing the contraction in the *2* direction for a tension in the *1* direction; v_{21} = Poisson's ratio governing the contraction in the *1* direction for a tension in the *2* direction; G_{12} = (in-plane) shear modulus.

There are five material constants in equation (*6.1*), but only four of these are independent because of the following symmetry relation[1]:

$$
\frac{v_{12}}{E_1} = \frac{v_{21}}{E_2}
\tag{6.2}
$$

For unidirectional tape of the type being considered here, E_1 is much larger than either E_2 or G_{12} because the former is a "fiber-dominated" property, while the latter are "matrix dominated". For a bi-directional cloth, $E_1 = E_2$ and both are much larger than G_{12}. For tape, v_{12} is matrix dominated and is of the order of 0.3, whereas the contraction implied in v_{21} is resisted by the fibers and so is much smaller.

The above equations are all related to a single ply but, because the ply thickness does not enter into the calculations, they also apply to a "unidirectional laminate" that is simply a laminate in which the fiber direction is the same in all of the plies. In fact, most of the material constants for a single ply are obtained from specimen tests on unidirectional laminates, a single ply being itself too thin to test conveniently.

For much of the following analysis, it is more convenient to deal with the inverse form of equation (*6.1*), namely

$$
\begin{bmatrix} \sigma_1 \\ \sigma_2 \\ \tau_{12} \end{bmatrix} =
\begin{bmatrix}
Q_{11}(0) & Q_{12}(0) & 0 \\
Q_{12}(0) & Q_{22}(0) & 0 \\
0 & 0 & Q_{66}(0)
\end{bmatrix}
\begin{bmatrix} \varepsilon_1 \\ \varepsilon_2 \\ \gamma_{12} \end{bmatrix}
\tag{6.3}
$$

where the $Q_{ij}(0)$, commonly termed the *reduced stiffness coefficients*, are given by

$$
Q_{11}(0) = \frac{E_1}{1 - v_{12}v_{21}} \qquad Q_{22}(0) = \frac{E_2}{1 - v_{12}v_{21}}
$$

$$
Q_{12}(0) = \frac{v_{21}E_1}{1 - v_{12}v_{21}} \qquad Q_{66}(0) = G_{12}
\tag{6.4}
$$

It is conventional in composite mechanics to use the above subscript notation for Q, the point of which becomes evident only when three-dimensional anisotropic problems are encountered. The subscript 6 is for the sixth component of stress or strain that includes three direct terms and three shear terms.

6.2.2 Stress-Strain Law for Single Ply in Laminate Axes: Off-Axis Laminates

As already noted, when a ply is incorporated in a laminate, its fibers will make some prescribed angle θ with a reference axis fixed in the laminate. Let this be the x-axis, and note that the angle θ is measured from the x-axis to the 1-axis and is positive in the counterclockwise direction; the y-axis is perpendicular to the x-axis and in the plane of the ply (See Fig. 6.2.). All subsequent calculations are made using the x-y, or "laminate" axes, therefore it is necessary to transform the stress-strain law from the material axes to the laminate axes. If the stresses in the laminate axes are denoted by σ_x, σ_y, and τ_{xy}, then these are related to the stresses referred to the material axes by the usual transformation equations,

$$\begin{bmatrix} \sigma_x \\ \sigma_y \\ \tau_{xy} \end{bmatrix} = \begin{bmatrix} c^2 & s^2 & -2cs \\ s^2 & c^2 & 2cs \\ cs & -cs & c^2 - s^2 \end{bmatrix} \begin{bmatrix} \sigma_1 \\ \sigma_2 \\ \tau_{12} \end{bmatrix} \tag{6.5}$$

where c denotes $\cos \theta$ and s denotes $\sin \theta$. Also, the strains in the material axes are related to those in the laminate axes, namely, ε_x, ε_y, and γ_{xy}, by what is essentially the strain transformation:

$$\begin{bmatrix} \varepsilon_1 \\ \varepsilon_2 \\ \gamma_{12} \end{bmatrix} = \begin{bmatrix} c^2 & s^2 & cs \\ s^2 & c^2 & -cs \\ -2cs & 2cs & c^2 - s^2 \end{bmatrix} \begin{bmatrix} \varepsilon_x \\ \varepsilon_y \\ \gamma_{xy} \end{bmatrix} \tag{6.6}$$

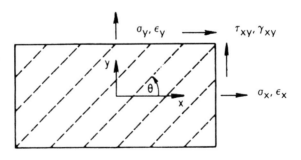

Fibres $- - - - -$

Fig. 6.2   Laminate axes for a single ply.

Now, in equation (6.5), substitute for σ_1, σ_2, and τ_{12} their values as given by equation (6.3). Then, in the resultant equations, substitute for ε_1, ε_2, and γ_{12} their values as given by equation (6.6). After some routine manipulations, it is found that the stress-strain law in the laminate axes has the form

$$
\begin{bmatrix} \sigma_x \\ \sigma_y \\ \tau_{xy} \end{bmatrix} = \begin{bmatrix} Q_{xx}(\theta) & Q_{xy}(\theta) & Q_{xs}(\theta) \\ Q_{xy}(\theta) & Q_{yy}(\theta) & Q_{ys}(\theta) \\ Q_{xs}(\theta) & Q_{ys}(\theta) & Q_{ss}(\theta) \end{bmatrix} \begin{bmatrix} \varepsilon_x \\ \varepsilon_y \\ \gamma_{xy} \end{bmatrix}
\tag{6.7}
$$

where the $Q_{ij}(\theta)$ are related to the $Q_{ij}(0)$ by the following equations:

$$
\begin{bmatrix} Q_{xx}(\theta) \\ Q_{xy}(\theta) \\ Q_{yy}(\theta) \\ Q_{xs}(\theta) \\ Q_{ys}(\theta) \\ Q_{ss}(\theta) \end{bmatrix} = \begin{bmatrix} c^4 & 2c^2s^2 & s^4 & 4c^2s^2 \\ c^2s^2 & c^4+s^4 & c^2s^2 & -4c^2s^2 \\ s^4 & 2c^2s^2 & c^4 & 4c^2s^2 \\ c^3s & -cs(c^2-s^2) & -cs^3 & -2cs(c^2-s^2) \\ cs^3 & cs(c^2-s^2) & -c^3s & 2cs(c^2-s^2) \\ c^2s^2 & -2c^2s^2 & c^2s^2 & (c^2-s^2)^2 \end{bmatrix}
$$

$$
\times \begin{bmatrix} Q_{11}(0) \\ Q_{12}(0) \\ Q_{22}(0) \\ Q_{66}(0) \end{bmatrix}
\tag{6.8}
$$

Observe that, in equation (6.7), the direct stresses depend on the shear strains (as well as the direct strains), and the shear stress depends on the direct strains (as well as the shear strain). This complication arises because, for non-zero θ, the laminate axes are not axes of material symmetry and, with respect to these axes, the material is not orthotropic; it is evident that the absence of orthotropy leads to the presence of the Q_{xs} and Q_{ys} terms in equation (6.7). Also, for future reference, note that the expressions for $Q_{xx}(\theta)$, $Q_{xy}(\theta)$, $Q_{yy}(\theta)$ and $Q_{ss}(\theta)$ contain only even powers of $\sin\theta$ and therefore these quantities are unchanged when θ is replaced by $-\theta$. On the other hand, the expressions for Q_{xs} and Q_{ys} contain odd powers of $\sin\theta$ and therefore they change sign when θ is replaced by $-\theta$.

Analogous to the previous section, the above discussion has been related to a single ply, but it is equally valid for a laminate in which the fiber direction is the same in all plies. A unidirectional laminate in which the fiber direction makes a non-zero angle with the x-laminate-axis is known as an "off-axis" laminate and is sometimes used for test purposes. Formulas for the elastic moduli of an off-axis laminate can be obtained by a procedure analogous to that used in deriving equation (6.7). Using equation (6.1) with the inverse forms of equations (6.5) and (6.6) leads to the inverse form of equation (6.7), in other words, with the strains expressed in terms of the stresses; from this result, the moduli can be written. Details can be found in most of the standard texts, for example page 54 of Ref. 3.

Only the result for the Young's modulus in the x direction, E_x, will be cited here:

$$\frac{1}{E_x} = \left(\frac{1}{E_1}\right)c^4 + \left(\frac{1}{G_{12}} - \frac{2v_{12}}{E_1}\right)c^2s^2 + \left(\frac{1}{E_2}\right)s^4 \qquad (6.9)$$

The variation of E_x with θ for the case of a carbon/epoxy off-axis laminate is shown in Figure 6.3. The material constants of the single ply were taken to be

$$E_1 = 137.44\,\text{GPa} \qquad E_2 = 11.71\,\text{GPa} \qquad G_{12} = 5.51\,\text{GPa}$$
$$v_{12} = 0.25 \qquad v_{21} = 0.0213$$

It can be seen that the modulus initially decreases quite rapidly as the off-axis angle increases from $0°$; this indicates the importance of the precise alignment of fibers in a laminate.

6.2.3 Plane Stress Problems for Symmetric Laminates

One of the most common laminate forms for composites is a laminated sheet loaded in its own plane, in other words, under plane stress conditions. In order for out-of-plane bending to not occur, such a laminate is always made with a lay-up that is symmetric about the mid-thickness plane. Just to illustrate the type of symmetry meant, consider an eight-ply laminate comprising four plies that are to be oriented at $0°$ to the reference (x) axis, two plies at $+45°$, and two plies at $-45°$. An example of a symmetric laminate would be one with the following ply sequence:

$$0°/0°/+45°/-45°/-45°/+45°/0°/0°$$

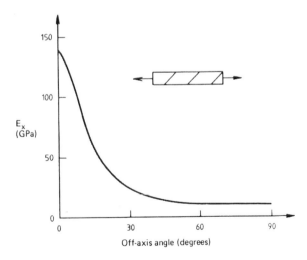

Fig. 6.3   Extensional modulus off-axis laminate.

On the other hand, an example of an unsymmetric arrangement of the same plies would be:

$$0°/0°/0°/0°/+45°/-45°/+45°/-45°$$

These two cases are shown in Figure 6.4 where z denotes the coordinate in the thickness direction.

6.2.3.1 Laminate Stiffness Matrix.

Consider now a laminate comprising n plies and denote the angle between the fiber direction in the kth ply and the x laminate axis by θ_k (with the convention defined in Fig. 6.2). Subject only to the symmetry requirement, the ply orientation is arbitrary. It is assumed that, when the plies are molded into the laminate, a rigid bond (of infinitesimal thickness) is formed between adjacent plies. As a consequence of this assumption, it follows that under plane stress conditions the strains are the same at all points on a line through the thickness (i.e., they are independent of z). Denoting these strains by ε_x, ε_y, and γ_{xy}, it then follows from equation (6.7) that the stresses in the kth ply will be given by:

$$\sigma_x(k) = Q_{xx}(\theta_k)\varepsilon_x + Q_{xy}(\theta_k)\varepsilon_y + Q_{xs}(\theta_k)\gamma_{xy}$$

$$\sigma_y(k) = Q_{xy}(\theta_k)\varepsilon_x + Q_{yy}(\theta_k)\varepsilon_y + Q_{ys}(\theta_k)\gamma_{xy} \qquad (6.10)$$

$$\tau_{xy}(k) = Q_{xs}(\theta_k)\varepsilon_x + Q_{ys}(\theta_k)\varepsilon_y + Q_{ss}(\theta_k)\gamma_{xy}$$

The laminate thickness is denoted by t and the thickness of the kth ply is $h_k - h_{k-1}$ with h_i defined in Figure 6.5. Assuming all plies are of the same thickness (which is the usual situation), then the thickness of an individual ply is simply t/n. Now consider an element of the laminate with sides of unit length parallel to the x- and y-axes. The forces on this element will be denoted by N_x, N_y,

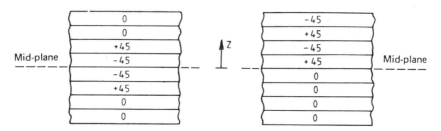

Fig. 6.4   Symmetric (*left*) and non-symmetric (*right*) eight-ply laminates.

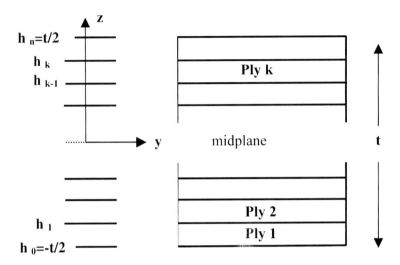

Fig. 6.5   Ply coordinates in the thickness direction, plies numbered from the bottom surface.

and N_s, (Figure 6.6); the N are generally termed *stress resultants* and have the dimension "force per unit length." Elementary equilibrium considerations give

$$N_x = \sum_{k=1}^{n} \sigma_x(k)(h_k - h_{k-1}), \quad N_y = \sum_{k=1}^{n} \sigma_y(k)(h_k - h_{k-1}),$$

$$N_s = \sum_{k=1}^{n} \tau_{xy}(k)(h_k - h_{k-1}) \tag{6.11}$$

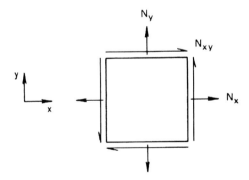

Fig. 6.6   Stress resultants.

Substituting from equations (*6.10*) into (*6.11*), and remembering that the strains are the same in all plies, the following result is readily obtained:

$$N_x = A_{xx}\varepsilon_x + A_{xy}\varepsilon_y + A_{xs}\gamma_{xy}$$

$$N_y = A_{xy}\varepsilon_x + A_{yy}\varepsilon_y + A_{ys}\gamma_{xy} \qquad (6.12)$$

$$N_s = A_{xs}\varepsilon_x + A_{ys}\varepsilon_y + A_{ss}\gamma_{xy}$$

where:

$$A_{ij} = \sum_{k=1}^{n} Q_{ij}(\theta_k)(h_k - h_{k-1}) \qquad (6.13)$$

The quantities A_{ij} are the terms of the laminate "in-plane stiffness matrix." Given the single-ply moduli and the laminate lay-up details, they can be calculated routinely by using equations (*6.4*), (*6.8*), and (*6.13*). Equation (*6.12*) are generally taken as the starting point for any laminate structural analysis.

6.2.3.2 Laminate Stress—Strain Law.

As was just implied, it seems to be the current fashion in laminate mechanics to work in terms of the stress resultants, rather than the stresses. However, for some purposes, the latter are more convenient. From the stress resultants, the average stresses (averaged through the thickness of the laminate) are easily obtained; writing these stresses simply as σ_x, σ_y, and τ_{xy} then:

$$\sigma_x = \frac{N_x}{t}, \quad \sigma_y = \frac{N_x}{t}, \quad \tau_{xy} = \frac{N_s}{t} \qquad (6.14)$$

Hence, in terms of these average stresses, the stress-strain law for the laminate becomes:

$$\sigma_x = A_{xx}^*\varepsilon_x + A_{xy}^*\varepsilon_y + A_{xs}^*\gamma_{xy}$$

$$\sigma_y = A_{xy}^*\varepsilon_x + A_{yy}^*\varepsilon_y + A_{ys}^*\gamma_{xy} \qquad (6.15)$$

$$\tau_{xy} = A_{xs}^*\varepsilon_x + A_{ys}^*\varepsilon_y + A_{ss}^*\gamma_{xy}$$

where:

$$A_{ij}^* = \frac{A_{ij}}{t} = \frac{1}{t}\sum_{k=1}^{n} Q_{ij}(\theta_k)(h_k - h_{k-1}) \qquad (6.16)$$

In some cases, equation (*6.15*) is more convenient than is equation (*6.12*).

6.2.3.3 Orthotropic Laminates.

An orthotropic laminate, having the laminate axes as the axes of orthotropy, is one for which $A_{xs} = A_{ys} = 0$;

clearly, this implies that:

$$\sum_{k=1}^{n} Q_{xs}(\theta_k)(h_k - h_{k-1}) = 0, \quad \sum_{k=1}^{n} Q_{ys}(\theta_k)(h_k - h_{k-1}) = 0 \qquad (6.17)$$

Thus, the stress-strain law for an orthotropic laminate reduces to:

$$\sigma_x = A_{xx}^* \varepsilon_x + A_{xy}^* \varepsilon_y$$

$$\sigma_y = A_{xy}^* \varepsilon_x + A_{yy}^* \varepsilon_y \qquad (6.18)$$

$$\tau_{xy} = A_{ss}^* \gamma_{xy}$$

The coupling between the direct stresses and the shear strains and between the shear stresses and the direct strains, which is present for a general laminate, disappears for an orthotropic laminate. Most laminates currently in use are orthotropic.

It can be readily seen that the following laminates will be orthotropic:

(1) Those consisting only of plies for which $\theta = 0°$ or $90°$; here it follows from equation (6.8) that in either case $Q_{xs}(\theta) = Q_{ys}(\theta) = 0$.
(2) Those constructed such that for each ply oriented at an angle θ, there is another ply oriented at an angle $-\theta$; because, as already noted from the odd powers in equation (6.8),

$$Q_{xs}(-\theta) = -Q_{xs}(\theta), \quad Q_{ys}(-\theta) = -Q_{ys}(\theta)$$

There is then a cancellation of all paired terms in the summation of equation (6.17).
(3) Those consisting only of $0°$, $90°$, and matched pairs of $\pm \theta$ plies are also, of course, orthotropic.

An example of an orthotropic laminate would be one with the following ply pattern:

$$0°/+30°/-30°/-30°/+30°/0°$$

On the other hand, the following laminate (while still symmetric) would not be orthotropic:

$$0°/+30°/90°/90°/+30°/0°$$

6.2.3.4 Moduli of Orthotropic Laminates.   Expressions for the moduli of orthotropic laminates can easily be obtained by solving equation (6.18) for simple loadings. For example, on setting $\sigma_y = \tau_{xy} = 0$, Young's modulus in the x direction, E_x, and Poisson's ratio v_{xy} governing the contraction in the y direction for a stress in the x direction are then given by:

$$E_x = \frac{\sigma_x}{\varepsilon_x}, \qquad \nu_{xy} = -\frac{\varepsilon_y}{\varepsilon_x}$$

Proceeding in this way, it is found that:

$$E_x = A_{xx}^* - \frac{A_{xy}^{*2}}{A_{yy}^*} \qquad E_y = A_{yy}^* - \frac{A_{xy}^{*2}}{A_{xx}^*}$$

$$\nu_{xy} = \frac{A_{xy}^*}{A_{yy}^*} \qquad \nu_{yx} = \frac{A_{xy}^*}{A_{xx}^*} \qquad G_{xy} = A_{ss}^* \tag{6.19}$$

As illustrative examples of the above theory, consider a family of 24-ply laminates, symmetrical and orthotropic, and all made of the same material but with varying numbers of $0°$ and $\pm 45°$ plies. (For the present purposes, the precise ordering of the plies is immaterial as long as the symmetry requirement is maintained; however, to ensure orthotropy, there must be the same number of $+45°$ as $-45°$ plies.) The single-ply modulus data (representative of a carbon/epoxy) are:

$$E_1 = 137.44 \text{ GPa} \quad E_2 = 11.71 \text{ GPa} \quad G_{12} = 5.51 \text{ GPa}$$
$$\nu_{12} = 0.2500 \quad \nu_{21} = 0.0213 \tag{6.20}$$

The lay-ups considered are shown in Table 6.1. The steps in the calculation are as follows:

(1) Calculate the $Q_{ij}(0)$ from equation (6.4).
(2) For each of the ply orientations involved here $\theta = 0°$, $+45°$, and $-45°$, calculate the $Q_{ij}(\theta)$ from equation (6.8). [Of course, here the $Q_{ij}(0)$ have already been obtained in step 1.]

Table 6.1 Moduli for Family of 24-ply $0°/\pm 45°$ Laminates
Constructed Using Unidirectional Tape

			Lay-up				
No. $0°$ Plies	No. $+45°$ Plies	No. $-45°$ Plies	E_x, GPa	E_y, GPa	G_{xy}, GPa	ν_{xy}	ν_{yx}
24	0	0	137.4	11.7	5.51	0.250	0.021
16	4	4	99.4	21.1	15.7	0.578	0.123
12	6	6	79.5	24.5	20.8	0.647	0.199
8	8	8	59.6	26.4	25.8	0.693	0.307
0	12	12	19.3	19.3	36	0.752	0.752

(3) Calculate the A_{ij}^* from equation (6.16); in the present case, equation (6.16) becomes:

$$A_{ij}^* = [n_1 Q_{ij}(0) + n_2 Q_{ij}(+45) + n_3 Q_{ij}(-45)]/24$$

where n_1 is the number of $0°$ plies, n_2 of $+45°$ plies and n_3 of $-45°$ plies.
(4) Calculate the moduli from equation (6.19).

The results of the calculations are shown in Table 6.1.

The results in Table 6.1 have been presented primarily to exemplify the preceding theory; however, they also demonstrate some features that are important in design. The stiffness of a composite is overwhelmingly resident in the extensional stiffness of its fibers; hence, at least for simple loadings, if maximum stiffness is required, a laminate is constructed so that the fibers are aligned in the principal stress directions. Thus, for a member under uniaxial tension, a laminate comprising basically all $0°$ plies would be chosen; in other words, all fibers would be aligned parallel to the tension direction. As can be seen from Table 6.1, E_x decreases as the number of $0°$ plies decreases. On the other hand, consider a rectangular panel under shear, the sides of the panel being parallel to the laminate axes (Fig. 6.7a). The principal stresses here are an equal tension and compression, oriented at $+45°$ and $-45°$ to the x-axis. Thus, maximum shear stiffness can be expected to be obtained using a laminate comprising equal numbers of $+45°$ and $-45°$ plies; this is reflected in the high shear modulus G_{xy} for the all $\pm45°$ laminate of Table 6.1.

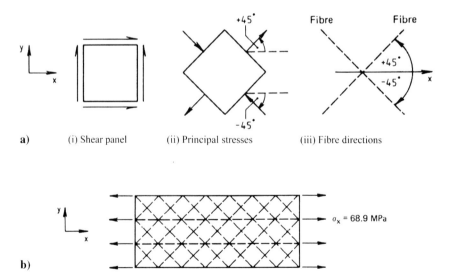

a)   (i) Shear panel   (ii) Principal stresses   (iii) Fibre directions

b)

$\sigma_x = 68.9$ MPa

Fig. 6.7 Ply orientations for example problems: a) fiber orientations for a shear panel: b) $0°\pm45°$ laminate under uniaxial tension.

It should also be observed that, although for an isotropic material, Poisson's ratio cannot exceed 0.5, this is not the case for an anisotropic material.

6.2.3.5 Quasi-Isotropic Laminates.   It is possible to construct laminates that are isotropic with regard to their in-plane elastic properties—in other words, they have the same Young's modulus E and same Poisson's ratio v in all in-plane directions and for which the shear modulus is given by $G = E/2(1+v)$. One way of achieving this is to adopt a lay-up having an equal number of plies oriented parallel to the sides of an equilateral triangle. For example, a quasi-isotropic 24-ply laminate could be made with 8 plies oriented at each of $0°$, $+60°$, and $-60°$. Using the same materials data (and theory) as were used in deriving Table 6.1, it will be found that such a laminate has the following moduli:

$$E = 54.2 \text{ Gpa}, \quad G = 20.8 \text{ Gpa}, \quad v = 0.305$$

Another way of achieving a quasi-isotropic laminate is to use equal numbers of plies oriented at $0°$, $+45°$, $-45°$, and $90°$. A quasi-isotropic 24-ply laminate (with, incidentally, the same values for the elastic constants as were just cited) could be made with 6 plies at each of $0°$, $+45°$, $-45°$, and $90°$. (For comparison, recall that Young's modulus and the shear modulus for a typical aluminum alloy are of the order of 72 and 27 GPa, respectively, and that the specific gravity of carbon/epoxy is about 60% that of aluminum.)

The term *quasi-isotropic* is used because, of course, such laminates have different properties in the out-of-plane direction. However, it is not usual practice to work with quasi-isotropic laminates; efficient design with composites generally requires that advantage be taken of their inherent anisotropy.

6.2.3.6 Stress Analysis of Orthotropic Laminates.   The determination of the stresses, strains, and deformations experienced by symmetric laminates under plane stress loadings is carried out by procedures that are analogous to those used for isotropic materials. The laminate is treated as a homogeneous membrane having stiffness properties determined as described above. It should be noted, though, that while the strains and deformations so determined are the actual strains and deformations (within the limit of the assumptions), the stresses are only the average values over the laminate thickness.

If an analytical procedure is used, then generally a stress function F is introduced, this being related to the (average) stresses by

$$\sigma_x = \frac{\partial^2 F}{\partial x^2}, \quad \sigma_y = \frac{\partial^2 F}{\partial y^2}, \quad \tau_{xy} = \frac{-\partial^2 F}{\partial x \partial y} \qquad \text{(Eq. 6.21)}$$

It can be shown that F satisfies the following partial differential equation:

$$\left(\frac{1}{E_y}\right)\frac{\partial^4 F}{\partial x^4} + \left(\frac{1}{G_{xy}} - \frac{2v_{xy}}{E_x}\right)\frac{\partial^4 F}{\partial x^2 \partial y^2} + \left(\frac{1}{E_x}\right)\frac{\partial^4 F}{\partial y^4} = 0 \qquad (6.22)$$

Solutions of equation (6.22) for several problems of interest can be found in Ref. 10.

Most structural analyses are now performed using finite element methods described in Chapter 16, and many general-purpose finite-element programs contain orthotropic membrane elements in their library. Once the laminate moduli are determined, they are used as input data for calculating the element stiffness matrix; the rest of the analysis proceeds as in the isotropic case.

As has already been emphasized, the stresses obtained from the above procedures are only the average stresses. To determine the actual stresses in the individual plies, it is necessary only to substitute the calculated values of the strains in equation (6.10). An elementary example may clarify this. Consider a rectangular strip under uniaxial tension (Fig. 6.7b) made of the 24-ply laminate considered earlier that had 12 plies at $0°$, 6 plies at $+45°$, and 6 plies at $-45°$. Suppose the applied stress is $\sigma_x = 68.9$ MPa. The average stress here is uniform in the xy plane and given by:

$$\sigma_x = 68.9\,\text{MPa}, \quad \sigma_y = \tau_s = 0$$

Using the values of E_x and v_{xy} given in Table 6.1, it follows that the associated strains are:

$$\varepsilon_x = 0.8667 \times 10^{-3}, \quad \varepsilon_y = -0.5607 \times 10^{-3}, \quad \gamma_s = 0$$

The stresses in the individual plies can now be obtained by substituting these values into equation (6.10), with the appropriate values of the $Q_{ij}(\theta)$. The results of doing this are shown in Table 6.2.

Thus, the actual stress distribution is very different from the average one. In particular, note that transverse direct stresses and shear stresses are developed, even though no such stresses are applied; naturally, these stresses are self-equilibrating over the thickness. It follows that there is some "boundary layer" around the edges of the strip where there is a rapid transition from the actual stress boundary values (namely, zero on the longitudinal edges) to the calculated values shown in the table. This boundary layer would be expected to extend in from the edges a distance of the order of the laminate thickness (from the Saint-Venant principle). In the boundary

Table 6.2   Stresses in Individual Plies of a 24-Ply Laminate (12 at $0°$, 6 at $+45$ and 6 at $-45°$) under Uniaxial Stress of 68.9 MPa

$\theta°$	$\sigma_x(\theta)$ MPa	$\sigma_y(\theta)$ Mpa	$\tau_{xy}(\theta)$ MPa
0	118.1	−4.1	0
+45	19.8	4.1	9.7
−45	19.8	4.1	−9.7

layer, the simple laminate theory presented above is not applicable and a three-dimensional analysis is required. The matter is of more than académic interest since faults, such as delaminations, are prone to originate at the free edges of laminates because of the above effect. Edge effects will be considered further in Section 6.3.2.

Finally, when discussing allowable design values for composite structures, it is common to cite values of strain, rather than stress. Clearly, strain is the more meaningful quantity for a laminate.

6.2.3.7 Laminate Codes.   Although the precise ordering of the plies of a laminate has not been of concern in the considerations of this section, generally there will be other factors that will determine such an ordering. In any case, when a laminate is being called up for manufacture, the associated engineering drawing should list the orientation of each ply. When referring to laminates in a text, some sort of abbreviated notation is necessary to specify the pattern. It is easiest to describe the code normally used with some examples.

Example 6.1

Consider an eight-ply uni-directional tape laminate with the following (symmetric) lay-up starting from the bottom ($z = t/2$) surface:

$$0°/0°/+45°/-45°/-45°/+45°/0°/0°$$

This is written in code form as:

$$[0_2/ \pm 45]_s$$

Note that:

(1) Only half the plies in a symmetric laminate are listed, the symmetry being implied by the *s* outside the brackets.
(2) The degree signs are omitted from the angles.
(3) In a + and − combination, the upper sign is read first.

Example 6.2

Consider a four-ply fabric laminate with the following (symmetric) lay-up:

$$(0°,90°)/(\pm 45°)/(\pm 45°)/(0°,90°).$$

This is written in code form as

$$[(0, 90)/(\pm 45)/(0, 90)] \quad \text{or} \quad [(0, 90)/(\pm 15)].$$

Example 6.3

Consider a fifty-ply tape laminate containing repetitions of the ply sequence:

$$0°/0°/ + 45°/ - 45°/90°$$

The order in the sequence being reversed at the midplane to preserve the symmetry. This would be written in code form as:

$$[(0_2/\pm 45/90)_5]_s$$

Sometimes, in general discussions, a laminate is described by the percentages of its plies at various angles. Thus, the laminate of example (6.1) would be described as having "50% 0, 50% ± 45." Similarly, the laminate of example (6.2) would be described as having "40% 0, 40% ± 45, 20% 90."

6.2.4   General Laminates Subjected to Plane Stress and Bending Loads

In this section the previous restriction to laminates that are symmetric about the mid-thickness plane will be dropped. It now becomes necessary to consider the plane stress and bending problems in conjunction, as in-plane loads can induce bending deformations and vice versa. Only the outline of the theory will be given below; for further details, including numerical examples, see Refs. 1–5.

6.2.4.1 General Theory.   In contrast to the situation for symmetric laminates, the position of each ply in the laminate is now important. Thus, consider an n-ply laminate with z the coordinate in the thickness direction, measured from the mid-thickness plane. The kth ply lies between h_{k-1} and h_k (Fig. 6.5). As before, the total thickness of the laminate will be denoted by t.

It is assumed that when a laminate is subjected to in-plane and/or bending loads, the strain varies linearly through the thickness and can therefore be written in the form:

$$\varepsilon_x = \varepsilon_x^o + \kappa_x z \quad \varepsilon_y = \varepsilon_y^o + \kappa_y z \quad \gamma_{xy} = \gamma_{xy}^o + \kappa_s z \tag{6.23}$$

where the superscript ^{o} quantities are the mid-plane strains and the κ_l are the midplane curvatures (as in the bending of isotropic plates). Both these sets of quantities are independent of z.

Substituting from equation (6.23) into equation (6.7), it follows that the stresses in the kth ply will now be given by:

$$\sigma_x(k) = Q_{xx}(\theta_k)\left(\varepsilon_x^o + z\kappa_x\right) + Q_{xy}(\theta_k)\left(\varepsilon_y^o + z\kappa_y\right) + Q_{xs}(\theta_k)\left(\gamma_{xy}^o + z\kappa_s\right)$$

$$\sigma_y(k) = Q_{xy}(\theta_k)\left(\varepsilon_x^o + z\kappa_x\right) + Q_{yy}(\theta_k)\left(\varepsilon_y^o + z\kappa_y\right) + Q_{ys}(\theta_k)\left(\gamma_{xy}^o + z\kappa_s\right) \tag{6.24}$$

$$\tau_{xy}(k) = Q_{xs}(\theta_k)\left(\varepsilon_x^o + z\kappa_x\right) + Q_{ys}(\theta_k)\left(\varepsilon_y^o + z\kappa_y\right) + Q_{ss}(\theta_k)\left(\gamma_{xy}^o + z\kappa_s\right)$$

Now introduce the stress resultants (in the form of forces per unit length and moments per unit length) defined by:

$$N_x = \int \sigma_x \, dz \qquad N_y = \int \sigma_y \, dz \qquad N_s = \int \tau_{xy} \, dz$$

$$M_x = \int \sigma_x z \, dz \qquad M_y = \int \sigma_y z \, dz \qquad M_s = \int \tau_{xy} z \, dz$$

(6.25)

where all of the integrals are over the thickness of the laminate (i.e., from $z = -t/2$ to $z = t/2$); see Figure 6.8. Because each of the integrals in equation (6.25) can be written in forms such as:

$$N_x = \sum_{k=1}^{n} \int_{h_{k-1}}^{h_k} \sigma_x(k) dz, \quad M_x = \sum_{k=1}^{n} \int_{h_{k-1}}^{h_k} \sigma_x(k) z \, dz$$

(6.26)

it follows that substituting from equation (6.24) into equation (6.26), and performing some elementary integrations, leads to the result:

$$\begin{bmatrix} A_{xx} & A_{xy} & A_{xs} & B_{xx} & B_{xy} & B_{xs} \\ A_{xy} & A_{yy} & A_{ys} & B_{xy} & B_{yy} & B_{ys} \\ A_{xs} & A_{ys} & A_{ss} & B_{xs} & B_{ys} & B_{ss} \\ B_{xx} & B_{xy} & B_{xs} & D_{xx} & D_{xy} & D_{xs} \\ B_{xy} & B_{yy} & B_{ys} & D_{xy} & D_{yy} & D_{ys} \\ B_{xs} & B_{ys} & B_{ss} & D_{xs} & D_{ys} & D_{ss} \end{bmatrix} \begin{bmatrix} \varepsilon_x^o \\ \varepsilon_y^o \\ \gamma_{xy}^o \\ \kappa_x \\ \kappa_y \\ \kappa_s \end{bmatrix} = \begin{bmatrix} N_x \\ N_y \\ N_s \\ M_x \\ M_y \\ M_s \end{bmatrix}$$

(6.27)

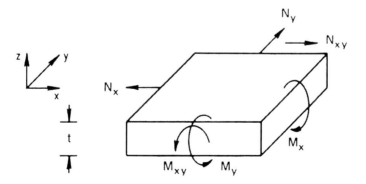

Fig. 6.8 Stress and moment resultants for a laminate.

The elements in the above combined "extensional-bending stiffness matrix" are given by:

$$A_{ij} = \sum_{k=1}^{n} Q_{ij}(\theta_k)(h_k - h_{k-1}) \qquad (6.28)$$

$$B_{ij} = \sum_{k=1}^{n} Q_{ij}(\theta_k)(h_k^2 - h_{k-1}^2)/2 \qquad (6.29)$$

$$D_{ij} = \sum_{k=1}^{n} Q_{ij}(\theta_k)(h_k^3 - h_{k-1}^3)/3 \qquad i,j = x, y, s \qquad (6.30)$$

[The above definition for A_{ij}, is, of course, equivalent to that of equation (6.13).] Equation (6.27) can be used to develop a theory for the stress analysis of general laminates, but this is quite formidable mathematically. It involves the solution of two simultaneous fourth order partial differential equations.

6.2.4.2 Uncoupling of the Stiffness Matrix.   It can be seen from equation (6.27) that the plane stress and bending problems are coupled unless all the B_{ij}, are zero. It follows from equation (6.29) that the B_{ij} are indeed zero for a symmetric lay-up. [For a symmetric pair of plies, if that ply below the mid-plane has coordinates $h_{k-1} = -a$ and $h_k = -b$, then its mate above the mid-plane will have $h_{k-1} = b$ and $h_k = a$. Because each ply has the same Q_{ij}, there is a cancellation in the summation of equation (6.29).]

It is possible to achieve an approximate uncoupling of equation (6.27) for a multi-ply unsymmetric laminate by making it in the form of a large number of repetitions of a given ply grouping. It can be seen intuitively that such a laminate will be symmetric in the group of plies if not in the individual plies; as long as the number of plies in the group is small compared with the total number of plies in the laminate, the B_{ij}, will turn out to be small quantities. For example, a 48-ply laminate containing 24 groups of 45° plies laid up in the sequence $+/-/+/-$ etc. (without there being symmetry about the mid-plane) would be expected to behave much as a symmetrical laminate of the same plies.

6.2.4.3 Bending of Symmetric Laminates.   The moment-curvature relation governing the bending of symmetric laminates out of their plane, as extracted from equation (6.27), is:

$$\begin{bmatrix} D_{xx} & D_{xy} & D_{xs} \\ D_{xy} & D_{yy} & D_{ys} \\ D_{xs} & D_{ys} & D_{ss} \end{bmatrix} \begin{bmatrix} \kappa_x \\ \kappa_y \\ \kappa_s \end{bmatrix} = \begin{bmatrix} M_x \\ M_y \\ M_s \end{bmatrix}. \qquad (6.31)$$

Analogously to the definition of orthotropy in plane stress, a laminate is said to be orthotropic in bending if $D_{xs} = D_{ys} = 0$. However, it is important to note that a laminate that is orthotropic in plane stress is not necessarily orthotropic in bending. For example, consider the four-ply laminate $[\pm 45]_s$. Here the coordinates for the $+45°$ plies may be written as $(-t/2, -t/4)$ and $(t/4, t/2)$, whereas those of the $-45°$ plies are $(-t/4, 0)$ and $(0, t/4)$; t, of course, is the laminate thickness. It is easy to establish that, while A_{xs} and A_{ys} are zero, D_{xs} and D_{ys} are not. On the other hand, a laminate, containing only $0°$ and $90°$ plies will be orthotropic in both plane stress and bending. These laminates are called specially orthotropic. (It is also worth noting that for multi-ply laminates made of groups of plies, if the group is orthotropic in plane stress, then the laminate will at least be approximately orthotropic in both plane stress and bending.)

As an example, consider the bending of the simply-supported beam shown in Figure 6.9a under a uniform distributed load. The laminate consists of a lay-up $[0_4\ 90_4]_s$. Using the single-ply modulus data given in equation (6.20) and a ply thickness of 0.125 mm, equation (6.31) becomes:

$$\begin{bmatrix} 81.584 & 1.962 & 0.0 \\ 1.962 & 18.382 & 0.0 \\ 0.0 & 0.0 & 3.673 \end{bmatrix} \begin{bmatrix} \kappa_x \\ \kappa_y \\ \kappa_s \end{bmatrix} = \begin{bmatrix} M_x \\ M_y \\ M_s \end{bmatrix} \text{Nm/m} \qquad (6.32)$$

If the moment per unit width at the center of the beam is $M_x = 100\ \text{N/m}$, $M_y = M_s = 0$, solving for the curvature gives $\kappa_x = 1.229$, $\kappa_y = -0.131$, and $\kappa_s = 0.0$, indicating the anti-elastic curvature effect typical of plates. Solving for strains in the laminate involves substituting in equations (6.23) and (6.24) with zero for the mid-plane strains. The stress and strain through the thickness are given in Figure 6.9b.

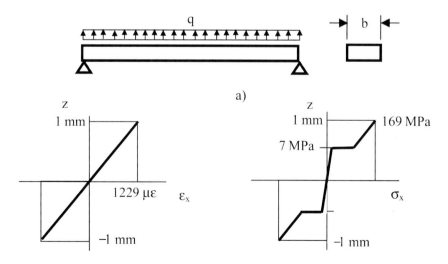

Fig. 6.9   **Configuration and results for simply-supported beam.**

To estimate the deflection at the center of the beam, the matrix of coefficients in equation (6.32) is inverted to give:

$$
\begin{bmatrix} \kappa_x \\ \kappa_y \\ \kappa_s \end{bmatrix} = \begin{bmatrix} d_{xx} & d_{xy} & d_{xs} \\ d_{xy} & d_{yy} & d_{ys} \\ d_{xs} & d_{ys} & d_{ss} \end{bmatrix} \begin{bmatrix} M_x \\ M_y \\ M_s \end{bmatrix}
$$

$$
= \begin{bmatrix} 0.01229 & -0.00131 & 0.0 \\ -0.00131 & 0.05454 & 0.0 \\ 0.0 & 0.0 & 0.27223 \end{bmatrix} \begin{bmatrix} M_x \\ M_y \\ M_s \end{bmatrix} \text{rad/m}
$$

In simple beam theory, a total moment M applied to a beam gives the curvature that satisfies the equation:

$$
\kappa_x = -\frac{d^2 w}{dx^2} = \frac{M}{EI}
$$

Imposing a moment per unit width on the laminate $M_x = M/b$, $M_y = M_s = 0$ on the laminate of width b, then $d_{xx}/b = 1/(EI)_{\text{effective}}$. This effective bending stiffness can be substituted in the simple beam relation $\delta = 5qL^4/384EI$, where q is the load per unit length applied to the beam, to obtain a first order approximation of the deflection of the laminate.[4] For short beams, the simple bending theory is inaccurate, and shear deformation needs to be included.

Composite beams are often stiffened using a lightweight core of Nomex honeycomb or expanded foam.[11] The laminate can be analyzed by including a layer in the center of the laminate with negligible in-plane properties. Use of the laminate theory implies that the core material has sufficient transverse shear and through-thickness compression stiffness to ensure that the top and bottom skins and the core material are constrained to behave as an integral laminate. Repeating the calculation with a 10-mm core added at the center of the previous laminate gives the D_{ij} indicated in the following equation:

$$
\begin{bmatrix} 4896.046 & 178.552 & 0.0 \\ 178.552 & 4200.829 & 0.0 \\ 0.0 & 0.0 & 334.273 \end{bmatrix} \begin{bmatrix} \kappa_x \\ \kappa_y \\ \kappa_s \end{bmatrix} = \begin{bmatrix} M_x \\ M_y \\ M_s \end{bmatrix} \text{Nm/m}
$$

which represents an increase of bending stiffness approaching two orders of magnitude.

For an orthotropic plate in bending, the deflection w satisfies the following equation:

$$
D_{xx}\frac{\partial^4 w}{\partial x^4} + 2(D_{xy} + 2D_{ss})\frac{\partial^4 w}{\partial x^2 \partial y^2} + D_{yy}\frac{\partial^4 w}{\partial y^4} = q
$$

where q is the applied pressure. Solutions of this equation can be found in Ref. 3. In this reference, the related problem of the buckling of laminated plates is also discussed.

6.3 Stress Concentration and Edge Effects

The strain variation through the thickness of the laminate defined by equation (6.23) is linear. Stresses vary discontinuously from ply to ply through the thickness as indicated in Figure 6.9. The determination of the stress in the kth ply requires the definition of the z-position of the ply in the laminate. Substitution into equation (6.23) defines the strains in the ply. These strains can then be substituted into equation (6.24) for the appropriate ply to define the stresses. These strains and stresses are defined in the laminate (x, y, z) coordinate system. When assessing failure in the ply, the stresses and strains are required in the material (1, 2, 3) axis system. Equation (6.5) for stress and equation (6.6) for strain can be implemented to achieve these transformations. Inverting the transformation in equation (6.5) gives the required relation:

$$
\begin{bmatrix} \sigma_1 \\ \sigma_2 \\ \tau_{12} \end{bmatrix} = \begin{bmatrix} c^2 & s^2 & 2cs \\ s^2 & c^2 & -2cs \\ -cs & cs & c^2 - s^2 \end{bmatrix} \begin{bmatrix} \sigma_x \\ \sigma_y \\ \tau_{xy} \end{bmatrix}
$$

6.3.1 Stress Concentration Around Holes in Orthotropic Laminates

A common feature with isotropic materials is the stress-raising effect of holes and changes in geometry that modify the load paths. Several analytical solutions for the stresses around holes in (symmetric) orthotropic laminates are cited in Ref. 7. Details of the derivations of these are given in Ref. 10. It turns out that the value of the stress concentration factor (SCF) depends markedly on the relative values of the various moduli. This can be illustrated by considering the case of a circular hole in an infinite sheet under a uniaxial tension in the x-direction (Fig 6.10). Here, the stress concentration factor at point A in Figure 6.10 ($\alpha = 90°$), defined as the ratio of the average stress through the thickness of the laminate to the average applied stress $\bar{\sigma}_x$, is given by the following formula:

$$
\text{SCF} = K_T = \frac{\bar{\sigma}_{x\,\text{max}}}{\bar{\sigma}_x} = 1 + \left\{ 2\left[\left(\frac{E_X}{E_Y}\right)^{1/2} - v_{xy} \right] + \frac{E_X}{G_{XY}} \right\}^{1/2} \tag{6.33}
$$

The stress concentration factors for the laminates of Table 6.1 have been calculated from this formula, and the results are shown in Table 6.3.

For comparison, the SCF for an isotropic material is 3. As can be seen, when there is a high degree of anisotropy (e.g., an all 0° laminate), SCFs well in excess of that can be obtained. It should also be pointed out that, as the laminate pattern changes, not only does the value of the SCF change, but the point at which the SCF attains its maximum value can also change. Whereas for the first four laminates of Table 6.3, the maximum SCF does occur at point A, for the remaining laminate the maximum occurs at a point such as B in Figure 6.10.

Care should be taken when relating these results to the strength of the laminate. A laminate with all $\pm 45°$ plies has the lowest SCF at 2, but may also

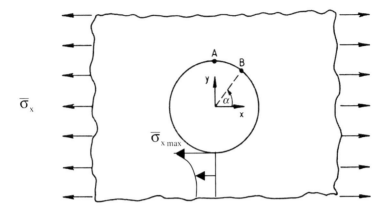

Fig. 6.10   Stress concentration on circular hole in infinite tension panel.

have the lowest strength due to the absence of 0° plies to carry the load. The best laminate has sufficient 0° plies to carry the load, but also ± 45° plies to reduce the stress concentration factor.

6.3.2   Edge Effects

Edge effects are caused by the requirement for strain compatibility between the plies in the laminate. They lead to interlaminar shear and through-thickness peel stresses near the free edges of the laminate. For example, if a laminate consisting of alternating 0° and 90° unidirectional plies is subject to a tensile load parallel to the 0° fibers, then the difference in Poisson's ratio leads to different transverse contraction, as indicated in Figure 6.11. However, the plies in the assembled laminate are forced to have the same transverse strain by the bonding provided by the resin. Therefore, an interlaminar shear develops between the plies, forcing the 0° ply to expand in the transverse direction and the 90° ply to contract. The shear stress is confined to the edge of the laminate because once the required tension σ_y is established in the 0° ply, for example, the compatibility will

Table 6.3   SCF at Circular Hole in Tension Panel (Laminate Data from Table 6.1)

Lay-up		SCF
No. 0° Plies	No. ± 45° Plies	Point A
24	0	6.6
16	8	4.1
12	12	3.5
8	16	3.0
0	24	2.0

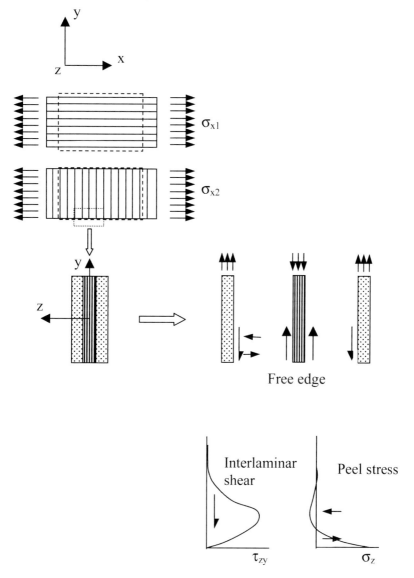

Fig. 6.11   Ply strain compatibility forced in a 0°/90° laminate and interlaminar shear and peel stresses at the edge of the laminate.

be ensured across the middle of the laminate. At the free edge, however, this tension stress must drop to zero if there is no applied edge stress.

The shear stress shown in Figure 6.11 is offset from the axis of the resultant of the stress σ_y, and therefore a turning moment is produced. To balance this moment, peel stresses σ_z develop in the laminate having the distribution indicated in Figure 6.11. These peel stresses can cause delamination at the edge. Similar stress distributions will be identified in Chapter 9 for bonded joints and bonded doubler plates.

Interlaminar shear stresses also occur in angle ply laminates as the individual plies distort differently under the applied loads. A more thorough treatment of edge effects is contained in Ref. 1.

6.4   Failure Theories

6.4.1   Overview-Matrix Cracking, First Ply Failure and Ultimate Load

The prediction of failure in laminates is complex. Failure is not only influenced by the type of loading, but also the properties of the fiber and properties of the resin, the stacking sequence of the plies, residual stresses, and environmental degradation. Failure will initiate at a local level in an individual ply or on the interface between plies but ultimate failure in multi-directional laminates may not occur until the failure has propagated to several plies.

Strains in the laminate are constant through the thickness for in-plane loading of symmetric laminates, or vary linearly if the laminates are subject to out-of-plane curvature. However, the stresses in each ply given by equations (6.7) and (6.24) depend on the modulus of the ply and vary discontinuously through the thickness of the laminate. Failure of the laminate described by a mean stress averaged through the thickness of the laminate will therefore apply only to a particular lay-up. The prediction of failure in multi-directional laminates usually requires the determination of strains and stresses for each ply in the material (1, 2, 3) axes for the ply. The prediction of ultimate failure then requires following the progression of failure through the laminate. A number of different types of failure therefore need to be assessed when evaluating the strength of a laminate:

(1) matrix cracking, which may have important implications for the durability of the laminate;
(2) first ply failure, where one of the plies in the laminate exceeds its ultimate stress or strain values;
(3) ultimate failure when the laminate fails; and
(4) transverse failure or splitting between the layers of the laminate.

Matrix cracking depends on the total state of stress or strain in the matrix. It depends on the residual stress in the matrix due to the curing processes as well as stress and strain due to mechanical loads. For example, in a thermoset laminate cured at elevated temperature, the resin can be considered to cure at or near the glass transition temperature. Because the thermal expansion coefficient of the matrix is much higher than that of the fibers, cooling to room temperature introduces tension into the matrix as it tries to shrink relative to the fibers. Matrix cracking under load then usually occurs at the interface between the most highly loaded ply aligned with the load direction and an off-axis ply.

To determine the load for first ply failure, the stress and strain in the principal material (1, 2, 3) axes in each ply are determined using the theory given in Section 6.2. Hence, the problem can be reduced to establishing a criterion for the ultimate strength of a single ply with the stresses or strains referred to the material axes. As before, these stresses will be denoted by σ_1, σ_2, and τ_{12}. A number of well-tried theories, including maximum stress and maximum strain, are discussed in the subsequent sections.

It is important to note that failure of the first ply does not necessarily constitute failure of the laminate. The stiffness of the failed ply can be reduced, say, to a defined percentage of its undamaged value, and the laminate re-analyzed to check whether the remaining plies can carry the load. If the load can be carried, the applied is increased until the next ply fails. When the load cannot be carried, ultimate failure has occurred.

The prediction of through-thickness failure has proved more difficult. This transverse failure occurs in the matrix. It is failure of the resin in either shear or tension. It depends on the total state of stress or strain in the matrix, including the stresses introduced by manufacturing of the component. Several approaches will be discussed in the following sections. When a flaw is present, a fracture mechanics approach is used to predict the growth of the flaw leading to de-lamination and structural failure. In the fracture mechanics approach, the strain energy release rate is determined and compared with the critical value for the matrix material. The approach has proved useful for predicting stiffener separation and delamination growth.[12]

6.4.2 Stress-Based Failure Theory

Stress-based failure theory can be classified into two categories: maximum stress theories[13-16] and quadratic stress failure theories.[17,18] The stresses are first determined for each ply and transformed to the material (1, 2, 3) axes.

Maximum stress theory directly compares the maximum stress experienced by the material with its strength. The maximum stress across a number of failure modes is compared with the strength in each failure mode. First ply failure will not occur if:

$$\max\left(\frac{\sigma_1}{X_T}, \left|\frac{\sigma_1}{X_C}\right|, \frac{\sigma_2}{Y_T}, \left|\frac{\sigma_2}{Y_C}\right|, \left|\frac{s_{12}}{S_{12}}\right|\right) \prec 1 \qquad (6.34)$$

The quadratic failure criteria include the affect of biaxial (multiaxial) load. The most used quadratic failure theories are:

Tsai-Hill Theory

$$\frac{\sigma_1^2}{X^2} - \frac{\sigma_1\sigma_2}{X^2} + \frac{\sigma_2^2}{Y^2} + \left(\frac{\tau_{12}}{S_{12}}\right)^2 \prec 1 \qquad (6.35)$$

If $\sigma_1 > 0$, $X = X_T$; otherwise, $X = X_C$. If $\sigma_2 > 0$, $Y = Y_T$; otherwise, $Y = Y_C$. This failure criterion is a generalization of the von Mises yield criterion for isotropic ductile metals. When plotted with σ_1 and σ_2 as the axes and with constant values of τ_{12}/S_{12}, this equation defines elliptical arcs joined at the axes.[1]

A more general theory can be developed based on an interactive tensor polynomial relationship. The Tsai-Wu criterion is invariant for transformation between coordinate systems and is capable of accounting for the difference between tensile and compressive strengths.[1]

Tsai-Wu Theory [17]

$$F_1\sigma_1 + F_2\sigma_2 + F_{11}\sigma_1^2 + F_{22}\sigma_2^2 + F_{66}\tau_{12}^2 + 2F_{12}\sigma_1\sigma_2 \prec 1 \qquad (6.36)$$

The Tsai-Wu coefficients are defined as follows:

$$F_1 = \frac{1}{X_T} + \frac{1}{X_C}$$

$$F_2 = \frac{1}{Y_T} + \frac{1}{Y_C}$$

$$F_{11} = -\frac{1}{X_T X_C}$$

$$F_{22} = -\frac{1}{Y_T Y_C}$$

$$F_{66} = \frac{1}{S_{12}^2}$$

The coefficient F_{12} requires biaxial testing. Let σ_{biax} be the equal biaxial tensile stress ($\sigma_1 = \sigma_2$) at failure. If it is known, then:

$$F_{12} = \frac{1}{2\sigma_{\text{biax}}^2}\left(1 - \left(\frac{1}{X_T} + \frac{1}{X_C} + \frac{1}{Y_T} + \frac{1}{Y_C}\right)\sigma_{\text{biax}} + \left(\frac{1}{X_T X_C} + \frac{1}{Y_T Y_C}\right)\sigma_{\text{biax}}^2\right)$$

otherwise,

$$F_{12} = f^1\sqrt{F_{11}F_{22}}$$

where $-1.0 \leq f^1 \leq 1.0$. The default value of f^1 is zero.

The maximum stress theories define simple regions in stress space. Stresses lying inside the limits defined by the solid lines in Figure 6.12 will not cause failure. Failure occurs for combinations of stresses that lie outside the failure envelope. The polynomial theories define elliptical regions. The plot appearing as a dashed line in Figure 6.12 is for the Tsai-Wu criterion for combinations of direct stress with zero shear stress. In this case, the ellipse crosses the axes at the four points corresponding to X_T, X_C, Y_T, and Y_C.

6.4.2.1 Stress-Based Theories: Considering Actual Failure Modes.
The Tsai-Hill and Tsai-Wu criteria do not identify which mode of failure has

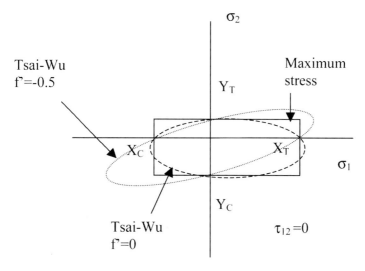

Fig. 6.12 Stress failure envelopes for a typical unidirectional carbon fiber.
(X_T = 1280 MPa, X_C = 1440 MPa, Y_T = 57 MPa, Y_C = 228 MPa)

become critical. Failure theories in the second category treat the separate failure modes inde-pendently. The maximum stress criteria and the Hashin-Rotem failure criterion treat the separate failure modes independently.[15,19]

The two-dimensional Hashin-Rotem failure criterion has the following components for unidirectional material. For tensile fiber failure ($\sigma_{11} > 0$):

$$\left(\frac{\sigma_{11}}{X_T}\right)^2 + \left(\frac{\tau_{12}}{S_{12}}\right)^2 = 1 \tag{6.37a}$$

For compressive fiber failure ($\sigma_{11} < 0$):

$$\left(\frac{\sigma_{11}}{X_C}\right)^2 = 1 \tag{6.37b}$$

For tensile matrix failure ($\sigma_{22} > 0$):

$$\left(\frac{\sigma_{22}}{Y_T}\right)^2 + \left(\frac{\tau_{12}}{S_{12}}\right)^2 = 1 \tag{6.37c}$$

For compressive matrix failure ($\sigma_{22} < 0$):

$$\left(\frac{\sigma_{22}}{2S_{23}}\right)^2 + \left[\left(\frac{Y_C}{2S_{23}}\right)^2 - 1\right]\frac{\sigma_{22}}{Y_C} + \left(\frac{\tau_{12}}{S_{12}}\right)^2 = 1 \tag{6.37d}$$

For through-thickness failure, the combination of through-thickness stresses predicts delaminations will initiate when:

$$\left(\frac{\sigma_{33}}{Z_T}\right)^2 + \left(\frac{\sigma_{23}}{S_{23}}\right)^2 + \left(\frac{\sigma_{31}}{S_{31}}\right)^2 = 1$$

Here σ_{11}, σ_{22} and τ_{12}, are the longitudinal stress, transverse stress, and shear stress, respectively, and X, Y, Z, and S are the longitudinal strength, transverse strengths (Z is through thickness), and shear strength, respectively, that are obtained from testing. The subscripts T and C refer to tension and compression mode, respectively.

If the matrix failure parameter is satisfied first, then an initial crack forms in the matrix.

Zhang[20] separated the through thickness mode into stear and tension.

For interlaminar shear failure occurs when:

$$\sqrt{\tau_{13}^2 + \tau_{23}^2} \geq \text{interlaminar shear strength}$$

For interlaminar tension:

$$\frac{\sigma_{\text{peel}}}{Z_T} = 1 \tag{6.38}$$

6.4.2.2 Stress-Based Methods: Application to Laminates.
To predict ultimate failure, the lamina failure criterion is applied to examine which ply undergoes initial failure. The stiffness of this ply is then reduced and the load is increased until the second ply fails. The process is repeated until the load cannot be increased indicating the ultimate failure load has been reached. Residual stresses can be taken into account at the laminate level.

Hashin and Rotem[15] used a different stiffness reduction method for predicting ultimate failure. A stiffness matrix represents the laminate where the stiffness of the cracked lamina decreases proportionally to the logarithmic load increase in the laminate. Residual stresses are considered, and a non-linear analysis is used.

Liu and Tsai[18] use the Tsai-Wu[17] linear quadratic failure criterion. The failure envelope is defined by test data. The data are obtained from uniaxial and pure shear tests. After initial matrix failure, cracking in the matrix occurs. The stiffness is reduced for the failed lamina by using a matrix degradation factor that is computed from micromechanics. This process is repeated until the maximum load is reached. Thermal residual stresses, along with moisture stresses, are estimated using a linear theory of thermoelasticity. This assumes that the strains are proportional to the curing temperature.

Through-thickness failure is failure in the matrix caused by tensile stresses perpendicular to the plies. A typical example is shown in Figure 6.13. The delamination can be predicted by the interlaminar tension criterion of Zhang.[20]

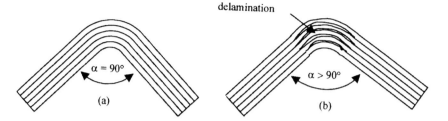

Fig. 6.13   Interlaminar failure—splitting in a curved beam.

Wisnom et al.[21,22] use a stress-based failure criterion to predict through-thickness failure in composite structures. This matrix failure criterion uses an equivalent stress σ_e, calculated from the three principal stresses:

$$\sigma_e^2 = \frac{1}{2.6}[(\sigma_1 - \sigma_2)^2 + (\sigma_2 - \sigma_3)^2 + (\sigma_3 - \sigma_1)^2 + 0.6\sigma_e(\sigma_1 + \sigma_2 + \sigma_3)]$$

(6.39)

Interlaminar strength is considered to be related to the volume of stressed material. Therefore, the stressed volume is taken into account using a Weibull statistical strength theory. The criterion can be applied to three-dimensional geometric structures with any lay-up. Residual stresses and the effect of hydrostatic stress are accounted for.

6.4.3 Strain-Based Failure Theories

The simplest strain-based failure theories compare strains in the laminate with strain limits for the material.[23,24] Failure occurs if

$$\max\left(\frac{\varepsilon_1}{\varepsilon_{1T}}, \left|\frac{\varepsilon_1}{\varepsilon_{1C}}\right|, \frac{\varepsilon_2}{\varepsilon_{2T}}, \left|\frac{\varepsilon_2}{\varepsilon_{2C}}\right|, \left|\frac{\gamma_{12}}{\gamma_{12C}}\right|\right) = 1$$

(6.40)

where the subscripts T and C, as before, refer to critical strains for tension and compression, the 1-2 axes are the material axes, and γ_{12C} is the critical shear strain.

The failure envelope for this failure criterion is sketched in Figure 6.14a. If the Poisson's ratio for the laminate is non-zero, tensile strain of the laminate in the 1-direction will be accompanied by contraction in the 2-direction. Transforming the failure envelope from strain axes to stress axes therefore leads to the distorted failure envelope shown in Figure 6.14b.

Puck and Schurmann[25] have developed a strain-based theory for fiber failure in tension, including deformation of fiber in the transverse direction.

$$\frac{1}{\varepsilon_{1T}}\left(\varepsilon_1 + \frac{\nu_{f12}}{E_{f1}}m_{\sigma f}\sigma_2\right) = 1$$

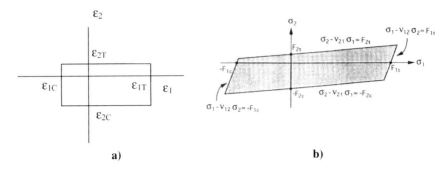

Fig. 6.14   Maximum strain failure envelope: *a*) **maximum strain failure envelope with strain axes;** *b*) **maximum strain failure envelope on stress axes.**

where ε_{1T} is tensile failure strain of a unidirectional layer, and m_{of} is mean stress magnification factor for the fiber in y-direction, due to the difference between the transverse modulus of the fiber and the modulus of the matrix. For carbon fiber, m_{of} is equal to about 1.1.

6.4.3.1 Strain Invariant Failure Theory.

Although the strain invariant failure theory (SIFT) is not new for isotropic metallic materials,[26] its application to the failure of the matrix in composite materials is a development initiated by Gosse and Christensen.[27] Theoretically, for an isotropic material like steel, yield under complex stress must directly result from the magnitude of stress or strain and must be independent of the direction of the coordinate system defining the stress field. Similarly, a strain-base criterion not linked to a location and direction in the laminate must be a function of invariant strains so that it is unaffected by a transformation of the coordinates.

Under complex stress, the strain invariants can be determined from the following cubic characteristic equation determined from the strain tensor.[26]

$$\varepsilon^3 - (\varepsilon_x + \varepsilon_y + \varepsilon_z)\,\varepsilon^2 + \left(\varepsilon_x\varepsilon_y + \varepsilon_y\varepsilon_z + \varepsilon_z\varepsilon_x - \frac{1}{4}\gamma_{xy}^2 - \frac{1}{4}\gamma_{yz}^2 - \frac{1}{4}\gamma_{zx}^2\right)\varepsilon$$

$$- \left(\varepsilon_x\varepsilon_y\varepsilon_z + \frac{1}{4}\gamma_{xy}\gamma_{yz}\gamma_{zx} - \frac{1}{4}\varepsilon_x\gamma_{yz}^2 - \frac{1}{4}\varepsilon_y\gamma_{zx}^2 - \frac{1}{4}\varepsilon_z\gamma_{xy}^2\right) = 0$$

The coefficients of the cubic equation are invariant to transformation of coordinates, designated as invariant strains. We can write:

$$\varepsilon^3 - J_1\varepsilon^2 + J_2\varepsilon - J_3 = 0$$

where:

$$J_1 = \varepsilon_x + \varepsilon_y + \varepsilon_z = \varepsilon_1 + \varepsilon_2 + \varepsilon_3 \tag{6.41}$$

$$J_2 = \varepsilon_x \varepsilon_y + \varepsilon_y \varepsilon_z + \varepsilon_z \varepsilon_x - \frac{1}{4}\gamma_{xy}^2 - \frac{1}{4}\gamma_{yz}^2 - \frac{1}{4}\gamma_{zx}^2$$

$$= \varepsilon_1 \varepsilon_2 + \varepsilon_2 \varepsilon_3 + \varepsilon_3 \varepsilon_1 \tag{6.42}$$

$$J_3 = \varepsilon_x \varepsilon_y \varepsilon_z + \frac{1}{4}\gamma_{xy}\gamma_{yz}\gamma_{zx} - \frac{1}{4}\varepsilon_x \gamma_{yz}^2 - \frac{1}{4}\varepsilon_y \gamma_{zx}^2 - \frac{1}{4}\varepsilon_z \gamma_{xy}^2 = \varepsilon_1 \varepsilon_2 \varepsilon_3 \tag{6.43}$$

and 1, 2, 3 denote principal strains.

6.4.3.2 First Invariant Strain Criterion for Matrix Failure. Obviously, the simplest criterion of such a kind is a function of the first invariant strain J_1, which indicates the part of the state of strain corresponding to change of volume. However, it is well known that a material would not yield under compressive hydrostatic stress; consequently, this first invariant strain criterion is applicable only to tension-tension load cases experiencing volume increases.

6.4.3.3 Second Deviatoric Strain Criterion. To consider material yielding by the part of the state of strain causing change of shape (distortion) and to exclude the part of state of strain causing change of volume, a function of the second deviatoric invariant strain J_2' has been suggested where:

$$J_2' = \frac{1}{6}((\varepsilon_x - \varepsilon_y)^2 + (\varepsilon_y - \varepsilon_z)^2 + (\varepsilon_z - \varepsilon_x)^2)$$

$$+ \frac{1}{4}\gamma_{xy}^2 + \frac{1}{4}\gamma_{yz}^2 + \frac{1}{4}\gamma_{zx}^2 \tag{6.44}$$

A more convenient form for use as a failure criterion is:

$$\varepsilon_{eqv} = \sqrt{3J_2'}$$

$$= \sqrt{\frac{1}{2}((\varepsilon_x - \varepsilon_y)^2 + (\varepsilon_y - \varepsilon_z)^2 + (\varepsilon_z - \varepsilon_x)^2) + \frac{3}{4}\gamma_{xy}^2 + \frac{3}{4}\gamma_{yz}^2 + \frac{3}{4}\gamma_{zx}^2} \tag{6.45}$$

This criterion can be simplified using principal strains to:

$$\varepsilon_{eqv} = \sqrt{((\varepsilon_1 - \varepsilon_2)^2 + (\varepsilon_2 - \varepsilon_3)^2 + (\varepsilon_3 - \varepsilon_1)^2)/2}$$

This equivalent strain, often referred to the Von Mises shear strain, is a combination of invariants:

$$\varepsilon_{eqv} = \sqrt{J_1^2 - 3J_2}$$

Consequently, it is also invariant to any transformation of axis.

6.4.3.4 SIFT Applied to Laminates.

Use of the strain invariant failure criteria for composite laminates[30] is a break from traditional methods because it considers three planes of strain as opposed to the conventional maximum principal strain. Two mechanisms for matrix failure are considered. These are dilatational failure, characterized by the first strain invariant, J_1, and distortional failure, characterized by a function of an equivalent shear strain, ε_{eqv}. Initial failure occurs when either of these parameters exceeds a critical value. The calculation of strain includes micromechanical models that take into account residual stresses and a strain amplification factor that includes strain concentration around the fiber. The criterion is a physics-based strain approach, based on properties at the lamina level. It can be applied to three-dimensional laminates with any lay-up, boundary, and loading conditions.

Gosse and Christensen[27] undertook several test cases on laminates, each with different lay-ups, for verification of the strain invariant failure criterion. These tests gave a good correlation between interlaminar cracking and the first strain invariant. Hart-Smith and Gosse[28] extended the SIFT approach to map matrix damage to predict final failure. This is done using a strain-energy approach.

6.4.4 Matrix Failure Envelopes

The matrix failure envelope[27] for the SIFT criterion can be seen in Figure 6.15. When the cylindrical section is cut by the plane formed by the first two principal axes, an ellipsoid is formed. The ellipsoidal region of the envelope is governed by shear components of strain characterized by the equivalent strain, ε_{eqv}. The 45° cut-off plane, dominated by transverse tensile strain, is characterized by the first strain invariant, J_1.

The insert in Figure 6.15, developed by Sternstein and Ongchin,[29] is a failure envelope for polymers constrained within glass fibers, where the strain in the 3-direction is equal to zero. When the SIFT failure envelope is transferred to stress axes both sections become segments of an ellipse as indicated in Figure 6.16.

6.4.5 Comparison of Failure Prediction Models

Soden et al.[31] have compared the failure predictions achieved by several theories and compared them to experimental results.[31,32,34,35] Almost all of the failure envelopes presented give an ellipsoidal shape in the negative stress region corresponding to shear loading. Transverse tensile loading causes failure in the

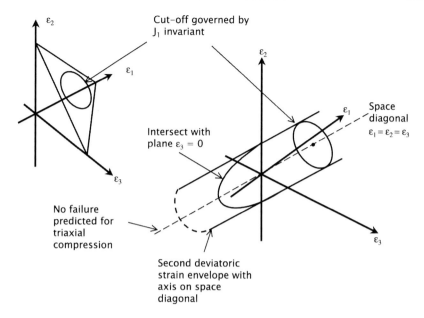

Fig. 6.15   The SIFT matrix failure envelope.

positive stress-strain region.[30] SIFT represents failure in this region with a cut-off plane characterized by the first strain invariant J_1, whereas most of the other failure theories continue with either an ellipsoidal shape or a curved, irregular shape.

6.5   Fracture Mechanics

In the fracture mechanics approach, failure is predicted to occur when a crack grows spontaneously from an initial flaw.[33] This approach has found application in predicting stiffener debonding[36] and for predicting interply failures.

Fracture toughness and crack growth was discussed in Chapter 2. It is apparent from that discussion that cracks are likely to grow parallel to the fibers (splitting) and parallel to the plies (delamination). Failure can also occur in assembled structures in adhesive bonds between the components. The prediction of when a delamination or disbond will grow is important for the assessment of damage tolerance where the initial defect can be assumed to arise due to manufacturing processes or due to impact or other damage mechanisms for the structure. The size of the defect is usually linked to the limits of visual inspection or the inspections that follow manufacture because known defects will be repaired.

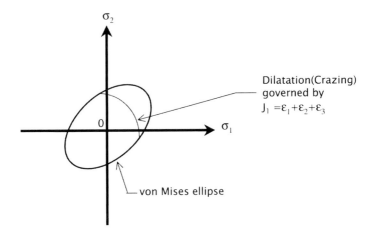

Fig. 6.16   SIFT failure envelope for polymeric materials.

The requirement is that damage that cannot be detected should not grow under operational loads.

The prediction of the growth of interlaminar splitting and disbonds in bonded joints is based on three modes of crack opening. Mode I is crack opening due to interlaminar tension, mode II due to interlaminar sliding shear, and mode III due to interlaminar scissoring shear. The components G_I, G_{II}, and G_{III} of the strain energy release rate, G, can be determined using a virtual crack closure technique in which the work done by forces to close the tip of the crack are calculated. If mode I and mode II crack opening is contributing to the growth, the delamination is predicted to grow when:

$$\left(\frac{G_I}{G_{IC}}\right)^m + \left(\frac{G_{II}}{G_{IIC}}\right)^n = 1 \qquad \text{(Eq. 6.46)}$$

where m and n are empirically defined constants. The finite element analysis depicted in Figure 16.11 identifies the role that buckling of a panel and flanges of a stiffener can play in driving a disbond in a bonded joint.

6.6   Failure Prediction Near Stress Raisers and Damage Tolerance

The behavior of carbon fiber laminates with epoxy resins is predominantly linearly elastic. However, some stress relief occurs near stress concentrations that is similar to the development of a plastic zone in ductile metals. Microcracking in the laminate softens the laminate in the vicinity of the notch. In the case of

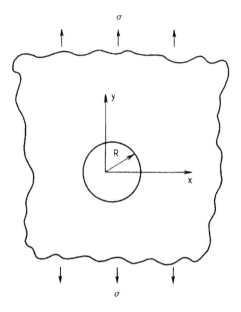

σ

Fig. 6.17   Reference axes for a hole in an orthotropic panel under uniform tension.

holes in composite laminates, two different approaches have been successfully developed to predict failure based on the stress distribution. These are the average stress failure criterion and the point stress failure criterion.

Consider a hole of radius R in an infinite orthotropic sheet (Fig. 6.17). If a uniform stress σ is applied parallel to the y-axis at infinity, then, as shown in Ref. 21, the normal stress σ_y along the x-axis in front of the hole can be approximated by:

$$\sigma_y(x,0) = \frac{\sigma}{2}\left\{2 + \left(\frac{R}{x}\right)^2 + 3\left(\frac{R}{x}\right)^4 - (K_T - 3)\left[5\left(\frac{R}{x}\right)^6 - 7\left(\frac{R}{x}\right)^8\right]\right\} \qquad (6.47)$$

where K_T is the orthotropic stress concentration factor given by equation (6.33).

The average stress failure criterion[40,41] then assumes that failure occurs when the average value of σ_y over some fixed length a_o ahead of the hole first reaches the un-notched tensile strength of the material. That is, when:

$$\frac{1}{a_o}\int_R^{R+a_o}\sigma_y(x,0)dx = \sigma_o$$

Using this criterion with equation (6.47) gives the ratio of the notched to un-notched strength as:

$$\frac{\sigma_N}{\sigma_o} = \frac{2(1 - \phi)}{2 - \phi^2 - \phi^4 + (K_T - 3)(\phi^6 - \phi^8)}$$

where:

$$\phi = \frac{R}{R + a_o}$$

In practice, the quantity a_o is determined experimentally from strength reduction data.

The point stress criterion assumes that failure occurs when the stress σ_y at some fixed distance d_o ahead of the hole first reaches the un-notched tensile stress,

$$\sigma_y(x, 0)|_{x=R+d_o} = \sigma_o$$

It was shown in Ref. 40 that the point stress and average stress failure criteria are related, and that:

$$a_o = 4d_o$$

The accuracy of these methods, in particular the average stress method, can be seen in Figure 6.18, where a_o was taken as 3.8 mm. The solid lines represent predicted strength using the average stress criterion, and the dotted lines are the predicted strengths from the point stress method. Tests in Ref. 41 were carried out on various 16-ply carbon/epoxy laminates (AS/3501-5) with holes. The laminates were: $(0/\pm45_2/0/\pm45)_s$, $(0_2/\pm45/0_2/90/0)_s$, and $(0/\pm45/90)_{2s}$. The results are shown in Table 6.4 and are compared with predicted values using the average stress method with $a_o = 2.3$ mm.

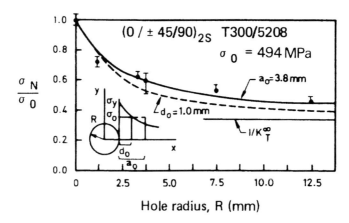

Fig. 6.18   Comparison of predicted and experimental failure stresses for circular holes in $(0/\pm45/90)_{2s}$, T300/5208.

Table 6.4 Static Strength Predictions[45]

Number of Holes, Hole Size and Placement		Laminate No.	% of Unnotched Strength	
			Test	Avg Stress
2 4.8-mm diameter countersunk.		1 2 3	58.9 48.1 51.8	53.6 51.4 53.2
2 4.8-mm diameter countersunk.		3	48.7	45.9
2 4-mm diameter countersunk.		3	53.1	50.3
1 4-mm diameter noncountersunk		2	54.0	52.6

As can be seen from the examples given, the average stress criterion provides accurate estimates of the strength reduction due to the presence of holes. This method is widely used in the aerospace industry[42] and has been applied to biaxial stress problems,[43] to the estimation of strength reduction due to battle damage,[44] and to problems in which the stress is compressive.[45]

Damage tolerance in laminates is considered in Chapters 8 and 12. The analysis requirements include prediction of the growth of defects caused by impact and the determination of the compressive strength after impact. The analysis of the growth of disbonds can be based on fracture mechanics approaches. The compression after impact strength has often been analyzed by approximating the damaged zone as an open hole and assessing the strength of the laminate under compressive loads using the procedures described above.

6.7 Buckling

In laminated composites, buckling can occur at the laminate or fiber level.

6.7.1 Buckling of the Laminate

Buckling loads for the laminate can be estimated using classical analysis for orthotropic plates. In general, buckling loads are increased by arranging the lay-up with plies aligned with the compressive load in the outer layers. The effect is to increase the bending stiffness of the laminate. Data sheets for the buckling coefficient for specially orthotropic laminates are presented in the ESDU data sheets.[46] Data for plates loaded either uniaxially or bi-axially is presented in terms of the coefficients K_o and C for a variety of edge conditions. The buckling load is given by

$$N_{xb} = \frac{K_o(D_{11}D_{22})^{1/2}}{b^2} + \frac{C\pi^2 D_o}{b^2} \qquad \text{where} \quad D_o = D_{12} + 2D_{33}$$

and the coefficients D_{ij} are the coefficients derived in Section 6.2 and equations (6.30) and (6.31).

6.7.2 Buckling of the Fibers

Buckling failures can also be associated with lamina. These failures are identified by kink zones that form normal to the layers. Typical kink bands are shown in Figure 6.19. In the most common mode of buckling, the fibers buckle in an in-phase or shear mode. Fiber buckling has been discussed in Chapter 2.

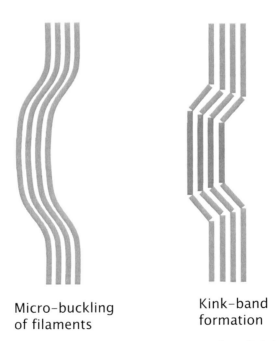

Micro−buckling
of filaments

Kink−band
formation

Fig. 6.19   Microbuckling of fibers. Taken from Ref. 1.

6.8 Summary

Classical laminate analysis has been introduced in this chapter. The analysis gives a relationship between in-plane load resultants and strain, and between out-of-plane bending moments and curvatures for panels consisting of layers or plies of unidirectional and fabric material. Once these relationships have been derived, the analysis of composites becomes equivalent to the classical analysis of anisotropic materials. A laminate analysis, for example, precedes a finite element analysis in which the algorithm calculates the equivalent plate properties from the A, B, and D matrices. Once this step is completed, the full power and versatility of finite element analysis (See Chapter 16) can be applied to the analysis and design of composite structures. Data sheets for design using composite panels can also be based on stiffness and strains produced by a laminate analysis as indicated for the case of buckling in Section 6.7. Finally the laminate analysis can be used to define the equivalent stiffness of the panel enabling the application of standard formulas to check the stiffness of plate and beam structures.

The prediction of failure in composites is a difficult problem. The materials consist of both fibers and a matrix—both of which exhibit distinct failure modes. In addition the interface between the fibers and the resin, the ply stacking sequence and the environmental conditions all contribute to failure. To compound the problem, the manufacturing processes introduce significant residual stresses into the resins. These residual stresses become apparent when the structure distorts due to the phenomenon called spring-in and when the matrix cracks after cure even before the structures are loaded. The failure theories discussed in this chapter are still being developed. Tension fiber failures are generally well predicted, and design margins of safety can be small. However, much still remains to be done to improve the reliability of the techniques for predicting matrix failures and the growth of delaminations.

References

[1] Daniel, I. M., and Ishai, O., *Engineering Mechanics of Composite Materials*, Oxford University Press, 1994.

[2] Staab, G. H., *Laminated Composites*, Butterworth-Heinemann, 1999.

[3] Jones, R. M., *Mechanics of Composite Materials*, Tokyo, McGraw-Hill, Kogakusha, 1975.

[4] Tsai, S. W., and Hahn, H. T., *Introduction to Composite Materials*, Technomic Publishing, Westport, CT, 1980.

[5] Agarwal, B. D., and Broutman, L. J., *Analysis and Performance of Fiber Composites*, Wiley, New York, 1980.

[6] Broutman, L. J., and Krock, R. H., (eds.), *Composite Materials*, Vols. 7 and 8 "Laminate Design and Analysis", Parts I and II, edited by C. C. Chamis, New York, Academic Press, 1975.

[7]"Plastics for Aerospace Vehicles," *Pt.* 1, *Reinforced Plastics*, MIL-HDBK-17A, Washington, DC, U.S. Department of Defense, 1971.

[8]Hearmon, R. F. S., *An Introduction to Applied Anisotropic Elasticity*, London, Oxford University Press, 1961.

[9]Lekhnitskii, S. G., *Theory of Elasticity of an Anisotropic Body*, Moscow, Mir Publishers, 1981.

[10]Lekhnitskii, S. G., *Anisotropic Plates*, Gordon and Breach, New York, 1968.

[11]Vinson, J. R., *The Behaviour of Sandwich Structures of Isotropic and Composite Materials*, Technomic, 1999.

[12]Davies, G. A. O., and Zhang, X., "Impact Damage Predictions, in Carbon Composite Structures," *International Journal of Impact Engineering*, Vol. 16, No. 1, 1995, pp. 149–170.

[13]Sun, C. T., and Tao, J. X., "Prediction Failure Envelopes and Stress/Strain Behaviour of Composite Laminates," *Composites Science and Technology*, Vol. 58, 1998, pp. 1125–1113.

[14]Zinoviev, P., Grigoriev, S. V., Labedeva, O. V., Tairova, L. R., "The Strength of Multilayered Composites under Plane Stress State," *Composites Science and Technology*, Vol. 58, 1998, pp. 1209–1223.

[15]Hashin, Z., and Rotem, A., "A Fatigue Failure Criterion for Fibre Reinforced Materials," *Journal of Composite Materials*, Vol. 7, 1973, pp. 448–464.

[16]Edge, E. C., "Stress Based Grant-Sanders Method for Predicting Failure of Composite Laminates," *Composites Science and Technology*, Vol. 58, 1998, pp. 1033–1041.

[17]Tsai, S. W., and Wu, E. M., "A General Theory of Strength for Anisotropic Materials" *Journal of Composite Materials*, Vol. 5, 1971, pp. 58–80.

[18]Liu, K. S., and Tsai, S. W., "A Progressive Quadratic Failure Criterion for a Laminate," *Composites Science and Technology*, Vol. 58, 1998, pp. 1023–1032.

[19]Rotem, A., "The Rotem Failure Criterion Theory and Practice," *Composites Science and Technology*, Vol. 62, 2002, pp. 1663–1671.

[20]Zhang, X., "Impact Damage in Composite Aircraft Structures—Experimental Testing and Numerical Simulation," *Journal of Aerospace Engineering*, Vol. 212, No. 4, 1998, pp. 245–259.

[21]Wisnom, M. R., Hill, G. F. J., Jones, M., *Through-Thickness Failure Prediction of Composite Structural Elements*, 2001, 13th Inter. Conference of Composite Materials, Beijing, 1623.

[22]Wisnom, M. R., Hill, G. F. J., Jones, M., "Interlaminar Tensile Strength of Carbon Fiber-Epoxy Specimens Size, Lay-up and Manufacturing Effects," *Advanced Composites. Letters*, Vol. 10, No. 4, 2001.

[23]Eckold, G. G., "Failure Criteria for Use in Design Environment," *Composites Science and Technology*, Vol. 58, 1998, pp. 1095–1105.

[24]Hart-Smith, L. J., "Predictions of the Original and Truncated Maximum Strain-Strain Failure Models for Certain Fibrous Composite Laminates," *Composites Science and Technology*, Vol. 58, 1998, pp. 1151–1178.

[25]Puck, A., and Schurmann, H., "Failure Analysis of FRP Laminates by Means of Physically Based Phenomenological Models," *Composites Science and Technology*, Vol. 58, 1998, pp. 1045–1067.

[26]Ford, H., and Alexander, J., *Advanced Mechanics of Materials*, 2nd Ed, Ellis Horwood, Chichester, UK, 1977.

[27] Gosse, J. H., and Christensen, S., *Strain Invariant Failure Criteria for Polymers in Composite Materials*, Paper AIAA-2001-1184, Phantom Works, Seattle, 2001.

[28] Hart-Smith, L. J., Gosse, J. H., Christensen, S., *Characterizing the Strength of Composite Materials from the Perspective of Structural Design*, Boeing, Paper MDC00K0103, Seattle, WA, 2000.

[29] Sternstein, S., and Ongchin, L., *Yield Criteria for Plastic Deformation of Glassy High Polymers in General Stress Fields*, Polymer Preprints, Vol. 10, 1969, pp. 1117–1124.

[30] Li, R., Kelly, D., and Ness, R., "Application of a First Invariant Strain Criterion for Matrix Failure in Composite Materials," *Journal of Composite Materials*, Vol. 37, No. 22, 2003, pp. 1977–2000.

[31] Soden, P. D., Hinton, M. J., Kaddour, A. S., "A Comparison of the Predictive Capabilities of Current Failure Theories for Composite Laminates," *Composites Science and Technology*, Vol. 58, 1998, pp. 1225–1254.

[32] Soden, P. D., Hinton, M. J., Kaddour, A. S., "Lamina Properties, Lay-up Configurations and Loading Conditions for a Range Reinforced Composite Laminates," *Composites Science and Technology*, Vol. 58, 1998, pp. 1011–1022.

[33] Gotsis, P. K., Chamis, C. C., Minnetyan, L., "Prediction of Composite Laminate Fracture: Micromechanics and Progressive Fracture," *Composites Science and Technology*, Vol. 58, 1998, pp. 1137–1149.

[34] Rotem, A., "Prediction Laminate Failure with Rotem Failure Criterion," *Composites Science and Technology*, Vol. 58, 1998, pp, 1083–1094.

[35] Wolfe, W. E., and Butalia, T. S., "A Strain-Energy Based Failure Criterion for Nonlinear Analysis of Composite Laminates Subjected Biaxial Loading," *Composites Science and Technology*, Vol. 58, 1998, pp. 1107–1124.

[36] Yap, J., Scott, M., Thomson, R., Hachenberg, D., "The Analysis of Skin-to-Stiffener Debonding in Composite Aerospace Structures," *ICCS-11*, Monash University, 2001.

[37] Sih, G., Paris, P. C., Irwin, G. R., "On Cracks in Rectilinearly Anisotropic Bodies," *International Journal of Fracture Mechanics*, Vol. 1, 1965, p. 189.

[38] Kelly, A., *Strong Solids*, Oxford University Press, London, 1973.

[39] Harrison, N. L., "Splitting of Fibre-Reinforced Materials," *Fibre Science and Technology*, Vol. 6, 1973, p. 25.

[40] Nuismer, R. J., and Whitney, J. M., "Uniaxial Failure of Composite Laminates Containing Stress Concentrations," ASTM STP 593, 1975, pp. 117–142.

[41] Nuismer, R. J., and Labor, J. D., "Applications of the Average Stress Failure Criterion, Part 1: Tension," *Journal of Composite Materials*, Vol. 12, 1978, p. 238.

[42] Pimm, J. H., *Experimental Investigation of Composite Wing Failure*, AIAA Paper 78–509, 1978.

[43] Daniel, I. M., "Behaviour of Graphite Epoxy Plates with Holes under Biaxial Loading," *Experimental Mechanics*, Vol. 20, 1980, pp. 1–8.

[44] Husman, G. E., Whitney, J. M., Halpin, J. C., *Residual Strength Characterization of Laminated Composites Subjected to Impact Loading*, ASTM STP 568, 1975, pp. 92–113.

[45] Nuismer, R. J., and Labor, J. D., "Application of the Average Stress Failure Criterion: Part 2-Compression," *Journal of Composite Materials*, Vol. 13, 1979, pp. 49–60.

[46] Engineering Science Data Unit (ESDU) Data Item 80023 *Buckling of Rectangular Specially Orthotropic Plates*, ESDU International London.

7
Mechanical Property Measurement

7.1 Introduction

Mechanical testing of materials and structural details is conducted to satisfy one or more of the following objectives: 1) characterization of materials or processes, 2) development of design allowables, 3) qualification of materials for certain applications, 4) quality control, 5) assessment of strength and durability under sustained or cyclic loads, or 6) assessment of the influence of damage or degradation on residual strength.

Aerospace wrought metal alloys are available in standard pre-fabricated forms with well-characterized properties. By contrast, composites are usually formed at the same time as the component is manufactured and therefore can have a very wide range of properties depending on the fiber, resin, lay-up, volume fraction, etc. Some properties of composites are more sensitive to environmental conditions. Thus, testing requirements are generally more demanding than is the case for metals.

The use of mechanical testing for developing design allowables for composites is described in Chapter 13, and its use in the testing of adhesively bonded or mechanically fastened joints is described in Chapter 9.

7.1.1 Types of Mechanical Tests

Most tests are conducted under static tensile, compressive, or shear loading. They may also be conducted under flexural loading, which induce tensile, compressive, and shear stresses in the various zones of the specimen. The static loading may be of short duration, taking only a few minutes, as in a standard tensile test to measure strength or stiffness.

Static tests, most generally performed under tensile loading, may be also be prolonged for weeks or months, as in a creep test, to measure the long-term strength and strain stability—often at elevated temperature. These tests are usually conducted at various percentages of the short-term ultimate tensile strength, typically 10–50%.

Cyclic loading tests to measure resistance to degradation and cracking under varying loads are essentially repeated static loading.[1] The frequency of application is generally low, in the case of composites around 5–10 Hz, to avoid heating. Loading may be tension/tension, tension/compression, or reversed

213

shear at constant amplitude or under spectrum loading, and may be aimed at simulating the actual loading conditions in a particular application.

Dynamic loads are used to measure the resistance of the materials to impact or ballistic conditions. These tests are also conducted under tension, compression, shear, or flexure, or they may be conducted using an impactor or penetrator of some type. In some tests, the impact event may occur while the specimen is under tensile or compressive loading. Typically, loading occurs over a 1-millisecond time interval.

Testing may be conducted at different temperatures and levels of absorbed moisture. They may also include exposure to a range of other environmental conditions, such as UV and solvents.

The specimens may be simple coupons or they may be structural details with representative stress-raisers such as holes, filled with a fastener or open. The coupons or details may include representative damage such as sharp notches or impact damage.

Test machines consist of loading frames, one fixed and one moving crosshead, separated either by a simple electromechanical screw action or by a servo-hydraulic piston. For simple static testing, the screw-driven machines are simpler and less costly and there is less danger of overload caused by accidental rapid movement of the crosshead. However, for versatility in loading (e.g. spectrum loading in fatigue testing) and in load capacity, the servo-hydraulic machines are unmatched.

7.1.2 Special Requirements for Testing Composites

During the early development of composites, many of the test techniques used for metals and other homogenous, isotropic materials were used to determine the properties of composite materials. It was soon recognized that anisotropic composite materials often required special consideration in terms of mechanical property determination. Much of the test method development was also undertaken within individual organizations, thus standardization was difficult and many methods developed were not adequate for the newer, emerging materials.

Since those early days, there has been a great deal of effort devoted to the standardization of test methods, and there are a number of reference sources that can be used to identify the relevant techniques. Test standards have been published by the American Society for Testing and Materials (ASTM)[2-9] and the Suppliers of Advanced Composite Materials Association (SACMA),[10,11] together with other information sources such as the U.S. Department of Defense Military Handbook 17 (MIL-HDBK 17; Polymer Matrix Composites). MIL-HDBK 17 is specifically suited to composite materials for aerospace applications and is generally used for test method selection.

The test techniques briefly described here are the ones most commonly used when measuring stress and strain in the tensile, compressive, flexural, and shear load states, but they are not the only techniques that can be used. The most critical issues that must be satisfied are that the test method used accurately creates the required stress state in the material and that the specimen failure be consistent with this stress state and not be artificially influenced by the test method.

Because of the variabilties encountered in coupon testing, airworthiness authorities require multiple tests across several batches. MIL-HDBK 17 recommends a minimum of six specimens per test point and five batches of material to be tested. These requirements mean that the exploration of even a minimum of material properties entails a very large number of test specimens.

When conducting tests to determine the strength and stiffness of a composite material, the first question that must be answered is "What mode of its performance is to be measured?" Composites, as with other materials, can have significantly different mechanical properties when tested in different ways. The main loading modes that are generally of interest are tension, compression, flexure, and shear—each has its own particular test techniques and difficulties.

To facilitate design computations, the elastic properties of the composite lamina discussed in Chapter 6 are usually obtained first through simple coupon tests. Recall the relationships for in-plane elastic properties, noting that in most cases, in-plane properties will be used to design the laminate:

$$
\begin{vmatrix} \varepsilon_1 \\ \varepsilon_2 \\ \gamma_{12} \end{vmatrix} = \begin{vmatrix} 1/E_1 & -v_{12}/E_2 & 0 \\ -v_{12}/E_1 & 1/E_2 & 0 \\ 0 & 0 & 1/G_{12} \end{vmatrix} \begin{vmatrix} \sigma_1 \\ \sigma_2 \\ \tau_{12} \end{vmatrix}
$$

And since $v_{12}/E_1 = v_{21}/E_2$ (See Chapter 6), only three tests are required to establish the in-plane elastic properties, in other words, $0°$ tension, $90°$ tension, and in-plane shear.

Because it is not possible to conduct tests on single plies, the coupons are laid up with multiple plies, all orientated in the same direction. The exception is the in-plane shear in which, if a $45°$ tension test is selected (see below), plies are alternated between $+$ and $-45°$ symmetric about the center line.

Strength values should not, in general, be taken from these coupons although they are very often taken to failure. The reasons for this are explained in Chapter 12. Laminate strength should be obtained from tests on representative laminates in which the orientations of the fiber lay-up are similar to those anticipated in the design. These values that are used in initial design are generally substantiated by tests on structural elements and often finally on full-scale structures. This is often referred to as the Testing Pyramid, which is illustrated in Figure 7.1.

It must be understood that issues such as scale effects[12] and complex load conditions[13] can become important when testing composite components, and the data obtained from simple coupon tests can often only be used for comparing materials and not as accurate predictions of component behavior.

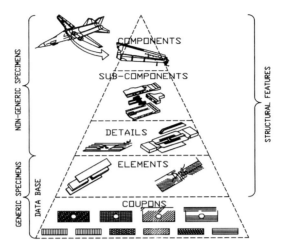

Fig. 7.1   Testing pyramid for composite structures.

7.2   Coupon Tests

7.2.1   Tension

Valid axial tension testing, particularly of strong unidirectional composites, can be a challenge. The load must be transferred from the testing apparatus into the specimen via shear, and the shear strengths of composites are often significantly lower than their tensile strength. Thus shear failure within the gripping region is often a problem.

The standard test technique (outlined in Refs. 2 and 3 for open-hole tension) describes the use of a parallel-sided, rectangular specimen with bonded end tabs. However, these tabs, which are normally made from a glass fabric/epoxy composite, are not strictly required. The key factor is the successful introduction of load into the specimen. Therefore, if acceptable failures are being obtained with reasonable consistency, then it can be assumed that the gripping method is working. A wide variety of bonded tab or unbonded shim configurations have been used successfully. One unbonded shim material sometimes used is a coarse mesh made of carborundum-coated cloth.

Load measurement is performed via the load cell in the test machine, and strain measurement is done by an extensometer secured to the specimen or by adhesively bonded strain gauges. To measure Poisson's ratio, both the axial and transverse strain must be measured concurrently. Extensometers are normally preferred because they are reusable, easier to mount, and often more reliable at elevated temperatures or in high-moisture-content environments. If strain gauges are used, then the active gauge length (length of specimen over which the strain is measured) is recommended to be at least 6 mm for tape composites and at least as large as the characteristic repeating unit of the weave for woven materials.

A successful test must cause failure within the gauge region. Failure at the tab edge (or gripped edge) or within the tab is unacceptable. Failure due to early edge delamination, which is normally caused by poor machining, is also unacceptable. Figure 7.2 illustrates typically a) unacceptable and b) acceptable specimen failures. Poor load system alignment is often a major contributor to premature failure, and it is highly desirable to evaluate system alignment with a suitably strain-gauged, alignment coupon.

7.2.2 Compression

There is still a great amount of debate among researchers as to the most appropriate method for compression testing or indeed whether there is a true axial compression test for composites.[14,15] Generally, compression failure occurs through buckling, ranging from classical column buckling of the entire specimen

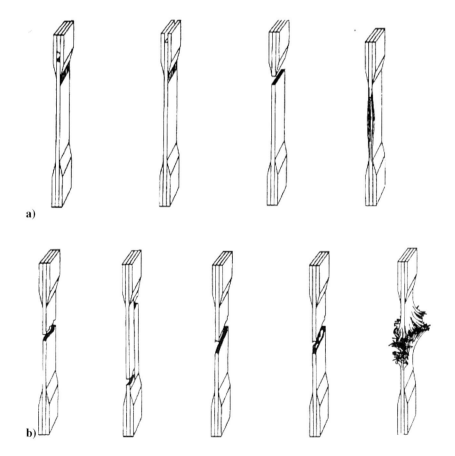

Fig. 7.2   Failure modes in tensile testing: *a*) **unacceptable;** *b*) **acceptable.**

cross-section to local microbuckling of fibers that often leads to failure through the process of kink band formation.[4] Therefore, the greater resistance to buckling the test fixture provides to the specimen, the higher the value of compressive strength that is obtained.

Many different test methods and specimen configurations have been developed over the decades in an attempt to limit specimen buckling, and there are a number of tests that have become the most widely used in current practice. The Illinois Institute of Technology Research Institute (IITRI) method,[4] which has become an ASTM standard, and the modified ASTM D695 method[10] (currently a SACMA standard), are two methods used for un-notched specimens (Figs. 7.3 and 7.4, respectively). The SACMA Recommended Test Method 3R-94[11] is commonly used for open-hole compression testing Fig. 7.5.

As with the tension test, tabs are not absolutely required for the specimen, although they are strongly recommended for specimens made with unidirectional reinforcement. The main criteria is that correct failure occurs within the gauge

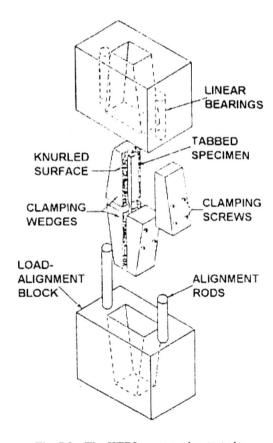

LINEAR
BEARINGS

TABBED
SPECIMEN

KNURLED
SURFACE

CLAMPING
WEDGES

CLAMPING
SCREWS

LOAD-
ALIGNMENT
BLOCK

ALIGNMENT
RODS

Fig. 7.3   The IITRI compression test rig.

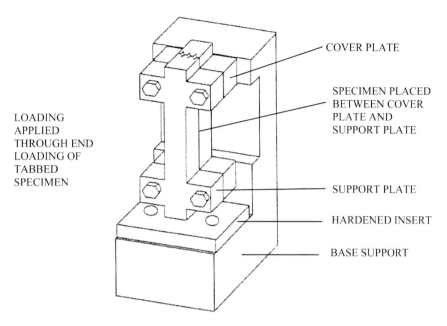

Fig. 7.4   Modified ASTM D695 compression test rig.

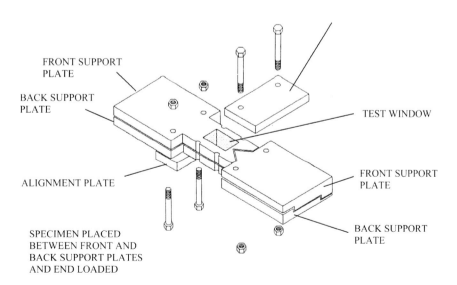

Fig. 7.5   Rig for the SACMA recommended test method 3R-94 for open-hole compression testing.

area; if this does not occur correctly, then the data point should not be used. Figure 7.6 illustrates examples of acceptable and unacceptable failures, with any failure residing solely in the tabbed or gripped region being considered unacceptable. Due to the very short gauge length, it is likely that the failure location could be near the grip/tab termination region; this is still an acceptable failure.

Compression tests are very sensitive to the flatness and parallelism of the specimens and/or tabs, and within the test specifications, the required tolerances are outlined. Gripping of the specimens and system misalignment are generally the biggest cause of data scatter, and of particular relevance to the test methods that use stabilizing lateral supports (SACMA SRM 1R-94 and 3R-94) is the issue of bolt torque. An over-torque of the bolts allows more of the applied load to be carried by the lateral supports through friction, thereby increasing the apparent compressive strength. Generally, the bolts are tightened up to a "finger-tight" level, a fairly arbitrary measurement; however studies[15] have shown that the torque should not exceed approximately 1 Nm.

7.2.3 Flexure

A flexure test is, without doubt, one of the simplest types of tests to perform and thus has long been popular (Fig. 7.7). The main difficulty is that it does not

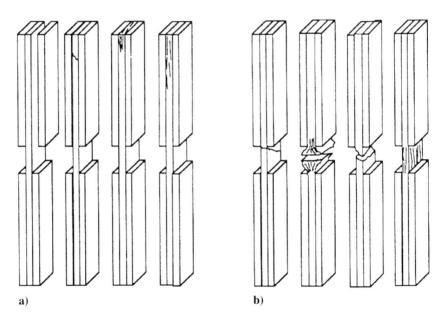

a)   b)

Fig. 7.6   Failure modes in compression testing: *a*) unacceptable; *b*) acceptable.

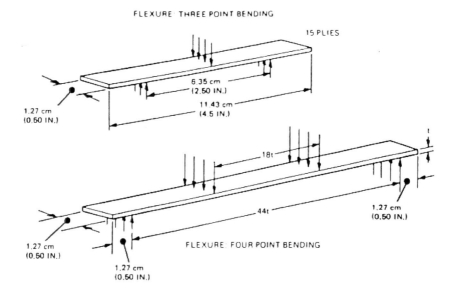

Fig. 7.7   ASTM test methods for the flexure test.

provide basic material property information because of the variation in stress-state within the specimen. The stress-state on the loading side is compression and on the supported side is tension; the mid-plane of the specimen is in pure shear. Therefore, depending on the relative values of the tension, compression, and shear strengths of the material, any one of these properties may be measured. The ratio of the support span length to specimen thickness is normally set long enough so that shear failure does not occur (32 : 1 is common) but whether failure initiates on the tensile or compressive face will be dependent on the material.

Although the flexure test does not provide basic design data, its use is normally justified if the actual components are subjected to flexure. This is a valid argument if the span length to thickness ratio is similar to the laboratory test specimens. If not, the failure mode of the component in service may be different, and thus any comparison of the laboratory testing is not valid.

The details of the standard flexure test are contained within the ASTM specification D790–84a[5] and this provides the recommended dimensions and cross-head speeds for various materials. There are two possible test configurations that can be used: three-point bending and four-point bending (Fig. 7.7). Although the three-point bending test requires less material, the four-point bending has the advantage that uniform tensile or compressive stresses (with zero shear) are produced over the area between the loading points, not just under the loading point as in three-point bending test. In the three-point test, the high local stresses at the loading point affects the failure mode and load. It should be noted that excessive bending of the specimen before failure can render the test invalid due to slipping of the specimen over the support points. This situation is discussed within the test specification.

In specimens with sandwich construction having relatively thin skins on a honeycomb (or other suitable) core, loading in flexure simultaneously provides tensile stresses in one skin and compressive stresses in the other. This form of testing is particularly advantageous for compression testing of composites because a much larger area of skin can be tested than is possible in the standard tests, and the loading is far more realistic.

7.2.4 Shear

Shear testing of composites is often a cause of confusion. Many different test procedures have been used, and only now are some gaining acceptance. This situation is hampered by the fact that many techniques cannot provide both shear strength and modulus from the one test.

The ideal test for shear is torsion of a thin-walled tube, which provides a pure shear stress-state, yet this method is not often used. The specimens are relatively expensive, fragile, and difficult to hold and align correctly, and the technique requires a torsion-testing machine of sufficient capacity. Currently, the two-rail shear test[6] (Fig. 7.8) and the Iosipescu test[7] (Fig. 7.9) are the most commonly used, although, it should be noted that the rail shear test is currently issued by ASTM as a Standard Guide, not a Standard Method. Both of these tests are not recommended for specimens containing only $\pm 45^\circ$ fibers; rather, these specimens should be tested using the method outlined in Ref. 8, which involves the use of a routine tensile test.

Difficulties can arise when using the rail shear test because the specimens generally fail by out-of-plane buckling, therefore the measured values of strength and strain will be affected. Stress concentrations can also occur at the rail attachments, and suitable design of the rail area is critical to prevent failure occurring here. Due to these problems, shear data obtained using this test is often questioned.

The Iosipescu test, nevertheless, is gaining in popularity due to having none of the disadvantages of the rail shear test and having the added advantages of using much less material and producing an essentially pure shear stress; however, shear stress concentrations develop at the root of the notches. Another advantage is that the test can be used to measure shear properties in any orientation. Thus, the Iosipescu method can be used to provide interlaminar shear properties by machining the specimen so that the interlaminar plane is parallel to the plane of the gauge area. The test specification contains recommendations for dimensions, but it is critical that the gauge area contain a sufficient number of fabric repeat units to ensure material properties are obtained. ASTM gives no guidelines on this but it is generally accepted that a minimum of 3 repeat units are used, therefore the specimen should be scaled up to achieve this. Twisting of the

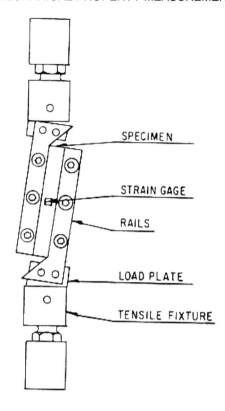

SPECIMEN

STRAIN GAGE

RAILS

LOAD PLATE

TENSILE FIXTURE

Fig. 7.8   Two-rail shear test rig.

specimen can occur during the test, therefore accurate machining (precision grinding or milling techniques) and specimen placement are critical.

The $\pm 45°$ Off-Axis Tensile Shear Test (ASTM D3518) consists of loading a $\pm 45°$ symmetric laminate uniaxially in tension. It is cheap and easy, and good correlation has been obtained with other test methods. It is argued that it provides a value more reflective of the actual stress-state in a laminated structure.

The discussion above relates to in-plane shear testing; however, for laminates there is often the need to measure interlaminar shear properties. This is normally accomplished through the use of a short-beam shear test, such as defined by ASTM D2344,[9] that is, a three-point flexure test of a very short beam (ratio of support span to specimen depth is generally less than 5). It should be noted that, although this test method provides reasonable comparative interlaminar shear strength values, it cannot provide shear stiffness or strain information. MIL-HDBK 17 does not recommend its use for strength prediction, however this is sometimes done on the absence of other data.

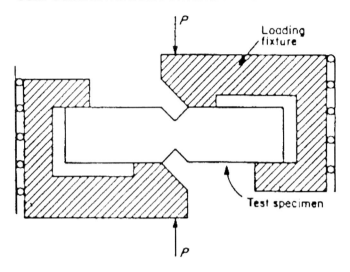

Fig. 7.9   Iosipescu shear test rig.

7.2.5 Fatigue

Due to the very good fatigue performance of high volume-fraction carbon fiber composite materials, there has been less emphasis on this aspect of performance than on other mechanical properties. Constant amplitude fatigue testing on undamaged coupons under axial load exhibit very flat S-N curves, indicating an insensitivity of life to cyclic load.

Fatigue performance is, however, influenced by the presence of damage and out-of-plane loading, and consequently testing is usually concentrated at the detail, sub-element, and full-scale levels, where realistic loading can be applied. As a consequence, there are no standard coupon tests recommended by testing or material authorities. Typical specimens include lap joints of both bonded and mechanically fastened configuration, stiffener run-outs, and cut-out panels. It is common to introduce damage (typically impact damage; see Chapter 12) to the expected critical areas of these specimens, and testing involves measurement of any growth of this damage.

There are increasingly moves towards developing techniques for predicting damage growth under cyclic loading using fracture mechanics approaches; however, most designs still resort to demonstration of the unlikelihood of no-flaw-growth through the service life of the aircraft.

This is not usually penalizing because the static strength reduction arising from the introduction of flaws, damage, or stress raisers means that working stresses are below the fatigue limit.

Despite the apparent resistance to fatigue, no major composite structure has been certified without a full-scale test. These tests usually include demonstration of minimum residual strength after fatigue load cycling and with the presence of damage. A typical program would be:

(1) Fatigue spectrum testing to two or more lifetimes with minor (barely visible) damage present
(2) Static ultimate load test
(3) Introduction of obviously visible damage by way of impacts and saw-cuts
(4) Fatigue cycle for a period equivalent to two or more inspection intervals
(5) Static limit load test
(6) Repair damage
(7) Fatigue for a further lifetime
(8) Residual strength test

The above would mean that all full-scale testing could be accomplished on a single structure, and although the program appears fairly conservative, it covers the fact that there is considerable scatter in fatigue life.

A point to note is that, although high volume-fraction carbon/epoxy and other carbon fiber–based laminates exhibit extremely good fatigue resistance, this is not the case for lower stiffness laminates such as glass/epoxy. These materials tend only to be used for personal aircraft and gliders for which the airworthiness requirements are less stringent.

7.3 Laboratory Simulation of Environmental Effects

The moisture content levels typically found in composite materials after many years of long-term service can be simulated in the laboratory using environmental chambers. Although the exact moisture profile present in components exposed to the elements cannot be easily reproduced, a good indicator of material performance can be gained by exposing the composite to a humidity level representative of the operating conditions until an equilibrium moisture content is achieved. MIL-HDBK 17 recommends that a humidity level of 85% represents a worst-case humidity level for operating under tropical conditions.

The simulation of the combination of mechanical loading and environmental conditions such as humidity and moisture can also be simulated in the laboratory through the use of servo-hydraulic testing machines and environmental generators (see Section 7.3.2).

7.3.1 Accelerated Moisture Conditioning

Conditioning composite materials to a particular moisture content can be a time-consuming process. This process can be shortened if care is taken with regard to the exposure conditions. The obvious means to accelerated conditioning is to increase temperature. This is a valid approach provided that the mode of diffusion remains unchanged and that no matrix damage is introduced.

MIL-HDBK 17 recommends conditioning at a level of up to 77°C for 177°C curing composites and 68°C for 121°C curing composites. The use of boiling water to condition composites, as sometimes occurs, is unlikely to faithfully represent exposure conditions. A higher initial humidity level can be used to force moisture more rapidly into the sample center before equilibrium is achieved at the target humidity level. MIL-HDBK 17 notes that this practice is acceptable provided the humidity level does not exceed 95% relative humidity (RH). This method was published by Ciriscioli et al.[16] and describes a method for the accelerated testing of carbon/epoxy composite coupons that has been validated using mechanical testing.

7.3.2 Combined Loading and Environmental Conditioning

The combination of representative loading with environmental conditioning is perhaps the best way to determine the effects of environment on composites in a short space of time in the laboratory. One such method, ENSTAFF, exists for use and includes flight types as well as ground storage conditions. The ENSTAFF[17] method of accelerated testing combines mission profiles, cyclic loads, environment, and associated temperature excursions during typical combat aircraft usage. A service condition, including loads and environment, is defined for each aircraft component, and these conditions are then applied in a reduced time frame. This allows many "flights" to be performed within a relatively short time and allows the prediction of the part performance over an extended period. The standard is designed specifically for testing of composite materials for the wing structure of combat aircraft operating under European conditions. ENSTAFF has been acknowledged by European aircraft manufacturers to cover the design criteria for composite structure in new fighter aircraft. It is applicable for tests performed at both coupon and structural level. The standard was developed jointly by West Germany, the Netherlands, and the United Kingdom.

Temperature changes due to aerodynamic heating, temperature variation with altitude, and solar radiation are all included and superimposed onto any load that may be experienced. A moisture level in the sample representing exposure to a humidity of 85% RH is maintained at all times. This is achieved by pre-conditioning the sample before testing and re-conditioning when moisture is lost. ENSTAFF is conservative in its approach in that all loads and temperature cycles are carried out at the maximum moisture content produced at the worst-case 85% RH condition. Typical service conditions will produce moisture contents below this level.

Although ENSTAFF represents a quite realistic way of accelerated testing, it must be noted that long-term degradation mechanisms (if present) may not be adequately represented by this method. This includes mechanisms such as UV exposure, erosion, or chemical reactions that may change the material properties.

7.4   Measurement of Residual Strength

For metallic structures, the term *residual strength* is used to define the strength of a structure after the formation of cracks, for example, by fatigue or stress corrosion. Because composite structures are brittle in nature and sensitive to the presence of even slight damage, the definition of residual strength includes its static strength when damage due to low-energy-level impacts or other flaws are present. Although high energy may lead to penetration with a little or no local delamination in a laminate, low energy may cause damage in the form of local fracture of the fibers, delamination, disbonding, or matrix cracking. These defects can occur with little visible surface damage [damage commonly known as barely visible impact damage (BVID)]. Low-energy impact damage is a concern to the composite structural designers because it may not be visible on the surface but may cause the reduction of residual strength of the structure. Numerous researchers have extensively studied the effect of impact damage on the static and fatigue strengths of composite structures. It has been demonstrated that impact damage is of more concern in compression than in tension loading, and consequently residual strength testing is usually carried out under compression loading.

Defects may arise during various stages of manufacture of materials and processing, machining, drilling, trimming, and assembly and accidental handling, or during service of the component. Some of the possible defects are summarized in Table 7.1.

Residual strength in the presence of these defects depends on various parameters such as structure, geometry, size and shape, material, damage type and its size, loading, and environmental exposure. Figure 7.10 from Ref. 18 shows the relative severity of defects such as porosity, delamination, open or filled hole, and impact damage on static strength for carbon/epoxy composite laminates. The important issue of impact damage on residual strength is discussed further in Chapters 8, 12, and 13.

Of all defects, impact damage appears to be the most critical. The laminate will typically lose up to 50% or more of its original static strength after an impact that may be barely visible to the naked eye. Consequently, most residual strength testing is carried out on coupons and structures containing impact damage, and it is assumed that this will encompass the effects of the other defects.

The following section deals with the measurement of residual strength through testing and with the reduction of the generated data.

7.4.1   Coupon Testing

The design of a suitable coupon test program will depend on the methods that are intended and be used in establishing values for subsequent design, often termed *design allowables.* It is sometimes assumed that flaws and service damage can be represented by holes in test coupons. A 0.25-inch (6-mm) hole in a 1.0-inch

Table 7.1   Types and Causes of Defects in Composite Structures During
Manufacture and Service

Cause	Process	Defect type
Manufacturing	Part lay-up	Fibre breakage; ply missing, ply cut, ply wrinkling or waviness, ply distortion, ply overlap, incorrect lay-up or missing plies, foreign objects inclusion, etc.
	Curing	Low or high local curing temperatures causing unevenly cured part or burn marks on surface, resin richness, resin starvation or dryness, porosity or voids, disbond or delamination, etc.
	Handling, machining, and assembly	Scratches, gouges or dents, damaged, over-size, distorted, mislocated or misoriented holes, impact damages
In service defects		Impact damage by runway debris, bird strike, vehicles, hailstones, and maintenance tools
		Lightning strike
		Environmental damage

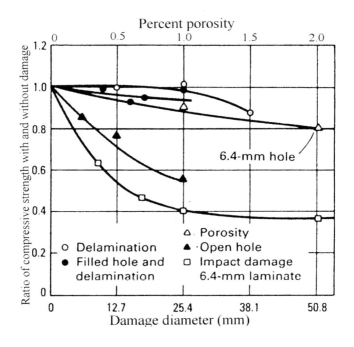

Fig. 7.10   Effect of damage diameter on compression strength.

(25-mm) wide specimen is often chosen as such a representative specimen. The evidence suggests that this is a reasonable assumption (Fig. 7.10) but is somewhat unconservative for the representation of certain impacts. The preferred approach is to apply an impact to a specimen of a specified energy using an impactor such as the one shown in Figure 7.11 and to obtain compression-after-impact (CAI) strength from a subsequent compression test on the impacted specimen.

The specimen configuration most widely used is given in Ref. 19. These specimens are 11.5×7.0 inches (292×178 mm) and are designed to represent a typical panel when constrained by supports on each of the four sides during the impact.

The appropriate impact energy is calculated as a function of laminate thickness from the formula:

$$\text{Impact energy} = 960 \, (\pm 20) \text{ inch lbs inch}^{-1}$$

$$(4.27 \pm 0.09 \text{ joules mm}^{-1}) \text{ laminate thickness}$$

This is assumed to be sufficient to inflict damage to the extent defined as *barely visible* (BVID) (see Chapter 12).

The specimen is trimmed after impact to 10.0×5.0 inches (254×127 mm) and mounted in a fixture such as illustrated in Figure 7.12 for compression testing. The fixture is designed to support the specimen from buckling. The side supports are a snug fit, yet they allow the specimen to slide in a vertical direction. A 0.05-inch (1.25-mm) clearance is provided between each side of the specimen to prevent any transverse load due to Poisson's deformation during the test. The upper and lower edges of the specimen are clamped between steel plates to prevent brooming. The loading rate is approximately 0.05 inches min^{-1}.

In some cases, the specimens are conditioned in a hot/wet environment after impact and before compression testing. The period of exposure is to last until the specimens are saturated. This is determined by repeated weighing until the weight stabilizes, indicating that no more moisture can be absorbed. For most carbon/epoxy laminates, this weight gain (i.e., moisture uptake) is around 1%. This eliminates the need to apply any subsequent "knockdown factor" (See Chapter 12) to the design allowable.

Test data are reduced as follows:

$$\text{CAI strength } \sigma_{\text{cai}} = P/bd$$
$$\text{compression modulus } E_{\text{cai}} = (P_3 - P_1)/0.002bd$$
$$\text{CAI failure strain } \varepsilon_{\text{cai}} = \sigma_{\text{cai}}/E_{\text{cai}}$$

where:

P = maximum load
P_3 = load at 3000 microstrain
P_1 = load at 1000 microstrain
b = average specimen width
d = number of plies $\times$ nominal ply thickness

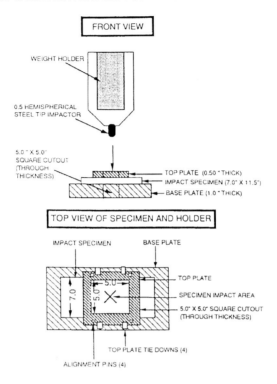

Fig. 7.11   Specimen impactor.

Residual strength testing may also be carried out on coupons with defects (impact damage or manufacturing flaws) that have also been subjected to fatigue loading. If the fatigue loading is such that the damage will grow, then clearly residual strength will be further reduced. To avoid this, most designs are based on a "no-flaw-growth" basis (see Chapter 12). This philosophy involves limiting design strain levels to a level that fatigue loading will not cause growth of a defect of a size that would otherwise be missed in a routine inspection. In most cases, this value is close to the limit strain (ultimate strain/1.5), and the compounding effect of fatigue loading may therefore be ignored. Figure 7.13 shows an example in which impact damage grew at cyclic strains below the nominal limit strain. In this case, the fatigue limit had to be set somewhat lower (at 60% limit static strain) to eliminate the possibility of growth in service.

7.4.2   Full-Scale Testing

Final qualification or certification of the airframe will usually involve demonstration of residual strength on a full-scale structure. Generally, the structure will have gone through several equivalent lifetimes of fatigue cycling to the given loading spectrum before damage is introduced by impacting in the

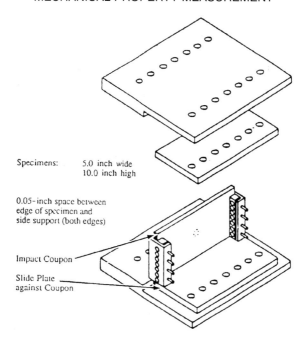

Specimens: 5.0 inch wide
                10.0 inch high

0.05-inch space between
edge of specimen and
side support (both edges)

Impact Coupon

Slide Plate
against Coupon

Fig. 7.12   Compression testing fixture.

critical locations. Fatigue loading is then continued to establish the damage growth rate. If the damage grows, the cycling must be continued from the time it is first visible until at least the next scheduled service inspection. Usually, the designers and airworthiness authorities prefer to be conservative and assume that the next inspection will miss the damage and continue for a further interval. Provided the structure has been designed to a no-flaw-growth philosophy, this will not elicit further penalty.

Mostly, full-scale tests have to be conducted at room temperature and in a nominal dry condition (actually, a significant amount of moisture is absorbed even in a laboratory environment), in which case, adjustments have to be made to the loading to account for the strength reductions at elevated temperatures. These load enhancements are effectively the reciprocal of the knockdown factors. Chapter 12 provides further explanation.

In other cases, the detrimental environmental effects are included in the test. One method used on wing structures has been to fill the wing tanks with hot water during the entire test sequence.

7.5   Measurement of Interlaminar Fracture Energy

Of major interest for practical application of polymer-matrix composites is their resistance to interlaminar fracture. This concern is also relevant to

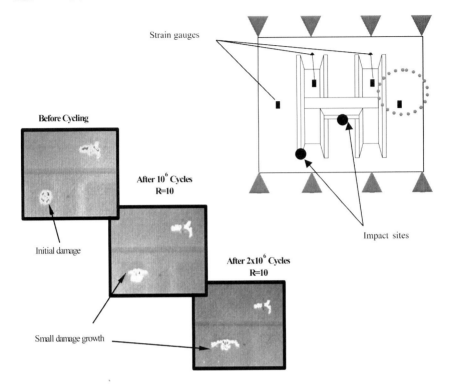

Fig. 7.13   Fatigue loaded specimens, thermography results. Peak cycle strain 0.67 ultimate. Courtesy of the Cooperative Research Centre for Advanced Composite Structures.

adhesively bonded composite joints, as discussed in Chapter 9. Interlaminar fracture toughness is much less of a concern with three-dimensional composites, as discussed in Chapter 14.

In addition to these microscopic failure mechanisms, at the macroscopic level, there are other discontinuities, such as delamination between plies that interact with crack growth. Delamination may develop during manufacturing due to incomplete curing or the introduction of a foreign object. Other sources of delamination are impact damage, cyclic loading, and interlaminar stresses that develop at stress-free edges or discontinuities. Delamination growth redistributes the stresses in the plies of a laminate and may influence residual stiffness, residual strength, and fatigue life.

In general, a delamination will be subjected to a crack driving force with a mixture of mode I (opening), mode II (forward shear), and mode III (anti-plane shear) stress intensities. Several test methods have been developed to evaluate the interlaminar fracture resistance of composites. In this section, a review of these methods is given.

7.5.1 Mode I Interlaminar Fracture Test

Double-cantilever-beam (DCB) specimens are used to measure the mode I interlaminar fracture toughness of composite laminates. There are two basic configurations of the DCB geometry: the constant width and the tapered width, as shown in Figure 7.14. In the latter geometry (because of constant strain energy release rate under a constant load), the crack length does not need to be monitored during testing. Two data-reduction methods have been applied in mode I interlaminar test compliance and fracture energy methods.

7.5.1.1 Compliance Methods. These methods are based on the Gurney and Hunt[20] critical strain energy release rate, G_{IC}, which is given by:

$$G_{IC} = \frac{P^2}{2b}\frac{dC}{da} \qquad (7.1)$$

where P is the critical load taken when the delamination crack propagates, b the specimen width, and a the crack length. Assuming a perfectly elastic and isotropic material, and taking into account the strain energy due to the bending moment compliance (C), is given by:

$$C = \frac{2a^3}{3EI} \qquad (7.2)$$

where E is the flexural modulus and I the second moment of area. Therefore, the mode I strain energy release rate in equation (7.2) for DCB specimens ($I = bh^3/12$) becomes:

$$G_{IC} = \frac{12P^2a^2}{Eb^2h^3} \qquad (7.3)$$

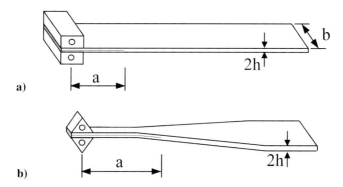

Fig. 7.14   Mode I interlaminar fracture specimens: *a*) constant width; *b*) tapered width.

Equation (7.3) also applies to the tapered-width DCB specimens where a/b is constant so that G_{IC} can be determined directly from the critical load P.

Because practical composites are mostly anisotropic/orthotropic laminates, and due to test limitations (e.g., end rotation, deflection of the crack tip) the value of the apparent elastic modulus, E, calculated from equation (7.3) varies with displacement or crack length. Therefore, by introducing some correction factors, several efforts have been made to interpret the experimental data. Some of these approaches have been simplified and used in ASTM D5528[21] standard for mode I interlaminar measuring of unidirectional composite laminates. Among these is the modified beam theory (MBT) method. In this approach:

$$G_{IC} = \frac{3P\delta}{2b(a + |\Delta|)} \qquad (7.4)$$

where δ is the displacement and Δ is a correction to the crack length to take account of the imperfectly clamped beam boundary condition and defined as the intercept on the x-axis of a plot of the cube root of compliance versus crack length. In this approach, the modulus (E), can be determined from:

$$E = \frac{64(a + |\Delta|)^3 P}{\delta b h^3} \qquad (7.5)$$

The compliance calibration (CC) method has been developed on the basis of an empirical compliance calibration, and G_{IC} is given by:

$$G_{IC} = \frac{nP\delta}{2ba} \qquad (7.6)$$

where the coefficient n is obtained from a least squares line of a log-log plot of C versus a. A further modification is made to the CC method given by equation (7.6) and proposed by JIS (Japanese Industrial Standards); in other words, the modified compliance calibration (MCC) method:[21]

$$G_{IC} = \frac{3P^2 C^{2/3}}{2\alpha_1 b h} \qquad (7.7)$$

where α is the slope of the least squares fit of the plot of a/h versus $C^{1/3}$. It is worth noting that in Ref. 22 G_{IC} values determined from three methods of data reduction—MBT, CC, and MCC methods—differed by no more than 3.1%, whereas the MBT method yielded the most conservative value of G_{IC} for 80% of the specimens tested.

7.5.1.2 Fracture Energy/Area Method.

In the fracture energy/area method, the crack extension is related to the area, ΔA, enclosed between the loading and unloading paths for extension of a known crack length, Δa, as shown in Figure 7.15. The mode I strain energy release rate in this case can be defined

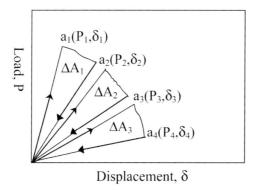

Fig. 7.15   Loading and unloading experiments used to determine the interlaminar fracture toughness based on the area method.

as:

$$G_{IC} = \frac{\Delta A}{b \Delta a} = \frac{1}{2b} \frac{P_1 \delta_2 - P_2 \delta_1}{a_2 - a_1}$$ (7.8)

By using equation (7.8), an average value of G_{IC} for an extension of crack length $a_2 - a_1$ is determined by measuring the force, P, and the corresponding displacement, δ. However, stable crack propagation is necessary for reliable application of equation (7.8). For this reason, interpretation of DCB test data should always be carried out in conjunction with an examination of the fracture surfaces, looking for lines of crack arrests.

7.5.1.3 Mode II Interlaminar Fracture Test.

Both the end-notched flexure (ENF) and the end-loaded split (ELS) specimens can be used to measure pure mode II interlaminar fracture energy (Fig. 7.16).The major difficulty of the ENF specimens, which are essentially three-point flexure specimens with an embedded delamination, is in preventing any crack opening without introducing excessive friction between the crack-faces. To overcome this, it was suggested that a small piece of PTFE 0.15-0.3-mm-thick film is inserted between crack surfaces after removing the starter film.[23]

The strain energy release rate in an ENF specimen based on linear beam theory with linear elastic behavior, and by neglecting shear deformation, is given by:

$$G_{IIC} = \frac{9Pa^2 \delta}{2b(2L^3 + 3a^3)}$$ (7.9)

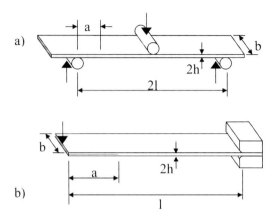

Fig. 7.16   Mode II interlaminar fracture specimens: *a*) ENF; *b*) ELS.

Due to unstable crack growth in this type of test specimen, the ELS configuration has been favored. For the ELS test, the corresponding expression for G_{IIC} is given by:

$$G_{IIC} = \frac{9 \, a^2 \, P \, \delta}{2b(L^3 + 3a^3)} \tag{7.10}$$

7.5.1.4 Mixed Mode Interlaminar Fracture Test.   Mixed mode (I and II) fracture toughness has been measured by a variety of test methods, including the cracked-lap shear (CLS) specimen, as shown in Figure 7.17. Using the CLS specimen, the force-displacement (P-δ) curves may be obtained for various crack lengths and dC/da be determined. Mixed mode fracture toughness, G_{I-IIC} can then be evaluated using equation (*7.7*), or alternatively, from Ref. 24:

$$G_{I-IIC} = \frac{P^2}{2b^2} \left[\frac{1}{(Eh)_2} - \frac{1}{(Eh)_1} \right] \tag{7.11}$$

where the subscripts 1 and 2 refer to the sections indicated in Figure 7.17. Using finite element analysis, the individual components of strain energy in mode I and II can be evaluated from the CLS test results. For unidirectional specimens with the delamination placed at the mid-plane, beam theory gives a value of $G_I/G_{I-II} = 0.205$.[25]

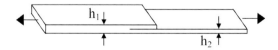

Fig. 7.17   CLS specimen for mixed mode interlaminar fracture test.

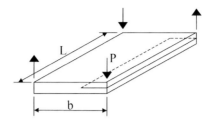

Fig. 7.18   Mode III edge crack torsion test (ECT).

7.5.1.5 Mode III Interlaminar Fracture Test.   The measurement of mode III interlaminar fracture energy can be done based on the out-of-plane torsion of a cracked plate specimen,[26] as shown in Figure 7.18. A series of edge-crack torsion (ECT) specimens with different initial crack lengths are prepared. These are loaded in torsion by pushing down on one corner. The compliance can be determined from the initial parts of the load-load point displacement plots:

$$\frac{1}{C} = A\left[1 - m\left(\frac{a}{b}\right)\right] \tag{7.12}$$

Plotting $1/C$ against a/b gives m. The strain energy release rate for mode III, G_{IIIC}, is then obtained from the expression:

$$G_{IIIC} = \frac{mP^2 C}{2Lb(1 - m(a/b))} \tag{7.13}$$

References

[1] Adams, D. F., "Test Methods for Mechanical Properties," *Comprehensive Composite Materials*, edited by A. Kelly and C. Zweben, Elsevier, 2000.

[2] "Standard Test Method for Tensile Properties of Polymer Matrix Composite Materials," ASTM Standard D3039/D3039M-95a.

[3] "Standard Test Method for Open-Hole Properties of Unidirectional or Crossply Fibre-resin Composites," ASTM D5766/D5766M-95.

[4] "Standard Test Method for Compressive Properties of Unidirectional or Crossply Fibre-resin Composites," ASTM Standard D3410/3410M-95

[5] "Flexural Properties of Unreinforced and Reinforced Plastics and Electrical Insulating Material," ASTM Standard D790-84a.

[6] "Standard Guide for Testing In-Plane Shear Properties of Composite laminates," ASTM Guide D4255/D4255-83 (94).

[7] "Standard Test Method for Shear Properties of Composite Materials by the V-Notched Beam Method," ASTM Standard D5379/D5379M-93.

[8] "Standard Test Method for In-Plane Shear Response of Polymer Matrix Composite Materials by Tensile Test of a $\pm 45°$ Laminate," ASTM Standard D3518/D3518M-94.

[9] "Standard Test Method for Apparent Interlaminar Shear Strength of Parallel Fibre Composites by Short-Beam Method," ASTM Standard D2344-84.

[10] "Compressive Properties of Oriented Fiber-Resin Composites," SACMA Recommended Test Method 1R-94.

[11] "Open Hole Compression Properties of Oriented Fiber-Resin Composites," SACMA Recommended Test Method 3R-94.

[12] Zweben, C., "Is There a Size Effect in Composites," *Composites*, Vol. 25, 199, p. 451.

[13] Chen, A. S., and Matthews, F. L., "A Review of Multiaxial/Biaxial Loading Tests for Composite Materials," *Composites*, Vol. 24, 1993, p. 395.

[14] Welsh, J. S., and Adams, D. F., "Current Status of Compression Test Methods for Composite Materials," *SAMPE Journal*, Vol. 33, 1997, p. 35.

[15] Componeschi, E. T., Jr, "Compression of Composite Materials: A Review," *Composite Materials: Fatigue and Fracture*, ASTM STP 1110, Vol. 3, p. 550.

[16] Ciriscioli, P. R., Lee, W. I., and Peterson, D. G., "Accelerated Environmental Testing of Composites," *Journal of Composite Materials*, Vol. 21, 1987, pp. 225–242.

[17] Gerharz, J. J., "Standardised Environmental Fatigue Sequence for the Evaluation of Composite Components in Combat Aircraft ENSTAFF = Environmental FalSTAFF," National Aerospace Laboratory NLR, The Netherlands, Report NLR TR 87053 U. Also published as LBF Report No. FB-179(1987), IABG Report a No. B-TF 2194 (1987), and RAE Report No. TR 87048

[18] Horton, R. E., and McCartney, J. E., "Damage Tolerance of Composites," *Composite Materials Analysis and Design*, 1984, pp. 260–267

[19] "Standard Tests for Toughened Resin Composites, Revised Edition," NASA Referenced Publication 1092—Revised 1983.

[20] Gurney, C., and Hunt, J., "Quasi-Static Crack Propagation," *Proceedings of the Royal Society of London*, Vol. A299, 1967, pp. 508–524.

[21] "Mode I Interlaminar Fracture Toughness of Unidirectional Fibre-Reinforced Polymer Matrix Composites," ASTM D5528, 1994.

[22] O'Brien, T. K., and R. H. Martin, "Round Robin Testing for Mode I Interlaminar Fracture Toughness of Composite Materials," *Journal of Composites Technology and Research*, Vol. 15, 1993, pp. 269–281.

[23] Tanaka, K., Kageyama, K. and Hojo, M., "Prestandardization Study on Mode II Interlaminar Fracture Toughness Test for CFRP in Japan," *Composites*, Vol. 26, 1995, pp. 257–267.

[24] Russel, A. J., and Street, K. N., "Moisture and Temperature Effects on the Mixed-mode Delamination Fracture of Unidirectional Carbon/Epoxy," *Delamination and Debonding of Materials*, ASTM STP 876, edited by W. S. Johnson, ASTM, Philadelphia, 1985, pp. 349–372.

[25] Brussat, T. R., Chiu, S. T., and Mostovoy, S., *Fracture Mechanics for Structural Adhesive Bonds*, AFML-TR-77-163, Air Force Materials Laboratory, Wright–Patterson AFB, Dayton, OH, 1997.

[26] Lee, S. M., "An Edge Crack Torsion Method for Mode III Delamination Fracture Testing," *Journal of Composites Technology and Research*, Vol. 15, 1993, pp. 193–201.

8
Properties of Composite Systems

8.1 Introduction

The mechanical properties of simple unidirectional continuous fiber composites depend on the volume fraction and properties of the fibers (including flaw and strength distribution), the fiber/matrix bond strength, and the mechanical properties of the matrix. The alignment (waviness) of the fibers also has a significant effect on some properties—notably, compression strength. Elevated temperature and moist environments also significantly affect properties dependent on matrix properties or interfacial strength.

Because of these and several other factors, the efficiency of translation of fiber properties into those of the composite is not always as high as may be expected. Stiffness can be predicted more reliably than strength, although static tensile strength is easier to predict than other strength properties. Chapter 2 provides some elementary equations for estimating the mechanical properties of unidirectional composites, which are reasonably accurate in estimating elastic properties, providing fiber alignment is good. The equations can also provide ball-park figures for the matrix-dominated shear and transverse elastic properties and the fiber-dominated tensile strength properties. However, estimation of matrix-dominated or fiber/matrix bond strength–dominated strength properties, including shear and compression, is complex. Prediction problems also arise when the fibers are sensitive to compression loading, as is the case for aramid fibers, as discussed later.

Chapter 7 describes the experimental procedures for measuring the mechanical properties, including those for assessing tolerance to damage and fatigue. These tests are used to develop a database for design of aerospace components and as part of the information required for airworthiness certification, as described in Chapter 12.

Table 8.1 lists relevant mechanical and physical properties of the composites discussed in this chapter. Details of aerospace structural alloys aluminum 2024 T3 and titanium 6Al4V are also provided for comparison. The nomenclature used for the properties is similar to that used in Chapter 2. The data provided for the composites can be used as an estimate of ply properties for making an approximate prediction of laminate properties.

The first four sections of this chapter provide an overview of the mechanical properties of composite systems based on glass, boron, aramid, or carbon fibers.

Table 8.1   Unidirectional Properties (Mostly Approximate) of Various Composites Considered in This Chapter and, for Comparison, Airframe Titanium and Aluminum Alloys. Based Largely on Ref. 2

	Units	Glass fiber composites		Boron	Aramid K 49	Carbon fiber composites			Al	Ti
		E	S			HT	HM	UHM		
SG	—	2.1	2.0	2.0	1.38	1.58	1.64	1.7	2.76	4.4
α_1	$\mu m/^\circ C$	7.1	6.3	4.5	-1	-0.16	—	—	23	9
α_2	$\mu m/^\circ C$	20	—	—	70	24	—	—	23	9
σ_{1tu}	MPa	1020	1620	1520	1240	1240	760	620	454	1102
σ_{1cu}	MPa	620	690	2930	275	1100	690	620	280*	1030*
σ_{2tu}	MPa	40	40	70	30	41	28	21	441	1102
τ_u	MPa	70	80	90	60	80	70	60	275	640
ILS	MPa	70	80	90	60	80	70	60	—	—
E_1	GPa	45	55	210	76	145	220	290	72	110
E_2	GPa	12	16	19	5.5	10	6.9	6.2	72	110
G_{12}	GPa	5.5	7.6	4.8	2.1	4.8	4.8	4.8	27	41
ν_{12}	—	0.28	0.28	0.25	0.34	0.25	0.25	0.25	0.33	0.31
ε_{1u}	—	0.022	0.029	0.006	0.016	0.01	0.03	0.02	0.12	0.06
ε_{2u}	—	0.4	0.4	0.4	0.5	0.4	0.4	0.3	—	—

Notes: Ti = Ti 6Al4V; Al = 2024 T3 *yield value
V_f ~60% in the composites; SG, specific gravity; ILS, interlaminar shear. See Chapters 2 and 12 for definition of other terms.

Further information on the properties of carbon-fiber composites is also provided throughout this book. In the last three sections, more generic discussion is provided on important impact, fatigue, and environmental properties, while a focus on carbon-fiber systems is maintained.

8.2   Glass-Fiber Composite Systems

As described in Chapter 3, several types of glass reinforcements are suitable for the manufacture of aircraft and helicopter composite components. E-glass composites are used extensively in gliders and in non-structural components that do not require high stiffness, such as radomes. S-glass composites have better mechanical properties and therefore are used in more demanding applications. A third type of reinforcement known as D-glass has good dielectric properties and is occasionally used in aircraft to minimize the impact of lighting strikes. E- and S-glass are used in the form of epoxy-based pre-preg or as fabrics containing unidirectional, woven, or chopped strand filaments.

A major advantage of E-glass fibers over the other types of fibers used in aircraft is their low cost. Figure 8.1 compares typical material costs for E-glass composites against costs for carbon, aramid (trade name, Kevlar), and boron/epoxy composites; the relative cost of boron pre-preg shown is divided by a factor of 10 to make the chart readable. Costs are given for composites made of pre-preg or fabric (woven roving, chopped strand mat). The costs are approximate and do not include the expense of fabricating the composite into an aircraft component, which is usually much higher than the raw material cost. E-glass composites are

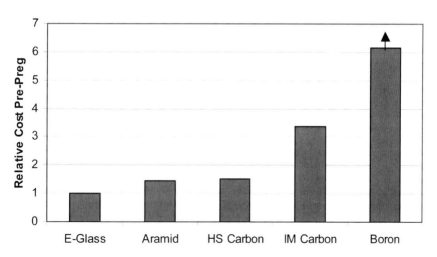

Fig 8.1   Relative costs of some fiber composite systems used in aerospace applications. Boron is shown at about 1/10 of its actual relative cost.

by far the cheapest, particularly when chopped strand mat or woven fabric is used. S-glass composites are much more expensive than the E-glass composites and only marginally less expensive than carbon/epoxy.

Figures 8.2 and 8.3 provide comparisons[1] of the strength and stiffness of some of the available forms of E-glass fiber materials. The forms are chopped-stand mat, woven rovings, and unidirectional pre-preg material. The comparisons in these figures are based on relativities that will also be relevant to the other fiber types if made from similar geometrical forms.

Table 8.1 provides relevant physical, thermal, and mechanical property data for unidirectional E- and S-glass/epoxy composites. Glass fibers have a specific gravity of about 2.5 g cm^{-3}, which is slightly lower than the density of boron fibers (2.6 g cm^{-3}) but is appreciably higher than carbon (~ 1.8 g cm^{-3}) and Kevlar (1.45 g cm^{-3}) fibers. The specific gravity of thermoset resins is around 1.3 g cm^{-3}, and as a result, glass/epoxy composites have a specific gravity that is higher than for other types of aerospace composites (except boron/epoxy) with the same fiber volume content. However, depending on the fiber volume fraction, it is still somewhat lower than that of aircraft-grade aluminum alloys (2.8 g cm^{-3}). The Young's moduli and strengths of both E- and S-glass composites are lower than those of other aerospace structural composites and metals. The combined effects of low stiffness and high specific gravity makes glass/epoxy or

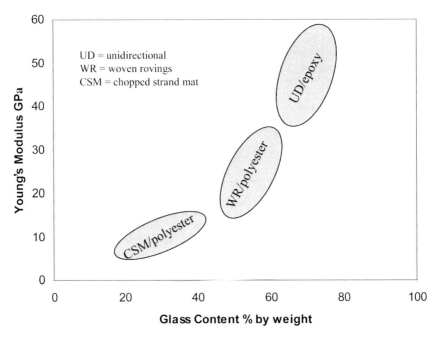

Fig 8.2 Typical Young's modulus for various types of glass-fiber composites. Adapted from Ref. 1.

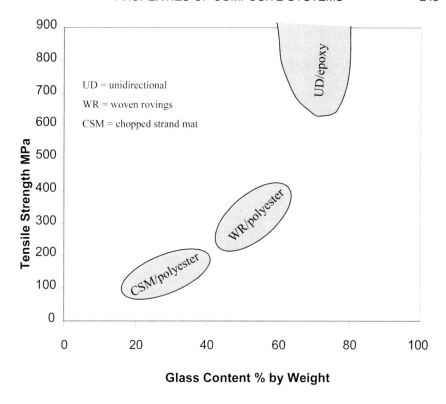

Fig 8.3   Typical strengths of various types of glass-fiber composites. Adapted from Ref. 1.

other glass fiber composites unattractive for use in weight-critical load-bearing primary structures on larger aircraft.

8.2.1   Fatigue Performance of Glass-Fiber Systems

Another drawback of using glass/epoxy composites in aircraft structures is their relatively poor fatigue performance compared with the other composites discussed in this chapter. Glass/epoxy composites are more prone to fatigue-induced damage (e.g., microscopic cracks, delaminations) and failure than other aerospace composite materials. Figure 8.4 shows a typical fatigue-life curve for a unidirectional glass/epoxy composite that was tested under cyclic tension-tension loading. Fatigue-life curves for unidirectional carbon/epoxy and Kevlar/epoxy laminates that were also tested under tension-tension loading are shown for comparison. In the figure, the normalized fatigue strain ($\varepsilon_f/\varepsilon_o$) is the maximum applied cyclic tensile strain (ε_f) divided by the static tensile failure strain of the composite (ε_o). Of the three materials, the fatigue-life curve for the glass/epoxy

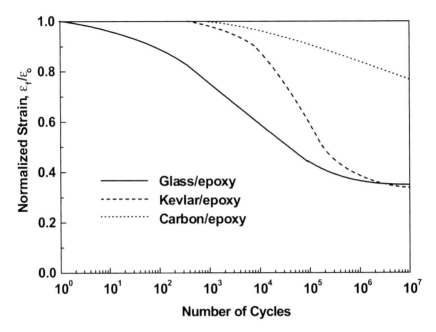

Fig 8.4   Fatigue-life curves for unidirectional composites subject to tension-tension loading.

composite drops the most rapidly, with increasing number of cycles. This indicates that glass/epoxy is the most susceptible to fatigue-induced failure under tension-tension loading, and this is due to the low stiffness of the glass reinforcement, resulting in damaging strains in the matrix, as discussed in Section 8.8.

The fatigue performance of glass/epoxy composites is degraded further when cyclic loading occurs in a hostile environment, such as in hot and wet conditions. The microscopic cracks and delaminations caused by fatigue loading create pathways for the rapid ingress of moisture into the composite. Moisture can then cause stress-corrosion damage to the glass fibers, which may dramatically reduce the fatigue life. Cracks and delaminations caused by fatigue also cause large reductions to the stiffness and strength of glass/epoxy. Figure 8.5 shows that the static tensile modulus and strength of [0/90]s glass/epoxy composites decrease rapidly with increasing number of load cycles before reaching a constant level. The residual modulus and strength remain relatively constant until near the end of the fatigue life. For some glass/epoxy materials, a reduction in stiffness and strength can occur within the early stage of the fatigue process, when the damage is not visible.

Finally, glass fibers composites and other composites having fibers with low thermal conductivity and low stiffness are prone to heat damage under cyclic

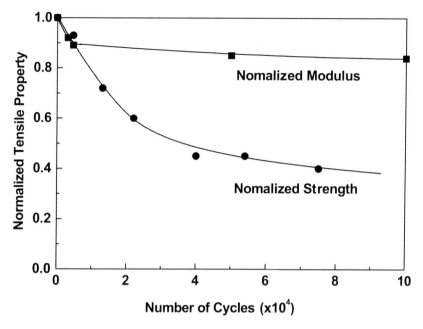

Fig 8.5   Effect of number of tensile load cycles on the Young's modulus and strength of a [0/90]ₛ glass/epoxy composite.

loading at high frequencies[2] above around 5 Hz. This is because the heat generated by stress/strain hysteresis in the polymer matrix cannot be easily dissipated. The problem increases in thick composites, in which heat dissipation is even more difficult and with off-angle fibers where matrix strains are higher.

The performance of composites under cyclic loading is discussed further in Section 8.

8.2.2 Impact Strength of Glass-Fiber Systems

Although many mechanical and fatigue properties of glass/epoxy composites are lower than those of other carbon/epoxy and aramid/epoxy materials, they generally have a superior ability to absorb energy during impact. Figure 8.6 illustrates the relative energies for failure under impact of glass fiber and other composites considered in this chapter and some aluminum alloys, as measured with the Charpy test method. The exceptionally high impact toughness of S-glass fibers has led to their use in ballistic protective materials.

As shown, glass/epoxy composites have the highest impact energies, with S-glass/epoxy composites being 4–7 times more impact-resistant than high-strength carbon/epoxy laminates and about 35 times more resistant than high-modulus carbon/epoxy materials. Glass/epoxy composites are even 9–11 times more impact-resistant on this basis than aircraft-grade aluminum alloy.

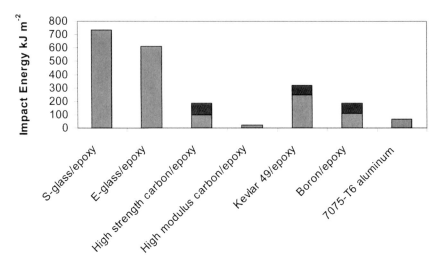

Fig 8.6   Charpy impact energy absorption of some composite and, for comparison, non-composite materials, as indicated.

8.2.3   Stress and Environmental Effects

As discussed in Chapter 3, glass fibers are prone to fracture when subjected to high stress for prolonged periods of time. This behavior, known as static fatigue or stress rupture, is exacerbated by exposure to moisture, as shown in Figure 8.7.

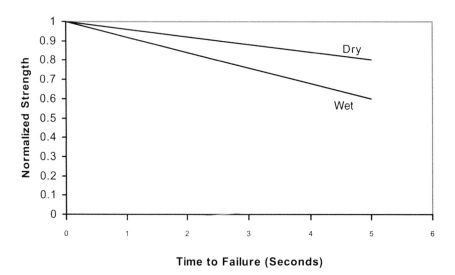

Fig 8.7   Stress rupture strength of E-glass fibers in air and water. Adapted from Ref. 1.

The influence of moisture on fiber strength is much reduced if the fiber is embedded in a polymer matrix, but can still be of concern in highly loaded applications such as pressure vessels.

Glass fiber composites, when exposed to moist environments or other aggressive environments, are also prone to degradation caused by weakening of the fiber/matrix interface. This weakening generally occurs by chemical attack at the fiber surface. The degree of weakening experienced depends on the matrix, the coating (called size or finish) used on the fiber, and the type of fiber. Weakening of the interface will result in significant loss in matrix-dominated mechanical properties such as shear, off-angle, and compression strength.

Environmental degradation is thus of significant concern for structural applications in which the ability to carry high loads is required and particularly where the loading is sustained.

8.3 Boron Fiber Composite Systems

Boron fibers (Chapter 3) were first discovered in 1959 and were subsequently developed during the 1960s into the first true high-performance fibers. Until that time, glass fiber was the only other high-strength fiber available in continuous lengths, and the low modulus of glass severely restricted its use in high-performance structures. The high-temperature capability of boron also provided the opportunity for producing metal-matrix composites, although it was a boron/epoxy (b/ep) composite that produced much of the initial commercial success. These composites were used successfully in several important aircraft component programs during the 1970s including the skins of the horizontal stabilizers on the F-14 and the horizontal and vertical stabilizers and rudders on the F-15. Boron/epoxy pre-preg materials are currently available in commercial quantities, and their unique properties make them suited to a range of specialized applications.

Because of the presence of a dense tungsten boride core (Chapter 3), the diameter of boron fibers is significantly greater than that of carbon fibers, to minimize fiber density and to ensure the properties of the fiber are not greatly influenced by the properties of the core. Fibers are currently produced in 100- and 140-μm diameters and therefore boron fibers have a very high bending stiffness (proportional to the fourth power of the radius). This restricts the radius that the composite can be formed into. For the 100-μm diameter fibers, a radius of around 30 mm is the practical limit. Although this is not of concern in the production of large, relatively flat aircraft components, it is sometimes a limiting factor in the selection of this composite system for the manufacture of a part with complex geometry.

The large diameter of boron fibers means that it is virtually impossible to weave these fibers into a fabric in the same way that glass, kevlar, and carbon fibers can. It is, however, possible to hold parallel boron fibers together with a weft thread of polyester to form a dry unidirectional preform. Boron pre-pregs are unidirectional and have a fine polyester scrim material (similar to that in structural film adhesives) incorporated into the resin on one side of the fibers to provide some lateral strength to the pre-preg during handling.

8.3.1 Mechanical Properties of Boron-Fiber Systems

Typical properties of unidirectional boron/epoxy composites are shown in Table 8.1. Boron composites typically have high compressive strength due to the large-fiber diameter, and this is one of their distinguishing features compared with carbon composites. Most of the advanced composite systems provide a significant improvement in specific stiffness over the conventional aircraft metallic materials, which have a common specific stiffness of around 25 GPa. Also apparent from Table 8.1 is the fact that although the density of cured boron composites is higher than carbon composites, it is appreciably lower than that of aluminum or titanium.

There are several types of carbon fibers on the market, some of which have properties that the densites of exceed either the tensile modulus or strength of boron fibers. Boron fiber composites, however, still have a blend of tensile and compressive properties that no single carbon fiber type is able to match. A form of pre-preg is available in which boron and carbon fibers are mixed together in the same pre-preg and this is marketed by Textron Specialty Materials as Hy-Bor. The properties of this material exceed those of conventional boron/epoxy composite due to the higher volume fraction of fibers.

8.3.2 Handling and Processing Properties of Boron-Fiber Systems

Boron is an extremely hard material with a Knoop value of 3200, which is harder than tungsten carbide and titanium nitride (1800–1880) and second only to diamond (7000). Cured boron composites can be cut, drilled, and machined with diamond-tipped tools, and the pre-pregs are readily cut with conventional steel knives. In practice, the knives cannot actually cut the hard fibers; however, gentle pressure fractures the fibers with one or two passes. Although it is possible to cut complex shapes with the use of templates, laser-cutting has been shown to be the most efficient way to cut a large amount of non-rectangular boron plies.

Boron fibers are currently available in several forms. As well as the two fiber diameters, pre-pregs are available with either 120°C or 175°C curing epoxies. With the exception of the reduction in formability mentioned above, in most other aspects, boron pre-pregs handle and process in a similar fashion to the more common carbon pre-preg materials.

8.3.3 Aircraft Applications of Boron-Fiber Composites

The fiber manufacturing process described in Chapter 3 shows that the fibers are produced as monofilaments on an expensive precursor filament, and this basic method has not changed since the early 1960s. This is the main reason that boron fibers are more costly than carbon fibers (an equivalent quantity of boron/epoxy pre-preg is roughly 12 times the price of carbon/epoxy pre-preg). The high cost of boron fiber was, initially, not critically important in defense applications and, because of its excellent specific mechanical properties, was selected for some of the empennage skins in the F-14 and F-15, and is also used in the B-1 bomber, in several components. However, in the 1970s, as the quantity of carbon fiber production rapidly increased, the cost of carbon fibers fell considerably, so that for most common aircraft applications, it became a more cost-effective fiber than boron in other than specialized applications.

One application for which boron/epoxy is well suited is as a repair material for defective metallic structures.[3] When repairs to aircraft components are considered, for example, the amount of boron/epoxy required is usually not great, and so the comparatively high cost of the material is not a critical factor. The high specific tensile and compressive properties of b/ep are ideally suited to repair applications. Carbon/epoxy can also be used for these applications; however, this material has several disadvantages. Because repairs are adhesively bonded to the structure with high-temperature curing adhesives, the lower coefficient of expansion of carbon/epoxy results in higher residual stresses in the repaired structure. These residual stresses can increase the local stresses at the defect. In addition, carbon fibers are electrically conducting, which inhibits the use of eddy-current non-destructive inspection methods through the repair material to confirm that there has been no growth of the damage. Boron fibers do not produce a galvanic couple with aluminum, so there is no danger of a boron repair causing corrosion of an aluminum aircraft structure.

8.4   Aramid Fiber Composite Systems

When Kevlar 49/epoxy composites were introduced by DuPont in the mid 1960s, they had a higher specific tensile strength than similar composites, based on the then available carbon fibers. However, the subsequent development of carbon fibers with greatly improved strength properties displaced aramid composites from this position. Now they fill a property gap in specific strength and stiffness between glass and carbon fibers.[4]

In contrast to their high tensile properties, compression strength of aramid composites is low. Under compression loading, aramid fibers[5] undergo non-linear deformation at strain levels around 0.5% by the formation of kink bands. Essentially, this mode of deformation occurs because the extended chain structure of the aramid fibers is unstable under compression loading. Figure 8.8 illustrates the extreme asymmetry in stress/strain behavior tension and compression loading for a typical aramid/epoxy composite.

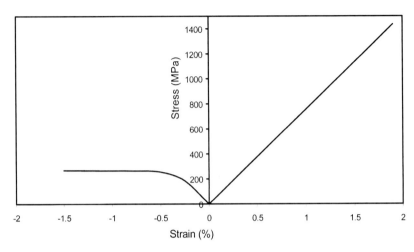

Fig 8.8   Typical tensile and compression stress-strain curves for aramid composites at ambient temperature. Adapted from Ref. 4.

The low compression resistance of aramid composites is a major disadvantage in applications requiring high strength or stiffness under compression or flexural loading. However, the non-linear behavior in compression, combined with a high strain capacity under tension, is a significant advantage in applications in which resistance to severe mechanical contact or penetration is required. Thus, in aerospace applications, aramid composites were favored for use in secondary structures such as fairings subject to impact damage. Thin-skin honeycomb panels based on aramid fibers were used extensively in some civil applications; however, the skins suffered from severe moisture penetration. This problem was mainly attributed to microcracking of the skins, possibly caused in part by moisture absorption and swelling of the fibers, coupled with the relatively weak fiber-to-resin bond strength.

The properties of high tensile strength and resistance to penetration damage continue to favor aramid composites for use in filament-wound vessels and for containment rings in engines. Ballistic protection is another important use of aramid composites, for example, in structural or non-structural components on helicopters for protection against small arms fire.

Finally, aramid fibers are used as the reinforcement in aircraft radomes, as they have favorable dielectric properties.

For components that require both good compressive properties and impact resistance, aramid fibers may be used in combination with carbon or glass fibers. They can be used to enhance the toughness properties of carbon-fiber composites or to improve strength in the presence of stress raisers. Hybrid aramid/carbon composites have been used in helicopter fuselage panels and in civil aircraft for fairings.

8.4.1 Manufacturing Issues with Aramid Composites

A significant issue in manufacturing aramid-fiber composites is the difficulty in achieving adhesion between the fibers and polymer matrix. Thus, the fibers must be surface-treated to enhance adhesion. However, in some applications, notably those requiring good ballistic properties, a fairly low-level of adhesive strength between fiber and matrix is desirable to obtain optimum energy absorption properties. In the case of aramid filament-wound pressure vessels, burst strength is highest at some intermediate level of bond strength.

Various treatments have been used to improve fiber/matrix adhesion,[6] including gas plasma treatment in Ar, N_2, or CO_2, which typically results in a 20% improvement in interfacial bond strength to epoxy.

Aramid fibers absorb moisture, up to around 6% by weight, if exposed to a humid environment. This can affect fiber/matrix adhesion and other properties, so the fibers are either stored in low humidity conditions or dried before usage.

8.4.1.1 Matrix Systems for Aramid Composites.

Some thermoset resin systems such as anhydride-cured bisphenol A epoxies are inherently more compatible with aramid fibers than other matrix resins and provide relatively high interlaminar strengths. Vinyl esters are more compatible with aramid fiber than polyesters and are used for marine-type applications. To obtain optimum tensile properties, it is important that the resin has high elongation. About 6% appears to provide the best balance of properties. Thermoplastic such as PEEK and polysulphones can also be successfully used. However, as processing temperatures can exceed 260°C in the case of polysulphones, and as high as 400°C in case of PEEK, there is some degradation of the fiber strength.

8.4.1.2 Cutting, Drilling and Machining Aramid Composites.

The high toughness of aramid fibers, including their tendency to defibrillate (separate into microfilaments) under high compressive and shear stresses, makes aramid composites very difficult to cut or machine. Indeed, dry aramid cloths themselves are difficult to cut and require the use of special shears, although heavy-duty upholstery scissors can be used. Special carbide-tipped tools are required for drilling and machining. Water jet is an excellent method for cutting aramid composites and also minimizes the creation of airborne fibers.

8.4.2 Mechanical Properties of Aramid Composites

As mentioned previously, under tensile loading, the strength of aramid/epoxy pre-preg laminates can match or exceed those of similar carbon/epoxy or glass/epoxy composites. Their elastic modulus is below that of carbon/epoxy but exceeds that of glass/epoxy. Typical values, including those for similar carbon and E-glass/epoxy composites, are listed in Table 8.1 The Table shows that although the elastic modulus is similar under tension and compression loading, strength is much reduced. Apparent interlaminar shear strength (ILSS) is also relatively low compared with the other composites. One reason for this is the low fiber/matrix bond strength. Another reason is the poor compression properties of these composites because failure in the standard short-beam ILSS test is rarely pure shear and often includes a significant component of compression failure.

8.4.2.1 Fatigue Resistance.
Under tensile-dominated cyclic loading, as illustrated schematically in Figure 8.9, unidirectional aramid composites are superior to aluminum alloys and to S-glass/epoxy composites but inferior to carbon/epoxy (not shown). For unidirectional composites, the fatigue damage occurs mainly as matrix microcracking. As may be expected, the rate of damage accumulation depends on the strain level experienced by the matrix, which is directly dependent on the fiber elastic modulus and volume fraction—hence, the relative ranking. The relative advantage of the composites over aluminum alloys is reduced in cross-plied laminates, normally used in aircraft structures. Nevertheless, a marked advantage over aluminum alloys is maintained for the aramid- and carbon-fiber composites.

As is to be expected from the poor compression strength of the fibers, aramid composites are inferior to both glass and carbon composites under compression-dominated fatigue.

8.4.2.2 Creep and Stress Rupture.
Aramid fibers and composites have a similar low creep rate to glass fibers but, as illustrated in Figure 8.10, they are less

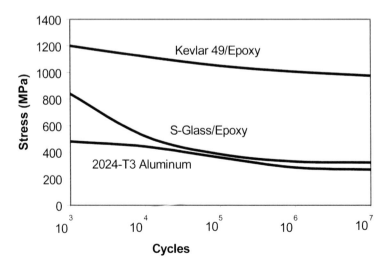

Fig 8.9   Plot of tension-tension fatigue results for unidirectional composites and for an aluminum alloy. Adapted from Ref. 4.

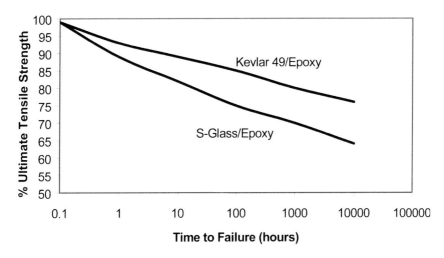

Fig 8.10   Stress rupture properties of unidirectional aramid and glass fibers in epoxy resin. Adapted from Ref. 4.

prone to stress rupture. Glass fibers are particularly sensitive to humid environments, where they have much lower stress rupture properties. Generally, carbon fibers are significantly more resistant to creep and stress rupture than glass or aramid fibers. Although, in unidirectional composites, the creep behavior is dominated by the fiber properties, the relaxation of the matrix makes a small contribution to the relatively short-term creep behavior. The creep rate increases and the stress rupture decreases as a function of both temperature and humidity.

8.4.2.3 Environmental Effects.   Aramid fibers absorb moisture; at 60% relative humidity, the equilibrium moisture content is about 4%, which rises to around 6% when the RH is 100%. The result is a decrease of tensile strength and stiffness at room temperature of around 5% (probably significantly greater at elevated temperature), which would be reflected in the properties of the composite. However, the effect of moisture on the fibers appears to be reversible. Tensile strength of the dry fiber is reduced by up to 20% at 180°C. Room temperature strength is also reduced by about 20% after prolonged (80 h) exposure at 200°C.

The effects of temperature and moisture on tensile and compression properties are illustrated in Figure 8.11. Tensile properties are unaffected up to a relatively high temperature (177°C) when the loss is around 30% hot/wet. The loss in compression strength at this temperature is quite dramatic and is around 70%. However, similar carbon/epoxy composites would also experience a significant loss of compression strength under wet conditions close to the cure temperature.

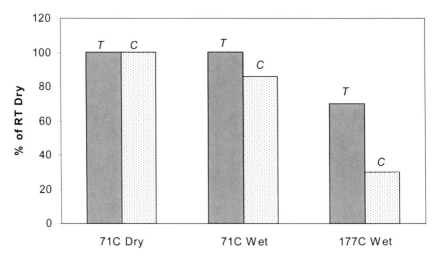

Fig 8.11 **Effect of temperature and moisture on tensile T and compression strength C of Kevlar 49/epoxy composites in a 171 °C cure epoxy resin, compared with value at room temperature. Adapted from Ref. 4.**

8.4.3 Other Useful Properties of Aramid Composites

8.4.3.1 Impact and Ballistic Properties.   Aramid composites have the capacity to absorb large amounts of energy during penetration (Figure 8.12). In part, this is due to the high strain-to-failure and moderate elastic modulus that

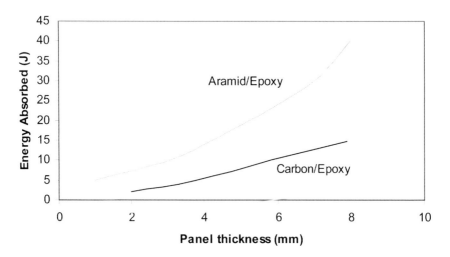

Fig 8.12   Drop-weight impact resistance of aramid/epoxy (Kevlar 49) and carbon/ epoxy (Thornel 300) quasi isotropic laminates in Hexcell F-155 resin. The energy parameter is for through-cracking, but not penetration. Adapted from Ref. 4.

results in a very large area under the stress-strain curve. This is an indication of the large energy-absorbing capacity of aramid composites in tension. In addition, the complex fiber-failure modes involving kinking in compression and defibrillization during final fracture, together with the strong tendency for disbonding, greatly add to the energy-absorbing capacity of aramid composites under dynamic loading.

One way of comparing ballistic performance of composite laminates is based on the V_{50} parameter. This is the velocity at which there is a 50% probability that the projectile will penetrate a target of the laminate. The V_{50} number for laminates of a given areal density is one way of making the comparison, where the areal density is the thickness multiplied by the density. Alternatively, the areal density for a given V_{50} can be used as the basis of comparison. Figure 8.13 shows results for a Kevlar (aramid) composite compared with S- and E-glass composites. This shows that S-glass composites provide a level of protection similar to that of aramid, and that both are much superior to E-glass and an aluminum alloy.

8.4.3.2 Vibration Damping. Composites based on aramid fibers exhibit very high damping qualities, particularly under reversed cyclic loading. In part, the high damping results from the non-linear deformation of the fibers in compression. This is an important advantage of aramid-fiber composites for aircraft applications where reduced noise and vibration are design objectives. Figure 8.14 illustrates the damping behavior of aramid composites compared with some other structural materials also having relatively high damping.

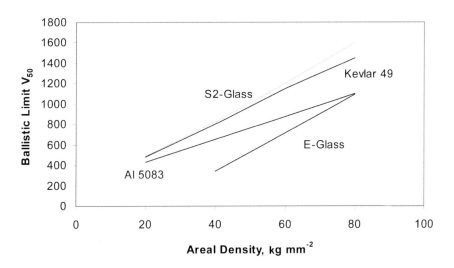

Fig 8.13 Relative ballistic performance of lightweight armor materials. Adapted from Ref. 4.

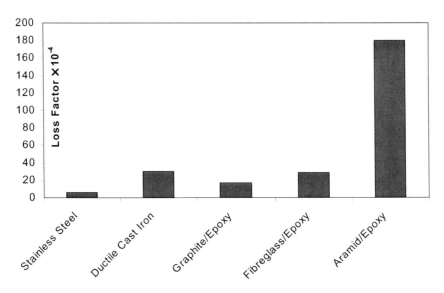

Fig 8.14   Loss factor from decay of free vibration for various materials. Adapted from Ref. 4.

8.4.3.3 Aramid Composites for Pressure Vessels and Containment rings.   Aramid composites are particularly well suited for use as pressure vessels because of their excellent specific tensile properties and their resistance to mechanical damage. The comparative performance of pressure vessels is often made on the basis of the parameter PV/W where PV is pressure $\times$ volume and W is the weight. A comparison on this basis of pressure vessels made with the three fiber types in epoxy matrices is shown in Figure 8.15. The influence of a 20-J impact on strength, adapted from some relevant data, is also shown.

As a result of their excellent performance under pressure loading and their damage resistance, aramid composites are frequently used as containment rings for jet engines, which prevent fractured engine parts (such as broken blades), exiting the casing of the engine, and damaging other parts of the aircraft.

8.4.3.4 Properties of Aramid-Hybrid Composites.   As discussed earlier, hybridization with fairly low volume fractions of aramid composites can be used to reduce stress concentrations around holes or cut-outs or to improve resistance to impact damage in carbon-fiber-based composites and to improve stiffness in glass/epoxy composites. Alternatively, carbon-fiber composites can be hybridized with aramid to improve toughness while maintaining the favorable compression strength properties of the carbon-fiber composites.

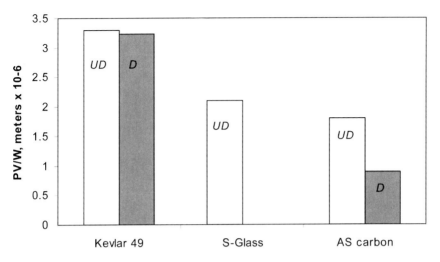

Fig 8.15   Performance of damaged (D) and undamaged (UD) pressure vessels made in the various composites. Adapted from Ref. 4.

Figure 8.16 shows the effectiveness of using 20% of 0° aramid layers in a quasi isotropic carbon/epoxy composite to improve open-hole tensile strength. The high-strain aramid fibers inhibit propagation of fiber and matrix cracking.

8.5   Carbon Fiber Systems

A discussion of the key mechanical properties of carbon-fiber composites is provided in Chapter 12 on design issues and in Chapter 13 on airworthiness issues, which should be read in conjunction with this chapter. The topic of impact damage of these composites is also covered in Chapter 12.

Carbon-fiber composite systems are used more extensively for structural applications within the aerospace industry than other high-performance fiber systems. This is primarily due to the overall high specific stiffness and strength properties that can be achieved from these composites compared with other composites and structural metals, as shown in Table 8.1.

The mechanical properties of carbon-fiber composites can be varied significantly through the choice of the carbon fiber. Table 3.1 in Chapter 3 lists the properties of the various grades of carbon fiber and Table 8.2 provides details of relevant mechanical properties of some carbon/epoxy systems widely exploited in aircraft structures.

PAN-based carbon-fiber composites dominate the market because of their lower cost, better handling characteristics (due to the higher failure strains of the

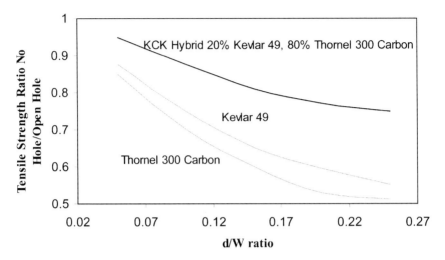

Fig 8.16   Tensile strength of laminates with open holes. Adapted from Ref. 4.

PAN fibers), and attractive overall composite mechanical properties. Pitch-based fiber composites tend to be used extensively in satellite applications, where their superior stiffness and thermal properties, including high conductivity and low coefficient of expansion, are a major advantage.

Carbon-fiber reinforcements can be produced in an extensive range of forms that also influence the properties of the composite system. These forms, ranging from short chopped fiber mats, through a variety of woven fabric products, to unidirectional tapes and advanced multi-layer fabrics such as non-crimp materials, are discussed in Chapter 3. Advanced forms such as three-dimensional carbon composites are covered in Chapter 14.

8.5.1   Matrix Systems for Carbon-Fiber Systems

The polymer matrix systems used with carbon fibers are discussed in Chapter 4. Thermoplastic matrices, such as PEEK and PPS, are becoming increasingly used for applications in the epoxy temperature range because of their higher toughness and low moisture absorption. However, recent developments in toughened epoxies have reduced the toughness advantage.

Epoxy resin systems have an upper limit of service temperature of around 180–200°C. For higher temperatures (up to approximately 250°C) BMI systems are often used, whereas for even higher temperatures (up to around 320°C) polyimide matrix systems may be used. Compared with epoxies, all the other matrix systems are more expensive and give rise to either processing or durability problems.

Table 8.2 Mechanical Properties of Selected Current Carbon-Fiber Composite Systems, Based on Data Provided in Ref. 2

Property	Units	Standard carbon/epoxy AS4/3501-6	Intermediate-modulus carbon/epoxy IM6/1081	High-modulus carbon/epoxy GY-70/934	Carbon/thermoplastic AS4/PEEK	Standard carbon/bismaleimide T300/V378
SG	—	1.58	1.6	1.59	1.57	1.6
V_f	—	0.63	0.65	0.57	0.58	0.65
σ_{1tu}	MPa	2280	2860	589	2060	1586
σ_{1cu}	MPa	1440	1875	491	1080	1324
σ_{2tu}	MPa	57	49	29.4	78	—
τ_u	MPa	71	83	49.1	157	—
E_1	GPa	142	177	294	131	138.6
E_2	GPa	10.3	10.8	6.4	8.7	—
G_{12}	GPa	7.2	7.6	4.9	5	—
ν_{12}	—	0.27	0.27	0.23	0.28	—
ε_{1u}	—	0.015	0.016	0.002	0.016	—
ε_{2u}	—	0.006	0.005	0.005	0.009	—

8.5.2   Adhesion and Bonding of Carbon Fibers in Composites

Carbon fibers are normally surface-treated to develop adequate bonding to epoxy or other matrices. To achieve adequate toughness, it is important that the fiber is able to disbond from the matrix to alleviate local stress concentrations, for example, at matrix cracks. Ductile matrices such as those based on thermoplastic matrices may inhibit disbonding, possibly resulting in reduced toughness and fatigue properties.

Surface treatments are based on oxidation of the fiber surface either by a wet chemical process (e.g., with sodium hypochlorite or chromic acid) or a dry process involving ozone. The treatment removes weak films, roughens the surface on a microscopic scale, and introduces chemically active sites onto the fiber. Only minor weakening of the fibers occurs as a result of these treatments. A coating of a compatible resin, generally similar to the thermosetting matrix resin, is sometimes used to protect carbon fibers from damage during reinforcement manufacture and also to provide lubrication. The coating can also improve adhesion and wetting.

There are various methods of measuring the fiber/matrix bond strength, including bulk tests based on measurement of transverse strength of composites and single-fiber tests.[7]

It appears that an upper value for the shear strength of the fiber/matrix bond for standard carbon fibers such as AS4 in an epoxy matrix is between 40–75 MPa, depending on the strength and ductility of the resin system. Interlaminar shear (ILSS) values for similar composites lie between 90 and 130 MPa. However, ILS tests often result in failure modes other than shear as the stress state in the failure zone is complex.

The fiber/matrix interface is often considered and modelled as the third phase in a composite, called the interphase. Significant effort has been directed at quantifying the effect of this phase on composite behavior in the case of carbon fiber composites.[8]

8.5.3   Effect of the Matrix and Fiber/Matrix Bond Strength of Carbon-Fiber Composites

8.5.3.1 Tension and Compression.   Studies on unidirectional carbon-fiber composites made using a standard epoxy matrix and a range of fibers of differing properties surprisingly exhibit no consistent improvement in composite strain to failure with fibers of differing strain to failure or stiffness.[7] In general, however, high strain-to-failure matrices provide the best translation of fiber properties. Fiber surface treatment appears to have only a minor effect on tensile properties of the resulting composites.

Under compression loading, elastic properties of the matrix play a more important role because they support the fibers against microbuckling, which is the predominant failure mode. Also, as may be expected from this mode of failure, the straightness of the fibers is a very important factor contributing to good translation of fiber properties. Often, compression strengths are quoted at just 50–60% of the corresponding tensile value. However, compression strength of unidirectional composites is difficult to measure, as discussed in Chapter 7, so that different test methods can result in different conclusions.

8.5.3.2 Intra-and Interlaminar Properties of Carbon-Fiber Composites. It is to be expected that, for a particular carbon-fiber composite, intra- and interlaminar properties would depend strongly on the fiber/matrix bond strength, which is related to the level of surface treatment. In Ref. 7, it is shown that an improvement of around 100% in transverse strength (and interlaminar toughness, G_{1c}) is obtained after applying a surface treatment of only 25% of that required to achieve maximum fiber/matrix bond strength.The values of the interlaminar tensile strength are nominally similar to the transverse tension strength. However, as mentioned earlier, ILSS values obtained from short-beam shear tests are often significantly higher, but direct comparison is not possible because this test produces complex loading and multiple failure modes.

Interlaminar toughness is related both to the properties of the matrix and the fiber/matrix bond strength. Further, the matrix is highly constrained by the fiber and therefore cannot achieve its potential toughness. This behavior is well known in adhesive bonding, where the toughness is greatly reduced when the adhesive thickness is not sufficient for full development of the plastic zone at the crack tip. Thus, a direct correlation of toughness of the composite with matrix toughness properties may not be expected, at least for the tougher matrices.

Similar comments can be made regarding mode 2 fracture toughness (which is significantly higher than mode 1 toughness). Interlaminar strength and impact resistance, discussed later, are expected to be related to interlaminar toughness. This is the case although the relationship is generally not straightforward and depends on mixed-mode (combined mode 1 and mode 2) behavior. Some of these issues are discussed in relation to adhesive bonds in Chapter 9.

8.5.3.3 Long-Term Deformation Behavior. Carbon fibers do not show any significant increases in strain with time (creep) over the working temperature range and are significantly less susceptible to stress rupture than aramid- or glass-fiber composites.[2] Thus, for a unidirectional composite under tensile or compressive loading, creep deformation will be low, and what does occur will result from loss of stiffness due to stress relaxation in the matrix. The situation regarding creep is, however, quite different for highly matrix-dominated composites, such as one based on $\pm 45°$ ply layers, where significant creep or stress-relaxation occurs at elevated temperatures. However, creep is not expected to be a major concern for a quasi isotropic laminate working within its stress and temperature design range.

8.6   Properties of Laminates

8.6.1   Tensile Strength of Cross-Ply Properties

Multilaminate cross-plied composites are, in the majority of cases, made up of families of $0°$, $\pm 45°$ and $90°$, plies (although other ply angles are sometimes included, for example $15°$, $30°$ and $60°$).

As discussed in Chapter 2, very significant losses in strength in unidirectional materials and changes in failure mode occur when the load is aligned at small angles to the $0°$ direction. The resulting off-axis mechanical properties depend on both the matrix and fiber/matrix interface properties. When considering the tensile strength of cross-plied laminates, it is obvious that the strength of the laminate will be determined by the capacity of the stiffer $0°$ plies (providing that these are present in sufficient proportions) because these plies are the most highly loaded. However, the strain level that can be achieved by the $0°$ plies in the cross-plied laminate is usually much more dependent on the matrix and fiber/matrix bond strength properties than is the case for the unidirectional material and is also dependent on the specific ply configuration.

As may be expected, fracture behavior is even more complex under combined loading, particularly when some fibers are in compression. A further issue is that for composites with brittle matrix or low fiber/matrix bond strength, the off-axis plies (most usually the $90°$ plies) may have a lower strain capacity than the $0°$ plies and may crack first. Cracking before final failure of the $0°$ plies (and hence the laminate) is called first ply failure (FPF). FPF usually occurs in the form of fine microcracks and does not greatly affect stiffness of the laminate; however, it can greatly aid the penetration of the environment into the composite and can lead to delamination and a lower strain-to-failure of the $0°$ plies. In some cases, due to high residual stresses, microcracking may occur in the absence of external load; this was a notable feature of some of the very early carbon/epoxy composites because of the very low strain capability of the epoxy matrix.

As previously mentioned, some microcracking leading to minor delaminations is actually desirable at stress concentrators, such as holes, because they can markedly reduce stress concentrations.

Even with a brittle matrix system the adverse effect of $90°$ ply cracking on the $0°$ plies is much less in a thick laminate with the $0°$ and $90°$ plies concentrated into thicker layers, because delamination of these layers and therefore removal of the stress concentration is likely. Fine dispersion of $0°/90°$ plies is likely to have the opposite effect.

Factors other than those discussed above that can affect strength of cross-plied laminates include mode of loading, ply stacking sequence, presence of free edges, specimen width, and residual stresses, which in some cases can be high enough to cause failure, even in the absence of external stresses.

Chapter 6 describes the various approaches used to estimate the strength of cross-ply laminates under complex loading.

8.7 Impact Damage Resistance

Figure 8.6 provides a comparison of Charpy impact behavior of various composites. This shows that the S-glass-fiber composites have the highest capacity for energy absorption followed by E-glass and then aramid composites. High-strength carbon/epoxy has a significantly lower energy-absorbing capability than these materials and high-modulus carbon/epoxy, the lowest of all the composites.

The capacity for energy absorption of some glass and aramid composites greatly exceeds that of aluminum alloys and even steel. This behavior is attributed to the high-strain capacity of fibers when loaded in the fiber direction. However, other than providing some idea of energy absorption capacity under dynamic loading conditions such as in a crash, these tests provide no information on the important issue of the effect of impact damage on residual strength and stiffness—that is, the remaining strength of the composite structure after damage. Here, the concern is the effect of in-service impacts in the plane of the laminate.

Impact damage can result, for example, from dropped tools, runway stones, or large hailstones. The drastic reduction in residual compression strength and less reduction in tensile strength that can result from impact damage is a major issue in the design and airworthiness certification of these composites, as discussed in Chapters 12 and 13.

The type of damage resulting from impact on composites depends on the energy level involved in the impact. High-energy impact, such as ballistic damage, results in through-penetration with some minor local delaminations. Lower-energy-level impact, which does not produce penetration, may result in some local damage in the impact zone together with delaminations within the structure and fiber fracture on the back face. Internal delaminations with little, if any, visible surface damage may result from low-energy impact.

The actual damage response depends on many intrinsic and extrinsic factors, including the thickness of the laminate, the exact stacking sequence, the shape and kinetic energy of the impactor, and the degree to which the laminate is supported against bending. The strain-to-failure capability of the fibers will determine the degree of back-face damage in a given laminate, and the area of the damage depends on the toughness of the matrix and fiber/matrix bond strength as well as the failure strain and stiffness of the fibers. Also, composites based on woven fibers show less internal damage for a given impact energy than those based on unidirectional material. This is because damage growth between layers is constrained by the weave.

High and medium levels of impact energy thus cause surface damage that is relatively easily detected. Low-energy impact produces damage that is difficult to observe visually and is therefore commonly termed barely visible impact damage (BVID). This type of damage is of concern because it may occur at quite low-energy levels and is by definition difficult to detect.

Figure 8.17 shows the area of BVID as a function of matrix toughness. Residual strength with BVID correlates quite well with the area of the damage zone, although different composite systems will have somewhat different sensitivities, depending on the matrix toughness as well as other factors.

The morphology of a BVID level impact is shown in Figure 8.18, taken from Ref. 9. It is seen that the damage occurs within a conical (Hertzian) contact zone with the apex at the point of impact. Within the cone, the damage consists of delamination between and within plies, and on the back-face (base of the cone) fiber fracture. The fiber fracture in this region results from the high strain caused by local bending in a thin laminate. Thick laminates do not usually suffer back-face fiber damage; however, at high-impact energies, fibers are crushed at the point of impact.

Delaminations occur as lobes between plies of significantly different orientation (e.g., $+45°$, $-45°$, $0°$, $90°$) and extend in the direction of the outermost reinforcing ply. Within thick laminates, damage only occurs as interply cracking.

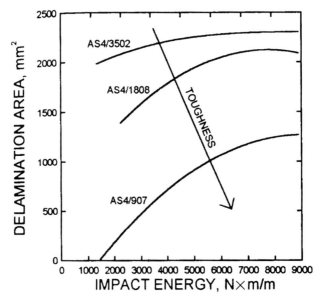

Fig 8.17   Delamination area as a function of impact energy for some carbon/epoxy composites with differing matrix toughness. Taken from Ref. 2.

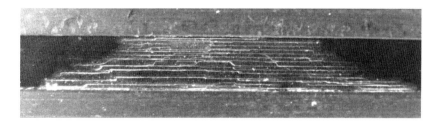

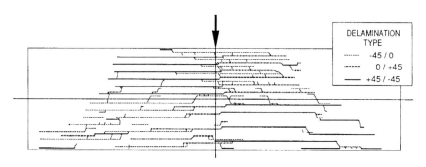

Fig 8.18   Impact damage in a 56-ply XAS-914C laminate and schematic of delamination pattern. Taken from Ref. 9.

8.7.1   Effect of BVID on Residual Strength

The effect of BVID on reducing residual compressive strength is well characterized experimentally. However, the actual mechanism has yet to be fully understood. It is clear that in the case of compression loading, the damage constitutes a zone of instability allowing the fibers to buckle at much lower strain levels than in the undamaged region. The marked effect of BVID on residual compression strength is shown in Figure 8.19 for four types of carbon composite.

In general, the reduction in residual strength is a similar function of damage size for all matrix systems. However, for a given impact energy, the damage size is less in tougher composite systems, such as those based on thermoplastic matrices.

Damage is most simply modelled as a softened zone or in more detail as a zone where the plies have become locally decoupled. Decoupling allows the plies to distort at relatively low strains. F-E models using composite interply fracture energy parameters, for example, G_{Ic} and G_{IIC}, are used to estimate onset of catastrophic damage growth. At this stage, these are suited only to the study of simple delaminations and cannot deal with the complexity of a real impact zone that includes broken fibers and matrix cracks as well as delaminations.

As yet, therefore, no model is sufficiently well developed for use as a predictive tool, for example, as linear elastic fracture mechanics (LEFM) is used as a predictive tool to estimate the residual strength of metals with cracks. Efforts

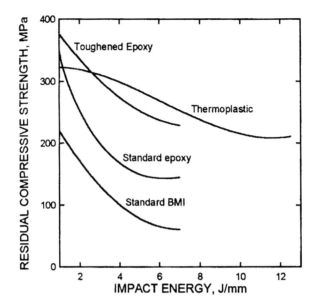

Fig 8.19 Residual compression strength versus impact energy for carbon-fiber composites with four common matrix systems. Taken from Ref. 2.

have increased over the past 10 years to develop predictive capabilities for both the consequences of the impact event (degree and characterization of damage) and residual static strength.

Software such as PAMSHOCK and LSDYNA is able to simulate the elastic response to the impact event; however, to characterize damage, multi-mode failure criteria have to be established for the material, lay-up, and configuration. This requires a significant amount of material testing and does not yet lead to an economic means of certification for typical structures.

Generally, the strength reduction in composites is determined empirically as a function of damage area and type. Most designs are based on the presence of an assumed damage zone for carbon composites; these issues are discussed further in Chapter 12.

Finally, cyclic loading and hot/wet environments have an influence on residual strength with BVID. These issues are discussed in the following sections.

8.8   Fatigue of Composite Laminates

In addition to maintaining static strength in service, structural composites are required to maintain an acceptable level of strength under fluctuating stress conditions, as experienced in service. The ability to maintain strength under cyclic stresses is called fatigue resistance. In an aircraft wing and empennage, the cyclic stresses are generally highly variable within the design limits; however, in fuselages, where the main stresses result from internal pressurization, the stress cycles to approximately constant peak values. These two types of loading are, respectively, called spectrum and constant amplitude.

In testing for fatigue resistance, there are two basic forms of measurement. The first is simply the life-to-failure (or to a certain level of stiffness degradation) at various stress levels; this is the S-N curve, where S is stress and N number of cycles. The second form is the rate-of-growth of damage as a function of cycles at various levels of stress. For metals, the damage is a crack; for composites, it is delamination or a damage zone consisting of localized microcracking and fractured fibers.

The ratio between the minimum and maximum stresses in constant amplitude cycling is an important parameter called the R ratio and is given by R = minimum/maximum stresses. Thus, an R of -1 is a cycle that involves full reversed loading, R = 0.1 is tension-tension, and a large positive value, for example R = 10 compression/compression. The ratio R generally has a marked influence on fatigue resistance.

8.8.1 Tension-Tension Fatigue, R ~ 0.1

The tension-tension fatigue properties of unidirectional composites having high fiber/volume fractions are dominated by the fatigue properties of the fibers. However, fiber-to-matrix-stiffness ratio is also important, as the matrix is fatigue sensitive. If the fiber-to-matrix-stiffness ratio is not sufficiently high, the strain in the matrix can become critical. Provided the matrix is cycled below its strain limit for a given number of cycles, it will not be expected to experience fatigue cracking. Above this strain level, microcracking of the matrix will occur. Note that, due to constraint by the fibers, this strain level may be higher than the fatigue strain limit of the bulk matrix. However, the residual stresses resulting from the mismatch thermal expansions and Poisson ratio between the fiber and matrix are superimposed on the external stresses, which complicates the stress state in the matrix.

When a fatigue-resistant fiber such as carbon is loaded to a high percentage of its average ultimate stress or strain, some fibers with relatively large flaws or defects will fail, and the adjacent fibers will be more highly stressed over the region of the load transfer length. If the composite is unloaded and reloaded, a few more fibers will fail in these regions. Thus, when this is repeated over many thousands of cycles, a definite fatigue effect is observed, as shown in Figure 8.20 The S-N curve is relatively flat, but scatter is very high; this is a major feature of carbon-fiber-based polymeric matrix composites, particularly when subject to tension-tension fatigue.

If, however, the fiber itself exhibits a degradation of strength under cyclic loading, then a much more pronounced fatigue effect is observed. For example, glass fibers show a pronounced degradation under cyclic straining at high proportions of their ultimate strain, which is probably more related to cumulative

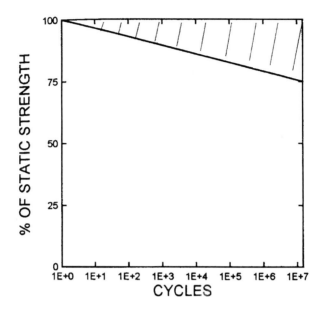

Fig 8.20   Typical scatter band for a unidirectional carbon-fiber/epoxy composite subjected to tension-tension cycling. Taken from Ref. 2.

time at high strain levels (stress rupture) than to damage caused by the cyclic loading. In addition, because of the low modulus of glass fibers, the resulting higher matrix strain results in matrix cracking that exacerbates fatigue sensitivity in two ways, first by strain concentration and second by allowing access of the environment to the fiber surface. As mentioned earlier, glass fibers are degraded by contact with moisture. To minimize stress on adjacent fibers, it is highly desirable that the fiber disbond from the matrix when fracture occurs. Similarly, when fiber fractures accumulate in a region, it is desirable that this region become isolated from the bulk of the composite by the formation of more macro-scale delaminations. Thus, composites with well-bonded tough matrices often exhibit inferior fatigue properties to those with brittle matrices.

8.8.1.1 Fatigue-Life Diagrams.   Talreja[10] developed fatigue-life diagrams to explain the behavior of unidirectional composites under tension-tension cycling. Figure 8.22 shows a schematic diagram of a typical fatigue-life diagram for a carbon-fiber/epoxy composite that is divided into three regimes corresponding to different types of fatigue damage:

(1) Region 1 occurs at high stress levels and is a scatter band for failure of the fibers and therefore is centered on the strain-to-failure of the fibers. In this region, random fiber breaks occur at flaws on each loading cycle and may subsequently focus stresses on surrounding fibers. If disbonding of the

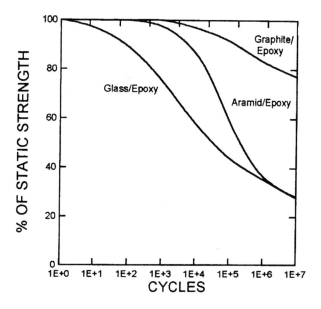

Fig 8.21   Schematic plot of S-N curves for unidirectional composites based on carbon, aramid, or glass fibers subjected to tension-tension cycling. Taken from Ref. 2.

broken fibers does not occur (because fiber/matrix bond strength is high), matrix cracks will form, increasing stresses on surrounding fibers. Even if debonding does occur, the accumulation of breaks in any cross-section increases net stresses, increasing the rate of random fiber fractures.

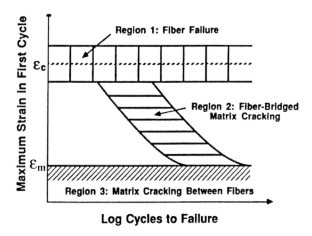

Fig 8.22   Schematic representation of a fatigue-life diagram showing damage zones for a unidirectional carbon-fiber/epoxy composite tested under unidirectional loading. Taken from Ref. 2.

(2) Region 2 is a region where cumulative matrix cracking and fiber matrix debonding occur. If debonding does not occur, the matrix cracking may result in fiber fractures, particularly if they impinge on a fiber flaw. Otherwise, the fibers are left bridging matrix cracks and will eventually fracture, as a bundle of fibers is weaker than those bonded as a composite (as explained in Chapter 2).

(3) Region 3 is below the fatigue limit for the composite because the strains are less than ε_m the nominal fatigue strain limit for the matrix. In this region, some matrix cracking may occur because of the local high thermal stresses and stress concentrations, but the cracks are non-propagating and therefore do not damage the fibers. However, cracking in this region will allow environmental ingress and lead to degradation in systems with environmentally sensitive fibers, such as glass fibers.

8.8.2 Tension Fatigue of Cross-Ply Composites

As may be expected, the fatigue behavior of cross-plied laminates is more complex than is the case for laminates with unidirectional fibers. This is because the off-angle plies are cyclically strained at some angle to the fiber direction, at a strain level that is largely dictated by the $0°$ fibers. As with static strength, microcracking of these plies between the fibers (FPF) can result in local strain elevation in the critical $0°$ fibers. Even if cracking of these plies does not result in failure of the $0°$ fibers, it is undesirable because it reduces the integrity and stiffness of the composite, even though the loss in stiffness is often fairly minor.

As cycling proceeds, the cracking pattern continues to accumulate until it saturates at what is called the characteristic damage state of the composite. Perhaps the greatest concern with this damage is that it opens the composite to ingress by the environment.

In laminates with fatigue-insensitive carbon fibers; provided there is a sufficient proportion of $0°$ fibers in the laminate, fatigue behavior is similar to unidirectional material—in other words, a flat S-N curve and high scatter. If the damage parameter is based on cyclic strain, the S-N curves could be fairly similar. However, with a low fraction of $0°$ fibers, in a quasi isotropic laminate, for example, fatigue sensitivity will be more marked with failure of the cross-plies, both reducing stiffness and concentrating strain on the $0°$ plies.

Three phases can be identified in the fatigue process, as illustrated schematically in Figure 8.23:

(1) Matrix cracking in $90°$ plies and, to a lesser extent, in the other non-zero plies is the first phase, which may initiate from the first load cycle depending on stress level—this is the FPF and will reduce laminate stiffness as the cracking accumulates. Eventually a characteristic damage state (CDS) develops as the cracking saturates.

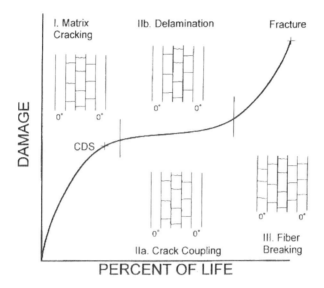

Fig 8.23 Schematic plot of fatigue damage mechanisms in a composite laminate. Taken from Ref. 2.

(2) Further cycling will result in the interaction and coupling of the matrix cracks through disbonding and the formation of delaminations. Depending on the construction of the laminate, edge delamination can also occur because of the high interlaminar stresses. The $[0°/\pm 45°/90°]_s$ is an example of an edge-delamination prone laminate. In this case, the edge plies become decoupled, and the delaminations propagate into the laminate, resulting in a marked elevation of the stresses in the 0° plies.

(3) As the off-angle plies become ineffective in carrying load, the stresses in the 0° plies will gradually increase and may cause accumulation of fiber fracture and eventual failure. The stress level for damage leading to final failure depends strongly on the volume fraction and stiffness of the 0° fibers, because, at a given stress level, they control the strain experienced by the composite and the load that can be carried when the off-angle fibers become ineffective.

Figure 8.24 schematically shows the reductions in residual strength and stiffness in a cross-ply laminate resulting from damage accumulation during cyclic loading.

8.8.3 Effect of Stress Concentrations

Stress raisers such as fastener holes and cut-outs are a feature of many composite components. Although these features often have marked detrimental effects on static strength in the as-manufactured component, they may not be a concern under cyclic loading. This is because the formation of minor

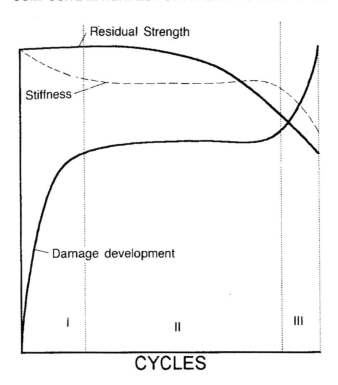

Fig 8.24   Schematic illustration of the changes in stiffness and residual strength as fatigue damage accumulates. Based on Ref. 2.

microcracking and delaminations in the high-strain regions can markedly reduce the stress concentration. This issue is further discussed in Chapter 12. It is, however, of interest to note the marked contrast in behavior with metals, where local plastic flow eliminates stress concentrations under static loading but results in fatigue cracking when the loading is cyclic.

Stress raisers also arise at ply-drop offs and at the ends of bonded or integral stiffeners. These features cause elevated through-thickness stresses transverse to the plane of the reinforcement. In this region, the rather poor fatigue resistance of the matrix, the ply/ply interface, and the fiber/matrix interface controls fatigue life. This situation is obviously highly undesirable, therefore considerable effort is made to minimize interlaminar stresses by careful design and test evaluation.

8.8.4 Effect of Loading Frequency

Unlike glass-fiber composites, discussed earlier, carbon-fiber composites with similar fiber architecture and matrix material are much less prone to temperature rise when loaded at high frequencies (5–10 Hz). This is because the high stiffness of the fibers limits the cyclic strain experienced by the matrix at a given stress level and, in addition, the high thermal conductivity of the carbon fibers conducts heat away from hot spots. However, for matrix-dominated composites (e.g., with $\pm 45°$ fibers) matrix hysteresis is much greater, and significant temperature increases can occur. Other factors that have a major influence on matrix temperature rise include the properties of the matrix material and the thickness of the composite.[2]

8.8.5 Compression Fatigue, R∼ 10

The main concern regarding compression loading is the strength degradation caused damage such as BVID, which is discussed in the next section. In the absence of damage and providing the laminate has a high proportion of fatigue-resistant 0° plies, compression fatigue can be quite good under ambient conditions and can be similar to that for R ∼ 0.1. Fatigue behavior is dependent on the ability of the matrix and fiber/matrix interface to suppress microbuckling of the fibers, which in turn depends on the resistance to microcracking under the negative loading. Because microcracking should be suppressed under compression cycling, quite good fatigue properties can be expected. However, compression fatigue sensitivity under hot/wet conditions will be more marked than under tension because of reduced support of the fibers by the softer matrix. Markedly reduced compression fatigue resistance is to be expected at temperatures near to T_g when the matrix softens.

Finally, as may be expected and because of their low resistance to compression loading, aramid-fiber composites exhibit quite poor compression fatigue properties.

It is of note that it is quite difficult to conduct fatigue tests under high compressive stresses because of the need to suppress global buckling of the composite. To achieve this, the use of anti-buckling guides is generally required, which allows only a small proportion of the cross-section to be tested. Thus, tension and compression results quoted may not always be directly comparable.

8.8.6 Tension/Compression Fatigue, R ∼ −1

The influence of a negative R ratio on fatigue resistance of a unidirectional carbon/epoxy composite is adverse. The reason for the poorer performance under reversed cycling is that the damage caused to the matrix and various interfaces during the tensile cycle limits the ability of the laminate to support the fibers against buckling in the compression cycles. This behavior is evident in both unidirectional and cross-plied laminates.

8.8.7 Effect of BVID on Fatigue Strength

Unlike glass- and aramid-fiber composites, in which fatigue strength for undamaged structures may be a concern, fatigue of carbon-fiber composites is only a real concern when the laminate also contains low-level impact damage (BVID). Under these circumstances, there is a gradual reduction in residual strength with cycles.

The effect of BVID and fatigue on the compressive residual strength of carbon/epoxy composites is shown in Figure 8.25, taken from Ref. 11, which schematically shows the reduction in normalized residual strength that occurs as a function of impact damage size, and the further reduction caused by strain cycling at various normalized strain levels. The static failure strain plateau of around 4500 microstrain shown, which occurs at a damage size of about 25 mm, is typical for carbon/epoxy composites after BVID. The Figure also shows that a further reduction of the plateau to around 3000 microstrain results after cycling at a strain of around 0.6 × 4500 microstrain for around 10^5 cycles.

Some further experimental results showing damage growth[12] are presented in Figure 8.26. These are for a 56-ply-thick (approximately quasi isotropic) laminate with BVID subjected to a compression-dominated spectrum loading typical of that for a fighter upper wing skin. Results for both ambient temperature dry and hot/wet are presented. The influence of environment is discussed again in Section 8.9 of this chapter.

The reduction in residual strength, which results from cycling under compression-dominated loading, is associated at least in part with growth of the BVID delaminations. Some observations on growth of the delamination damage from BVID in carbon-fiber/epoxy composites during cycling under representative spectrum loading[13] are shown in Figure 8.27.

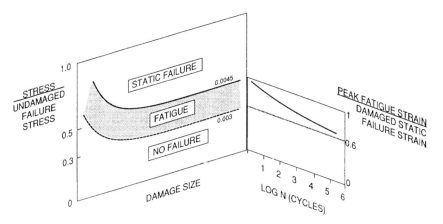

Fig 8.25 Schematic representation of the damage size on the fatigue life of composite laminates. Taken from Ref. 11.

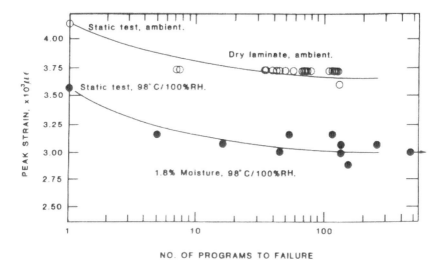

Fig 8.26   Compression residual strength for a 56-ply XAS/914C laminate as a function of spectrum loading representative of that experienced in a fighter wing skin. Behavior under ambient dry and hot/wet is presented. Taken from Ref. 9.

8.8.8 Damage (or Defect) Growth

Metal structures have long been designed with an understanding of the mechanics of flaw growth, allowing establishment of inspection intervals based on knowledge of the critical (unstable) flaw size and the growth under (spectrum) loading. The problem is much less well understood in composite materials. The common experience is that defects or damaged areas do not grow at repeated strain levels, even as high as 80% of limit strain, generally around 2000–3000 microstrain.

Figure 8.28 shows a comparison of residual strength reduction under spectrum loading (representative loading for the component) for metal and composite with,

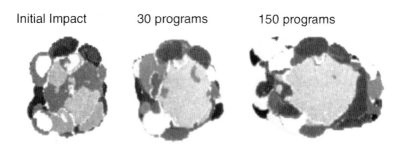

Fig 8.27   Growth of BVID delaminations under spectrum loading, representative of a compression-dominated wing top surface. Taken from Ref. 9.

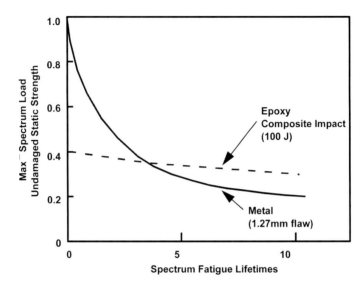

Fig 8.28   Residual strength as a function of spectrum cycles for 7075 T6 aluminum alloy and carbon/epoxy AS4/3501-6. Adapted from Ref. 14.

respectively, a crack-like flaw and impact damage.[14] In the metal, the flaw grows as a fatigue crack, causing a gradual reduction in residual strength until final failure. By contrast, the reduction in residual strength in the composite is marked immediately after impact. This reduction is followed by a relatively small further reduction in residual strength, with cyclic loading with or without limited flaw growth.

8.9   Environmental Effects

The mechanical properties of polymer-matrix composites may be degraded by a range of physical and chemical effects. It is therefore important to understand both the material and the operating environment. The environment must be understood before the suitability of a composite material for a particular application is assessed. The details include humidity, temperature (of air and material surface), ultraviolet and infra red radiation levels, wind conditions and, rainfall. Additional details that need to be defined specifically for flight include variations of these conditions with altitude, rates of heating and cooling during maneuvers, and frequency and duration of each exposure. The different mission profiles that the aircraft experiences will affect the severity and frequency of these conditions. Materials on different parts of the aircraft will experience different environmental conditions. A set of conditions or flight profiles must then be defined for each specific part of the aircraft. Aircraft components are also subjected to a wide range of chemicals, including fuel, fuel additives, hydraulic fluids, de-icing fluids, paint and paint strippers, dye penetrants, and ultrasonic couplant gels and detergents/wash systems.

These chemicals and environmental factors can significantly change the mechanical properties of a composite material. It is important to note that the matrix, fiber, and fiber/matrix interface will be affected differently by the operating environment. It is therefore vital to assess potential effects on each of these components with appropriate mechanical tests before certifying the material for use. Tests may need to be conducted to include the possible synergy between the various exposure environments. For example, the combination of humidity and temperature creates what is often termed a hot/wet environment. For epoxies and other thermosetting-based composites, the composite matrix absorbs moisture from humid air, which, when combined with elevated temperature, significantly reduces mechanical properties. Typically, for a carbon/epoxy composite cured at 180°C, moisture uptake reduces matrix-dominated mechanical properties (such as compressive strength) by up to 10% for subsonic aircraft and up to 25% for supersonic aircraft.

8.9.1 Moisture Absorption

Diffusion of moisture into a carbon/epoxy composite occurs quite slowly at ambient temperatures but will eventually saturate the material to an equilibrium concentration of moisture which will depend on operating conditions. It is important to understand the diffusion of moisture into the composite so as to allow the prediction of the long-term moisture content of a component in service. This moisture-content level can then be reproduced in the laboratory, and the effects on performance can be evaluated using mechanical tests.

The effect of diffused moisture on the mechanical properties of a composite is often reversible upon drying of the material. The absorption and desorption of moisture will occur on a continual basis for the life of a component in service as it is exposed to a changing environment. In the long term, the bulk of the material will come to moisture-content equilibrium, whereas the exposed outer surface plies may have a fluctuating moisture concentration.

Immediately after manufacture, the matrix material in a composite material will begin to absorb moisture from humid air, even in an air-conditioned environment. The effect of this absorbed moisture on mechanical performance is critical and needs to be evaluated for specific composite systems. The level and extent of moisture diffusion are highly dependent on the type of matrix material. As discussed in Chapter 4, thermoplastic resins absorb very low levels of moisture (typically much less than 1% by weight) while epoxy resins absorb over 4% moisture by weight. Therefore, it is not valid to assess all composite matrices to a fixed moisture content, but rather, the approach should be to expose the matrix to a representative environmental condition and assess the effects on the material over time. It is assumed in most cases that the fibers do not absorb moisture. This is true for carbon, boron, and glass but not for aramid and other polymeric fibers.

Moisture diffusion characteristics are often quoted in the literature as *Fickian* or *non-Fickian*. Fickian behavior, the simplest to deal with mathematically,[15] fortunately represents the diffusion behavior of most aerospace, thermoset matrix materials. It is characterized experimentally by an uptake of moisture that reaches an asymptotic value after a period of time (Figure 8.29). If the weight gain of a sample exposed to constant humidity and temperature is plotted against the square root of time, there will be an initial linear region up to about 60% of the maximum moisture uptake followed by a gradual approach toward a constant or asymptotic value. This asymptotic value is equal to the concentration of moisture experienced at the surface layer of the material exposed to a given humidity level.

Considering a common aerospace composite in laminate form, diffusion will occur primarily through the laminate faces, and only a small effect will be seen from edge diffusion. Fick's first law states that the flux of moisture in the through-thickness direction x, will be dependent only on the moisture concentration gradient through the sample in that direction:

$$MoistureFlux = -D \cdot \frac{\partial c}{\partial x} \tag{8.1}$$

where D is the diffusivity or diffusion constant, and c is the concentration of moisture. Fick's second law defines the differential equation for the diffusion process if diffusivity, D, is independent of x:

$$\frac{\partial c}{\partial t} = D \cdot \frac{\partial^2 c}{\partial x^2} \tag{8.2}$$

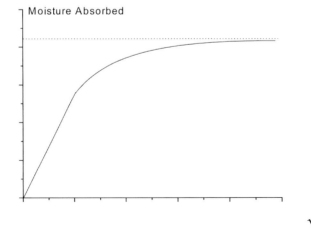

Fig 8.29 Schematic illustration of moisture uptake versus root time under constant humidity and temperature conditions for Fickian diffusion behavior.

The diffusion constant D will be independent of time and assumed to be constant through the thickness of the sample. The diffusion constant, however, varies exponentially with temperature:

$$D = D_o \cdot \exp[-E_d/R.T] \qquad (8.3)$$

where T is temperature, R is the universal gas constant, and D_0 and E_d are constants.

The absorption of moisture through the thickness of the composite with time is shown in Figure 8.30. After manufacture, the composite is essentially completely dry (t_0). Exposure to humid air allows moisture to begin to diffuse through the outer plies of the composite and through to the specimen center after time (t_1). After a longer period of time under constant humidity conditions, an even moisture distribution arises (t_∞)

It is important to note that at stages other than the fully dry or fully saturated case, a profile of moisture concentration will exist in the matrix. Because moisture affects the mechanical properties of the matrix, this also implies that a profile of properties will exist through the thickness. If the humidity conditions are transient (as found in normal weather patterns), a complex profile of moisture (and hence properties) through the specimen thickness may result.

The moisture content of a composite material is typically quoted as a percentage by weight:

$$\text{Moisture uptake concentration } (\%) = \frac{\text{Weight (final)} - \text{Weight (initial)}}{\text{Weight (initial)}} \times 100$$

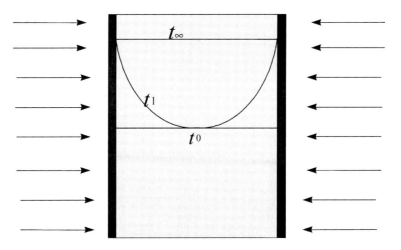

Fig 8.30   Diffusion of moisture into composite over time.

It has been shown for many composite materials that the maximum moisture uptake is related to humidity by:

$$\text{Maximum moisture uptake} = k.\phi^n \qquad (8.4)$$

where ϕ is the relative humidity in %, k is a constant, and n is close to unity for many aerospace composite materials. For a typical carbon/epoxy composite (60% fiber volume fraction), the maximum moisture uptake for exposure at 100% RH is about 2%. Figure 8.31 illustrates the influence of humidity on moisture absorption.

The diffusion of moisture into a composite matrix over time varies exponentially with temperature. An increase in temperature of $10°C$ typically doubles the diffusion rate. Figure 8.32 shows the effect of increasing temperature on the profile of weight-gain versus time for a constant humidity level.

The effect of specimen thickness is straightforward; the time taken to reach equilibrium is proportional to the square of the specimen thickness.

8.9.2 Real-Time Outdoor Exposure

The true performance of a composite material can only be established when all the exposures that will be encountered in service are allowed for. Real exposures to test coupons can be obtained by attaching the coupons to aircraft structure and assessing performance after differing lengths of service. This is somewhat inconvenient, and the alternative of simply exposing coupons of material to the environment at ground level is often substituted. Ground exposure coupons are more likely to absorb greater levels of moisture because they are unlikely to dry during flights at altitudes where the humidity is low. Consequently, this approach should be conservative.

The degradation of composite materials exposed on the ground to tropical conditions is described in Ref. 16. This trial used carbon/epoxy material as used

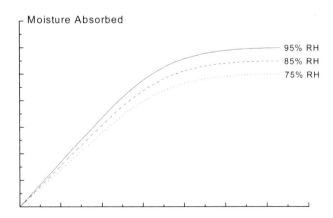

Fig 8.31   Effect of relative humidity on the amount of moisture absorbed with time.

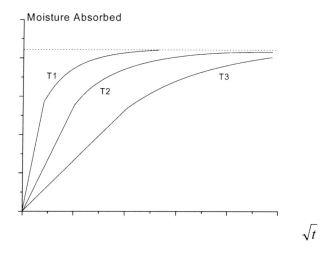

Fig 8.32   Effect of temperature on the weight-gain profile T1 > T2 > T3 (constant humidity).

on the F/A-18 aircraft. The trial investigated a number of variables, including different exposure conditions, the influence of paint schemes, and differing infrared and UV levels in an Australian tropical environment.

It can be seen (Figure 8.33) that it takes a very long time for the level of moisture to come to equilibrium, particularly if the sample is protected from sunlight. Note also that fully exposed (and to a lesser extent, shaded) samples lose mass due to erosion and UV degradation of surface matrix or paint layers. Typical equilibrium moisture contents for epoxy-based composites were found to range from about 0.7% to about 0.9% after long-term outdoor exposure.

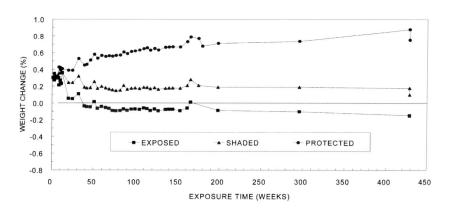

Fig 8.33   Weight changes for unpainted composite coupons (20-ply AS4/3501-6) exposed at Butterworth Air Force Base in Malaysia. Taken from Ref.16.

8.9.3 Effect of Moisture and Temperature on Mechanical Properties

Moisture plasticizes the matrix, leading to a reduction in T_g and changes in mechanical properties, such as Young's modulus. These properties can be restored on drying, assuming no permanent matrix damage, such as microcracks, occurred during the exposure. As discussed several times previously, the glass-transition temperature, T_g, is an important material property because it defines the temperature at which material properties are drastically reduced as the matrix changes from a glassy, stiff state to a pliable one. Figure 8.34 shows a plot of T_g versus exposure conditions for AS4/3501-6 carbon/epoxy composite.

As expected, the degradation in matrix properties mostly affects matrix-dominated composite properties at elevated temperatures. For example, Figure 8.35 shows that moisture has a marked effect on reducing the elevated temperature strength of $\pm 45^\circ$ AS4/3501-6 laminates,[17] but little effect on the properties at ambient temperature.

The open-hole compression strength is often used as a key comparative measure of compression strength. Figure 8.36 plots the influence of temperature and temperature combined with moisture on this property for the AS4/3501-6 system and shows that moisture has a marked effect on elevated-temperature properties but, again, only a fairly small effect on the ambient-temperature properties.

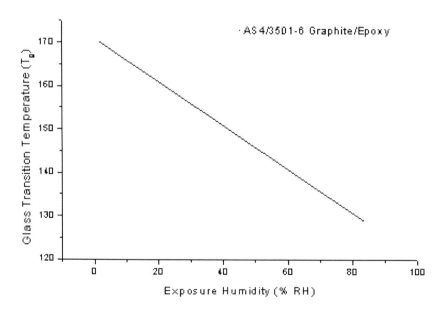

Fig 8.34 Plot of T_g versus saturation moisture content resulting from exposure to humidity for a typical carbon/epoxy composite.

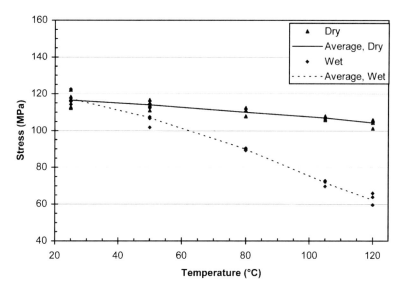

Fig 8.35   Effect of temperature and temperature and moisture of the tensile strength of $\pm 45°$ laminates of AS4/3501-6. Taken from Ref. 17.

The environmental effects on fatigue behavior of composites for aircraft structures are as important as the effects on static properties.[18] Mechanical properties of the resin in carbon-fiber composites were not degraded after conditioning to a moisture level of around 0.9%. In fact, it was found that the

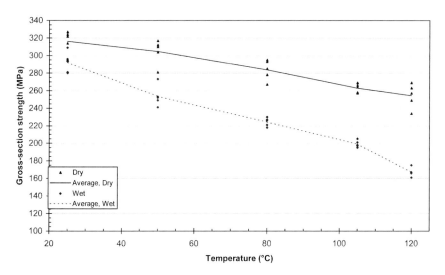

Fig 8.36   Effect of temperature and temperature and moisture open-hole compression strength of AS4/3501-6. Taken from Ref. 17.

interlaminar shear fatigue strength of the composite was moderately higher than dry, possibly due to the effect of plasticization of the matrix and a relaxation of residual thermal stress during processing. It was also found that $\pm 45°$ laminates conditioned to 0.9% moisture content had a better fatigue resistance than dry specimens.

The effect of absorbed moisture and temperature on the residual compression strength of impact-damaged specimens is shown in Figure 8.26 It seems likely, from the preceding discussion, that temperature rather than moisture causes the degradation, and the damage may be partially alleviated by the softening effect of the moisture.

8.9.4   Temperature Effects and Thermal Spiking

Both reversible and irreversible effects may be observed when a composite matrix is exposed to high temperature. If the temperature exceeds the T_g, the material modulus will decrease markedly. The original modulus will return upon cooling, provided no thermal decomposition or other permanent damage has occurred. Thermal decomposition is not an effect that is likely to be important on aircraft except on exposure to fire or other high-temperature sources (over 250°C). Irreversible damage effects include emission of volatiles and plasticizers, altering the nature of extent and cross-linking of the matrix and residual stresses induced through thermal cycling. Thermal cycling to high temperatures may cause trapped volatiles to expand and create high pressures within matrix voids and cracks. These stresses can lead to permanent mechanical damage and loss of properties. Service temperature values must be chosen such that the material wet T_g value is not exceeded (MIL-HDBK 17 recommends at least a 28°C safety factor).

Low temperatures can also have a serious effect on composite properties. Water trapped in voids or cracks within composite materials may freeze when exposed to cold conditions at high altitude. Temperature decreases by 3°C for every 500 m of altitude, and even moderately low altitudes can produce freezing conditions. Water expands by 8.3% in volume upon freezing and has a bulk modulus that is three to four times that of epoxy resin. Thus, water trapped within cavities will create pressure on the surrounding material that can result in permanent matrix damage. It is therefore important to consider the potential problems associated with free water entering voids and micro-cracks in composites. This can also be a more serious problem on a much larger scale for water entering honeycomb sandwich structures.

Thermal spiking is the terminology used to describe the effect of exposing a composite with high moisture content to rapid rises in temperature. Thermal spiking is an effect that is investigated to determine the useful maximum operating temperature of a composite. This is designed to simulate a supersonic dash in flight. Spiking is thought to create matrix damage that allows greater levels of moisture to absorb into the composite. Work by Clark et al.[19] shows that spiking creates the most amount of damage when conducted during moisture uptake or at the peak moisture uptake level. Thermal spiking before moisture conditioning did not appear to create any damage to the material.

8.9.5 Swelling Strains

The absorption of moisture by the composite matrix also causes it to swell and exert a resultant strain on the material, although, as mentioned above, these swelling strains may counteract residual strains from curing. The coefficient of moisture expansion defines the way a volume changes when taking up moisture. The volume change in a composite due to swelling may be represented by the empirical relation[20]:

$$\frac{\Delta V}{V_o} = 0.01 \cdot c + \frac{\Delta M}{M_o} \cdot d \tag{8.5}$$

where V_o and M_o represent initial volume and mass and c and d are swelling constants. For 3501–6 resin, swelling constants are given as $c = -0.61$ and $d = 0.87$.

8.9.6 Stress Effects

The effect of stress superimposed over a hot/wet condition can produce a greater detriment to composite mechanical properties than can each of these factors alone.[21] It is found that the level of moisture uptake increased with increasing stress level, and this behavior can be modelled using Fick's law. The greatest effect is on the value of diffusivity that increased with applied stress. The equilibrium moisture-content value is also found to be proportional to the applied stress level. Stress induced damage in the form of microcracks will increase the equilibrium moisture uptake level. Moisture present within these microcracks will have a significantly different effect than moisture absorbed by the matrix. Viscoelastic relaxations within the resin may occur at sustained stress levels that may alter the diffusion properties.

8.9.7 Ultraviolet Damage

Ultraviolet (UV) damage in composites occurs when the radiation breaks the chemical bonds in any exposed epoxy resin, and the degraded resin is then eroded away by wind and rain. Such damage can be minimized by the application of UV-resistant coatings. High-quality paints are equipped to deal with high UV levels and prevent the matrix from being affected. UV damage is restricted to the topmost layers of the composite and is unlikely to affect the bulk properties of a composite laminate. Other matrix resins, such as polyesters, are less susceptible to UV degradation, however, because they have inferior mechanical properties, these resin systems are not considered for structural applications on aircraft.

8.9.8 Chemical Changes in Matrix

Time may have an effect on the matrix because of chemical reactions that may occur on a long-term basis. The matrix may leach chemical components that will affect the T_g and mechanical properties such as fracture toughness. The reaction of moisture with some of the matrix chemical components may also need to be considered. These reactions are likely to be hastened by increased temperature. The long-term chemical stability of most aerospace thermoset resins is excellent under normal exposure conditions and therefore generally does not need to be determined, unless the suitability of the matrix for an unusually severe environment is a concern.

References

[1] Sims, G. D., and Broughton, W. R., "Glass Fibre Reinforced Plastics," *Comprehensive Composite Materials*, edited by A. Kelly and C. Zweben, Elsevier, 2000.

[2] Mall, S., "Laminated Polymer Matrix Composites," *Composites Engineering Handbook*, edited by P. K. Mallick, Marcel Decker, 1997.

[3] Baker, A. A., "Bonded Composite Repair of Metallic Aircraft Components: Overview of Australian Activities," AGARD Conference Proceedings 550, Conference on Composite Repair of Military Aircraft Structures, October 1994.

[4] Wardle, M. W., "Aramid Fibre Reinforced Plastics," *Comprehensive Composite Materials*, edited by A. Kelly and C. Zweben, Elsevier, 2000.

[5] Pigliacampi, J. J., "Organic Fibres," *Engineered Materials Handbook, Composites*, ASM, Vol. 1, 1987.

[6] Drzal, L. T., and Ishihara, S., "Aramid Fibre Surface Treatments to Improve Adhesion to Epoxy Matrices," Proceedings of 33rd SAMPE International Conference, November 2001.

[7] Smith, P. A., "Carbon Fibre Reinforced Plastics-Properties," Comprehensive Composite Materials, edited by A. Kelly and C. Zweben, Elsevier, 2000.

[8] Drzal, L. T., Herra-Franko, P. J., and Hoe, H., "Fibre-Matrix Interface Tests," *Comprehensive Composite Materials*, Vol. 2, edited by A. Kelly and C. Zweben, Elsevier, 2000.

[9] Clark G., and Saunders, D. S., "Morphology of Impact Damage Growth by Fatigue in Carbon Fibre Composite Laminates," *Materials Forum*, Vol. 15, 1991, pp. 333–342.

[10] Talreja, R., "Fatigue of Polymer Composites," *Comprehensive Composite Materials*, Vol. 2, edited by A. Kelly, and C. Zweben, Elsevier, 2000.

[11] Clark, G., and van Blaricum T. J., "Load Spectrum Modification Effects on Fatigue of Impact Damaged Carbon Fibre Composite Coupons," *Composites*, Vol. 18, 1987, pp. 243–251.

[12] Saunders, D. S., Clark, G., van Blaricum, T. J., and Preuss, T. E., "Graphite/Epoxy Laminate Coupon Testing Program," *Theoretical and Applied Fracture Mechanics*, Vol. 13, 1990, pp. 105–124.

[13] Saunders, D. D., and Clark, G., "Fatigue Damage in Composite Laminates," *Materials Forum*, Vol. 17, 1983, pp, 309–331.

[14]Whitehead, R. S., "Certification of Primary Composite Aircraft Structures," 14th Symposium of the International Conference on Aeronautical Fatigue (ICAF), June 1987.

[15]Crank, J., *Mathematics of Diffusion*, Oxford University Press, London, 1959.

[16]Chester, R. J., and Baker, A. A., "Environmental Durability of F/A-18 Carbon/Epoxy Composite," *Polymers and Polymer Composites*, Vol. 4, 1996, pp. 315–323.

[17]Callus, P., Vodika, R., Baker A. A., and Bannister, M., "The Effect of Temperature and Moisture on the Shear and Compression Behaviour of Three Carbon Epoxy Composites," Prceedings of ACUN 4, July 2002.

[18]Jones, C. J., Dickson, R. F., Adam, T., Reiter, H., and Harris, B., "The Environmental Fatigue Behaviour of Reinforced Plastics," *Proceedings of the Royal Society*, London, Vol. 396, 1984, pp. 315–338.

[19]Clark, G., Saunders, D. S., van Blaricum, T., and Richmond, M., "Moisture Absorption in Graphite/Epoxy Laminates," *Journal of Composites Science & Technology*, Vol. 39, 1990, pp. 355–375.

[20]Delasi, R., and Whiteside, J. B, "Effect of Moisture on Epoxy Resins and Composites," *Advanced Composite Materials: Environmental Effects*, ASTM STP 658, edited by J. R Vinson, 1978, pp. 2–20.

[21]Gillat, O., and Broutman, L. J, *Advanced Composite Materials: Environmental Effects*, ASTM STP 658, edited by J. R. Vinson, 1978, pp. 61–83.

9
Joining of Composite Structures

9.1 Introduction

Airframe structures consist essentially of an assembly of simple elements connected to form a load transmission path. The elements, which include skins, stiffeners, frames, and spars, form the major components such as wings, fuselage, and empennage. The connections or joints are potentially the weakest points in the airframe so can determine its structural efficiency.

In general, it is desirable to reduce the number and complexity of joints to minimize weight and cost. A very important advantage of composite construction is the ability to form unitized components, thus minimizing the number of joints required. However, the design and manufacture of the remaining joints is still a major challenge to produce safe, cost-effective, and efficient structures.

This chapter is concerned with joints used to connect structural elements made of advanced fiber composite laminates, mainly carbon/epoxy, to other composite parts or to metals. Sections 9.3 and 9.4 deal, respectively, with bonded and mechanical joints typical of those used in the manufacture of airframe components. Joints are also required to repair structural damage; this topic is dealt with in Chapter 10. Both design and materials aspects are considered. The aim of this chapter, when discussing design, is to outline simple analytical procedures that provide a physical insight into the behavior of joints involving composites. The materials aspects covered will be those essential to the manufacture of sound joints.

Joint types used in airframe construction can be broadly divided into joints that are mechanically fastened using bolts or rivets, adhesively bonded using a polymeric adhesive, or that feature a combination of mechanical fastening and adhesive bonding.

In mechanical joints, loads are transferred between the joint elements by compression on the internal faces of the fastener holes with a smaller component of shear on the outer faces of the elements due to friction. In bonded joints, the loads are transferred mainly by shear on the surfaces of the elements. In both cases, the load transmission elements (fastener or adhesive) are stressed primarily in shear along the joint line; however, the actual stress distribution will be complex.

Joints can be classified as single or multiple load path. Single load path joints are joints in which failure would result in catastrophic loss of structural capability. Multiple load path joints are joints in which failure of a single element results in the load being carried by other load-carrying members. An apparently multiple load path joint would be classified as single load path if failure of one of the paths leads to an unacceptable reduction in the load capacity of the joint.

The alignment of the load path and the geometry of the structural elements are important considerations in the design of joints. Airframe structural elements are usually intended to be loaded in either tension/compression or shear. Primary bending is avoided by keeping the loading as close as possible to collinear. However, secondary bending induced by minor eccentricity of the loads occurs in many types of joint (and structure) and can cause serious problems.

Compared with metals, laminated fiber composites have relatively low through-thickness strength and bearing strength under concentrated loads. Thus metals, usually titanium alloys, are sometimes required to transmit loads in and out of highly loaded composite structure, particularly where stress fields are complex.

Typical design parameters for carbon/epoxy airframe components (for a high-performance military aircraft) are:

- Ultimate design strain: $\pm$ 3000 to 4000 microstrain for mechanically fastened structure, up to $\pm$ 5000 microstrain for bonded honeycomb structure
- Operating temperature $-55\,°C$ to $+105\,°C$
- Service fluids; presence of moisture, hydraulic oil, fuel, and (limited exposure to) paint stripper

Strain, rather than strength, is generally used as the basis for comparison of the structural capacity of composite structure because composites of differing stiffness tend to fail at a similar strain level—particularly when damaged. Microstrain is strain $\times 10^{-6}$.

9.2   Comparison Between Mechanically Fastened and Adhesively Bonded Joints

The advantages and disadvantages of forming joints by adhesive bonding and bolting or riveting are summarized in Table 9.1

Although there are many advantages for bonding composites from the performance view point, there are also many limitations or disadvantages that must be considered with each potential application. For a relatively thin-skinned structure, particularly where fatigue may be a problem, bonding is very attractive indeed. However, the use of suitable pre-bonding surface treatments and adhesives is essential to develop the required strength level and maintain it during a service life, which could be more than 30 years.

A high level of quality control is very important to obtain reliable adhesive bonding. This is because current non-destructive inspection (NDI) procedures are able to detect only gross defects such as severe voids and disbonds in bonded

Table 9.1   A Comparison of the Advantages and Disadvantages of Adhesively
Bonded and Bolted Composite Joints

Advantages	Disadvantages
Bonded Joints	
Small stress concentration in adherends	Limits to thickness that can be joined with simple joint configuration
Stiff connection	Inspection other than for gross flaws difficult
Excellent fatigue properties	Prone to environmental degradation
No fretting problems	Sensitive to peel and through-thickness stresses
Sealed against corrosion	Residual stress problems when joining to metals
Smooth surface contour	Cannot be disassembled
Relatively lightweight	May require costly tooling and facilities
Damage tolerant	Requires high degree of quality control
	May be of environmental concern
Bolted Joints	
Positive connection, low initial risk	Considerable stress concentration
Can be disassembled	Prone to fatigue cracking in metallic component
No thickness limitations	Hole formation can damage composite
Simple joint configuration	Composites's relatively poor bearing properties
Simple manufacturing process	Pone to fretting in metal
Simple inspection procedure	Prone to corrosion in metal
Not environmentaly sensitive	May require extensive shimming
Provides through-thickness reinforcement; not sensitive to peel stresses	
No major residual stress problem	

components but are unable to detect weak or (due to environmental degradation) potentially weak bonds. The limitations of NDI are a major reason why adhesive bonding has rarely been used in critical primary joints in metallic airframe structure; bonded metal joints are particularly prone to environmental degradation if not adequately surface-treated.

Mechanical fastening is usually the lower-cost option because of its simplicity and low-cost tooling and inspection requirements. However, hole-drilling can be highly labor intensive (unless automated) and, if not correctly done, can be highly damaging to the composite. Joints in aircraft usually require many thousands of expensive fasteners (usually titanium alloy), and extensive shimming may be required to avoid damage to the composite structure during bolt clamp-up. Thus adhesive bonding, despite the high tooling, process, and quality control costs, can in many cases offer significant cost savings.

9.3 Adhesively Bonded Joints

Symbols

Shear modulus (also used for strain energy release rate)	G	Young's modulus	E
Shear stress	τ	Stress	σ
Shear strain	γ	Strain	ε
Thickness	t	Displacement	U
Transfer length	L		
Plastic zone size	d	Applied load	P
Step length	N	Transmitted load	T
Scarf angle	θ	Thermal expansion coefficient	α
		Temperature range	ΔT

$$\Delta T = \text{(service temperature—cure temperature)}$$

Subscripts/Superscripts

Plastic condition	p	Outer adherend (also for mode 1 opening)	1
Elastic condition	e	Inner adherend (also for mode 2 opening)	2
Ultimate value	u	Maximum value	max
Adhesive	A	Minimum value	min
Temperature	T	Balanced	b
Value at infinite length	∞	Unbalanced	un
Critical value	C		

9.3.1 Introduction

Bonded joints used in aerospace applications can be classified as single (primary) or multiple (secondary) load path joints, as indicated in Figure 9.1. This section describes simple design procedures and some materials' engineering aspects relevant to the application of these types of joint in airframe structures.

In the design of bonded composite joints, consideration is given to each of the elements to be joined (adherends), including their geometry, size, materials of construction, actual or potential modes of failure, coefficients of thermal expansion, magnitude and nature of the loading involved, and operating environment.

Potential modes of failure are:

- Tensile, compressive, or shear of the adherends
- Shear or peel in the adhesive layer
- Shear or peel in the composite near-surface plies
- Shear or peel in the resin-rich layer on the surface of the composite
- Adhesive failure at the metal or composite/adhesive interface

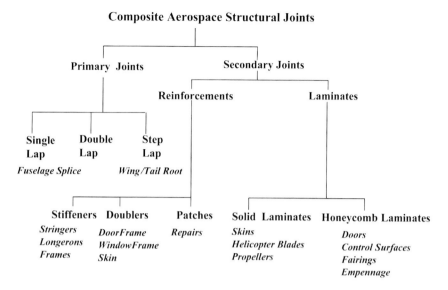

Fig. 9.1   Classification and applications of adhesively bonded joints used in airframe manufacture.

The design aim is for the joint to fail by bulk failure of the adherends. A margin of safety is generally included in the design to provide tolerance to service damage and manufacturing defects in the bond line. Generally, the adhesive is not allowed to be or to become the weak link[1] because adhesive strength can be highly variable, and the growth of damage or defects in the adhesive layer can be very rapid under cyclic loading. For composite adherends, the very thin, relatively brittle resin bonding the near-surface plies is more prone to failure than the adhesive layer, so great care must also be taken to ensure that this does not become the weak link.

The design input parameters include:

- Stiffness and strength (for metals usually the yield strength) of the adherends
- Shear modulus, yield strength, and strain-to-failure of the adhesive
- Thermal expansion coefficient of the adherends
- Magnitude and direction of the applied loads
- Overlap length of the adherends
- Thickness of the adherends
- Thickness of the adhesive

The properties used must be sufficient to handle the weakest state of the materials; for the adhesive and composite adherends, this is usually the hot/wet condition. It is most important to ensure that the strength of the adherend/adhesive interface does not become significantly weakened as a result of environmental degradation. For a degraded interface, there is no way of quantifying minimum strength; even zero is a possibility. Environmental degradation of the interface in service is much more likely if the adherends are not given the correct surface treatment before bonding. Suitable methods will be discussed later.

Fatigue damage or creep in the adhesive layer can be avoided, or at least minimized, by maintaining the adhesive in an elastic state for most of its service life. Ideally, significant plastic deformation of the adhesive should be permitted only when the joint is stressed to limit load. Limit load is the highest load expected during the service life of the aircraft. Even at ultimate load ($1.5\times$ limit), the strain in the adhesive should not approach the failure strain.

The design aim is to maintain the adhesive in a state of shear or compression. Structural adhesive joints (and composites) have relatively poor resistance to through-thickness (peel) stresses and, where possible, this type of loading is avoided. The classical joint types, suitable for joining composites to either composites or metals[2] (Fig. 9.2), are 1) the double lap, 2) the single lap, 3) the single scarf, 4) double scarf, 5) the single-step lap, and 6) the double-step lap.

Figure 9.3, by Hart-Smith,[3] illustrates schematically the load-carrying capacities of these joints and some simple design improvements.

The single-lap joint is generally the cheapest of all joints to manufacture. However, because the loads are offset (eccentric), a large secondary bending moment develops that results in the adhesive being subjected to severe peel stresses. This type of joint is therefore only used for lightly loaded structure or is supported by underlying structure such as an internal frame or stiffener.

The double-lap joint has no primary bending moment because the resultant load is collinear. However, peel stresses arise due to the moment produced by the unbalanced shear stresses acting at the ends of the outer adherends. The resulting stresses, although relatively much smaller in magnitude than in the single-lap joint, produce peel stresses limiting the thickness of material that can be joined. Peel (and shear) stresses in this region are reduced by tapering the ends of the joint. As shown in Figure 9.3, this markedly increases the load capacity of this joint.

The scarf and step-lap joints, when correctly designed, develop negligible peel stresses and may be used (at least in principle) to join composite components of any thickness.

To explore the feasibility of using primary lap joints that use only adhesive bonding, the USAF funded the Primary Adhesively Bonded Structure Technology (PABST) program[4] which, although concerned with the bonding of aluminum alloy airframe components, must be mentioned as a landmark in the development of bonded joints for aeronautical applications; many of its conclusions are relevant to bonded composite construction. The Douglas Aircraft Company was the major contractor. The program (based on a full-scale section of fuselage for a military transport aircraft) demonstrated that significant improvements could be obtained in integrity, durability, weight, and cost in an

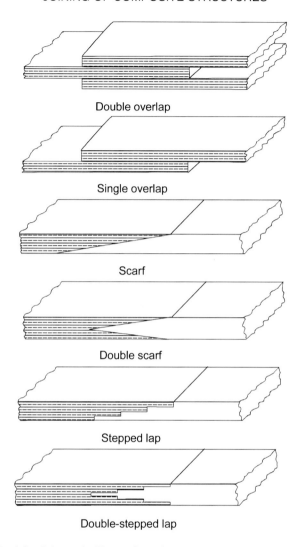

Double overlap

Single overlap

Scarf

Double scarf

Stepped lap

Double-stepped lap

Fig. 9.2   Schematic illustration of several types of bonded joint.

aluminum alloy fuselage component by the extensive use of bonded construction. The demonstrated weight-saving was about 15%, with a 20% saving in cost.

Lap joints relying solely on adhesive bonding, although structurally very attractive, are not generally used by major aircraft manufacturers in primary structural applications (such as fuselage splice joints) because of concerns with long-term environmental durability. These concerns stem from some early poor service experience with the environmental durability of adhesive bonds, resulting from the use of inadequate pre-bonding surface treatments and ambient-curing adhesives.

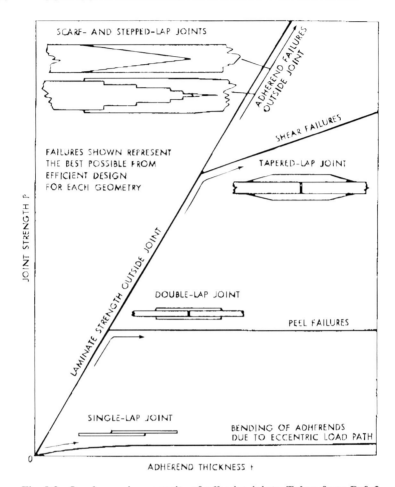

Fig. 9.3   Load-carrying capacity of adhesive joints. Taken from Ref. 3.

9.3.2   Design/Analysis of Bonded Lap Joints

Reviews of analytical procedures for joints involving composites are provided in Refs. 5 and 6. Hart-Smith undertook comprehensive analytical studies[7–9] on adhesive joints, particularly advanced fiber composite to composite and composite to metal joints. His studies, based on the earlier approaches, cover the important aspect of non-linear (elastic/plastic) deformation in the adhesive. The stress level for joint (adhesive) failure is determined by shear strain to failure of the adhesive ($\gamma_e + \gamma_p$) in the bondline; the design aim being that this stress level should well exceed adherend strength. Peel stresses are avoided by careful design rather than considered as a potential failure mode.

Several earlier attempts were made to represent non-linear behavior in the adhesive assuming realistic shear stress/shear strain behavior, but they were too

Table 9.2   Computer Programs Developed by Dr John Hart-Smith for
Stress Analysis of Bonded Joints

Joint to be analyzed	Program	Joint to be analyzed	Program
Single-lap joint: Joint strengths and efficiencies in non-dimensional form. *Deals only with identical adherends. Three failure cases are considered: a) adherend bending, b) adhesive shear, and c) adhesive peel.*	A4EA	Double-lap joint: Elastic adherend and elastic/plastic adhesive. *Can deal with unbalanced joints and allows for thermal mismatch between adherends. Provides ratio of maximum to average shear strength and non-dimensionalized joint strength.*	A4EB
Scarf Joint: Elastic adherend and elastic/plastic adhesive. *Provides a) shear stress distribution along the joint b) displacement of inner and outer adherends, and c) potential joint strength.*	A4EE	Step-lap joint: Elastic adherend and elastic/plastic adhesive. *Provides a) shear stress distribution along the joint, b) displacement of inner and outer adherends, and c) potential joint strength.*	A4EG
Step-lap joint: Elastic adherend and elastic/plastic adhesive. *Similar to A4EG but more comprehensive; allows for variations in adhesive thickness and adhesive defects. Bond width can also be varied.*	A4EI		

complex for most analytical approaches. However, as discussed later, Hart-Smith shows that a simple elastic/ideally plastic formulation gives similar results to more realistic representations of adhesive behavior, providing the strain energy density in shear in the adhesive (area under the stress-strain curve) is comparable to that expected for the real curve.

As a major part of these studies, software programs were developed for the analysis of double-overlap and the other types of joint discussed here; these are listed in Table 9.2. Similar programs are available through the Engineering Sciences Data Unit (ESDU)[9] and proprietary programs have been developed by manufacturers.

Inevitably, many of the complications in real joints are neglected or inadequately dealt with in these relatively simple studies. These include:

- Influence of flaws in the form of local porosity, local disbonds, etc.
- Adhesive thickness variations
- Through-thickness variation of shear stresses
- Through-thickness stresses
- Stress-free state at the ends of the adhesive
- Highly beneficial effect of adhesive spew, excess adhesive that forms a fillet at the edges of the joint
- True shear stress/shear strain behavior

Most of these complexities are best modelled using finite element procedures. For example, the simple analytical procedures for lap joints mentioned here predict that the maximum shear stress occurs at the free ends of the overlap. However, because the end of the overlap is a free surface, the principle of complimentary shears is violated because the horizontal shear force at the ends cannot be balanced by a vertical shear force. In reality, therefore, the stress along the bond line right at the edge must fall to zero. More realistic stress analysis—using the finite element approach[10] shows that this is the case—shear stress falls rapidly to zero over a distance of the order of the adherend thickness; these observations are confirmed by direct experimental observations. However, the shear stress distribution along the bond line and magnitude of the maximum stress predicted by the simple analytical procedures turns out to be approximately correct. Similar observations have been made concerning normal or peel stresses.

A further considerable complication, difficult to handle even with finite element methods, is the time dependency or viscoelastic (and viscoplastic) behavior of adhesives.

9.3.3 Models for Adhesive Stress/Strain Behavior

For analysis of stress distribution in the joint, a model for the shear stress/strain behavior of the adhesive is required. The simplest model assumes that the adhesive is strained only within its linear elastic range. This model may be adequate if fatigue is a major concern and the primary aim is to avoid plastic cycling of the adhesive; then the stresses must not be allowed to exceed τ_p. However, use of the elastic model is overly conservative for assessing the static strength of a joint, particularly if it is bonded with a highly ductile adhesive.

To account for plastic deformation, the actual stress/strain behavior must be modelled. In computer-based approaches such as the finite element method, the stress/strain curve can be closely modelled using the actual constitutive relationship. However, for analytical approaches, much simpler models are needed.

Figure 9.4 shows stress/strain behavior for a typical ductile adhesive and the models of this behavior used for joint analysis by Hart-Smith.[11] The intuitive simple non-linear model is the bilinear characteristic because this most closely approximates to the real curve. However, even use of this simple model is mathematically complex, greatly limiting the cases that can be analyzed to produce closed-form solutions.

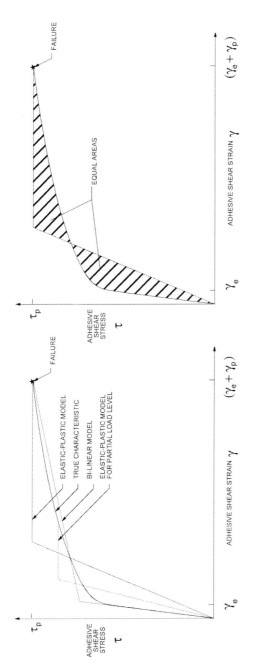

Fig. 9.4   Models for representing the shear stress/strain behavior in an adhesive. Taken from Ref. 11.

The ideally elastic/plastic models, (Fig. 9.4), greatly simplify the analysis, allowing closed-form solutions to be developed for a wide range of joints. It is shown that the requirement for the elastic/ideally plastic model is that it has the same shear strain energy (area under the curve) as the actual curve and intersects it at the required level of shear stress. Thus, as indicated in Figure 9.4, the effective shear modulus G_A and shear yield stress used in the model vary with the strain level.

In most joint designs, it is sufficient to undertake a simple elastic analysis to check that, for most of the operation of the joint (below limit load), the adhesive will not deform plastically and then, using the effective elastic/plastic parameters, assess the load-carrying capacity of the joint.

For the strength analysis to be conservative, the hot/wet shear yield strength should be used to assess the likelihood of fatigue damage, then the low-temperature stress/strain behavior of the adhesive used to estimate static strength (because the area under the stress–strain curve is then a minimum).

9.3.4   Load Transfer Mechanisms in Overlap Joints

The skin/doubler joint shown in Figure 9.5 provides a simple illustration of the main features of load transfer in a lap joint. The overlap length is assumed to be semi-infinite, which means that it is very much larger than the load-transfer length based on the exponent β.

Loading of the outer adherend occurs by the development of surface shear forces, which arise as the adhesive layer resists the shear displacement between the inner, directly loaded adherend and the outer, initially unloaded, adherend. Load transfer by the shear forces produces an increasing axial strain in the outer (reinforcing) adherend and a reducing strain in the inner adherend until, at some point, the strains in the two adherends become equal; the shear strain in the adhesive is then zero.

9.3.4.1 Elastic Model for the Adhesive.   The analysis assuming elastic behavior is outlined in Figure 9.5, and the outcome is illustrated in Figure 9.6. It is assumed here that failure occurs when $\tau_{\max} = \tau_p$ for the adhesive. Bending effects, for example, due to joint rotation, are not considered in this analysis. It therefore corresponds to a symmetric double-lap joint or symmetric doubler configuration, or a single-lap/single-sided doubler configuration in which bending is reacted by other supporting structure.

The main analytical results from this model are as follows:

Shear stress and strain distributions are given by:

$$\tau = \tau_P e^{-\beta x} \tag{9.1}$$

$$\gamma = \gamma_P e^{-\beta x} \tag{9.2}$$

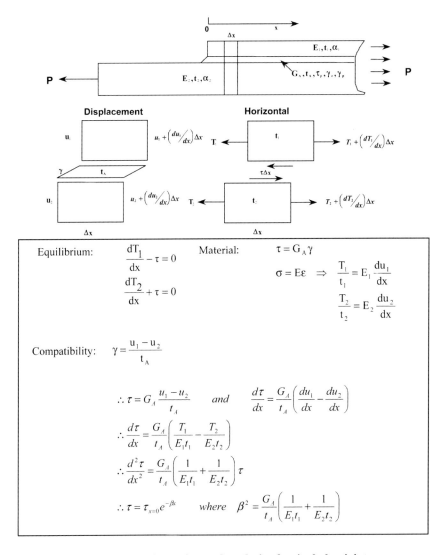

Fig. 9.5   Configuration and analysis of a single-lap joint.

where

$$\beta^2 = \frac{G_A}{t_A}\left[\frac{1}{E_1 t_1} + \frac{1}{E_2 t_2}\right] \qquad (9.3)$$

Because of the low shear moduli of polymer-matrix composites, a modification[12] of this equation is required to estimate β. This can be done (assuming a linear shear lag across the thickness) by replacing t_A/G_A with the

Shear stress/strain distribution at adhesive yield

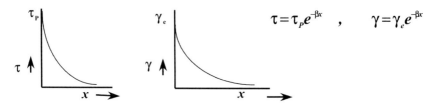

Load transfer

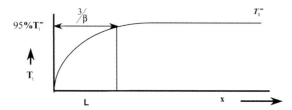

Fig. 9.6   Outcome of the analysis of the skin-doubler joint, assuming elastic behavior in the adhesive.

effective value:

$$\left(\frac{t_A}{G_A}\right)_{eff} = \frac{t_A}{G_A} + \frac{t_2}{G_2} + \frac{3t_1}{8G_1} \tag{9.4}$$

where G_1 and G_2 are, respectively, the shear moduli of the outer and inner adherend.

The maximum load that can be transferred from the inner to the outer adherend per unit width of joint before adhesive yield is given by:

$$T_{1\,max}^{\infty} = \tau_p \int_0^{\infty} e^{-\beta x} dx = \frac{\tau_P}{\beta} \tag{9.5}$$

which is the area under the shear-stress/length curve.

The distance to transfer most (95%) of the load, the load transfer length, is given by:

$$L_{min} = \frac{3}{\beta} \tag{9.6}$$

If the transfer length is less than $3/\beta$, it is not possible to obtain full load sharing between the adherends.

In the absence of residual stress due to thermal-expansion, mismatch between adherends, and a differential between operating and cure temperatures, the maximum load per unit width (P_{max}) that can be applied at the end of adherend 2 without yielding the adhesive is given by:

$$P_{\max} = \left(\frac{\tau_P}{\beta}\right)\left(1 + \frac{E_2 t_2}{E_1 t_1}\right) \tag{9.7}$$

If residual stresses can arise as a result of the difference in expansion coefficients between, say, a metal panel and a composite doubler, the maximum load that can be applied without yielding the adhesive is given by:

$$P^T_{\max} = P_{\max} + E_2 t_2 (\alpha_1 - \alpha_2)\Delta T \tag{9.8}$$

In this equation, ΔT (service temperature—cure temperature) is always negative so that the influence of residual stresses on the maximum load transfer depends on the sign of $\Delta \alpha$ If, for example, adherend 1 is carbon/epoxy and adherend 2 aluminum, then $\Delta \alpha$ is negative and almost equal in magnitude to α for aluminum; taking aluminum as $23 \times 10^{-6} \, °C^{-1}$ and α for a quasi isotopic carbon/epoxy composite to be $4 \times 10^{-6} \, °C^{-1}$.

The result is an increase in the maximum tensile load and a reduction in the maximum compressive load that can be carried by the joint after cooling from the cure temperature. This result is easily explained physically. The inner metallic adherend contracts as the joint is cooled from the cure temperature, producing shear stresses in the adhesive opposing those produced by the applied tensile load. Thus, a significant tensile load must be applied to the joint to overcome this contraction before adhesive starts to be sheared in the original direction. The converse occurs if the applied load is compressive. This topic of residual stress is discussed again later with respect to the double-overlap joint.

9.3.4.2 Elastic/Plastic Model for the Adhesive.
The shear stress/joint length relationship in the adhesive, assuming elastic/plastic behavior, is shown in Figure 9.7. In this figure, it is assumed that the adhesive is strained to its full

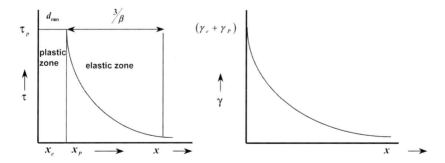

Fig. 9.7   Shear stress/length and shear strain/length distribution in the skin-doubler joint, assuming elastic/plastic behavior in the adhesive.

capacity (see Fig. 9.4), which is:

$$\gamma = \gamma_e + \gamma_P \tag{9.9}$$

As shown in Figure 9.7, a plastic zone length d develops in addition to the elastic zone length $3/\beta$.

Thus, the maximum load transfer capacity is:

$$T^\infty_{1\,\text{max}} = \tau_P \int_0^d dx_P + \tau_P \int_0^\infty e^{-\beta x_e} dx_e = \tau_p d_{\text{max}} + \frac{\tau_P}{\beta} \tag{9.10}$$

The length of the plastic zone at failure of the adhesive[11] is given by:

$$d_{\text{max}} = \frac{1}{\beta}\left[\left(1 + 2\left(\frac{\gamma_P}{\gamma_e}\right)\right)^{1/2} - 1\right] \tag{9.11}$$

Using these equations, it can be shown[3] that the maximum load that can be applied to adherend 2 without failing the adhesive is given by:

$$P_{\text{max}} = \left\{\left[2t_A E_2 t_2\left(1 + \frac{E_2 t_2}{E_1 t_1}\right)\right]\left[\tau_P\left(\frac{\gamma_e}{2} + \gamma_P\right)\right]\right\}^{1/2} \tag{9.12a}$$

and, for thermal mismatch,

$$P^T_{\text{max}} = P_{\text{max}} + E_2 t_2(\alpha_1 - \alpha_2)\Delta T \tag{9.12b}$$

The area under the shear stress–strain curve for the adhesive appears explicitly within the second square bracket in equation (9.12a). This suggests that the load transfer capability should not change significantly with temperature because experimental studies on stress/strain behavior (for ductile structural film adhesives) show that this area does not vary greatly with temperature. The area under the shear stress-strain curve multiplied by the adhesive thickness t_A is a measure of the maximum fracture energy per unit area of crack growth, as discussed in more detail later.

The length required to transfer the load, $T^\infty_{1\text{max}}$, is now given by:

$$L_{\text{min}} = d_{\text{max}} + \frac{3}{\beta} \tag{9.13}$$

The minimum transfer length L_{min} required to transfer T^∞_1 under arbitrary external load P is [based on equation (9.10)] obtained as follows:

$$T^\infty_1 = \int_0^\infty \tau dx = \tau_p d + \frac{\tau_P}{\beta}$$

also:

$$T^\infty_1 = P/(1 + E_2 t_2/E_1 t_1)$$

and since:

$$L_{\min} = d + \frac{3}{\beta}$$

then:

$$L_{\min} = P/[\tau_P(1 + E_2 t_2/E_1 t_1)] + 2/\beta \qquad (9.14)$$

9.3.4.3 End-Termination Shape.
The above models have assumed that the doubler (adherend 1) is of constant thickness. However, if its ends are tapered, the peak shear (and peel) stresses can be greatly reduced. This can be achieved by forming an end taper (or scarf) or, as illustrated in Figure 9.8, by stepping. Stepping is the usual configuration for composite joints since it arises naturally when laminating.

An analysis for the stress distribution in doublers with scarfed stepped skin ends is described by Chalkly[13]. Figure 9.8 illustrates part of the model used, and Figure 9.9 is a plot, for the elastic case, of step thickness versus peak shear strain in the adhesive, assuming a step thickness of 0.13 mm and material properties for the composite boron/epoxy; the maximum thickness is 0.65 mm. The peak shear strain asymptotes to a lower bound of about half the peak level after a step length of about 5 mm. Actually, in most practical doubler applications, a step length of approximately 3 mm is used. The peel stress in the adhesive will also be markedly reduced by stepping. Stepping (or scarfing) the ends of the doubler is required in most practical applications, unless the doubler is less than a few plies thick.

A useful estimate of the influence of stepping the ends of the doubler can be obtained using the simple analysis for a constant-thickness doubler, outlined in Figure 9.5. The results are shown as the bounds in Figure 9.9, taking the minimum thickness to be one ply and the maximum thickness that of the full five plies. The step length required to achieve the lower bound is of the order of 4 mm, which is about the minimum length required for full load transfer $(3/\beta)$.

It is of note that, for a similar thickness doubler and tapering distance, the analysis shows that the step configuration develops a lower peak shear strain than the scarfed configuration.

9.3.5 Double-Overlap Joint

Figure 9.10 shows schematically one side of a simple double-overlap joint. It is assumed in this diagram that the adherends are of similar (balanced) stiffness, the product of modulus and thickness (Et). At the left end, where the outer adherend terminates, the load distribution is identical to that in the skin-doubler joint shown in Figure 9.5. At the right end, where the inner adherend terminates, the load remaining in the inner adherend is transferred to the outer adherend—this configuration is Figure 9.5, inverted.

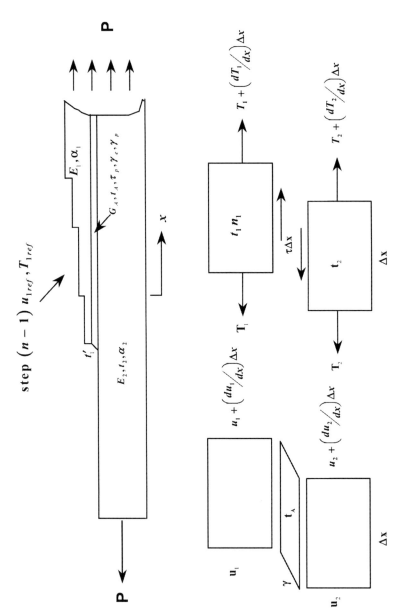

Fig. 9.8   Skin-doubler joint with stepped ends, showing part of the analytical model.

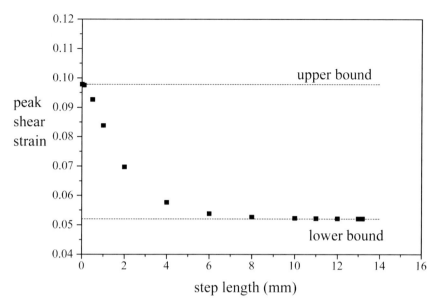

Fig. 9.9 Outcome of the analysis of the skin/doubler joint with stepped ends, assuming elastic behavior of the adhesive. The upper and lower bounds assume full thickness or thickness of one ply. Taken from Ref. 13.

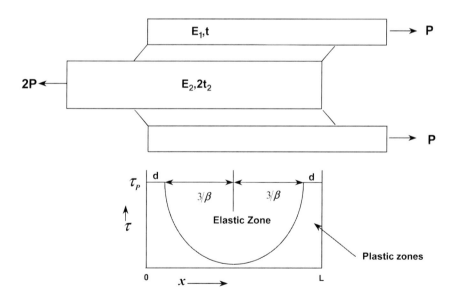

Fig. 9.10 Double-overlap joint showing shear stress/length distribution in the adhesive, assuming elastic/plastic behavior in the adhesive and stiffness-balanced adherends.

9.3.5.1 Overlap-Length, Balanced Joint.   Figure 9.10 shows schematically the shear stress distribution in the adhesive in the double-overlap joint. To minimize the weight penalty in the joint, it is desirable to use the shortest possible overlap length, with some allowance for defects and damage. The minimum overlap length, L_{min}, for $P < P_{max}$, is estimated as follows.

We have that:

$$L_{min} = 2d + 6/\beta \quad \text{minimum transfer length}$$

and:

$$T_{1\,max} = 2\tau_P d + 2\tau_P/\beta = P \quad \text{maximum load transferred}$$

so:

$$d = P/2\tau_P - 1/\beta$$

For adherend 1, failure $P = P_u = \sigma_{1u}t_1$.

Thus,

$$L_{min} = \frac{\sigma_{1u}t_1}{\tau_P} + \frac{4}{\beta} \tag{9.15}$$

Alternatively, for composites, it is usual to work to an ultimate design strain level ε_u, typically 4000 microstrain. The strain capacity to failure exceeds this value markedly, typically up to 13,000 microstrain, but this much more modest value allows for strength reduction due to damage and stress concentrations.

Then (per unit width of the joint):

$$P_u = E_1 \varepsilon_u t_1 \tag{9.16}$$

Here P_u is half the total load applied to the joint. Then:

$$L_{min} = E_1 \varepsilon_u t_1/\tau_P + 4/\beta \tag{9.17}$$

In this case, since $E_1 = E_2$ and the total thickness of the outer adherends equals the inner adherend $= 2t$, β is simplified in equation (9.3) to $\beta = \sqrt{2G_A/t_A Et}$.

However, longer overlaps are highly desirable (if cost and weight penalties are not too great) because they provide high levels of damage tolerance to voids and other flaws. It is important that the minimum value of shear stress τ_{min} not exceed about $\tau_P/10$, which approximately corresponds with the elastic trough of length $3/\beta$.

As overlap lengths decrease below L_{min}, the minimum shear stress in the elastic trough τ_{min} gradually increases until it becomes uniform (τ can reach a maximum level of τ_P when the whole adhesive layer becomes plastic). This results in 1) a loss of damage tolerance because the joint strength is sensitive to bond length, and 2) a susceptibility to creep strain accumulation.

9.3.5.2 Stiffness Imbalance. The load-carrying capacity of a double-overlap joint is estimated as follows.

For the right-hand end, from equation (*9.12*):

$$P_{max} = \left\{\left[2t_A E_1 t_1\left(1 + \frac{E_1 t_1}{E_2 t_2}\right)\right]\left[\tau_P\left(\frac{\gamma_e}{2} + \gamma_P\right)\right]\right\}^{1/2}$$

Similarly, for the left-hand end:

$$P_{max} = \left\{\left[2t_A E_2 t_2\left(1 + \frac{E_2 t_2}{E_1 t_1}\right)\right]\left[\tau_P\left(\frac{\gamma_e}{2} + \gamma_P\right)\right]\right\}^{1/2} \quad (9.18)$$

The strength is given by the lower of these two values.

For a stiffness-balanced joint $E_1 t_1 = E_2 t_2 = Et$, so

$$P_{max\,b} = 2\left[t_A Et\tau_P\left(\frac{\gamma_e}{2} + \gamma_P\right)\right]^{1/2} \quad (9.19)$$

If an unbalanced joint is created by reducing the stiffness of one of the adherends, let $S = E_1 t_1/E_2 t_2$ or $= E_2 t_2/E_1 t_1$, whichever is the smaller. Then:

$$P_{max\,un} = \left\{\left[2t_A SEt(1 + S)\right]\left[\tau_P\left(\frac{\gamma_e}{2} + \gamma_P\right)\right]\right\}^{1/2}$$

then:

$$\frac{P_{max\,un}}{P_{max\,b}} = \frac{\sqrt{2S(1 + S)}}{2} \quad (9.20)$$

Because this ratio must always be less than 1, the unbalanced joint is always weaker than the balanced joint. The weaker end of the joint is where the lower stiffness adherend extends. This is intuitively obvious because this is the end with the greater deformation of the adherend, resulting in the larger shear deformation in the adhesive.

9.3.5.3 Thermal-Expansion Mismatch. As with the skin-doubler joint, residual stresses have a significant influence on the strength of the double-overlap joint. Unlike the skin-doubler joint, the residual stress has a different effect at each end of the joint, being beneficial at one end and detrimental at the other,[7] as illustrated in Figure 9.11.

For a balanced joint the load-carrying capacity is given by the smaller value of:

$$P_{max} = 2\left[t_A Et\tau_P\left(\frac{\gamma_e}{2} + \gamma_P\right)\right]^{1/2} \pm Et\Delta\alpha\Delta T \quad (9.21)$$

where $\Delta\alpha$ is the difference in expansion coefficients between adherends.

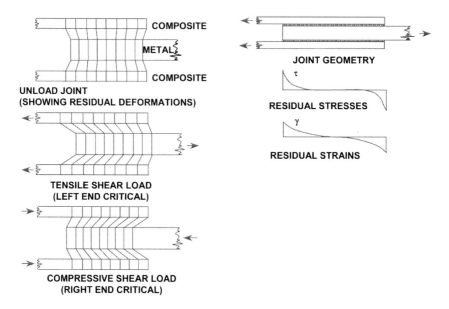

Fig. 9.11 Schematic illustration of the effect of thermal expansion mismatch in a double-overlap joint. Taken from Ref. 7.

The situation is somewhat more complicated when there is both stiffness imbalance and residual stress due to thermal-expansion mismatch. The load-carrying capacity of the joint in this case is given by:

$$P_{\max} = \left\{\left[2t_A E_1 t_1\left(1 + \frac{E_1 t_1}{E_2 t_2}\right)\right]\left[\tau_P\left(\frac{\gamma_e}{2} + \gamma_P\right)\right]\right\}^{1/2} + E_1 t_1(\alpha_2 - \alpha_1)\Delta T \quad (9.22a)$$

or

$$P_{\max} = \left\{\left[2t_A E_2 t_2\left(1 + \frac{E_2 t_2}{E_1 t_1}\right)\right]\left[\tau_P\left(\frac{\gamma_e}{2} + \gamma_P\right)\right]\right\}^{1/2} + E_2 t_2(\alpha_1 - \alpha_2)\Delta T \quad (9.22b)$$

9.3.5.4 Peel-Strength Limitation on Strength and Methods of Alleviation. The approach used by Hart-Smith[8] to estimate peel stress is outlined in Figure 9.12. The origin of the peel stress is the horizontal shear stress, which results from load transfer along the bond line at the ends of the joint. Because there are no complementary vertical shear stresses at this point, the unbalanced horizontal shear stress produces a bending moment that acts to bend the outer adherend away from inner adherend. To react-out this bending moment,

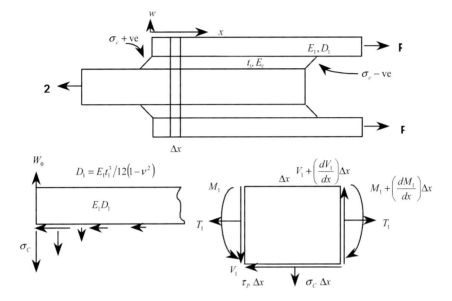

Fig. 9.12   Model analysis for peel stresses.

through-thickness (peel stresses) develop in the adhesive. Note that while the peel stress at the ends of the joint is positive for tensile loading, it is negative (compressive) for compressive loading, so not usually of concern.

Hart-Smith[14] also provides detailed treatment of design to minimize peel stresses in several other types of bonded joint. The simplifying assumption made in most of these analyses is that the shear stress at the ends of the adherends is constant at τ_p, the shear yield stress in the adhesive.

From the analysis outlined in Figure 9.12, the result is that the peel stress, σ_c, is given by:

$$\sigma_c = \tau_p \left(\frac{3E'_c t_1}{E_1 t_A} \right)^{1/4} \tag{9.23}$$

where E'_C is the effective transverse stiffness of the joint, including the adhesive and adherends. From this relationship, it can be seen that σ_c increases with increasing thickness of the outer adherend and is reduced with increasing modulus of the outer adherend and increasing thickness of the adhesive layer. Peel stresses can be alleviated by control of these parameters as well as by the various approaches illustrated in Figure 9.13. The presence of adhesive spew, as discussed in the next section, can also significantly reduce peel stresses.

Metallic adherends have very high peel strength, therefore peel failures occur in the adhesive layer. In contrast, peel is much more of a concern with composite

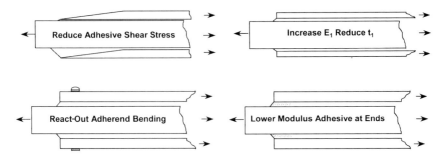

Fig. 9.13   Some methods for alleviating peel stresses.

laminates because they have much lower peel strength than do structural adhesives. Failure can occur in the plies close to the bond surface, or even in the resin-rich layer on the composite surface if this is not removed before bonding.

Comparison of peel resistance of composites can be made more conveniently on the basis of the relative mode I (opening or peel mode) fracture energy. This approach is described later.

9.3.5.5 Adhesive Spew.   As mentioned previously, in practical joints a fillet or spew of adhesive forms from adhesive squeezed out during the bonding process. Unless removed by machining, the spew forms part of the geometry of the joint and reduces the maximum shear and peel stresses at the ends of the joint. The spew also acts as a barrier to the ingress of fluids from the operating environment in this critical region of the joint. Thus, removal of the spew, as is sometimes done for cosmetic reasons, is very bad practice.

Classical analytical approaches cannot satisfactorily model this region, so finite element procedures are appropriate. The influence of the spew on stress distribution has been studied in some detail,[10,15] modelling it as a 45° triangle of varying size. In reality, the shape of the spew can vary considerably and can contain significant porosity.

It is found that, within the bond line away from the ends, the principal stresses are tension and compression of equal magnitude—showing that, as predicted by analytical procedures, the adhesive is in a state of pure shear. Within the spew, the principal stress is aligned approximately parallel to the angle of the fillet and is predominantly tensile.

It is predicted and found that for relatively low ductility adhesives, brittle failure occurs in the spew at right angles to the principal tensile stress. The maximum stresses occur very close to the corner of the adherend edge (if sharp) and result in failure at this point. Compared with the failure stresses with no fillet, the maximum shear and peel stresses are reduced by approximately 20% or 30%. A considerable further reduction in peak stresses (about 30%) is obtained by rounding off the corner of the adherends.

In the case of adhesives having significant ductility, it is shown that plastic deformation initiates at these points of high stress.[10]

One approach that considers adhesive spew and ductility[16] correctly predicts the experimentally observed effect of adhesive thickness. Most other theories (finite element as well as analytical) predict that the joint becomes stronger with increasing thickness, in contrast to the observed behavior.

It is assumed that failure occurs when the adhesive layer yields along the full length of the joint. Thus, once the joint is fully yielded (globally yielded), it can carry no further load, and failure ensues. It is shown that although yielding occurs at lower loads in a thin adhesive layer, it spreads more rapidly in a thick adhesive layer—because of lower constraint and more uniform stress distribution.

9.3.6 Effects of Defects in Lap Joints

Considerations have so far been confined to idealized joints having a uniform adhesive layer and uniform adherends. However, in real joints, manufacturing defects and service damage defects occur in the adhesive layer and should be taken into account in the analysis to assess their effect on strength. These defects include local disbonded regions, porosity, and locally thinned regions. The effects of such defects are addressed by Hart-Smith[17] and will be briefly outlined here with respect to the double-overlap joint. The effects of defects can also be evaluated using a fracture mechanics approach, as described later.

Provided the joint is otherwise sound, the effect of local disbonds at the ends of the double-overlap joint is simply to reduce overlap length. Thus, as long as the overlap length is greater than the minimum, no reduction in strength should occur.

A small region of disbond at the center of the joint would have no effect if the overlap length is large. Even if the overlap length were of the minimum length, the effect of the disbond would not be great because only a small proportion of the load is transferred through this region.

Porosity up to a few percent appears to have relatively little effect on static strength of the joint, even when located in the critical load transfer zone at the ends of the joint. It appears that the discrete ligaments between the pores act independently and do not link up to significantly reduce the shear strain capacity of the adhesive. To model the effect of porosity in the joint, it may be sufficient to reduce the effective shear modulus, G_A, the shear yield strain γ_e, and the strain capacity, γ_P The actual values used could be obtained analytically or experimentally. Cyclic loading may be of concern because the voids may link up and form a major disbond. This aspect is under investigation, but is unlikely to be of concern for most practical joints because of conservative design. However, fatigue may be much more of a concern in repair applications, where safety margins are often much lower.

Although it appears that limited porosity may not be of concern in a structural sense, durability problems may arise in service due to the easier path to the bond interface for moisture or other aggressive agents.

During manufacture, excessive adhesive flow may occur out of the ends of a joint. This situation arises because at the ends of the joint there is little resistance to flow of the adhesive and also because locally high pressures can arise in this region. In an extreme case most of the adhesive may be expelled, leaving only a very porous adhesive layer or, in the case of a structural film adhesive, a porous adhesive plus carrier.

Because very high strains will arise in the adhesive—leading to early failure—it is appropriate to consider this region a local disbond. Provided the overlap length is sufficient and tapering of the ends is not required, little loss of joint strength should result. However, disbonded regions at the ends of the joint, although not detrimental initially, can allow ingress of aggressive agents from the environment and so pose a durability problem.

9.3.7 Step-Lap Joint

The step-lap joint is essentially a series of overlap joints and is analyzed as such. Figure 9.14 is an outline of the simple one-dimensional analytical model.[9]

As with the overlap joint, the stepped-lap joint has a non-uniform shear stress distribution with high stresses at the ends of the each step. With correct design, the step-lap joint is capable of joining adherends of any thickness. It is

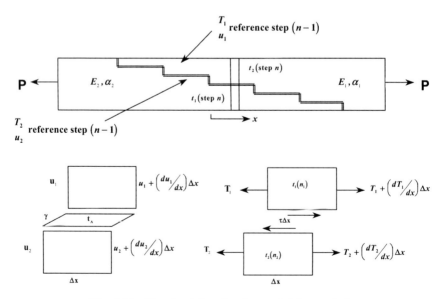

Fig. 9.14   Step-lap joint showing model for analysis.

particularly well-suited to joining laminated composite components because the step-lap configuration is readily produced by the laminating process.

Design of step-lap joints is considerably simplified using the software such as the programs listed in Table 9.2.

To maximize the load-carrying capacity of a stepped-lap joint, it is not sufficient just to increase the length of the steps, because the load-carrying capacity does not increase indefinitely with length. To increase load capacity, it is necessary to increase the number of steps. Furthermore, to avoid overloading thin end steps, it may actually be necessary to reduce their length.

Peel stresses are not usually a problem with step-lap joints because of the alignment of the primary loads and the small thickness change at the ends of each step.

One of the best-known examples of a step-lap joint is the wing-skin-to-fuselage attachment used in the F/A-18 aircraft, shown in Figure 9.15, consisting of (AS3501-2) carbon/epoxy skins bonded with adhesive FM300 to titanium alloy 6Al-4V. Similar joints are used to join boron/epoxy to titanium alloy for the empennage of the F-14 and F-15 aircraft As explained earlier, titanium alloy is used as the metallic component of the joint because it has a low thermal expansion coefficient (around $9 \times 10^{-6}\,^{\circ}C^{-1}$) and (unlike aluminum alloys) is not prone to galvanic corrosion when in electrical contact with carbon fibers.

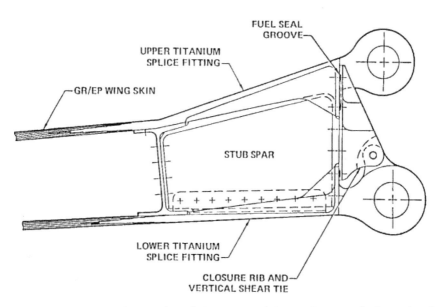

Fig. 9.15 Schematic illustration of the step-lap joint used to attach the carbon/ epoxy wing skin to the titanium alloy fuselage attachment lug of the F-18 military aircraft.

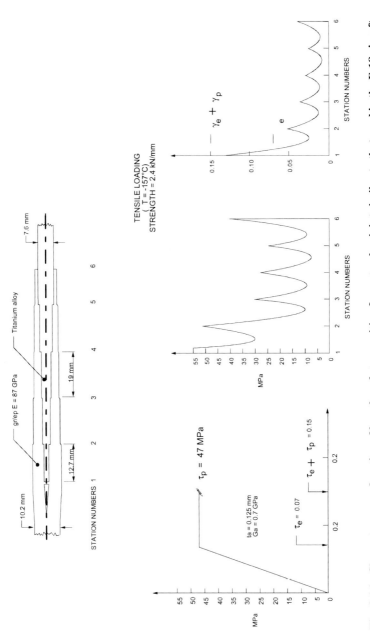

Fig. 9.16   Shear stress as a function of length and step position for a step-lap joint similar to that used in the F-18 aicraft. Taken from Ref. 8.

Figure 9.16 shows the predicted shear-stress distribution for the F/A-18 step-lap joint.

The manufacturing process for step-lap joints is as follows:

- Machine the titanium-alloy wing-root fitting to form the inner step-lap
- Surface-treat and prime the fitting to ensure durable bonding (bonding aspects will be discussed later)
- Apply a layer of adhesive to the lower surface of the fitting
- Place the fitting onto a carbon/epoxy lay-up already in place on the tool—this forms the lower half of the wing skin
- Place adhesive on the top of the fitting
- Lay-up the top half of the wing skin over the lower half of the skin and the fitting

Finally, the whole component is bagged and cured in an autoclave. In this process, it is most important that the plies be correctly positioned. If they are too long or too short for the step, they will cause out-of-plane distortion of the succeeding plies. The result of poor ply placement is development of transverse stresses, leading to the initiation and propagation of delaminations, which will degrade or ultimately cause failure of the joint.

9.3.8 Scarf Joint

Scarf joints (Fig. 9.17) are used mainly for repairs to composite structures, and are therefore discussed more fully in Chapter 10. A simple strength-of-materials

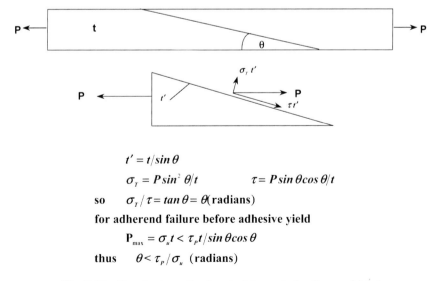

$$t' = t/\sin\theta$$

$$\sigma_T = P\sin^2\theta/t \qquad \tau = P\sin\theta\cos\theta/t$$

so $\quad \sigma_T/\tau = \tan\theta = \theta(\text{radians})$

for adherend failure before adhesive yield

$$P_{max} = \sigma_u t < \tau_p t/\sin\theta\cos\theta$$

thus $\quad \theta < \tau_p/\sigma_u$ (**radians**)

Fig. 9.17 Simple strength of materials analysis of a scarf joint.

analysis (based on resolution of stresses and areas), as shown in Figure 9.17, provides a reasonably close estimate of the shear stress in scarf joints where the stiffnesses and expansion coefficients of the adherends are similar,[18] as is generally the situation in a repair. The adhesive is assumed to undergo only elastic shear stress/strain behavior. This is a reasonable assumption in most cases because general yielding is generally not acceptable in a scarf joint for reasons discussed later.

The analysis predicts a uniform shear stress in the adhesive layer given by:

$$\tau = \frac{P \sin \theta \cos \theta}{t} \tag{9.24}$$

and a uniform normal stress in the adhesive given by:

$$\sigma_T = \frac{P \sin^2 \theta}{t} \tag{9.25}$$

The ratio of normal stress to shear stress is given by:

$$\frac{\sigma_T}{\tau} = \tan \theta = \theta \text{ (radians)} \tag{9.26}$$

Thus, for a taper angle of $5°$, the ratio is <0.1, showing that the normal stresses are negligible.

For adherend failure before adhesive yield, we have that:

$$P_{\max} = \sigma_u t \leq \frac{\tau_p t}{\sin \theta \cos \theta} \tag{9.27}$$

Thus:

$$\theta < \frac{\tau_p}{\sigma_u} \tag{9.28}$$

It will be shown in Chapter 10 that, for typical repair applications, this requires a θ of about $3°$.

The uniform shear stress in a balanced scarf joint is beneficial in that the strength of the joint is not limited by local high-stress concentrations at the ends, as in a lap joint. Thus, the load-carrying capacity of the joint increases in proportion to the thickness of the adherends so that, at least in principle, the thickness of material that can be joined is unlimited. However, because there is no elastic trough to limit continuous deformation under prolonged loading, creep leading to eventual failure must be expected if the effective adhesive shear yield stress is reached. Further, joint strength will be sensitive to damage to the tapered edge.

In practice, because of the viscoplastic nature of the adhesive, there is probably no lower limit to the adhesive yield stress under prolonged loading. The reduced yield stress and increased time-dependent behavior imposes a limitation on the allowable load in scarf joints under hot/wet conditions. Thus, design must be based on conservative estimates of elastic properties.

If the adherends are dissimilar in stiffness and/or thermal expansion properties, as in a composite-to-metal joint, a much more complex analysis will be required; part of the model for the one-dimensional elastic analysis[3] is shown in Figure 9.18. This analysis can be based on elastic or elastic/ideally plastic behavior in the adhesive. Table 9.2 provides details on computer programs for analyzing scarf joints.

The net result of the analysis for joints with adherends with different stiffnesses or thermal expansion coefficients is that the shear stress in the joint is no longer uniform. Assuming elastic behavior in the adhesive, it is found that the shear stress concentration, maximum-adhesive-stress/minimum-adhesive-stress (unity for a balanced joint), asymptotes to the lowest adherend stiffness ratio. The effect of adhesive plasticity is to extend the length over which the stress ratio is unity.

The effect of thermal expansion mismatch (stiffness-balanced adherends) is more complex with the shear stress concentration rising and falling with increasing scarf length; at large lengths (very small θ) the ratio approaches unity, as for no thermal mismatch.

9.3.9 Materials Aspects

Bonded joints, composite/composite or composite/metal, are made by secondary bonding or cocuring. In secondary bonding, the components of the joints are first manufactured and are then bonded with a structural adhesive in a secondary operation. In cocuring the joint, the component is cured along with the adhesive during the bonding process. In some all-composite joints, the adhesive is omitted during a cocure, the matrix (resin) being relied on to provide the bond.

The advantage of secondary bonding is that both joint components are processed under ideal conditions and can be inspected before bonding. The advantages of cocuring are that the process is reduced by one step, the critical adherend/adhesive interface is effectively removed and very good dimensional control is possible—even in very complex joints.

9.3.9.1 Structural Adhesives.
Most structural adhesives are based on epoxies because these form strong bonds to most suitably prepared substrates, and particularly to high-energy substrates such as metals. Epoxies exhibit little shrinkage during cure, minimizing residual bond-line stresses. Also, because only small amounts of volatiles are emitted during cure, they require only relatively low pressures.

However, even though epoxies have relatively high strength and stiffness and many other desirable properties, they are too brittle to be used in their unmodified form as structural adhesives. Thus, as described in Chapter 4, various approaches

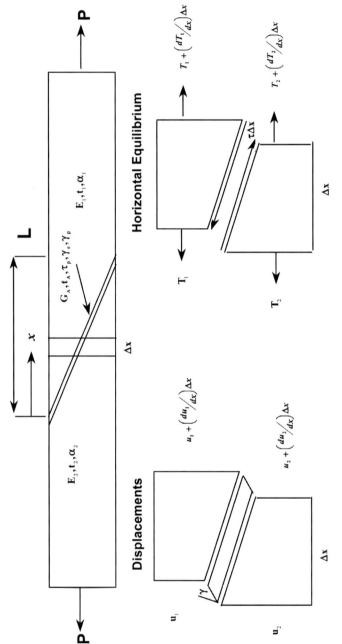

Fig. 9.18   Model for analysis of a scarf joint.

are used to provide toughening, including the formation of a solid solution with a more ductile polymer, precipitation of an elastomeric second phase, and development of an interpenetrating polymer network.

Adhesive forms.   Structural adhesives are generally available in two main forms—pastes and film. Paste adhesives are usually of two-component form (i.e., resin and hardener), which are mixed together just before use. In this form, they have the advantage that grades that cure at ambient temperature can be used—also, in most systems, there are no major life limitations before the mixing takes place.

Paste adhesives can also be single component. In this case, the curing agent is premixed with the adhesive. Only adhesives curing at elevated temperature can be stored in this form, and refrigeration is required to provide a reasonable storage life.

Film adhesives are usually formed by coating a fine woven cloth or random mat with the adhesive resin system, which is subsequently partially cured (advanced or staged) to increase viscosity. The fibers generally used for the carrier are polymers such as polyester or nylon; however, glass fibers are also used, mainly with high-temperature adhesives. The resultant film is packaged between release film.

The high-resin viscosity produced by staging prevents resin flow during storage and during the initial stages of bonding when the film is placed on the adherend surface. The degree of staging also determines the level of tack (stickiness) that is available to hold the adhesive and adherends in place before cure.

The carrier in structural film adhesives serves several purposes, including:

- Providing mechanical strength to the uncured (actually, part-cured) adhesive to aid handling
- Controlling flow and thus preventing over-thinning of the adhesive during joint formation
- Providing an insulating layer in the event of complete resin squeeze-out—this is important where carbon/epoxy adherends are bonded to a metal such as aluminum because electrical contact can result in severe galvanic corrosion of the aluminum

Film adhesives are widely exploited in the bonding of aircraft structures. Generally, they provide much higher strengths than the corresponding paste adhesives. Some other important advantages include:

- Ease with which the adhesive can be placed on the adherend surface
- Avoidance of the need for accurate weighing and mixing
- Avoidance of mess (compared with paste adhesives)
- Minimization of entrapped air and volatile materials (from solvent residues)
- Ability to hold adherends in position during cure

In addition, film adhesives assure a higher level of process and therefore quality control.

Disadvantages of film adhesives include high cost, the need for relatively high pressures (compared with single-component paste adhesives) to ensure adhesive flow, high temperatures for cure, and the need for low-temperature storage. Cure temperatures, depending on the hardener system, vary from ambient to around 180 °C, and pressures from zero for paste adhesives to 100–700 KPa for film adhesives.

Factors in the Selection of an Adhesive. Most structural adhesives are capable of bonding the adherends of interest, provided suitable surface treatments can be applied. However, if only very simple treatments are possible for economic or other reasons—such as in a repair application—certain types of adhesive may be favored. This is particularly the case if surface contaminants cannot be removed before bonding.

In rare cases, lack of compatibility of the structural adhesive with the adherend can cause problems. For example, the adhesive—or more likely, the solvent in an adhesive—might attack polymeric materials, particularly thermoplastics; acid or basic products from the adhesive, in the presence of moisture, can corrode some metals, with disastrous consequences to bond strength.

As described earlier, the problem of residual stress arises when joining adherends of different coefficients of thermal expansion with an elevated-temperature curing adhesive. This problem is particularly serious when joining metals such as aluminum to fiber composites such as carbon/epoxy where expansion coefficient mismatch is very large. Residual stress can be minimized by choosing adhesives having the lowest possible cure temperature (if necessary, extending the cure time), a high ductility, and low shear modulus.

Of paramount importance in the choice of an adhesive system is its resistance to attack or degradation in the operating environment. This requirement also applies to the adhesive/adherend interface. Moisture is the main agent responsible for degradation of a metal/adhesive interface whereas many other agents, particularly organic solvents and hydraulic fluids, might attack the adhesive itself.

High temperatures (e.g., above 100 °C) in addition to lowering mechanical properties can cause degradation of the adhesive, due to oxidation or other undesirable chemical reactions. Further, many adhesives exhibit a marked loss in toughness at low temperatures—particularly at temperatures as low as −40 °C, often encountered in aircraft structures. Modified epoxies, particularly some of the film adhesives, have outstanding resistance to loss of toughness at low temperature.

Important economic aspects include the cost of materials, including adhesives; their storage life; the need for expensive surface treatments; the requirement to provide heat and pressure in the cure of the adhesive; and the need for tooling—particularly very expensive items such as autoclaves. Other considerations could include the process time, again favoring adhesives that cure rapidly, and the level of skill required by the personnel in the use of the adhesive. Avoiding the need for accurate mixing of components can save time and the danger of mistakes but often involves the use of adhesives with limited shelf lives.

9.3.10   Assessment of Adhesive Stress/Strain Properties

Toughened epoxy-based film adhesives are generally used to form structural joints for aircraft applications, although paste adhesives are also used for some applications, particularly for repairs. Two film adhesives, FM73 and FM300 (by Cytec Engineered Materials Inc.), are used here as examples of typical adhesives used in composite-to-composite and composite-to-metal bonding. The FM73 and FM300 systems cure at 120 °C and 180 °C, respectively.

Adhesives are qualified for aerospace applications by a range of tests prescribed in ASTM, and the results of these tests are provided in the manufacturers' data sheets. The main joint test specified in these data sheets is the (unsupported) single-overlap joint, similar to that shown in Figure 9.2, with aluminum alloy adherends. The specimens are exposed to a wide range of environmental conditions and tested over a range of temperatures. However, the single-lap joint test, because of severe secondary bending caused by the loading eccentricity, is essentially a combined peel/shear test, therefore it does not provide useable shear stress/strain data, although it does provide very valuable comparative properties, including information on environmental durability.

Thus, to provide useful design data on adhesive shear stress/shear strain behavior for use in joint design, tests based on model joints that produce nominally uniform pure shear stress in the adhesive layer have been developed. Generally, there are significant differences between the results obtained from the various tests, and even between similar tests when undertaken by different laboratories. However, variability can be expected for several reasons, including:

- Properties are sensitive to strain rate, because the adhesive is viscoelastic (or viscoplastic).
- Tests differ in the uniformity of stress in the adhesive layer.
- Failure modes differ.
- Residual stresses due to thermal expansion mismatch differ in different test specimens.

The test most used is the thick-adherend, short-overlap shear specimen,[19] mainly because of its relative simplicity. Figure 9.19 is a schematic of this test specimen showing behavior of adhesive FM73 at two temperatures.

Several manufacturers of aerospace adhesive now include stress/strain behavior of the adhesive (usually using the short-overlap shear specimen) in their data sheets. Table 9.3 provides some of the properties used for design purposes.

Although it is tempting to use these plots as though they were as reproducible as a stress-strain curve for a metal, there are several complications, mainly

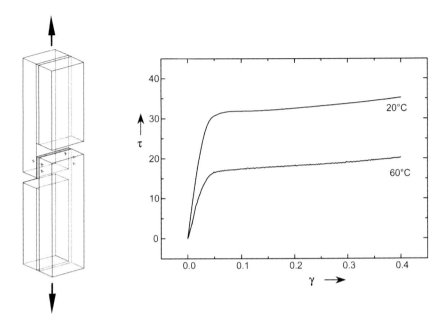

Fig. 9.19 Short-overlap shear specimen and shear stress–shear strain curves for adhesive FM73 at two temperatures obtained using this specimen. Taken from Ref. 20.

associated with time-dependent behavior. Figure 9.20 shows the effects of stress relaxation[20] (constant displacement) on FM73. As may be expected, the curve obtained by plotting the relaxed troughs is similar to the very slow strain rate curve. Thus, a curve obtained by joining the relaxed points could be taken as a master plot for static loading at ambient temperature.

To be useful in the design and analysis of practical joints, the shear stress-strain curve must allow the formulation of simple and consistent failure criteria. Two intuitive failure criteria for elastic/plastic behavior in the adhesive based on the shear stress/shear strain behavior are the plastic shear strain, γ_p, and the shear strain density (e.g., the area under the stress-strain curve to failure).

The failure criteria ideally should be invariant with adhesive thickness. Furthermore, design approaches based on these criteria should be capable of allowing for residual stresses and defects in the bond line and representative loading of the joint. While the above criteria are implicit in the Hart-Smith design approach used here, its validity has yet to be established. For example, it is a concern that the approach does not appear to correctly predict the experimentally observed influence of adhesive thickness. Generally, as mentioned earlier, it is found that (within certain limits) joints get stronger with decreasing adhesive thickness.

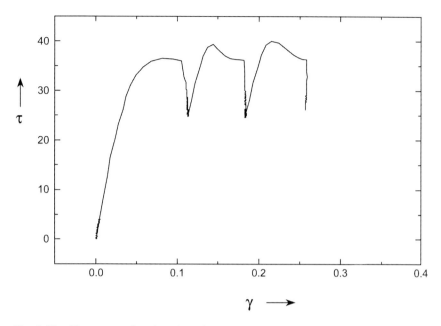

Fig. 9.20   Shear stress/strain relaxation behavior measured using the short-overlap shear specimen.

An entirely different approach to joint design is based on fracture mechanics that assumes the presence of pre-existing flaws, as discussed in the next section.

9.3.11   Assessment of Fracture Energy of Adhesives and Composites

Failure from pre-existing cracks can be categorized into the following basic modes based on the nature of the crack-face displacement: mode I opening or cleavage mode, mode II in-plane shear, and mode III torsional shear. Failure by a mixture of these modes is also possible.

These basic and mixed modes of failure occur in a bonded joint.[21] Generally, for adhesive joints, mode I (peel) is of most concern because this is the mode in which both the adhesive and the composite are weakest.

As may be expected, the fracture behavior of a polymer as an adhesive may differ markedly from that of the bulk material, mainly because of the constraint imposed on the adhesive by the adherends. Furthermore, the crack is constrained to propagate within the boundaries set by the adherends. Thus, while in the bulk material under complex loading, a crack can orient itself to propagate under mode I conditions; this is often not possible in the adhesive layer, so that propagation is forced to occur under mixed-mode conditions.

As previously discussed, various loci for the failure in composites are possible, including:

- In the adhesive layer
- At the adhesive/adherend interface
- In the resin layer near the composite surface
- In the composite surface plies
- Within the adherends

Failure within the adhesive, called cohesive failure, usually represents the maximum level of fracture resistance. Failure at the adherend/adhesive interface is called adhesive failure and represents an off-optimum mode of failure—generally resulting from inadequate pre-bonding surface preparation.

Studies are conducted on the fracture behavior of adhesives in joints for three purposes:

(1) To generate valid comparative data that will aid in the selection of adhesives
(2) To provide data and information that will aid in the development of improved adhesive materials
(3) To provide data to be used in the design of adhesive joints

The energy approach to fracture is based on two parameters:

(1) A mechanical component: the elastic strain energy release rate G in the specimen due to the extension of crack length by unit area. This depends only on the geometry and stiffness properties of the specimen (G_I, G_{II}, or G_{III}, depending on the mode of crack propagation).
(2) A materials component: the fracture energy R absorbed by extension of the crack by unit area (also called toughness). This is the materials parameter being measured and is given by the critical value of G at which the crack grows spontaneously ($R = G_{IC}$ for mode I). R is often related to the extent of plastic deformation that can develop at the crack tip, so it can be a strong function of adhesive thickness.[22]

Several tests based on stable crack growth are used to measure the fracture energy of composites in mode I, mode II, or mixed mode. These tests are also used to measure the fracture energy in bonded composite joints.[21]

Some of the most important tests for composites[23] are depicted in Figure 9.21, which also indicates the percentage G_I. It was found[24] that lap joint tests were unreliable for measuring fracture energy in bonded joints although, as discussed in the next section, they can be satisfactorily used to measure fatigue properties. To avoid the possibility of failure in the composite rather than in the adhesive, similar tests can be conducted using metallic adherends.

The interlaminar fracture energy of the composite is an order of magnitude lower than that of a structural film adhesive; for example, G_{IC} for the carbon/epoxy composite is around 150 J m^{-2} whereas for adhesives FM73 and FM300 it is, respectively, around 3 kJ m^{-2} and 1.3 kJ m^{-2}. Therefore, if a crack can move

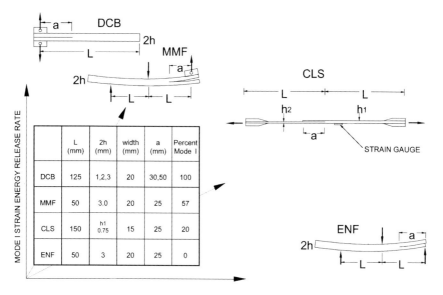

Fig. 9.21   Types of specimen used for measurement of fracture properties in laminated composites and bonded joints, showing percentage of mode 1, taken from Ref. 23. Note DCB; double cantelever beam, MMF; mixed-mode flexural, CLs; cracked lap shear, and ENF; edge-notched flexural.

from the adhesive layer into the composite or if a crack (delamination) already exists in the composite, failure of the composite surface plies will be the most likely failure mode under most loading conditions. Alternatively, if a layer of matrix resin remains on the composite surface after surface treatment, this may be the preferred path for failure.

As for the design approach based on the shear stress/shear strain behavior, the fracture mechanics approach to be useful must allow for adhesive thickness and residual stresses. In joints designed to minimize peel stresses, it is mainly the mode II behavior that is of interest. Use of G_{IIC} as the fracture criterion is thus an alternative approach to the strain capacity approach previously discussed. Generally, the fracture mechanics approach is to assume the presence of a delamination or disbond just below the size that could be readily found by non-destructive inspection, approximately 1 mm.

The fracture mechanics approach is more useful in the design of joints having a significant mode I (peel) component. In this case, the composite will usually be the most vulnerable component of the joint, therefore strength can be determined by its G_{IC} or by some combination of G_{IIC} and G_{IC} for mixed mode.

For a double-lap joint, it can be shown (based on a simple strength of materials approach and ignoring any peeling effects) that the strength and fracture mechanics approaches to predict joint strength P_{max} result in identical conclusions if G_{IIC} is taken as equal to $t_A \tau_p (\gamma_e/2 + \gamma_p)$ the area under the shear stress–strain curve for the adhesive; see, for example, equation (9.19).

For example, using the properties listed in Table 9.3 for adhesive FM73 at ambient temperature with an adhesive thickness of 0.2 mm gives maximum value of G_{IIC} of about 5 kJ m^{-2}, which agrees well with measured values at this adhesive thickness.

The above approach indicates that G_{IIC} should scale linearly with adhesive thickness. However, as previously mentioned due to constraint, it is found experimentally that G_{IC} is generally a non-linear function of adhesive thickness, and a similar situation may be expected to apply to G_{IIC}. Thus, tests are required to measure these parameters at approximately the same thickness as expected in the joint.

9.3.12 Fatigue

Fatigue verification is usually undertaken on critical joints to demonstrate that the joint can carry the ultimate load through its design life, under representative service conditions of stress, temperature, and humidity. The design of such joints is still very far from the point at which the influence on joint performance of aspects such as scale, spectrum stressing, and service environment can be inferred from data on simple specimens (coupons). However, fatigue tests on simple specimen and model joints (such as the short-overlap shear specimen) are often also undertaken at an early stage to screen candidate adhesives and provide design data. Preliminary tests may also be carried out on specimens much more

Table 9.3   Some approximate values for adhesive properties for two typical epoxy-nitrile film adhesives based on the actual shear stress-strain curves (idealized values used in lap-joint calculations will differ considerably, depending on shape of the stress-strain curve and the strain level; see Fig. 9.4)

Adhesive	Exposure temperature (°C)	G_A (GPa)		τ_p (MPa)		γ_p	
		Dry	Wet	Dry	Wet	Dry	Wet
FM73	−55	0.9	0.8	50	56	0.5	0.3
	24	0.8	0.7	32	29	0.9	1.0
	60	0.5	0.4	18	—	1.4	1.4
	82	0.3	—	11	—	1.6	1.6
FM300	−55	—	—	—	—	—	—
	24	0.9	—	42	—	0.9	—
	104	0.5	0.2	21	13	1.3	1.2

Note: $\gamma_e = \tau_p/G_A$.

representative of the actual joint; if these can also provide the design data, they may be used in place of the coupon specimen.

Simple endurance testing of adhesives is also often undertaken using the single-overlap shear specimen. However, for reasons already discussed, this test can provide only comparative data.

For the model joints (which are designed to have uniform shear in the adhesive) repeated cyclic stressing to high plastic strain levels can result in creep failure of the joint after a relatively small number of cycles.[25] This is because cyclic shear strains are cumulative. (If the cycle rate is high, full strain recovery cannot occur during the unloading cycle.) The result is an accelerated creep failure of the adhesive by a *strain ratcheting* mechanism. In practical lap joints, this situation is avoided by maintaining a sufficiently long overlap, so that much of the adhesive remains elastic. The elastic region on unloading acts as an elastic reservoir to restore the joint to its unstrained state preventing the damaging strain accumulation.

Data on crack propagation under loading is most usually obtained from the fracture mechanics-type lap joint tests, as depicted in Figure 9.21, using the edge-notched flexural specimen[26] for mode II, the double-cantilever beam specimen for mode I, and cracked lap-shear specimen for mixed mode.[21] In these tests, the rate of crack propagation in the adhesive is usually plotted as a function of the strain-energy-release-rate range. The empirical relationship between the range of strain-energy-release-rate determined is of the form:

$$\frac{da}{dN} = A\Delta G^n \qquad (9.29)$$

where a is the disbond or crack length in the adhesive, N the number of fatigue cycles, and ΔG the range of strain-energy release rate for the relevant mode. The parameters A and n are empirically determined constants. In the mixed-mode specimens, it was found[21] that the better correlation is with the total strain-energy strain range ΔG_T, showing that modes I and II contribute to damage growth. Figure 9.22a shows a typical result for the adhesive FM300.

Comparative studies[27] on several joint types have shown that the values of the crack-growth parameters are similar, indicating the potential value of this approach as a design tool.

For crack growth in airframe aluminum alloys (generally tested under mode I loading), n is of the order of 1.5–3, whereas for the typical structural film adhesive FM300 (film thickness, 0.2 mm), n is close to 5, both under pure mode I and mixed-mode loading.[21] This indicates that disbond growth in these adhesives is rapid. Thinner bondlines due to higher constraint would probably have much higher values of n. For a more brittle adhesive,[28] such as FM400, under mode I loading, n was as high as 12, confirming (the known) poor peel resistance.

For disbond propagation in the composite, n will also be very high because of the brittle matrix and thin effective bond line.

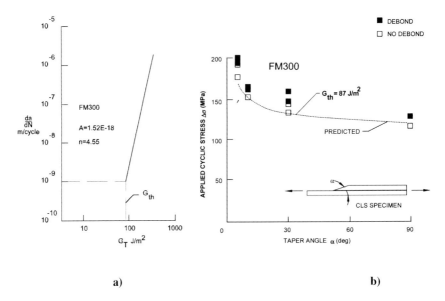

a)   b)

Fig. 9.22 *a*) **Schematic plot of** d*a*/d*N* **versus** ΔG_T **based on data for adhesive FM300;** *b*) **use of data to predict damage growth in CLS specimen with tapered end. Taken from Ref. 21.**

These observations strongly discourage the use of (damage-tolerant) designs based on controlled disbond growth under cyclic loading conditions. Thus, for most of the life of the joint, the design approach must be to hold ΔG below (a conservative estimate of) the threshold for crack initiation, ΔG_{Th}.

An alternative damage criterion for loading, involving mainly mode II crack propagation, is the cyclic strain range $\Delta\gamma$ experienced by the adhesive[29]. This parameter is more convenient to use than ΔG_{II} because it is easier to estimate from a one-dimensional joint analysis, described previously, and automatically includes the influence of adhesive thickness and residual stresses. However, its validity for use in fatigue loading has yet to be proved.

The threshold strain-energy-release-rate range ΔG_{Th} was used as a measure of the cyclic stress level for damage to occur in a (unidirectional) carbon/epoxy cracked-lap specimen bonded with adhesive FM300 or a paste adhesive.[21] The ends of the cracked-lap specimen had taper angles of either 5°, 10°, 30°, or 90°.

The estimated cyclic stress levels for the initiation of damage were compared with the observed level for the various taper angles. It was assumed that damage would grow when $\Delta G_T = \Delta G_{Th}$.

An FEA program was used to estimate G_T for the joint, assuming the presence of a small delamination 1-mm long for the tapered end. The value for ΔG_{Th} was taken as the strain-energy release range for a debond propagation rate of 10^{-9} m cycle^{-1}. For FM300, the value of ΔG_{Th} was found to be $87\,\mathrm{J\,m^{-2}}$ at this propagation rate.

Generally, as shown in Figure 9.22b, the correlation was very good between the predicted and observed cyclic stress levels for disbond growth for the various taper angles, indicating the potential of this approach for fatigue-critical joints having a significant mode I (peel) component. Sensitivity to adhesive thickness and other joint parameters remains to be demonstrated. However, use of the shear strain range ($\Delta\gamma$) in the adhesive as a parameter to assess the threshold for disbond growth may be simpler and equally effective.

9.3.12.1 Failure Modes Under Cyclic Loading.

Surface ply orientation.   Generally, the ply configuration (proportion of $0°$, $\pm 45°$, $90°$ and their stacking sequence) is determined by factors other than joint design. However, the strength of the bonded joint may be expected to depend on the orientation of the surface ply. The fatigue strength of the interface is intuitively expected to be a maximum when the interface layer of fibers is oriented in the same direction as the major applied load. This fiber orientation will inhibit any cracks in the adhesive layer entering the weaker (low fracture energy) internal composite interface. Most of the fatigue studies had $0°$ fibers at the bond interface, and fatigue cracking was generally within the adhesive layer. Fiber orientation will probably have less influence if a layer of matrix resin is present on the surface because this will become the preferred path for crack propagation.

Studies were conducted on cracked-lap shear specimens [with either film adhesive FM300 or a paste adhesive (EC 3445)] with $0°$, $\pm 45°$, or $90°$ plies at the interface.[30] It was found that fatigue damage with the $0°$ ply at the interface occurred within the adhesive, as expected from earlier work. However, with a $45°$ ply at the interface, damage grew both in the adhesive and as a delamination between the $\pm 45°$ plies. With the $90°$ interface, ply damage initiated by transverse cracking in this ply and then grew first by a combination of cracking and delamination in the nearby $\pm 45°$ plies and then by delamination between the $0°$ and $45°$ plies. The value for ΔG_{Th} was considered to be similar for specimens with the $0°$ and $45°$ plies. For the $90°$ plies, the minimum cyclic stress for cracking was much lower.

This suggests that fatigue resistance of the joints is seriously compromised only when the interface plies are $90°$. However, the best practice would seem to be to use $0°$ plies at the interface because the composite was undamaged in this case.

Temperature effects.   Studies using the edge-notched flexural specimen[26] were undertaken to assess the effect of temperature using adhesive FM300K. The specimens were made either by secondary bonding or cocuring. It was found that at ambient and elevated temperature ($100 °C$) damage growth was almost always in the adhesive. However, at low temperature ($-50 °C$) for the secondary bonded specimen (where a layer of matrix resin remained on the surface of the composite), damage grew preferentially in the composite matrix. This mode of failure did not occur in the cocured specimen or in the secondary bonded specimen if the specimen was machined to remove the surface layer.

The value of ΔG_{Th} for the matrix mode of failure was about one third of the value for cohesive failure in the adhesive. This change in mode is attributed to the increase in interfacial shear stress in the matrix layer resulting from the high shear modulus (G_A) of the adhesive at low temperature. The shear modulus of FM300 increases from around 0.5 GPa at 100 °C to about 0.9 at -50 °C. Atmospheric moisture absorbed into the adhesive will reduce G_A further at elevated temperature but cause little change at low temperature.

9.3.13 Moisture Effects

Epoxy and other thermosetting polymers used as a basis of both adhesives and the matrices of composites are hydrophilic and therefore absorb moisture from the atmosphere.[31] Thermoplastic polymers absorb relatively little moisture (they are generally much less polar) but are prone to absorb and be damaged or temporarily degraded by organic solvents. With metallic adherends, water can enter only through the exposed edges of the adhesive. However, with composite adherends having thermosetting matrices, water can diffuse through the composite matrix.

Moisture is absorbed at the surface to a level depending on solubility and relative humidity and diffuses into the bulk of the material. Diffusion can also occur through the carrier fibers if these are polymeric. However, because polymeric carrier fibers are thermoplastic, moisture transport is significantly less than it is through the thermosetting matrix polymer. Water can also enter along interfaces, as discussed later. Unfortunately, of all service liquids (including fuel, engine oil, and hydraulic oils), water causes the most degradation to joints bonded with thermosetting polymers, particularly if one of the adherends is a metal.

Absorbed moisture can:

- Plasticize the matrix, reducing its mechanical properties, particularly at elevated temperature; this is generally reversible on drying. The effect of plasticization could be modelled as a local reduction in G_A and τ_p. For relatively small reductions, joint strength may actually increase as a result of more uniform stress distribution. However, the effect on joint creep and fatigue properties may be detrimental.
- Reduce the glass transition temperature T_g, the temperature at which a dramatic change in mechanical properties occurs; this is reversible on drying. For example, for the adhesive FM73 cured at 120 °C, T_g is reduced from 98 to 81 °C with 3.4% absorbed moisture.
- Damage the adherend/adhesive interface, particularly with high-surface-energy adherends such as metals, by physically displacing the adhesive or by hydrating the surface oxide, as discussed later.
- Produce undesirable residual stresses by causing swelling and cracking of the adhesive; these stresses are usually removed on drying.

- Weaken the joint by leaching out unreacted components in the adhesive. The chemicals released can accelerate attack at the bond interface, for example, by changing the pH at the interface.
- Disrupt the joint at temperatures above 100 °C (e.g., during a supersonic dash) through the formation of vapor.

In addition to absorption and diffusion through the base polymer, which are discussed later, water can diffuse along interfaces such as the adhesive/adherend interface and the adhesive/filler interface. Often interfacial diffusion is more rapid than bulk diffusion, depending on the nature of the interfacial bond. The interface between carrier fiber and adhesive does not, however, appear to be a problem in most systems.

Very rapid transport of water by capillary action (wicking) can occur through regions of interfacial separation (disbonds) and cracks and crazes in the polymer.

9.3.13.1 Diffusion Calculations.
Moisture diffusion through thermosetting polymers is generally Fickian.[32] That is, at least to a good first approximation, the (one-dimensional) ingress of moisture for a distance x along a wide joint of length L with impermeable adherends (metals) is given by the relationship:

$$\frac{\partial c}{\partial t} = D \frac{\partial^2 c}{\partial x^2} \tag{9.30}$$

where $c(x, t)$ denotes the moisture concentration at distance x at time t, and D the diffusion coefficient does not vary with moisture concentration. Diffusion is classed as non-Fickian where D varies with moisture concentration, for example, glassy polymers. However, the diffusion coefficient is generally strongly dependent on temperature through the relationship $D = D_o e^{-k/T}$ where D_O and K are constants.

The boundary conditions are that:

$$c(0, t) = c(L, t) = c_0$$

where c_0, the moisture concentration at the boundaries, has a constant value depending on the humidity of the atmosphere and the solubility of moisture in the polymer, and L is the length of the joint.

Typical values for epoxy adhesives at around 40 °C are:

$$D = 10^{-12} \, \text{ms}^{-1} \text{ and } c_0 = 4\% \quad \text{for RH} \approx 100\%$$

For comparison, typical values for carbon/epoxy composites (through thickness diffusion) are:

$$D = 10^{-13} \, \text{ms}^{-1} \quad \text{and} \quad c_0 = 2\% \quad \text{for RH} \approx 100\%$$

Diffusion is slower for the composite because it contains only approximately 40% by volume polymer matrix, which also has a smaller concentration of rubber toughening additions than used in the adhesive.

The capacity of a polymer to transmit water is its permeability, given by the product Dc_0. Thus, the composite is about one order of magnitude less permeable than the adhesive.

A convenient solution to equation (9.30), which provides an approximate estimate of moisture concentration c for one end of a long joint, is:

$$c(x, t) = c_i + (c_0 - c_i)\left[1 - erf\left(\frac{x}{2\sqrt{Dt}}\right)\right] \qquad (9.31)$$

where c_i is the initial moisture content and the error function $y = x/2\sqrt{Dt}$ may be obtained from tables. Table 9.4 provides some values of $erf(y)$.

When c_i, the initial value of moisture, is zero equation (9.31) reduces to:

$$c = c_0\left[1 - erf\left(\frac{x}{2\sqrt{Dt}}\right)\right] \qquad (9.32)$$

It is useful to note that when $x = \sqrt{Dt}, c = c_0/2$. Thus, the time for the moisture level to rise to half of the surface concentration at distance x is given by $t = x^2/D$. For a typical adhesive, assuming zero initial moisture at $x = 5$ mm, half a typical load-transfer length, it would take only 10 months at 40 °C under conditions of high humidity to reach 2%.

It will be shown later[33] that, for metallic adherends, a critical level of moisture appears to exist for chemical attack to occur. Typically (for epoxy bonds to steel) this is of the order of 1.4%, which, for the assumed system, is reached at the 5-mm point in approximately 6 months.

For the case of composite adherends, moisture can simultaneously reach the whole surface by through-thickness diffusion. The rate of diffusion and the final level of moisture away from the edges of the joint is mainly determined by the composite adherend, so the adhesive layer can be neglected.

Table 9.4   Some Values of the Gauss Error Function for a Range of y Values

y	$erf(y)$	y	$erf(y)$
0.0	0.000	0.8	0.742
0.1	0.112	0.9	0.797
0.2	0.223	1.0	0.843
0.3	0.329	1.2	0.910
0.4	0.428	1.4	0.952
0.5	0.521	1.6	0.976
0.6	0.604	2.0	0.995
0.7	0.678	2.4	0.999

Assuming, for example, that the composite adherend has a thickness of 3 mm, the time for the adhesive layer to reach 1.4% at 40 °C (ignoring diffusion in from the ends of the adhesive) is approximately 6 years. Thus, diffusion through the bulk of the composite may not be a major concern. In a real exposure situation involving drying periods[34] by solar heating, the typical maximum moisture content in the composite is generally less than 0.7%.

However, moisture will diffuse more rapidly through the critical tapered-end regions. For example, considering diffusion only through the composite layer of 0.12 mm thick (one ply), a moisture concentration of 1.4% is reached in about 100 hours. Here the combined two-dimensional effect of diffusion through the composite and along the adhesive must be considered and will be significantly worse than with metal adherends.

9.3.13.2 Interfacial Strength Degradation.

As mentioned earlier, loss in interfacial strength due to moisture absorption can occur by two major mechanisms:

(1) Physical displacement of the adhesive by water, this occurs where bonding is of a physical nature and the energetics favor the adherend/moisture interface rather than the adherend/adhesive interface.
(2) Chemical disruption of the interface, this occurs where the surface can react with dissolved moisture. Hydration of the metal oxide in bonds involving metallic adherends is the main example of this problem.

The case of physical displacement at the interface may be analyzed by the following simple thermodynamic approach[33] in which only physical forces (e.g., hydrogen bonds) are considered to be acting. Such forces are believed to predominate in many types of adhesive bond.

First, in an inert medium, the work of adhesion is given by:

$$W_A = \gamma_a + \gamma_s - \gamma_{as} \qquad (9.33a)$$

where γ_a and γ_s are the surface free energies of the adhesive and substrate and γ_{as} is the interfacial free energy. In the presence of a liquid such as water, this equation must be modified for the free energies with a physically absorbed surface layer:

$$W_{Al} = \gamma_{al} + \gamma_{sl} - \gamma_{as} \qquad (9.33b)$$

where γ_{al} and γ_{sl} are, respectively, the interfacial free energy between adhesive/liquid and substrate/liquid.

In air W_A is generally positive, indicating thermodynamic stability of the bond. However, in water W_{AL} can be negative, indicating that the bond is unstable; it can be displaced by moisture. For the aluminum-oxide/epoxy-adhesive bond,[33] $W_A = 291$ mJ m^{-2} whereas in water $W_{AL} = -137$ mJ m^{-2}, indicating instability. In contrast, for the carbon/epoxy-epoxy bond, $W_A = 88-99$ mJ m^{-2} and $W_{AL} = 22-44$ mJ m^{-2}, indicating stability.

The case of chemical stability of the surface is much more complex to analyze. The stability of bonds to metals depends critically on the type of oxide produced by the surface treatment procedure. In the case of aluminum, some types of oxide are hydrated in a moist environment with catastrophic loss in bond strength. For attack to occur (in the absence of disbonds, etc.), the moisture level in the adhesive needs to reach a critical level; for the case of epoxy bonds to steel, this (as mentioned previously) was found to be about 1.4%.

Unless fairly elaborate surface treatment procedures and primers are used, metal bonds to epoxy adhesives are prone to degradation in humid environments, whereas similar bonds to epoxy-matrix composites appear to pose no durability problems, even with very simple abrasive surface treatments.

9.3.14   Treatment of Composite Surfaces for Bonding

A common factory approach for bonding precured composite adherends relies on the use of a peel ply, which is a layer of woven nylon cloth incorporated into the surface of the composite during manufacture. Before bonding, the nylon is peeled off, exposing a clean surface ready for bonding. However, it is generally considered that such bonds are inferior to those effected by grit blasting because the grid-like nature of the peeled surfaces encourages air entrapment; there is also the significant danger of small amounts of the peel ply[35,36] or, where used, silicone release agents transferring as a thin layer to the bonding surface.

For thermosetting-matrix composites, the most effective surface treatment for strong durable bonding is to grit-blast with alumina or silicon carbide particles.[37] When done correctly, this process provides a clean, uniform, high-energy surface.

Thorough abrasion of the surfaces with silicon-carbide paper or abrasive pad is a reasonable alternative,[38] but is less satisfactory because minor depressions in the surface are left untreated unless a considerable amount of surface material is removed. This will result in a weaker joint as areas of unbraided surface resin will remain. Because the surface resin on the composite has a much lower fracture energy than that of the adhesive, there is merit in removing all or most of this layer.

In contrast with thermosets, thermoplastic-matrix composites, because of the low surface energy, require aggressive chemical surface treatments to form strong bonds with thermosetting adhesives.[39] Methods based on chemical or plasma discharge etching have proved reasonably successful[40] but the bonds formed are generally weaker than those made to a thermosetting-matrix composite. Thermoplastic films with a lower melting point than the matrix polymer may be a better option. For example, PEI film can be used to join (or more likely repair) PEEK matrix composites.[41]

9.4 Mechanically Fastened Joints

Symbols

Allowable materials strength in tension	σ_{tu}	Elastic tensile stress concentration factor in infinitely wide plate with unloaded hole	K_t
، Allowable far-field tensile stress	σ_u	Elastic isotropic tensile stress concentration factor, with respect to net tension stress	K_{te}
Allowable far-field tensile strain	ε_u	Effective tensile stress, with respect to net tension stress	K_{tc}
Allowable materials strength in shear	τ_u	Effective tensile stress concentration factor for loaded hole, with respect to hole diameter	K_{tbc}
Through-thickness stress	σ_z	Load capacity of joint per unit width	P
Allowable materials strength in bearing	σ_{bgu}	Load on joint per unit width	p
Tensile stress bypassing hole	σ_{by}	Correlation coefficient between experimental and observed stress concentration factors	C
Bearing stress	σ_{bg}	Hole or fastener diameter	d
Modulus in load direction	E_x	Strip width	w
Modulus normal to load direction	E_y	Strip thickness	t
Shear modulus, in plane	G_{xy}	Edge distance	e
Major Poisson ratio	v_{xy}	Stress ratio, minimum/maximum	R
		Torque	T

9.4.1 Introduction

This section describes simple design procedures and materials engineering topics relevant to the application of mechanical joints in composite airframe structures.

Intuitively, it may be concluded that mechanical fastening is an unsatisfactory means of joining composites because the fastener holes must cut fibers, destroying part of the load path. However, although considerable loss in strength occurs (typically to half of the original strength), acceptable joints can be made. Indeed, mechanical fastening is usually the only feasible or economic means of joining highly loaded (thick) composite components.

9.4.1.1 General Design Considerations.
Although the aim of achieving smooth load transfer from one joint element to another is similar in bonding and mechanical fastening, the load transfer mechanisms are very different.

In mechanical fastening, load transfer is accomplished by compression (bearing) on the faces of holes passing through the joint members by shear (and, less desirably, bending) of the fasteners.

Some of the load is also transferred through friction on the face of the joint element if the clamping forces imposed by the fasteners is sufficient. However, although high clamping forces (bolt-tightening torque T) are very important to develop high-friction forces to maximize bearing strength, it may not be possible to maintain these levels of clamping force during prolonged service, for example, due to wear under service loading conditions.

Because high through-thickness reinforcement is provided by the fasteners, peel failure of the composite is generally not a problem. However, problems can arise resulting from the relatively low bearing and transverse strengths of the composite compared with those of metals. Bearing failure results in hole elongation, allowing bending and subsequent fatigue of the bolt or substructure. Alternatively, the fastener head may pull through the composite.

Figure 9.23 illustrates the failure modes of a composite joint.[42] In tension, the main modes are tension failure of the net section, bearing, and shear failure.

In addition (Fig. 9.23), mixed-mode failures can occur, including cleavage tension, essentially mixed tension/shear; bolt-head pulling through the laminate, a problem particularly with deeply countersunk holes; and bolt failure due to bearing failure.

The type of failure that occurs depends on the ratio of the effective width to the diameter of the fastener hole w/d, and the ratio of the edge distance to the diameter e/d. The variation of failure load with w/d and e/d for a quasi isotropic laminate is indicated in Figure 9.24. For large w/d and e/d, the joint fails in

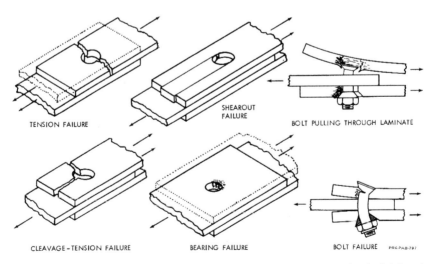

TENSION FAILURE

SHEAROUT FAILURE

BOLT PULLING THROUGH LAMINATE

CLEAVAGE-TENSION FAILURE

BEARING FAILURE

BOLT FAILURE

Fig. 9.23   Schematic illustration of the main failure modes in mechanical joints in composites. Taken from Ref. 42.

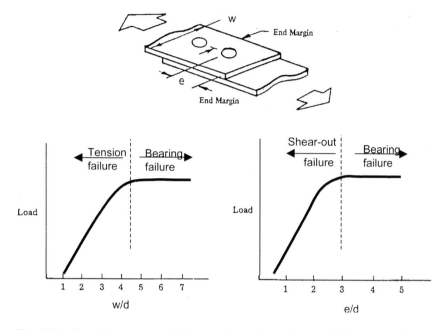

Fig. 9.24   Transition between failure modes with specimen width (rivet pitch) and edge distance.

bearing, and the failure load is independent of w/d or e/d. With reduced w/d tension failure of the net section will occur with the joint strength dropping to zero when $w/d = 1$. If the edge distance e is reduced, shear failure occurs with the strength of the joint dropping to zero when $e/d = 0.5$.

The allowable stresses in each of these modes is a function of:

• Geometry of the joint, including thickness
• Hole size, spacing, and bearing area, allowing for countersink
• Fastener loading, single or double shear; that is, loading symmetrical, as in a double-lap joint, or unsymmetrical, as in a single-lap joint
• Fastener fit tolerance
• Clamping area and pressure, allowing for any countersink
• Fiber orientation and ply sequence
• Moisture content and service temperature
• Nature of stressing: tension, compression, shear; cyclic variation of stressing; any secondary bending, resulting in out-of-plane loading. Stresses due to thermal expansion mismatch in metal-to-composite joints may also have an effect, but these are rarely considered in mechanical joints

The ply configuration in most bolted joints is usually chosen to be close to quasi isotropic, based on $0°$, $\pm 45°$, and $90°$ fibers. The non-zero fibers are needed to carry load around the hole to prevent shear or cleavage-type failures, whereas the $0°$ fibers carry the primary bearing loads and tension. The desired failure mode is usually net tension or compression; however, in some situations (the softer or less catastrophic) bearing failure may be preferred.

If stiff (highly orthotropic) laminates are required for a particular application, a higher proportion of $0°$ fibers may be used and further measures, discussed later, may be required to increase hole strength.

9.4.2 Design Criteria for Failure of Single-Hole Joints Under Static Tensile Loads

9.4.2.1 Stress Concentrations in Laminates with Unloaded Holes. It is instructive to consider the elastic stress concentration factor K_t for an unloaded hole in an infinite plate because this case has been solved analytically.[43] This situation is relevant to joints having significant bypass loads, as described later.

The analysis gives the effective K_t at the edge of the hole at $90°$ to an applied tension stress as:

$$K_t = 1 + \sqrt{\left\{2\left[\sqrt{\left(\frac{E_x}{E_y}\right)} - \gamma_{xy}\right] + \frac{E_x}{G_{xy}}\right\}} \qquad (9.34)$$

It is shown that K_t at the edge of the hole, at $90°$ to the applied load, varies from 7.5 for a 100% $0°$ laminate to about 1.8 for a 100% $\pm 45°$ laminate and approaches the isotropic value of 3.0 at 80% $\pm 45°$. Because the tensile strength falls with increasing $\pm 45°$, it can be shown that the optimum ply configuration is about 50% $\pm 45°$.

Actually, the peak stresses do not necessarily occur at $90°$ to the applied load. For example, in the case of an all $\pm 45°$ laminate, it occurs at $45°$ to the loading direction.

Stresses in the individual plies vary with their orientation and are complex involving in-plane and through-thickness components. It is thus difficult to develop suitable failure criteria, particularly because some of the failure modes, such as local splitting and delamination, are highly beneficial in reducing the peak stresses. Failure of the laminate is generally considered to have occurred (analytically) when the load is sufficient to cause fiber failure in one of the plies, based on criteria for complex loading, such as Tsai-Hill (see Chapter 6).

There are several semi-empirical methods of assessing the tensile strength of composite panels with unloaded holes of finite width. The main approaches[44] used are:

- Average stress criterion: Failure is considered to occur when the *average* value of the tensile stress over some characteristic length a_o from the hole reaches the unnotched failure strength σ_{tu} of the laminate.

- Point stress criterion: Failure is considered to occur when the *local* value of stress at some characteristic distance d_o from the hole reaches the unnotched failure strength σ_{tu}.

The values of a_o or d_o, considered to be materials properties, are determined from plots of strength reduction versus hole size to give the best fit to the experimental results. These criteria are related, through $a_o = 4d_o$.

Unfortunately, there are problems with these approaches; for example, they usually do not predict the actual locus of failure. However, the approaches are used extensively in the aerospace industry with some success and have been applied to more complex problems, including bi-axial and compressive loading of unloaded holes and to stresses arising from bearing loads.[45,46]

In the following sections, the tensile load capacity P is estimated for each of the main failure modes in a simple joint, such as shown in Figure 9.25. The more complex behavior in compression loading, non-symmetrical loading, or in multi-hole joints will be considered later.

The approach taken here is largely based on that developed by Hart-Smith and reported in several papers and reports, the most detailed being Ref. 42.

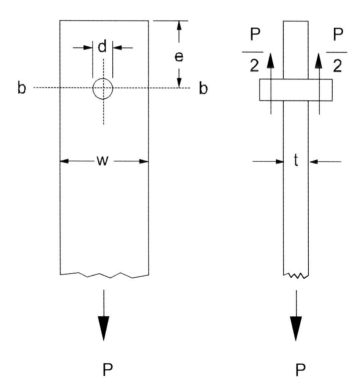

Fig. 9.25   Geometry of a simple double-lap bolted joint used to obtain test data.

9.4.2.2 Tension Failure.   The maximum tensile stress σ_{max} at the edges of a loaded hole in a joint under an arbitrary load P, such as shown in Figure 9.25, is given by:

$$\sigma_{max} = \frac{K_{tc}P}{t(w - d)}$$ (9.35)

where K_{tc} is the *effective* stress concentration factor, based on net section.

Thus, the joint strength efficiency, expressed as the ratio of (load capacity of the joint, P)/(unholed load capacity), is given by:

$$\frac{\sigma_u}{\sigma_{tu}} = \frac{P}{\sigma_{tu}wt} = \frac{(1 - (d/w))}{K_{tc}}$$ (9.36)

For metals at high stresses, the effective stress concentration factor $K_{tc} \approx 1$ because, as discussed previously, yielding reduces the elastic stress concentration so that the failure strength is simply dependent on net sectional area, whereas for a brittle material (or for the metal at stresses below yield) $K_{tc} = K_{te}$. For the composite, K_{tc} will fall somewhere between these two extremes with microcracking of a brittle matrix locally softening the material in the vicinity of a stress concentration.

Based on the early experimental work of others for an elastic isotropic joint element (having a large edge distance e), Hart-Smith[42] recommends the following empirical relationship for the elastic stress concentration:

$$K_{te} = \frac{w}{d} + 1 - 1.5\frac{(w/d - 1)}{(w/d + 1)}$$ (9.37)

Thus, for $d/w = 0.1$, $K_{te} \approx 10$ while for $d/w = 0.33$, $K_{te} \approx 3.3$, showing the large stress concentration associated with bearing loads acting on a small hole.

For an elastic isotropic material, using equations (9.35) and (9.36), the ratio joint strength/basic strength is given by:

$$\frac{P}{\sigma_{tu}tw} = \frac{1}{2/(1 - d/w) + 1/(d/w) - 1.5/(1 + d/w)}$$ (9.38)

This relationship is plotted in Figure 9.26 and shows that the peak strength of the joint is about 20% of nominal tensile strength at a d/w of about 0.4.

To allow for stress reduction in composites at failure loads, the relationship between K_{tc} and K_{te} is determined experimentally from strength tests on joints (as shown in Fig. 9.25), equation (9.36) is used to find K_{tc} and equation (9.37) to estimate K_{te}. An approximate linear relationship is found. Because the two coefficients must be equal at $K_{te} = 1$, the equation used is:

$$K_{tc} - 1 = C(K_{te} + 1)$$ (9.39)

where C is the correlation coefficient for the particular laminate, environmental conditions, and geometry of the joint. A value of $C = 0$ indicates full relief of the

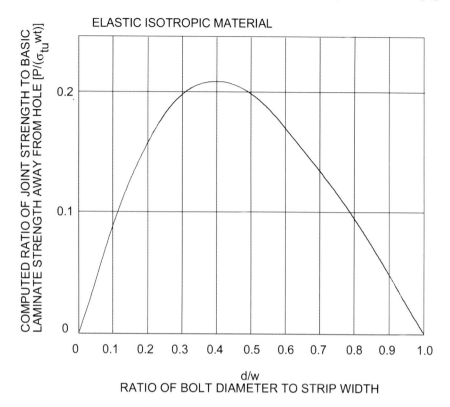

COMPUTED RATIO OF JOINT STRENGTH TO BASIC LAMINATE STRENGTH AWAY FROM HOLE [P/(σ_{tu}wt)]

ELASTIC ISOTROPIC MATERIAL

d/w
RATIO OF BOLT DIAMETER TO STRIP WIDTH

Fig. 9.26   Plot of ratio of joint strength to basic laminate strength versus d/w for an elastic isotropic material, assuming net tension failure. Based on Ref. 42.

stress concentration, whereas $C = 1$ indicates a brittle material where equation (9.38) applies.

For composites, C depends on fiber pattern and hole size and probably on temperature and moisture content in the laminate. For a first generation quasi isotropic composite, C was found to be around 0.25 for a standard 6.35-mm bolt hole; coincidentally, this is numerically similar to the fraction of $0°$ plies used in the experiments; although for a more highly anisotropic composite, C can range up to 0.5.

A comprehensive study[47] of the loaded hole strength of laminates based on carbon/epoxy cloth with a $[0°/45°]_{2s}$ lay-up provided the values for C listed in Table 9.5. This shows that the laminate becomes significantly more notch-sensitive at 180 °C. This is thought to be associated with the marked softening (effective toughening) of the matrix at elevated temperature, inhibiting the formation of delaminations around the hole. The effective stress concentration K_{tc} then becomes closer to the elastic value, Table 9.5, favoring fiber failure rather than delamination, and resulting in significant strength reduction. Similar behavior may be expected with thermoplastic-matrix composites (and even

Table 9.5   Data from Tensile Tests on Loaded Holes in $[0°/45°]_{2s}$ Carbon/Epoxy Cloth Laminates; the Bolt Size was 4.76 mm, $d/w = 0.375$, and the Computed K_{te} is 3.0

Temperature, °C	K_{tc}	C
24	1.36	0.18
120	1.33	0.18
180	1.71	0.36

highly toughened epoxies), even at ambient temperature, because these composites are highly resistant to delamination.

9.4.2.3 Bearing Failure.

The bearing capacity P of a joint, such as shown in Figure 9.25, involving metallic adherends, is generally based on the nominal bearing strength σ_{bgu} using the relationship:

$$P = \sigma_{brgu}dt \qquad (9.40a)$$

Thus, the joint efficiency ratio for bearing failure is given by:

$$\frac{P}{\sigma_{bgu}wt} = \frac{d}{w} \qquad (9.40b)$$

In carbon/epoxy composites, failure in bearing occurs by local buckling and kinking of the fibers and subsequent crushing of the matrix.[48] The compressive stress to predict microbuckling of the fibers is given by equation (2.28). Consequently, the bearing strength σ_{bgu}, and thus the load carrying capacity P, are strongly dependent on the degree of constraint (clamping stress σ_z) provided by the fastener and on the properties of the matrix.

Experimental studies[49] on the influence of clamping pressure σ_z on ultimate bearing strength σ_{bgu} (Fig. 9.27), show that an improvement in bearing load of 60–170% can be obtained over pin loading with σ_z up to around 20 MPa; above this pressure, little further improvement is obtained. A typical value for the optimum σ_{bgu} is about 1000 MPa.

The clamping pressure in these plots was estimated from:

$$\sigma_z = 1.658 \frac{T}{d^3} \qquad (9.41)$$

based on the clamping area with a standard washer, taking the diameter of the washer to be $2.2d$ and assuming a torque stiffness coefficient of 0.2.

There is also some load transfer simply due to friction between the fastener or washer and joint element. Tests[50] were undertaken to measure the *effective* bearing strength with 1) simple pin loading, 2) clamp up (no bolt), and 3) a standard bolt under moderate torque. Figure 9.28 plots the experimental results, showing that friction makes a significant contribution to bearing strength.

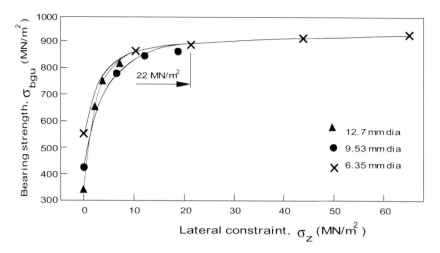

Fig. 9.27 Bearing strength versus clamp-up pressure for a 0°, ± 45° 12-ply laminate with various hole sizes. Taken from Ref. 49.

Because clamping plays such an important role in the bearing strength of composites, it is important to ensure that this pressure is maintained under service conditions.

Bearing strength initially increases with increasing proportions of 0° plies because these are the most efficient in carrying the bearing loads. However, once the proportion of 0° plies exceeds about 60%, failure occurs by splitting because the transverse strength then becomes insufficient to prevent shear failure, even at very large values of e, the edge distance. The optimum bearing strength for a $0°/\pm 45°$ laminate occurs at about 50% 0° and 50% ± 45° plies. It is found that the bearing strength is further improved as the ply sequence is made more homogeneous (dispersion of 0° and ± 45° plies). As is well known, interply stresses are reduced as the laminate becomes more homogeneous.

Although the compressive strength of the composite undergoes significant reduction at elevated temperature, particularly under hot/wet conditions, loss in bearing strength in joints can be reduced by maintaining high local constraint through bolt clamping. Furthermore, matrix softening may reduce local high loads through better contact of the fastener with the hole. Figure 9.29 shows that reasonable bearing strength for two extensively used (180 °C—curing) composite systems[47] is maintained well above 120 °C.

9.4.2.4 Shear-Out Failure.   For metallic adherends, load-carrying capacity in shear is usually estimated from the following simple relationship:

$$P = \tau_u 2et \qquad\qquad (9.42)$$

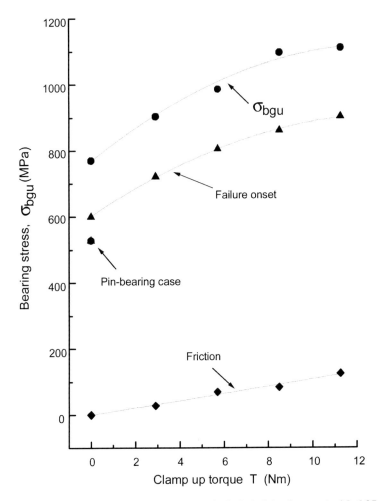

Fig. 9.28   Static strength versus torque for a single-hole joint fastened with 6.35-mm bolt or pin. Taken from Ref. 50.

Experimental results indicate that this relationship holds reasonably well for carbon/epoxy composites providing there are about 50% $\pm 45°$ plies, implying that there is little stress concentration for this loading condition. To ensure that the joint strength is not limited by either net-tension or shear-out strength (with laminates containing sufficient percentages of $\pm 45°$ plies) a minimum w/d of about 5 and an e/d ratio of about 3 are required.

In contrast, significant stress concentrations occur with high percentages of $0°$ plies because the apparent τ_u falls well below the value measured by standard shear tests. In fact, under these conditions, failure occurs by splitting rather than by shear (or bearing), and strength is unaffected by the shear distance e.

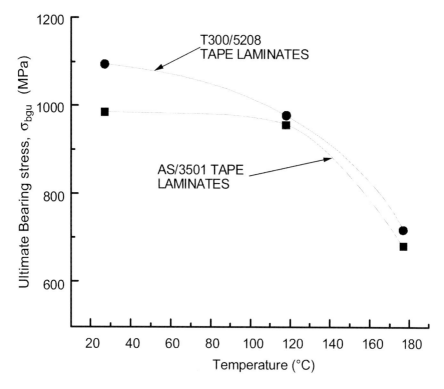

Fig. 9.29   Bearing strength as a function of temperature for two carbon/epoxy composite systems. Taken from Ref. 47.

9.4.3   Single Fastener Joint Loading Efficiency in Tension

The conclusion from the above consideration of failure modes for a single-hole joint is that a quasi isotropic laminate with well-dispersed plies provides the optimum strength in mechanical joints. Assuming that the joint is designed to avoid the shear and cleavage failures shown in Figure 9.23 by having appropriate ply configuration and an e/d of at least 3, only net-section tension and bearing failures need be considered.

Figure 9.30, taken from Ref. 42, plots $P/\sigma_{tu}wt$, the joint strength efficiency, versus d/w for the metal, brittle material (using equation (9.38), and composite (assuming $C = 0.25$). The cut-off in net-section strength for bearing failure is shown only for the metal and composite. For the brittle material, it is seen that a maximum strength of 21% of the strength of the virgin material is reached at $d/w = 0.4$.

In the case of both the metal and the composite, a change in failure mode from net-tension to bearing is predicted to occur at d/w of approximately 0.3. The net-tension/strength plot for the metal results from using equation (9.36) for P/σ_{tu}, taking $K_{tc} = 1$ with an appropriate value for σ_{tu}. The bearing strength plot results from using equation (9.40b) with an appropriate value for σ_{bgu}.

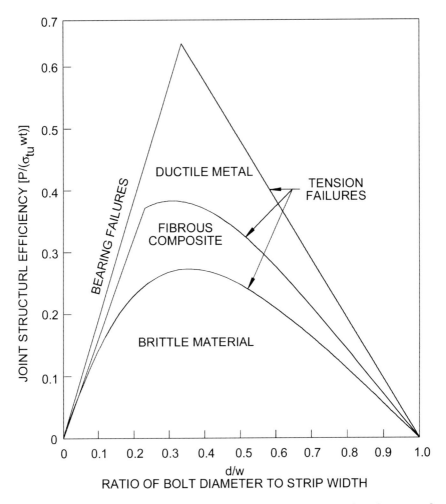

Fig. 9.30   Joint efficiency versus d/w for single fastener joints based on metal, composite, or brittle components under tensile loading. Only bearing or net tension strengths are considered. Taken from Ref. 42.

For estimating the net tension strength of the composite, equation (9.36) is used with equations (9.37) and (9.39) for K_{tc}, with an appropriate value for σ_{tu}, whereas for bearing strength equation (9.40b) is used with an appropriate value for σ_{bgu}.

For the composite, the maximum strength efficiency is only about 40%, whereas for the metal it is about 65%.

9.4.4   Single Fastener Joint Loading Efficiency in Compression

Compression strength is significantly higher than tension strength for a loaded hole because some of the compression load can be transmitted directly through the fastener. The degree to which this can occur is dependent on the fit of the fastener in the hole. For a fastener with large clearance, the stress concentration will be similar to that experienced under tension, although the actual failure mode would be quite different. Typical hole clearance for fasteners in composites range from 0.1 mm to zero for interference fit.

9.4.5 Multi-Row Joints

The main objective of using multi-row joints is to minimize the peak bearing load, avoiding the cut-off due to bearing failure shown in Figure 9.30. However, to achieve improved strength, the joint has to be designed to ensure even load sharing between the fasteners. An analysis for load distribution for a joint with three rows of fasteners is outlined in Figure 9.31, and the outcome is illustrated in Figure 9.32. Figure 9.33 illustrates, schematically, the comparison in load distribution between a multi-row metallic joint in which the elements are able to yield and a typical composite joint[51] with no yielding or softening. Computer programs have been developed to execute this elastic analysis.[56,57] Data is required for in situ flexibility of fasteners. If the joint has been correctly designed to reduce bearing loads, failure under tensile loading will occur in net tension. However, there are now two sources of tensile stress at the edge of the fastener hole:

Caused by the load reacting out on the fastener by bearing
Caused by the load bypassing the fastener to be reacted out on other fasteners along the joint

The experimental approach to finding the allowable load on a composite joint is to produce a plot, such as in Figure 9.34, in which the outer envelope of allowable gross strain ε_u (away from the fastener hole) is shown as a function of the bearing stress σ_{bg}. All that is then needed is to establish, by analysis, the peak bearing stress in the critical hole in the joint. In Figure 9.34 the allowable gross strain for pure bypass was established as 4000 microstrain, reducing to 3000 microstrain at the bearing stress cut-off at $\sigma_{bgu} = 690$ MPa for the configuration under examination.

These envelope plots can be produced by measuring 1) the failure strain of a joint element $3d$ or $4d$ wide with an *unloaded* fastener hole that should fail in tension at the fastener hole, 2) the bearing stress σ_{bgu} in a much wider strip (typically $6d$) forced to fail in bearing, and 3) the failure strain of a $3d$ or $4d$ wide specimen designed to fail in tension at the hole at some combinations of bypass and bearing.

A more sophisticated approach is described in Ref. 52 using a mechanical test machine based on two independent servo-loading systems. One servo loads the joint element while the other loads the bolt hole by directly applying load to the bolt.

Figure 9.35 shows (a simplified version of) the envelope obtained[52] under tension or compression bypass loading. The plot shows the results for the onset of

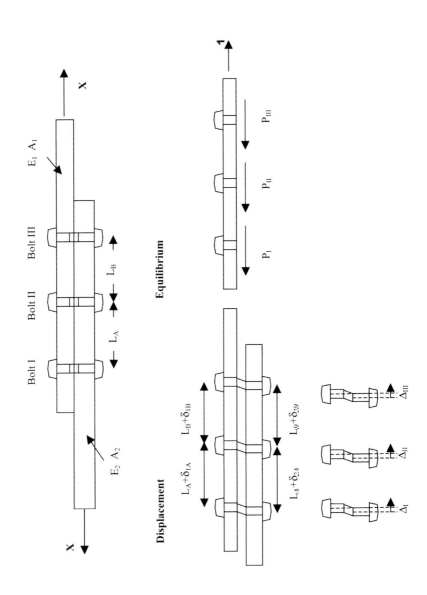

Compatibility

Equilibrium

$$\delta_{2A} - \delta_{1A} = \Delta_{II} - \Delta_I$$

$$\therefore \delta_{1A} - \delta_{2A} + \Delta_{II} - \Delta_I = 0$$

$$\therefore \delta_{1B} - \delta_{2B} + \Delta_{III} - \Delta_{II} = 0$$

$$P_I + P_{II} + P_{III} = X$$

Material

$$\delta_{1A} = \frac{L_A}{E_1 A_1} P_I \qquad \delta_{2A} = \frac{L_A}{E_2 A_2}(X - P_I)$$

$$\delta_{1B} = \frac{L_B}{E_1 A_1}(P_I + P_{II}) \quad \delta_{2B} = \frac{L_B}{E_2 A_2}(X - P_I - P_{II})$$

$$\Delta_I = P_I f_I$$

$$\Delta_{II} = P_{II} f_{II}$$

$$\Delta_{III} = P_{III} f_{III}$$

Hence

$$P_I + P_{II} + P_{III} = X$$

$$-\frac{L_A}{E_1 A_1} P_I + \frac{L_A}{E_2 A_2}(X - P_I) + P_{II} f_{II} - P_I f_I = 0$$

$$-\frac{L_B}{E_1 A_1}(P_I + P_{II}) + \frac{L_B}{E_2 A_2}(X - P_I - P_{II}) + P_{III} f_{III} - P_{II} f_{II} = 0$$

Fig. 9.31 Model and analysis of the joint with multiple rows of fasteners; f is fastener flexibility.

Joint design	Controlling property	Simplified equations	Bolt loads
Fasteners very flexible (or plates able to yield in bearing—metals at ultimate load)	$f_I = f_{II} = f_{III}$ large	$P_I + P_{II} + P_{III} = X$ $P_{II} = P_I$ $P_{III} = P_{II}$	$P_I = X/3$ $P_{II} = X/3$ $P_{III} = X/3$ 
Balanced stiffness, fasteners very stiff (composite panels —elastic behavior)	$E_1A_1 = E_2A_2$. $f_I = f_{II} = f_{III}$ small	$P_I + P_{II} + P_{III} = X$ $P_I - (X - P_I) = 0$ $(P_I + P_{II}) -$ $\qquad (X - P_I - P_{II}) = 0$	$P_I = X/2$ $P_{II} = 0$ $P_{III} = X/2$ 
Stiff fasteners — unbalanced joint 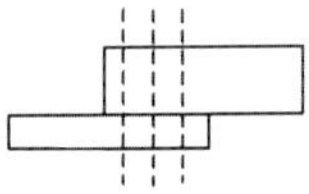	$E_1A_1 \gg E_2A_2$. $f_I = f_{II} = f_{III}$ small	$P_I + P_{II} + P_{III} = X$ $(X - P_I) = 0$ $(X - P_I - P_{II}) = 0$	$P_I = X$ $P_{II} = 0$ $P_{III} = 0$ 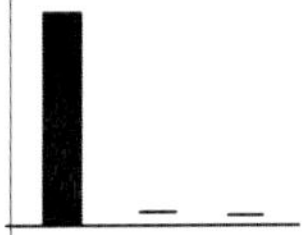
Stiff fasteners — unbalanced joint 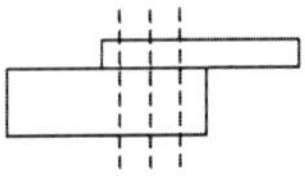	$E_1A_1 \ll E_2A_2$. $f_I = f_{II} = f_{III}$ small	$P_I + P_{II} + P_{III} = X$ $P_I = 0$ $P_I + P_{II} = 0$	$P_I = 0$ $P_{II} = 0$ $P_{III} = X$ 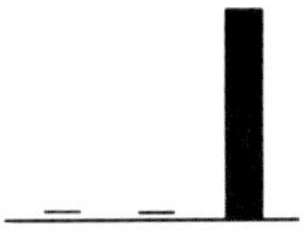

Fig. 9.32   Representative load distributions in a joint with three rows of fasteners.

damage, which is generally what is required for design purposes. Also noted are the various damage modes.

For tension loading, the conditions for onset of damage are similar to those shown schematically in Figure 9.34, indicating a cut-off of tension-reacted bearing strength (TRB) for net-tension (NT) failures as the magnitude of σ_{by}

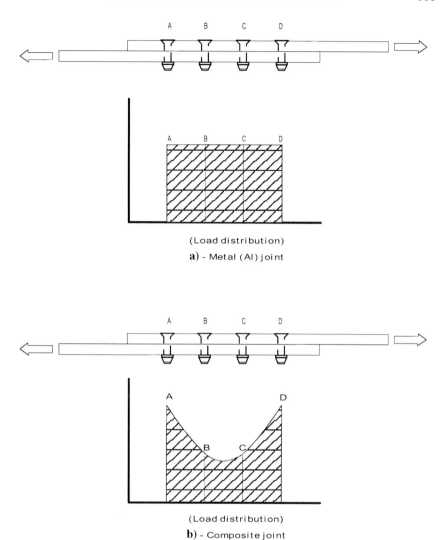

(Load distribution)

a) - Metal (Al) joint

(Load distribution)

b) - Composite joint

Fig. 9.33   Comparison of load transfer behavior, metals versus composites.

increases. The results are reasonably explained by the two straight-line plots, one for TRB failures and the other for NT failures.

Under compression loading, behavior is markedly different because the bolt (if clearances are small) can support the walls of the hole, transmitting part of the load directly and thus delaying the onset of net-compression (NC) failures. The predominant failure mode is thus compression-reacted bearing (CRB).

Hart-Smith[42] also developed an analytical approach for multi-row joints under tension in a strip width w, based on the hypothesis of linear interaction

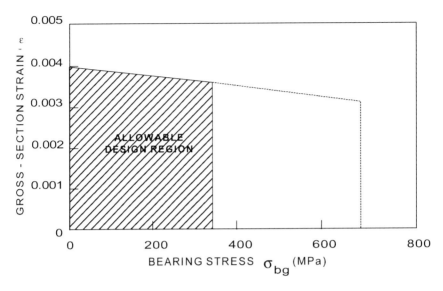

Fig. 9.34   Design allowables for bearing/bypass interaction under tensile loading.

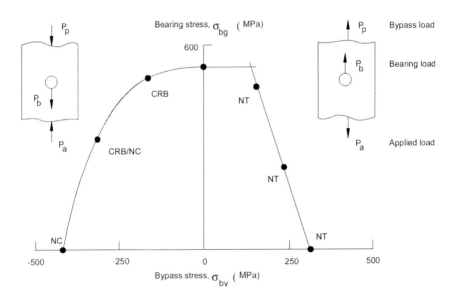

Fig. 9.35   Results of bearing/bypass experiments for tension or compression loading. Note failure in bearing (B), net tension (NT), net compression (NC), tension reacted bearing (TRB), and compression reacted bearing (CRB). Results are for a 16-ply quasi isotropic T300/5208 composite. Based on Ref. 52.

between the net-section bypass and bearing stresses, using the following relationship:

$$\sigma_{tu} = K_{tby}\sigma_{by} + K_{tb}\sigma_{brg}\left(\sigma_{brg} < \sigma_{brgu}\right) \qquad (9.43)$$

The relationship for horizontal load equilibrium (at failure) is used to eliminate σ_{by}:

$$\sigma_{max} = \sigma_{brg}\left(\frac{d}{w}\right) + \sigma_{by}\left(1 - \frac{d}{w}\right) \qquad (9.44)$$

Thus:

$$\sigma_{max} = \sigma_{brg}\left(\frac{d}{w}\right) + \left(1 - \frac{d}{w}\right)\left(\frac{\sigma_{tu} - K_{tb}}{K_{tby}}\right) \qquad (9.45)$$

It is more useful to express these results in terms of allowable gross strain using:

$$\varepsilon_{tu} = \frac{\sigma_{max}}{E_x} \qquad (9.46)$$

The results can also be expressed in terms of gross-section structural efficiency for NT failure σ_{tu}/σ_u

Now the values of K_{tc} and K_{tbc} must be determined. Based on early work of others, it was shown that for the stresses associated with σ_{by}, the elastic stress concentration factor K_{te} for an *unloaded* hole in an isotropic strip width is given by:

$$K_{te} = 2 + (1 - d/w)^3 \qquad (9.47a)$$

Thus, allowing for hole softening:

$$K_{tby} = 1 + C(K_t - 1) \qquad (9.47b)$$

Because the tensile failure load P with no bypass can be expressed either in terms of net-section [equation (9.35)] or in terms of the contact area dt, we have that:

$$P = \sigma_{tu}\frac{(w - d)t}{K_{tc}} = \sigma_{tu}\frac{dt}{K_{tbc}} \qquad (9.48a)$$

Thus,

$$K_{tb} = \frac{K_{tc}}{(w/d - 1)} \qquad (9.48b)$$

Using equation (9.45) with equation (9.46) to obtain allowable strain and equations (9.37), (9.39), (9.47) and (9.48) for the K values, plots were developed such as in Figure 9.36 for the allowable strain (and structural efficiency) in multi-row joints. The figure plots the far field strain allowables at the most critical hole as a function d/w for various nominal values of bearing stress σ_{bg}. The values of σ_{bg} range from 0, for no bearing stress, to $\sigma_{bg} = \sigma_{bgu}$ where failure would occur in bearing. At all values of σ_{bg} below σ_{bgu}, failure occurs in NT.

The above relationships are also applicable for a wide joint element, having many columns of multiple fasteners spaced at d/w, using slightly modified values for the K constants.

Finally, for comparison, the relationships for a similar single-hole joint are also plotted in Figure 9.36 using the following equations.

Based on section strain away from hole,

$$P = \varepsilon_{tu} E_x wt \qquad (9.49)$$

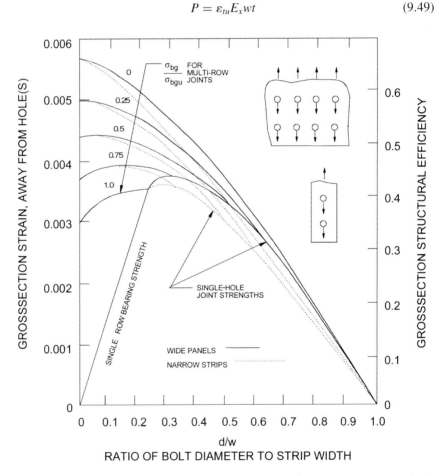

Fig. 9.36   Allowable strain and joint efficiency versus d/w for multi-row and single fastener composite joints under tensile loading. Only bearing or net-tension strengths are considered. Taken from Ref. 42.

Thus, for bearing,

$$\varepsilon_{tu} = \left(\frac{\sigma_{brgu}}{E_x}\right)\left(\frac{d}{w}\right) \tag{9.50}$$

and for NT failure,

$$\varepsilon_{tu} = \left(\frac{\sigma_{tu}}{E_x}\right)\left[\frac{(1 - d/w)}{K_{tc}}\right] \tag{9.51}$$

Figure 9.36 shows that:

• The maximum strength with multiple-row joints occurs when the bearing stress is zero, as expected. However, this is not a practical joint design, just the outer envelope of strength.
• At the optimum d/w ratio for a single-hole joint (approximately 0.3), the improvement with multi-row joints is not great for practical values of σ_{bg}. For example, for $\sigma_{bg}/\sigma_{bgu} = 0.5$, the improvement is only about 10%
• The only way of obtaining a major improvement over the single hole is to reduce d/w and also reduce bearing stresses by using joint designs that evenly share the bearing stress among several fasteners. This is difficult to achieve in practice and requires a very good design capability.

9.4.5.1 Optimum Design of Simple Multi-Row Joints.

In most joint designs, it is desirable to modify the major components as little as possible for reasons of cost and repairability; it is much more efficient to modify the splice plate in the case of lap joints. The use of local build-ups or local inserts in the major components is very expensive, and therefore usually unacceptable, except where used for a single major attachment hole such as a lug. Furthermore, repair of a structure with modified holes may not be feasible because such modifications cannot be reproduced during repair.

The key to the optimization of load sharing in bolted joints using the procedures defined in Fig. 9.31 is in the modelling of effective fastener flexibility. This is expressed in terms of the sum of the following compliances[53]:

• Shear deformation of the bolt
• Bending deformation of the bolt
• Bearing deformation of the bolt
• Bearing deformation of the hole

Figure 9.37 is an idealized plot of load versus deflection[53] for a fastener in a simple joint such as shown in Figure 9.25. This shows deflection at zero or low load for take-up of clearance between the bolt and the hole (zero if interference fit), an initial line representing reversible elastic deflection and a line of a reduced gradient representing non-linear deflection due to hole elongation.

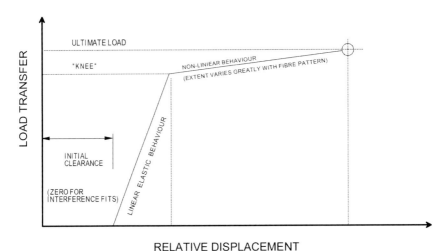

Fig. 9.37   Load versus deflection for a fastener, showing linear elastic region and non-linear region caused by hole elongation. Taken from Ref. 53.

Estimates can be made for the various compliances listed for the elastic region based on earlier studies on previous work on metallic joints.[53]

Using estimates of the compliances, based on earlier studies on metals, Hart-Smith produced the program (A4EJ), which allows estimation of load sharing between multiple fasteners.[56] Similar programs have been developed by the ESDU.[57]

An optimized design for a multi-row joint is shown in Figure 9.38. The approach (with reference to Fig. 9.36) involves use of tapered splice plates with various sized fasteners. The aim is to minimize the bearing stress in the inner (adjacent to the skin butt) fastener. Because in the skin this fastener has no bypass load, it is optimized as a single-hole joint with a d/w of 0.3 and a 15-mm bolt. The bypass and bearing loads in the splice plate are a maximum at this point. However, because the plate can be designed to be thick (more than half the equivalent thickness of the skin) at this point, with little weight penalty, it can

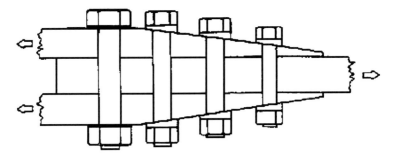

Fig. 9.38   Optimum design of multi-row lap joint. Taken from Ref. 53.

easily cope with these loads. The next two rows of fasteners have a smaller diameter with d/w of 0.25 because these experience some bypass load. The last (now critical) fastener, which has the maximum bypass load, is designed with a d/w of 0.2 to minimize bearing stresses (to 25% of σ_{bgu}). The gross strain allowable at this fastener, and consequently at the joint, is around 5000 microstrain, which is much higher than is possible with a single-hole joint.

9.4.6 Influence of Fatigue Loading

9.4.6.1 Open Holes. To understand the complex effects of cyclic loading on mechanically fastened joints, it is first helpful to appreciate degradation mechanisms in carbon/epoxy laminates with an unloaded hole. Under tension or compression-dominated loading,[54] failure initiates in the regions of high elastic stress concentration as matrix microcracking and local disbonding of fibers from the matrix. This damage significantly reduces the in-plane elastic stress concentrations thus *increasing* residual strength. The localized damage accumulates until it results in more extensive intralaminar cracking, eventually resulting in delaminations (separations between plies). The rate and extent of delamination formation depends on the magnitude of the interply peel and shear stresses, which are strongly dependent on the ply configuration. More homogeneous configurations (few groupings of plies having similar orientation) produce lower interply stresses.

From this stage, tension and compression behavior differ greatly. Under tension, the formation of the delaminations is generally beneficial because the damage is localized and generally does not propagate. Thus, for design purposes, it is usually necessary to consider only static strength, which is lowest before fatigue.

Under compression loading, although stress concentration at the edges of the hole is similarly reduced, the loss in section stiffness due to delaminations can lead to compression or buckling failure of the remaining sound material. Furthermore, the loss in laminate symmetry caused by the formation of delaminations produces interlaminar stresses that drive delamination growth and encourage instability. Compression fatigue strength similar to compressive static strength is degraded under hot/wet conditions.

It is of interest to compare this behavior with that of metals. Under relatively low cyclic stresses (below limit load for most of the life), the elastic stress concentrations at the edges of the hole are not relieved by gross plastic deformation. However, localized cyclic plastic deformation at the edge of the hole can occur at a relatively low stress (approximately one third limit load), leading to the initiation of fatigue cracks that can propagate predominantly under tensile components of the loading, eventually resulting in failure. Fatigue crack growth in metals usually cannot occur under pure compression loading. There is no equivalent to delamination growth, except under corrosive conditions in some aluminum alloys, in which exfoliation can occur in the material surrounding the hole.

9.4.6.2 Loaded holes.   In loaded holes, superimposed on the behavior just described for the composite are (1) bearing stresses, which are detrimental, (2) lateral support and pressure from the fastener, which are beneficial, particularly in compression, and (3) support of the hole by the fastener in compression, also beneficial. Generally, a composite with a loaded hole in which fastener pressure can be maintained will have superior fatigue resistance to a similar composite having an open hole, even allowing for bearing stresses in the former case. However, if fastener pressure or fastener support is lost, due to partial bearing failure or wear, these benefits will be reduced or lost.

In practice, hole enlargement and a loss in residual strength are not serious problems in the allowable strain range if load reversal does not occur, and residual strength may increase after exposure to cyclic stresses with no stress reversal; e.g., for $R = -\infty$ (compression/zero) or $R = 0$ (zero/tension).

Fatigue tests conducted on joints (similar to that shown in Figure 9.25, with a 6.35-mm pin or bolt) under R = 0.05 (small-preload/tension) under dry and wet conditions[50] showed that with simple pin loading (i.e., no load carried by friction) little hole elongation occurred before fatigue failure, although fatigue failure occurred at a relatively low bearing stress. However, marked hole elongation (about 1 mm) occurred at a similar fatigue life at loads about 50% higher with $T \approx 0$ (hand tight) because the washers provided sufficient constraint to delay failure. At normal levels of T (around 6 Nm), fatigue strength was markedly improved and hole elongation at bearing failure greatly reduced. The effect of wet conditions at modest levels of T was to reduce the threshold level of stress for hole elongation, reducing the fatigue strength (based on a threshold level of hole elongation) by about 40%. This behavior was considered to be associated in part with a reduction in friction, due to the lubricating action of moisture, resulting in increased bearing stresses for a given T.

Loss in strength can be marked even at modest stress levels if stress reversal occurs, for example, $R = -1$ (equal tension and compression), even at reasonable levels of T. This is because, under this type of loading, gross fastener movement can occur, causing damage to both ends of the hole, resulting in extensive hole enlargement. The result is lack of fastener support under compression loading and, due to the relative movement, loss of clamping pressure. Furthermore, lack of support in the hole due to elongation leads to fastener pull-out or to fastener bending resulting in fastener fatigue failure. Movement of the fastener can also lead to fatigue cracking of the substructure, if this is metallic.

Frequent removal and replacement of fasteners[55] appears to accelerate the development of damage around the composite hole, resulting in a reduction in fastener fatigue life.

9.4.6.3 Problems with Single-Shear Joints and The Use of Countersinking.   Double-shear joints, as shown in Figure 9.25 (similar to double-lap joints) are preferred because they usually provide the highest joint strength. This is because the symmetrical loading minimizes secondary bending and fastener rotation, so that loading on the bore of the fastener hole is reasonably uniform.

Single-shear joints (similar to single-lap joints) generally have lower joint strengths but are widely used in aircraft construction, for example, when access is limited to only one side during assembly. Strength loss can be minimized if the joint is well supported. However, in highly loaded applications, some degree of non-uniform loading of the bore of the fastener hole is inevitable.

Single-shear joints are often based on the use of blind fasteners. These are fasteners (described in more detail later) designed to be clamped up from one side. Alternatively, for blind fastening, bolts can be used that screw into nuts in nut plates applied to the (pre-drilled) skin before assembly. Typical applications for blind fastening are in the attachment of skins to substructure. In this type of application, countersunk or flush fasteners are often used to maintain aerodynamic smoothness.

This use of single-shear joints (even in the absence of secondary bending) and countersunk holes leads to two significant new problems: fastener rotation due to unsymmetrical loading of the joint, and reduced bearing area in the fastener hole caused by the countersink.

Considering first the use of countersinking, in the absence of fastener rotation, the bearing area is only that provided by the parallel section of the hole. This reduced bearing area could be factored into plots such as in Figures 9.30 and 9.36. Provided that clamping is sufficient and enough parallel section remains, bearing failure can be avoided, at least for lightly loaded applications. However, in many applications with thin composite skins, the countersinking may use up the entire skin thickness to accommodate the heads of available fasteners, leaving a knife-edge. Bearing strength will then be negligible, and hole elongation will occur in service unless bearing loads are very low.

Fastener rotation is a major problem in single-shear joints, resulting in marked strength reduction. It is particularly a problem with composites, even when not countersunk, because their relatively low bearing strength results in local bearing failure. Under extreme loading or due to hole elongation under cyclic loading, pull-out of the fastener or failure of the fastener head can occur, as illustrated in Figures 9.23.

With skins having countersunk holes, rotation of the faster results in the bearing surface moving onto the countersunk surface from the parallel section. However, this situation arises only once the parallel section has failed under the severe bearing pressure developed by the rotating fastener.

9.4.7 General Materials Engineering Aspects

9.4.7.1 Fasteners for Composites. Options for composite joints include either metallic or non-metallic fasteners. Flush fasteners are used for aerodynamic smoothness or to provide clearance in moving surfaces. A wide

variety of fasteners is available, many specially designed for use with composites. It is beyond the scope of this chapter to describe these special fasteners in any detail; more information is provided by Niu[51] and by the relevant manufacturers' data sheets.

Metallic fasteners. To avoid galvanic corrosion problems with carbon/epoxy metallic fasteners are limited to those made of titanium alloy, stainless steel, or Inconel. Other metals, such as aluminum and low-alloy steels, may be used if they can be insulated to avoid direct contact with the composite. Generally, tension head (large head) fasteners are used to avoid problems with fastener pull-through.

Metallic fasteners are, broadly, divided into:

- Rivets—permanent fasteners clamped by:
  - plastic deformation of the shaft of the rivet
  - direct swaging of a deformable sleeve over a solid shaft
  - deformation by drawing of a sleeve over a shaped hollow shaft; these are blind fasteners. To allow development of an interference fit, some fasteners of this type include a deformable metal sleeve.
- Bolts—permanent or demountable fasteners using a nut (of a softer material) on a threaded end of the shaft clamped by:
  - standard spanners or sockets, and locked by pins or self-locking nuts
  - a tool that deforms a collar (special nut) to a design level of torque, thereby locking the collar to the shaft
  - a nut, acting on the same side as the head, that draws the collar over a hollow shaft by means of a threaded bar passing through the shaft
  - a nut, attached by a nut plate to the lower skin

Non-metallic fasteners. Non-metallic fasteners are based on reinforced thermosets or thermoplastics. As outlined by Niu,[51] non-metallic fasteners are used to:

- Avoid fuel tank arcing during lightning strike
- Reduce weight
- Increase electromagnetic transparency, reducing radar cross section
- Eliminate corrosion problems

Non-metallic fasteners do not have the load-bearing capacity of titanium or steel fasteners, but, they can rival aluminum alloy fasteners in some applications.

Fasteners made of thermoplastic matrix composites are similar to those made of metals. For example, rivets based on short-discontinuous-fiber thermoplastic composites can be formed by using an ultrasonic punch or by a conventional punch following preheating of the rivet. Similar "blind" approaches to those described for metals can also be used on preheated rivets.

9.4.7.2 Fastener Hole Preparation. Hole formation in carbon/epoxy composites using well-maintained tungsten-carbide-tipped drills poses no particular problems, provided some simple precautions are taken. Diamond-tipped drills, though more expensive, provide the best performance. Care must be taken to support the laminate during drilling by clamping it either between scrap material or in a drilling jig. The tendency for delamination on the exit side of the drill can also be reduced by coating the composite on this side with a layer of adhesive. Delamination can also be minimized by using a pressure-controlled drill at a fairly slow feed rate. Under mass-production conditions, some minor delamination damage is probably inevitable, but generally not serious, and can be repaired by resin injection, as described in the next section.

Although very good tolerances can be maintained in holes in carbon/epoxy, interference fit fastening is generally (although not universally) avoided. This is because excessive interference can lead to delamination damage during fastener installation; significant stressing of the hole can also arise in service due to the higher thermal expansion of the fastener. However, tight fit of the fastener can considerably improve fatigue performance, particularly if load reversal occurs.

For applications involving flush fasteners, countersink depths should be limited to 65% of the depth of the hole to avoid the formation of knife-edge bearing surfaces, which are very fragile in composites.

9.4.7.3 Hole-Strengthening Procedures. Several procedures involving bonded reinforcements may be used to increase the bearing load of composites. These include incorporation of extra layers into the laminate, bonding of doublers over the region of the hole, and bonding of inserts into the fastener hole.

Although composites lend themselves well to modifications to the laminate structure, manufacturing costs are significantly increased. Also, the use of bonded reinforcements may make effective repairs more difficult, or even impossible, to implement. Consequently, these approaches are limited to use in critical locations such as highly loaded lugs. Use of expanded inserts or sleeves in the fastener hole is a more cost-effective approach that also allows repairs to be undertaken relatively easily.

The stress concentration at the edges of a loaded hole in carbon/epoxy can be reduced significantly, either by local reinforcement with a stiffer fiber, such as boron, or by local softening with a low-modulus fiber such as aramid or glass. These plies are incorporated into the laminate on each side of the prospective faster hole during manufacture.

Another method of softening is the incorporation of extra $\pm 45°$ carbon/epoxy plies or layers of thin titanium alloy sheet. These approaches are effective in improving both the net and bearing strength. The titanium alloy is particularly effective in increasing bearing strength. All inserts additionally reduce bearing stress by increasing the local skin thickness.

A simpler and much less costly approach is to reinforce the hole with an externally bonded doubler, made either of composite or titanium alloy.

The doubler must be appropriately scarfed to minimize shear and peel stresses in the adhesive.

In an experimental study in which the weight and extra thickness of each of these concepts were compared for a given load-carrying capacity, it was found that the extra $\pm 45°$ plies provided the lightest solution and the titanium interleaves the thinnest. However, the use of titanium created considerable manufacturing difficulties because of the bonding pretreatment required and the subsequent difficulty in forming the holes.

9.4.7.4 Corrosion Prevention.
Carbon/epoxy is electrically conducting and cathodic with respect to most airframe alloys other than titanium. Thus, to avoid galvanic corrosion on the metallic side of the joint, special precautions are required. In areas where carbon/epoxy and aluminum alloys may come into contact with one another, an insulating layer of glass/epoxy or aramid/epoxy is used. This is usually cocured onto the surface of the carbon/epoxy laminate during manufacture. In some cases, the insulating layer may also be used on the outside of the component to avoid electrical contact through the fasteners.

As mentioned earlier, unless insulation is possible, aluminum alloy or steel fasteners are avoided. Titanium alloy is the preferred fastener material, although stainless steel or Inconel are also suitable, but at a weight penalty. Where the titanium fasteners come into contact with the aluminum alloy side of the joint, a strontium chromate pigmented coating may be used for corrosion prevention. Corrosion-resistant steel nuts and washers, when used, will be cadmium plated if they are to come into contact with aluminum.

9.4.7.5. Component Alignment in Joints.
Joints in airframe structures often require shimming in assembly to maintain correct alignment. Use of shimming is one of the most costly operations in manufacturing airframe components. Composite parts require more shimming than similar metals parts for two main reasons:

(1) Manufacturing tolerances are lower because of thickness variations associated with slight changes in composite resin content, resulting from variation in pre-preg, in resin bleed during manufacture, and in manufacturing methods.
(2) Composites are much less tolerant to force-fitting due to their high modulus and inability to yield. This will be much more of a problem with thick-section material; use of force during assembly has resulted in delamination damage in several cases.

Various approaches are possible for shimming,[51] These are:

- Solid shims, laminated titanium or stainless steel, or composite
- Laminated (peelable) shims, titanium, stainless steel, or Kapton
- Moldable, cast-in-place plastic

The moldable shim, which is the most versatile and effective for gaps up to 0.5 mm (0.020 in), involves injection of the liquid shim material into the gap between the joint components, for example, through a fastener hole. The shim material must have medium viscosity (sufficient to flow into the gap and then stay there), low shrinkage, stability in the service operating environment (temperature, moisture, fuel, etc.), and have a working life of 1 to 4 hours. Once injected into the gap, it must cure within a reasonable time at ambient temperature or around an hour at 80–90 °C.

Considerable savings are possible with composite structure if suitable manufacturing techniques can be developed to avoid the need for shimming (e.g., the co-forming of parts to ensure accurate fit irrespective of minor variation in tolerances).

9.4.8   Bonded and Bolted Joints

A joint bonded with a structural adhesive is usually much stiffer than a similar joint joined by mechanical fastening, even when the mechanical joint is optimally designed and interference fit fasteners are used. Thus it is not possible to design a joint in which the load is effectively shared between the bonded and fastened regions. Hart-Smith,[56] using his A4EK program, showed that for an optimally designed step-lap joint the bolts transmit only around one percent of the total load. However, fastening and bonding can be beneficially used together for several reasons:

- Fasteners provide an alternate in-plane load path as well as through-thickness reinforcement and therefore can contain the spread of damage in thick-section composite-bonded joints where failure (for example, due to an overload or to the development of local bond or interlaminar flaws) would occur by disbonding of the adhesive layer or by delamination of the composite.
- Fasteners can be used at the end of a lap joint, (Fig. 9.13) to reduce peel stresses. However, this is a somewhat hazardous application because the fastener holes, unless very carefully sealed, allow environmental ingress into the bond interface in the most critical region.
- Fasteners can be used both as a jigging aid and to apply pressure during adhesive bonding of composite components; generally, this approach would be effective only with paste adhesives.
- Bonding can be used to alleviate local stresses in the metallic component in a mechanically fastened joint, markedly improving fatigue and static strength properties. For the reasons mentioned, the bond line carries most of the load, and the fasteners become effective only after bond failure. This approach is extensively used with riveting in the metallic longitudinal fuselage splice region in commercial aircraft. With composite construction, this approach is more likely to be used for rework of areas found to be prone to damage.

Use of combined bolting and bonding in the repair of composite structure is considered in Chapter 10.

References

[1] Hart-Smith, L. J., *An Engineers Viewpoint on Design and Analysis of Aircraft Structural Joints*, Douglas Paper MDC 91K0067, presented at the International Conference on Aircraft Damage and Repair, Melbourne, Australia, 1991.

[2] Baker, A. A., "Joining of Advanced Fibre Composite," Chapter 8 in *Composite Materials for Aircraft Structures*, edited by B. C. Hoskin and A.A. Baker, AIAA Education Series, AIAA, New York, 1986.

[3] Hart-Smith, L. J., *Analysis and Design of Advanced Composite Bonded Joints*, NASA CR-2218, 1974.

[4] Thrall, E. W., *Failures in Adhesively Bonded Structures, Bonded Joints and Preparation for Bonding*, AGARD-CP-102, 1979.

[5] Vinson, J. R., "On the State of the Technology in Adhesively Bonded Joints in Composite Material Structures," *Emerging Technologies in Aerospace Structures Design, Structural Mechanics and Materials*, edited by J. R. Vinson, ASME, Fairfield, NJ, 1980.

[6] Mathews, F. L., Kilty, P. F., and Godwin, E. W., "A Review of the Strength of Joints in Fibre-Reinforced Plastics," *Composites*, Vol. 13, 1982, pp. 29–37.

[7] Hart-Smith, L. J., "Stress Analysis: A Continuum Mechanics Approach," in *Developments in Adhesives 2*, edited by A. J. Kinloch, Applied Science Publishers, London, 1981.

[8] Hart-Smith, L. J., *Adhesive-Bonded Double Lap Joints*, NASA CR-l12235, Jan. 1973.

[9] "Guide to the Use of Data Items in the Design of Bonded Joints," Data Item 81022, Engineering Sciences Data Unit (ESDU), London, 1981.

[10] Adams, R. D., "Stress Analysis: A Finite Element Approach," *Developments in Adhesives 2*, edited by A. J. Kinloch, Applied Science Publishers, London, 1981.

[11] Hart-Smith, L. J., and Thrall, E. W, "Structural Analysis of Adhesive-Bonded Joints," *Adhesive Bonding of Aluminium Alloys*, edited by E. W. Thrall and R. W. Shannon, Marcel Dekker, New York, 1985, Chap. 13.

[12] Jones, R., "Crack Patching: Design Aspects," *Bonded Repair of Aircraft Structures*, edited by A. A., Baker and R., Jones, Martinus-Nijhoff, 1988.

[13] Chalkly, P. D., *Mathematical Modelling of Bonded Fibre: Composite Repairs to Metals*, Dept. of Defence and Technology Organisation, Aeronautical Research Laboratory, Research Report Commonwealth of Australia, AR-008–365, 1993.

[14] Hart-Smith, L. J., "Designing to Minimise Peel Stresses in Adhesive Bonded Joints," *Delamination and Debonding of Materials*, edited by W. S., Johnson, ASTM 876, 1985.

[15] Adams, R. D., and Peppiatt, N. A., "Stress Analysis of Adhesive-Bonded Lap Joints," *Journal of Strain Analysis*, Vol. 9, 1974, pp. 185–196.

[16] Crocombe, A. D., "Global Yielding As Failure Criterion for Bonded Joints," *International Journal of Adhesion*, Vol. 9, 1989, pp. 145–153.

[17] Hart-Smith, L. J., *Effects of Flaws and Porosity on Strength of Adhesive-Bonded Joints*, Douglas Paper 7388, 29th Annual SAMPE Symposium and Technical Conference, 1984.

[18] Lubin, J. L., "A Theory of Adhesive Scarf Joints," *Journal of Applied Mechanics*, Vol. 24, 1957, pp. 255–260.

[19] Kieger, R. B., "Stress Analysis Concepts for Adhesive Bonding of Aircraft Primary Structure," *Adhesively Bonded Joints: Testing, Analysis, and Design*, edited by W. S., Johnston, ASTM STP 981, 1988.

[20] Chalkley, P. D., and Chiu, W. K., "An Improved Method for Testing the Shear Stress/Strain Behaviour of Adhesives," *International Journal of Adhesion and Adhesives*, Vol. 4, 1993, pp. 237–242.

[21] Johnson W. S., and Dillard D. A., "Experimentally Determined Strength of Adhesively Bonded Joints," *Joining Fibre Reinforced Plastics*, edited by F. L. Mathews Elsevier Applied Science, 1987, pp. 105–183.

[22] Kinloch, A. J., and Shaw, S. J., "Fracture Resistance of a Toughened Epoxy Adhesive," *Journal of Adhesion*, Vol. 12, 1981, pp. 59–77.

[23] Russell, A. J., and Street, K. N., "Moisture and Temperature Effects on the Mixed Mode Delamination Fracture of Unidirectional Carbon/Epoxy," *Delamination and Disbonding of Materials*, edited by W. S., Johnson, ASTM STP 876, 1985.

[24] Loss, K. R., Ehlers, S. M., and Kedward, K. T., "An Evaluation of Cracked Lap Shear Testing for Bonded Joint Applications," *AIAA/ASME/ASCE/AAS Collection of Technical Papers*, New York, 1985, pp. 647–655.

[25] Hart-Smith, L. J., "Difference Between Adhesive Behaviour in Test Coupons and Structural Joints," Douglas Paper 7066, presented to ASTM Adhesives Committee, Phoenix, AZ, 1986.

[26] Russell, A. J., "Fatigue Crack Growth in Adhesively Bonded Carbon/Epoxy Joints Under Shear Loading," *ASME Symposium on Advances in Adhesively Bonded Joints*, edited by S. Mall, K. M. Liechti, and J. K. Vinson, Vol. 6, Book No GOO485, 1988.

[27] Lin, C., and Liechti, K. M., "Similarity Concepts in the Fatigue Fracture of Adhesively Bonded Joints," *Journal of Adhesion*, Vol. 21, 1987, pp. 1–24.

[28] Mall, S., and Yun, K. T., "Effect of Cyclic Ductility on Cyclic Debond Mechanism in Composite-to-Composite Bonded Joints," *Journal of Adhesion*, Vol. 23, 1987, pp. 215–231.

[29] Baker, A., "Crack Patching: Experimental Studies, Practical Applications," *Bonded Repair of Aircraft Structures*, edited by A. A. Baker and R. Jones, Martinus-Nijhoff, 1988.

[30] Johnson W. S., and Mall, S., *Influence of Interface Ply Orientation on Fatigue Damage of Adhesively Bonded Composite Joints*, ASTM Composite Technology Review, 1986.

[31] Comyn, J., "The Relationship Between Joint Durability and Water Diffusion," *Developments in Adhesives*, edited by A. J. Kinloch, Applied Science Publishers, London, 1981, Chap. 2.

[32] Crank, J., *Mathematics of Diffusion*, Oxford Univ. Press, 1956.

[33] Kinloch, A. J., "The Service Life of Adhesive Joints," *Adhesion and Adhesives: Science and Technology*, Chapman Hall, 1987, Chap. 8.

[34] Chester, R. J., and Baker, A. A., *Environmental Durability of Carbon/epoxy F/A-18 Composites*, Proceedings of ICCM-10 1995.

[35] Hart-Smith, L. J., Ochsner, R. W., and Radecky, R. L., *Surface Preparation of Fibrous Composites for Adhesive Bonding or Painting*, First Quarter Issue Douglas Service, 1984.

[36] Hart-Smith, L. J., Wong, S. B., and Brown, D. L., *Surface Preparations for Ensuring That the Glue Will Stick in Bonded Composite Structures*, NAWCADWAR-94096-60, 1994, (also McDonnell Douglas Paper 93K0126, 1993).

[37] Parker, B. M., and Waghorne, R. M., "Surface Pretreatment of Carbon Fibre Reinforced Composites for Adhesive Bonding," *Composites*, Vol. 13, 1982, pp. 280–288.

[38] Poncuis, A. V., and Wenz, R. P., "Mechanical Surface Preparation of Carbon-Epoxy Composites for Adhesive Bonding," *SAMPE Journal*, Vol. 21, 1985, pp. 50–57.

[39] Kinloch, A. J., and Taig, C. M., "The Adhesive Bonding of Thermoplastic Composites," *Journal of Adhesion*, Vol. 29, 1987, pp. 291–302.

[40] Kodokian, G. K. A., and Kinloch, A. J., "The Adhesive Fracture Energy of Bonded Thermoplastic Fibre-Composites," *Journal of Adhesion*, Vol. 29, 1989, pp. 193–218.

[41] Davies, P., Cantwell, W. J., Jar, P. Y., Bourban, P. E., Zyman, V., and Kauch, H. H., "Joining and Repair of Fibre-Reinforced Thermoplastic," *Composites*, Vol. 22, 1991, pp. 425–431.

[42] Hart-Smith, L. J., "Mechanically-Fastened Joints for Advanced Composites" *Fibrous Composites in Structural Design*, edited by E. M. Lenoe, D. W. Oplinger, and J. J. Burke, Plenum Press, New York, 1980.

[43] Leknitski, S. G., *Anisotropic Plates*, 2nd ed., Gordon and Breach, New York, 1968, pp. 171.

[44] Davis, M. J., and Jones, R., *Damage Tolerance of Fibre Composite Laminates in Composite Materials for Aircraft Structures*, edited by B. C. Hoskin and A. A. Baker, AIAA Education Series, AIAA, New York, 1986 Chap. 10.

[45] Soni, S. R., *Failure Analysis of Composite Laminates with a Fastener Hole*, edited by K. T., Kedward, ASTM STP 749, American Society for Testing Materials, 1981, pp. 145–164.

[46] Chang, F. K., Scott, R. A., and Springer, G. S., "Failure of Composite Laminates Containing Pin Loaded Holes: Method of Solution," *Journal of Composite Materials*, Vol. 18, 1984.

[47] Bailie, J. A., Duggan, M. F., Bradshaw, N. C., and McKenzie, T. G., "Design Data for Carbon Cloth Epoxy Bolted Joints at Temperatures up to 450 K," *Joining of Composite Materials*, edited by K. T. Kedward, ASTM STP 749, American Society for Testing and Materials, 1981, pp. 165–180.

[48] Wu, P. S., and Sun, C. T., "Modelling Bearing Failure Initiation in Pin-contact of Composite Laminates," *Mechanics of Materials*, Vol. 29, 1998, pp. 325–335.

[49] Collins, T. A., "The Strength of Bolted Joints in Multidirectional CFRP Laminates," *Composites*, Vol. 8, 1977, pp. 43–55.

[50] Crews J. H., Jr. "Bolt-Bearing Fatigue of a Carbon/Epoxy Laminate," *Joining of Composite Materials*, edited by K. T. Kedward, ASTM STP 749, American Society for Testing and Materials, 1981, pp. 131–144.

[51] Niu, M. C. Y., "Joining" *Composite Airframe Structures*, Conmilit Press, Hong Kong, 1992, Chap. 5.

[52] Crews, J. H., and Naik, R. A., "Combined Bearing and Bypass Loading on a Carbon/Epoxy Laminate," *Composite Structures*, Vol. 6, 1986, pp. 21–40.

[53] Nelson, W. D., Bunin, B. L., and Hart-Smith, L. J., *Critical Joints in Large Composite Structure*, Douglas Paper 7266, presented at Sixth Conference on Fibrous Composites in Structural Design, 1983.

[54] *Fatigue of Filamentary Composites*, ASTM STP 636, 1977.

[55] Saunders, D. S., Galea, S. C., Deirmendjian, G. K., "The Development of Fatigue Damage Around Fastener Holes in Thick Carbon/Epoxy Composite Laminates," *Composites*, Vol. 24, 1993, pp. 309–321.

[56] Hart-Smith, L. J., "Design Methodology for Bonded-Bolted Composite Joints," Vol. 1, *Analysis Derivations and Illustrative Solutions*, AFWAL-TR-81–3154.

[57] "Flexibility of, and bad distribution in, multi-bolt lap joints subject to in-plane axial loads," Data Item 98012, Engineering Sciences Data Unit (ESDU), London, 2001.

10
Repair Technology

10.1 Introduction

Carbon/epoxy (and other similar) composite airframe components are immune to the costly forms of deterioration, notably cracking and corrosion, that plague aluminum and most other alloys used in airframe structures. However, these composites are much more easily damaged in service, for example, by mechanical impact. Thus repairability of such damage[1,2] is an important consideration in the selection of composites for aircraft applications.

Table 10.1 lists the major sources of damage. Service damage includes:

- Mishandling
- Impact, for example, by dropped tools
- Contact damage in doors, often caused by poor rigging
- Delamination damage, often caused by inadequate shimming during component assembly
- Delamination caused during fastener removal or reinstallation
- Local overheating caused by impingement of hot exhaust gases or from a lightning strike

Light weight honeycomb structures most often require repair as the thin-face skins are easily damaged by mechanical contact. Moisture penetration can occur through damaged face skins as well as through badly sealed regions, resulting in corrosion damage if the core is aluminum alloy. Damage is more of a problem with the older-generation composites as these have relatively brittle matrices. The future trend in composite aircraft structures is thus away from honeycomb to (cocured) integrally stiffened structure, although damage over stiffener regions can be difficult to repair, particularly if a post-buckled design is used; in this design approach, the skins are allowed to buckle close to limit load.

10.2 Assessment of the Need to Repair

Methods of analytical assessment of residual strength in damaged composite components are needed to ensure that only necessary repairs are undertaken. Essentially, one of the following decisions is required:

- No repair action—damage is negligible.

Table 10.1   Major Types of Damage Suffered by Aircraft Composite Components

Defect	Typical Cause
Manufacturing Defects	
Voids	Poor process control
Delaminations	Inclusion of release film
	Poor process control
	Faulty hole-drilling procedures
	Poor fit of parts during assembly
Surface damage	Poor process control
	Bad handling
Misdrilled holes	Incorrect drilling procedure
	Faulty jigging
Mechanical Damage	
Cuts/scratches/abrasions	Mishandling
Penetrations	Mishandling/battle damage
Abrasion	Rain/grit erosion
Delaminations/disbonds	Impact: tools/hailstones/runway stones
	Freeze/thaw expansion
	Aerodynamic peeling
	Overload, e.g., during assembly or removal
	Lightning strike/static discharge/laser/overheat
Disbonds	Degradation of metallic interfaces, adhesive joints
Hole elongation	Fatigue-induced bearing failure, mechanically fastened joints
Dents/crushed core	Mishandling/impact
Edge damage, doors, etc.	Poor fit/mishandling
Environmental Damage	
Surface oxidation/burns	Lightning strike/laser/overheat
Core corrosion	Moisture penetration, metallic core
Surface swelling	Incorrect use of solvents or paint strippers

- Cosmetic or sealing repair is required to correct minor damage.
- Structural repair is required (if feasible) because strength is reduced below ultimate design allowable or has the potential to be reduced in subsequent service.
- Repair is not economic and component must be replaced.

When there is penetration damage, the requirement for a structural repair is obvious.

The decision is much more difficult for less obvious damage such as cuts, scratches, and barely visible impact damage (BVID). As yet, simple analytical approaches to estimate the strength of damaged composites (similar to fracture mechanics for metals) are unavailable, so empirical methods are generally used. For BVID, quite large areas of damage (typically 25 mm diameter) can be tolerated for older-generation carbon/epoxy systems without failures occurring below the ultimate design strain allowable, generally around 3000–4000 microstrain.

Fatigue studies[3] have shown that BVID will not grow under realistic cyclic strain levels for typical carbon/epoxy laminates. This is an important point because BVID will often not be detected until a 100% non-destructive inspection is undertaken. There is also the possibility of damage growth and resultant strength degradation under hygrothermal cycling conditions, but this does not appear to be a serious concern under moderate cycling conditions. However, catastrophic flaw growth is possible under severe hygrothermal cycling. This results from expansion of entrapped moisture due to freezing, or to steam formation on heating during supersonic flight.

10.3   Classification of Types of Structure

To evaluate the need for repair, it is also necessary to establish the criticality of the structure.

Structures are generally classified as follows:

- Primary—structure critical to the safety of the aircraft
- Secondary—structure that, if it were to fail, would affect the operation of the aircraft but not lead to its loss
- Tertiary—structure in which failure would not significantly affect operation of the aircraft

Inspection, damage assessment, and repair requirements differ significantly between these classifications. However, even within a single component, the allowable damage type and size (and consequently acceptable repair actions) will vary according to the criticality of the damaged region. The component is generally zoned by the original equipment manufacturer (OEM) in the structural repair manual (SRM) to indicate these regions. Mainly, the SRM will address repairs to non-primary structure. Repairs outside the scope of the SRM, particularly to critical regions of primary structure, require engineering design and approval by the OEM (or its delegate).

10.4   Repair Requirements

Generally, the repair scheme used for structural restoration should be the simplest and least intrusive that can restore structural stiffness and strain capability to the required level and be implemented in the repair environment, without compromising other functions of the component or structure.

It is usually necessary to restore the capability of the structure to withstand a design's ultimate loads and to maintain this capability (or some high percentage of it) for the full service life. Structural requirements for the repair vary according to the component or structural element. For example, wing skins are strength-critical in tension or compression, tail skins and control surfaces are often stiffness-critical (or flutter-critical), whereas spars and (unpressurized) fuselage skins may be stability- or buckling-critical.

The functions that must be restored include: 1) aerodynamic shape, 2) balance, 3) clearance of moving parts, and 4) resistance to lightning strike. The requirement in military to restore the stealth properties of the component may also have to be considered and may influence the type of repair chosen.

Important additional requirements are that implementation of the repair should minimize down-time of the aircraft, use readily available and easily storable materials, remove as little sound material as possible, minimize degradation or damage to the surrounding region, require only simple procedures or tooling, produce minimal increases in the weight of the component.

The type of structure and its accessibility are major considerations in determining the repair approach taken. For example, honeycomb structures with thin face skins are relatively easy to repair using core inserts and simple external patches. Highly loaded thick-skin components will usually require elaborate scarf repairs.

10.4.1 Repair Levels

A major consideration in the choice of repairs is the level at which the repair can be or needs to be implemented. Repair activities are performed at one of the following levels:

- Field level is undertaken directly on the aircraft, in a situation where skilled personnel and/or adequate facilities are unavailable. Such activities will generally be limited to minor repairs to non-primary structure or non-critical repairs to primary structure. Emergency field repairs may be undertaken in a battle situation to make the aircraft operational or to ferry it back to base. Battle-damage repairs (BDR) must be implemented rapidly by relatively unskilled technicians using minimum equipment. They may subsequently be replaced with permanent repairs.
- Depot level is undertaken in a situation where skilled personnel and facilities are available (up to factory capability in some cases). However, if the component is too large or difficult to remove from the aircraft, repairs are implemented directly on the aircraft.

An alternative system of classification is organizational, intermediate, and depot. Organizational equates with field; intermediate is a special repair facility having a capability above field and below depot.

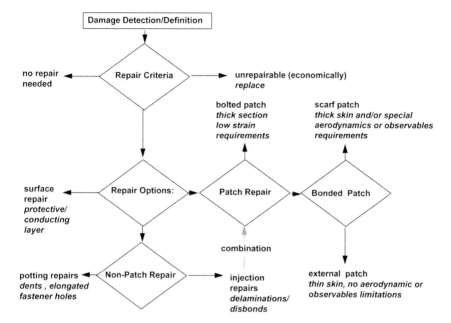

Fig. 10.1 Flow diagram indicating repair options.

Figure 10.1 shows that repairs can be broadly classified into non-patching techniques, for minor damage (detailed in Table 10.2) and patching techniques for more major damage, where restoration of the load path is required (detailed in Table 10.3). Patches can be attached by adhesive bonding or mechanically fastened by riveting or bolting.

Table 10.2 Non-patch Repair Procedures for Minor Damage

Procedure	Application
Resin injection	Connected small voids
	Small delaminations
	Small disbonds
Potting or filling	Minor depressions
	Skin damage in honeycomb panels
	Core replacement in honeycomb panels
	Fastener hole elongation
Fusion	Delaminations in thermoplastic-matrix composites
Surface coating	Seal honeycomb panels

Table 10.3   Patch Repair Procedures for Major Damage

Patch Approach	Comments
Bonded external patch – precured carbon/epoxy – precured carbon/epoxy bonded layers – cocured carbon/epoxy – titanium alloy foil – carbon/epoxy cloth patch (wet lay-up)	Suitable for repairs to laminates up to 16 plies thick Excellent restoration of mechanical properties Easy to implement; well suited for field applications Unobtrusive, minimum further damage to structure
Bonded scarf patch – cocured carbon/epoxy patch – precured carbon/epoxy patch	Suitable for repairs to thick laminates Excellent restoration of mechanical properties Obtrusive; requires significant material removal Difficult to implement; suited only to depot-level repairs
Bolted external patch – titanium alloy (usual) – aluminum alloy – carbon/epoxy cloth patch (wet lay-up)	Suitable for repairs to thick laminates Limited restoration of mechanical properties, but may be sufficient Obtrusive; requires large number of extra fastener holes Easy to implement; well suited for field applications

10.5   Non-patch Repairs

10.5.1   Filler or Potting Repairs

Potting repairs, illustrated in Figure 10.2, are made to fill the defective region with a resin. They may be used to fill minor indentations in a laminate, provided that non-destructive inspection (NDI) has shown that no extensive internal matrix cracking or delaminations are present. In the case of lightly loaded honeycomb panels where the composite skin has been penetrated, potting repairs may be made to stabilize the skin and to seal the damaged region. In this case, the damaged skin around the penetration is removed, together with the damaged part of the core—which is usually undercut to entrap the potting compound. The potting compound (which usually consists of a compatible resin, such as an epoxy, with either a chopped-glass-fiber or ultra-fine-glass-sphere filler) is then applied and cured. An alternative approach is to plug the cavity with glass-cloth/epoxy pre-preg or wet lay-up, but this imposes a high weight penalty that may not be acceptable for a control surface, for example.

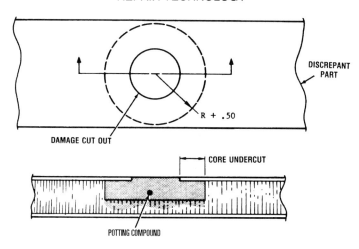

Fig. 10.2   Potted repair to a damaged honeycomb region.

Provided bearing loads are not too great, damage to attachment holes, such as minor hole elongation or wear, can be repaired by filling the hole with a machinable potting compound. A superior approach, particularly if bearing loads are high, is to adhesively bond a metal rod into the hole and redrill.

10.5.2 Injection Repairs for Delaminations

Resin-injection repairs, illustrated in Figure 10.3, are used for minor disbonds and delaminations in laminates or joints. The effectiveness depends on whether

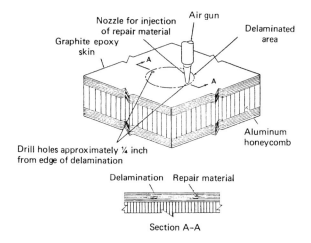

Fig. 10.3   Method of repairing delamination damage in the composite skin of a honeycomb panel by resin injection.

the defect arose during manufacture or was caused by mechanical damage during service. Manufacturing delaminations caused by a local lack of bonding pressure or contamination of the bonding surface have surfaces that are very difficult to bond without pretreatment, making injection repairs generally unsuccessful. In contrast, internal flaws caused by mechanical damage have surfaces that can be bonded reasonably well, provided contamination has not occurred by service fluids such as fuel or hydraulic oil; water can be removed by drying.

The repair procedure involves the injection of a compatible thermosetting resin under pressure directly into the delaminated or disbonded region. This can be done directly if the delaminations are exposed, as in the case of edges or fastener holes, or, if not, through injection holes (with bleeder holes to allow displacement of air, etc.—vacuum may be applied to aid this action). It is difficult, however, to ensure that these holes break into all the delaminations as many will not be internally connected.

The resin is generally injected after the part is preheated to about 70°C to decrease resin viscosity and improve wetting capability. Pressure can be applied to the component during cure; this is achieved under temperatures of about 150°C, to improve mating of the delaminated surfaces and to maintain contour. A fastener can be installed through the damaged and injected region in an attempt to further improve transverse strength.

Resin injection, although an attractive unobtrusive method for repairing delamination damage, is currently limited to non-critical applications. This is in part because resin systems recommended in the SRMs have relatively poor flow and wetting capabilities. This results in incomplete penetration of delaminations and consequently low strength recovery. Some improvement is being obtained with improved lower-viscosity adhesives.

A special resin has been developed that is optimized for injection repairs.[4,5] This resin provides excellent penetration of voids and delaminations, using either vacuum assistance or simple positive pressure, and produces a void-free well-bonded repair with a high T_g. Full recovery of compression strength after impact damage was demonstrated even when the internal delaminations were initially contaminated with environmental fluids including jet fuel, hydraulic fluid, detergent, or seawater.

10.5.2.1 Fusion Repairs for Thermoplastics.   For the reasons mentioned in Chapter 9, thermoplastics are difficult to bond with thermosetting adhesives. Thus, injection repairs to delaminations are unlikely to be successful. Because thermoplastic materials are fusible, it should be possible to repair them by applying pressure and heat to the delaminated region. Unfortunately, melting temperatures are so high (typically over 380°C) that with general heating the component must be pressurized on a suitable tool to avoid distortion and delamination. Control of cooling rate is also important to avoid degradation of the mechanical properties of the matrix. This makes in situ repairs infeasible in most cases. Another approach is to use thermoplastic adhesives with a lower melting temperature; however, because of their very high viscosity, thermoplastic adhesives are not suitable for injection repairs, though they may be suited as film adhesives for patch repairs. With mechanical abrasion, or better, with more elaborate surface treatment procedures, patching-type repairs using thermosetting adhesives may be feasible.

Several heating methods, based on either magnetic-induction, electrical-resistance, infrared, microwave, or ultrasonic welding, have been considered or evaluated in attempts to provide in situ heating. Induction[6] is probably the most promising for fusion of delamination damage.

10.6 Patch Repairs: General Considerations

Patch (reinforcement) repairs are intended to restore the load path removed by the damage, ideally, without significantly changing the original load distribution. Table 10.4 provides a summary of the performance requirements for bonded patch repairs. For a preliminary analysis, these repairs can be modelled as one of the simple joints discussed in Chapter 9.

The level of recovery of operating-strain possible, by a repair, is dependent on the stiffness of the laminate. The actual load to be transmitted by the joint is:

$$P = e_a E_x t \tag{10.1}$$

where e_a, E_X, and t are the allowable or ultimate design strain (often 4000 microstrain), the modulus in the primary loading direction, and the laminate thickness, respectively.

There are four main patching approaches:

(1) external bonded patches,
(2) flush or scarf-bonded patches,
(3) bolted patches, and
(4) bolted and bonded patches.

Adhesively bonded patches provide the most effective load transfer and, because fastener holes are not required, external patches minimize further damage to the structure. Bonded repairs are capable of restoring the original strength of the composite; however, these advantages are offset by the greater degree of complexity and skills required and the longer time required to complete the repair. Other problems with bonded repairs include the need to dry the composite before bonding to avoid porosity associated with the formation of water vapor during cure and the limited storage life of adhesives and other repair materials.

Bonded external-patch repairs are generally restricted to thin-skin applications (for example, up to 16 plies, around 2-mm-thick carbon/epoxy), whereas flush or bolted external patches are applicable to repairs for thick sections.

Scarf repairs are used when the thickness of composite exceeds the repair capability of simple external patches, around 2–3 mm of carbon/epoxy. Scarf

Table 10.4   Some Requirements for Patch Repairs to High-Performance Military Aircraft (Requirements Marked with * Refer to Bonded Repairs)

Requirement	Thick Primary Structure	Thin-skin Structure	Composite Substructure
Service temperature	$-54-104°C$	$-54-104°C$	$-54-82°C$
Ultimate strain/ strength recovery	± 4000 microstrain	± 4000 up to ± 6000 microstrain	Web shear and strength recovery; web cap strength and cap pull off recovery
Stiffness change	No decrease; moderate local increase acceptable		
Weight change	Minimum	Minimum; critical on control surfaces	Minimum
Aerodynamic smoothness	Maximum 2 mm change; less than 1 mm if stealth requirement	Less than 1 mm if control surface or for stealth requirements	No particular limitation
Skin configuration	Typically curved with varying thickness including ply drop-offs		
Moisture absorbed	1% prior to repair		
Spectrum loading	Durable for two lifetimes of severe loading		
Environment	Exposure to high humidity, fuel, and hydraulic fluids		
Maximum patch cure temperature*	$180°$ C, T_g must be similar to that of parent material		
Maximum cure pressure*	Usually non-autoclave, generally atmospheric or below		
Accessibility to damaged region	Usually from outside only		
Facilities/skills	Simple as possible, commensurate with efficient cost-effective repair		
Quality	Low porosity; low acoustic attenuation		

repairs are also used where it is required to maintain 1) aerodynamic smoothness, 2) radar cross-section, or 3) clearance—for example, where a component, such as a flap, must fit into a restricted space.

Compared with bolted or bonded external patches, scarf repairs to thick skins are difficult to apply and usually require depot-level facilities and highly skilled personnel. Scarf repairs to thick laminates have the serious disadvantage of requiring removal of a large amount of sound material because of the shallow scarf angles required, generally about 3°. Finally, (as discussed later) creep or stress relaxation may be a concern under prolonged high stress levels, particularly at elevated temperatures.

Bolted repairs are highly suited for the repair of thick composite skins. These repairs are simple to apply by technicians familiar with standard repairs to metallic airframe structures, require no drying, and involve minimal removal of the parent structure. However, bolted repairs are limited to relatively low strain levels, below 4000 microstrain, and usually involve the drilling of many extra fastener holes.

Bolted repairs are, however, unsuitable for the repair of honeycomb structure because (unless very carefully sealed) the bolt holes provide a path for environmental ingress and generally do not provide a sufficient strength recovery. They are also usually unsuitable for the repair of post-buckled structure because they lack the required flexibility.

10.7 Bonded Patch Repairs

10.7.1 Design Approaches

Repairs are often designed, at least to a first approximation, by modelling the repair region as a representative joint, as shown in Figure 10.4. Thus an external patch repair is modelled as an overlap joint, and a scarf repair is modelled as either a scarf or a step-lap joint. This one-dimensional approach essentially assumes the repair to be a single-load path joint. In a real repair situation, load shed by an inadequately stiff repair can be carried by the parent structure, provided its degraded strength allowables are not exceeded.

An important design input is the ultimate design strain in the repair region. This information is often difficult to obtain, particularly at short notice. If such information is unavailable, strain levels can be based on an assumed ultimate allowable design strain for the parent structure. A reasonable estimate for current (military) designs is an ultimate design strain level of between $\pm$ 3000 and 4000 microstrain. For the purpose of this chapter, the higher level is assumed for conservatism in the design of repairs.

For more realistic designs, several other factors need to be considered, including:

- The allowable strain at the edges of the (reinforced) cut-out, typically over 10,000 microstrain
- The geometry of the repair joint
- Through-thickness or peel stresses
- Extra load attracted to the region due to local stiffening by the repair

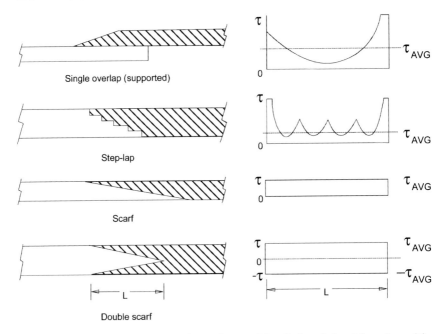

Fig. 10.4   Main types of joint configuration used for the bonded patch and resulting shear-stress distribution in the adhesive; _t_ is shear stress and τ_{AVG} is the average shear stress.

- Creep/stress relaxation in the adhesive (function of temperature and absorbed moisture)
- Secondary bending arising from the neutral-axis offset caused by external reinforcements
- Development of residual stresses where the coefficients of thermal expansion of patch and parent material differ
- Proximity of other repairs—multiple repair interaction
- Scale effects

To deal with most of these complications, particularly where significant through-thickness (peel) stresses are anticipated, structural analysis using a three-dimensional finite-element approach is probably the only option and in even more sophisticated designs may need to include non-linear to include geometrical effects and adhesive plasticity.

10.7.2 External Patch Repairs

Typical external patch repairs to thin-skinned honeycomb panels are illustrated in Figure 10.5. Patches generally cover a circular cut-out made to

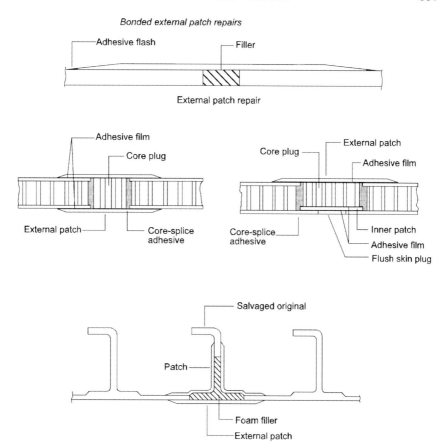

Fig. 10.5   **Typical external patch repairs to honeycomb and to stiffened panels.**

remove the damaged material. This shape is normally chosen for machining convenience and to minimize stress concentrations; however, a circular cut-out does not necessarily provide the lowest edge strain.

As a first approximation, an external patch repair can be modelled as one half of a double-overlap joint, assuming sufficient support is provided by the honeycomb core or substructure to react-out secondary bending. It is assumed for this analysis that:

- The patch is appropriately stepped at its ends to minimize peak shear and peel stresses (very important for patches thicker than about eight plies, or about 1 mm)—one ply drop per 3–4 mm about 3° effective taper.
- The edges of the cut-out are not tapered—this is a conservative assumption tapering improves the load-carrying capacity of the joint.

- The strength of the joint is limited by the load-carrying capacity of the adhesive in shear; this is most likely to be the case under hot/wet conditions. Under ambient or cold conditions, strength is more likely to be limited by the peel strength of surface resin or surface ply in the composite. This is a more complex scenario and therefore will not be considered here; however, in repair design it has to be ensured that peel is not the weakest failure mode. If it is, repair design will be based on a fracture-mechanics-type failure criterion related to ply or interface peel failure. The reality is that failure criteria for these modes have not been validated—this is an area of current research.

Two simple one-dimensional design approaches are considered here:

In the first, it is assumed that a patch of stiffness equal to that of the parent material is used and the strength of the joint is checked to see whether it will carry the ultimate design load. This assumes that the strain at the edges of the cut-out do not exceed the allowable ultimate design conditions.

In the second approach, the patch is designed so that the effective stiffness of the gap (cut-out) matches that of the parent material and then the strength is checked. This implies that there will be no strain concentration at the edges of the cut-out.

10.7.2.1 Simple Strength Analysis Based on Adhesive Strength.
In Chapter 9 the maximum load-carrying capacity per unit width of a balanced joint is given as:

$$P_{\max b} = 2[t_A E t \tau_P(\gamma_e/2 + \gamma_P)]^{1/2} \qquad (10.2)$$

where τ_p is the effective yield stress of the adhesive; γ_e and γ_p are, respectively, the elastic strain to yield and the plastic strain to failure; t_A is the adhesive thickness; t is the thickness of the patch (and the parent material); and E is its modulus.

Using, for a typical carbon/epoxy laminate and structural film adhesive (FM300), the following properties:

$\tau_p = 20$ MPa (hot/wet)	$t = t_p = 1.5$ mm (12 plies)
$E = 72$ GPa, typical for carbon/epoxy laminate	$t_A = 0.125$ mm
$G_A = \tau_p/\gamma_e = 0.4$ GPa	$\gamma_e = 0.05, \gamma_p = 0.5$

gives $P_{\max b} = 0.75$ kN mm^{1}.

It is necessary to show that the load capacity of the joint $P_{\max b}$ exceeds the allowable load (per unit width) in the patch or parent material P_u given by:

$$P_u = E e_u t \qquad (10.3)$$

where e_u is taken here as 4000 microstrain.

This gives $Pu = 0.43$ kN mm^{-1} showing that the joint has adequate strength. However, safe margin (factor of ~ 2) is not maintained for external patch repairs of carbon/epoxy laminates above about 16 plies thick.

If it is considered that the strength of the repair is adequate, the next step is to determine the overlap length L. The total patch length is twice this plus the diameter of the hole. The minimum design overlap length (excluding the length of the taper) is given by:

$$L_{min} = \frac{Ee_u t}{\tau_p} + \frac{4}{\beta}$$ (10.4)

where $\beta = \sqrt{2G_A/t_A Et}$ and $G_A = \tau_p/\gamma_e$

This gives L_{min} of about 40 mm on each side of repair cut-out.

Use of a generous overlap length is essential in repair designs. A long overlap ensures that the elastic trough (See Figure 9.10) is fully developed, thereby stabilizing the joint against creep in the adhesive and providing allowance for manufacturing defects, such as voids and disbonds, and service damage.

10.7.2.2 Stiffness Analysis.

For a one-dimensional model of this repair joint the displacement Δ of the gap (cut-out), length h, is given by:

$$\Delta = 2\gamma t_A + he_R$$ (10.5)

where e_R is the strain in the patch. The first component of Δ is the displacement due to shear of the adhesive, while the second is due to strain of the patch.

To obtain equivalence in strain between the parent material and gap, we have:

$$\frac{\Delta}{h} = \frac{2\gamma t_A}{h} + e_R = e_P$$ (10.6)

where, based on parent material stiffness E_p and thickness t_p, the strain e_p in the parent material is given by:

$$e_P = \frac{P}{E_p t_p}$$ (10.7)

Assuming elastic behavior in the adhesive the shear strain γ is given by τ/G_A which, in terms of the applied load P, is given by:

$$\gamma = P\beta/G_A(1 + E_p t_p/E_R t_R)$$ (10.8)

Elastic/plastic behavior should be assumed for the adhesive because this is more representative of the conditions in the adhesive at ultimate design loads; however, for simplicity, only elastic conditions are considered here.

Substituting equations (10.8) and (10.7) into (10.5) and letting $S = E_R t_R/E_p t_p$ yields the following equation, which can be solved to obtain $E_R t_R$ as a function of h and adhesive properties.

$$(S - 1)^2(S + 1)\frac{h^2}{4}\frac{G_A}{t_A}\frac{1}{E_p t_p} = S \tag{10.9}$$

This shows that S is a function of the gap size h, the adhesive thickness, the shear modulus, and the absolute value of stiffness $E_p t_p$ of the parent material.

For the same joint properties as in the previous example, assuming h values of (a) 5 mm (b) 10 mm (c) 20 mm, and (d) 40 mm gives, for the stiffness ratio S, (a) 2.7 (b) 1.8 (c) 1.4, and (d) 1.2 respectively.

Thus only when h is greater than 40 mm (for this relatively thin skin) is a balanced stiffness approach reasonable. Because the joint strength is reduced by having an unbalanced joint [See equation (9.20)] ideally h should be chosen so that $S = 1$, provided that the cut-out is not excessive.

10.7.2.3 Modified Load Path: Two-Dimensional Effects. A more realistic model of an external patch repair needs to account for the increase in stiffness of the patched region and the load diverted around the patched hole. Generally, a finite-element approach would be needed to undertake an analysis of this complexity; however, simple analytical approaches can be used to obtain a useful first estimate.

The influence of the stiffness of the patch on the strain in the repair region (assuming the cut-out region is small in size compared with the patch) can be estimated using an inclusion model developed by Rose[7] for composite patching of metallic components. The model, which allows for the shape and elastic properties of the patch material, shows that due to extra load attracted into the region, the strain in the parent material is somewhat higher than would be estimated on the basis of patch/parent stiffness ratio. For example, for a circular patch of equal stiffness to the parent, the strain in the repair region may be reduced by about 0.60 rather than the 0.5 expected. This implies an effective increase in P, the load on the joint per unit width, of around 20%.

The influence of the load carried around the hole can be estimated using the approach of Hart-Smith.[19] This simple analysis considers a hole reinforced by a central strip. Because the unreinforced hole can carry load, an estimate can be made of the load that the hole can carry and therefore the remaining load that the strip must carry on the basis of the relative stiffness. Because a hole experiences a deformation three times that of the surrounding sound material, it has an effective stiffness of $1/3E_p t_p$. Thus, if the patch has stiffness $E_R t_R$, the effective applied load per unit width is P and the hole diameter d is such that load transfer effects can be neglected (See preceding section), the actual load P' that the patch must carry is given by:

$$P' = P/(1 + E_p t_p / E_R t_R) \tag{10.10}$$

Thus, assuming $E_R t_R = E_p t_p$ the load P is reduced by 20%. Therefore, for this example, the two effects approximately cancel.

10.7.3 Scarf Repairs

Scarf patch repairs are illustrated in Figure 10.6. Note that the configuration is actually scarfed in the parent material but a small step-lap in the repair, as the

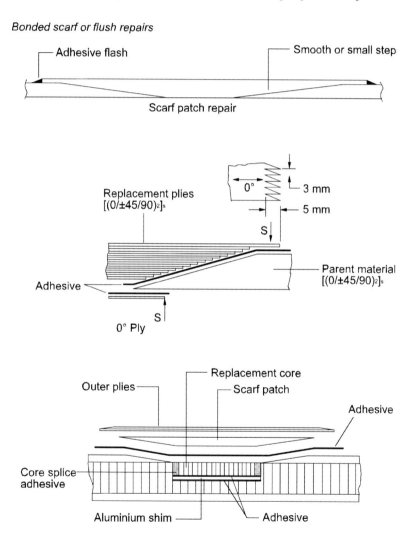

Fig. 10.6   General illustration of a simple scarf repair and, below, exploded views of a scarf repair to a thick-skinned honeycomb panel. S indicates serrated 0° plies sometimes used to reduce peel stresses in the outer plies.

repair patch is built up from individual plies. The condition of uniform shear stress in the adhesive layer holds only if the scarf is taken to a feather-edge. If the edge breaks away during repair implementation, or is damaged during service loading, significant stress concentrations arise that could lead to failure of the joint. To avoid this problem a thin external patch is bonded over the scarf region; the $0°$ plies may be serrated to reduce the peel stresses even further.

Scarf repairs can be modelled to a first approximation as a simple scarf joint. If the patch matches the parent material in stiffness and expansion coefficient, simple theory gives:

$$\tau = P \sin \theta \cos \theta / t \qquad (10.11)$$

At small θ the normal stress σ is negligible. The required minimum value of scarf angle θ for an applied load P can be obtained from the following, taking τ_p as the peak shear stress:

$$P = Ee_u t = \tau_p t / \sin \theta \cos \theta \qquad (10.12)$$

For small scarf angles, the condition for reaching the allowable strain e_u in the adherends is $\theta < \tau_p / Ee_u$ rad.

Taking e_u as 4000 microstrain, τ_p for hot/wet conditions as 13 MPa, and E as 72 GPa gives $\theta \leq 3°$

For a typical horizontal stabilator skin, for example, 4 mm, on a honeycomb core (tail skin) the minimum length of the scarf is about 80 mm, which with a hole size of, say, 80 mm, gives a total repair length of 240 mm. Because a bonded repair must be used in this case, the scarf repair would probably be accepted.

For a typical wing skin thickness around 13 mm, the minimum length of the scarf is about 250 mm which, for a hole size of 100 mm, gives a total patch length of 600 mm—far too long to be feasible in most cases. The problem is much less serious if the damage extends only part way through (a reasonable expectation in such a thick laminate) so that the repair length would be considerably shorter. Full-thickness repairs on such a thick laminate would be based on bolted repairs, as described later. The strength recovery in this case should be acceptable if (as is usually the case for at least one of the skins) the wing skins are attached by bolts to the substructure.

10.7.4 Studies on Scarf Joints Representing Repairs

The focus of this program[8] is the scarf repair of the relatively thick-skinned region of the F/A-18 horizontal stabilator—AS4/3501–6 carbon/epoxy, over 35 plies thick in this area. This repair is particularly challenging because the design ultimate strain is 5200 microstrain, unlike most of the other composite components on the aircraft, where design ultimate strains are usually around 3500 microstrain. The aim was to evaluate the strength of scarf joints under compression or tension loading over the design temperature range for the aircraft of $+104°C$ to $-40°C$. The adhesive used in these repairs is FM 300, having the following shear yield stress (τ_p) properties: approximately 40 MPa (RT dry) 13 MPa (hot/wet).

A honeycomb-sandwich beam specimen, developed for this program, corresponds to a section through a typical repaired region of the stabilator. The beams are loaded in four-point bending with the repaired region in either tension or compression. Figure 10.7 shows the configuration of the parent and repair laminate. The scarf joint consists essentially of a ply configuration similar to that of the parent material with doublers having extra 45° plies at the bottom and 0° and 45° plies at the top.

From the results provided in Figure 10.8, it is clear that hot/wet exposure (about 0.7% moisture in the skins) markedly reduces the failure strain of the joint. In the cold/wet and ambient temperature tests, failure almost invariably occurred in the honeycomb core so that these results represent a lower bound to the strain capacity of these specimens. In contrast, in the hot/wet tests failure was mainly cohesive in the adhesive layer.

A simple analysis of the shear stress in the scarf joint can be made, assuming a uniform (average) modulus through the thickness of the carbon/epoxy laminates.

Taking strain design ultimate for the parent material to be $e_u = 5200$ µε, E_p as 80 GPa, t as 2.7 mm, and θ as 3° (allowing for the load taken by the outer plies of the patch),s the average shear stress τ_{av} in the joint is estimated from equation *(10.12)* to be $\tau_{av} = 19$ MPa, just above the hot/wet yield.

However, because the in-plane stiffness of the carbon/epoxy skin varies in the through-thickness direction, and the configuration is actually a step-lap on in the repair plies, the shear stress along the "scarf" may not be constant. A simple first approximation of the variation in shear stress along the scarf is obtained by assuming that the shear stress in the adhesive adjacent to each ply step on the

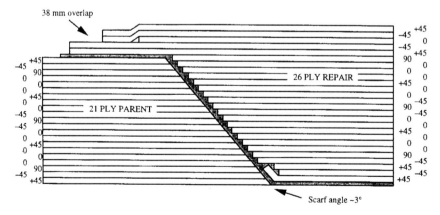

Fig. 10.7   Ply configuration of parent laminate (21 plies) and repair scarf laminate (26 plies). The adhesive (shown shaded) is either FM300 or FM300K structural film adhesive, and the scarf angle is nominally 3°. Taken from Ref. 8.

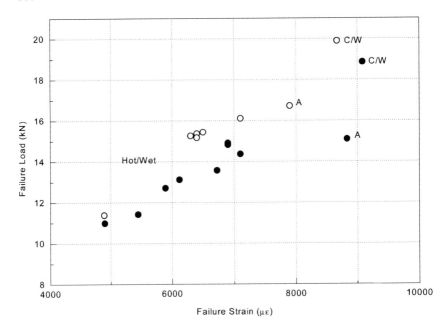

**Fig. 10.8   Plot of failure loads and strains for the carbon/epoxy scarf specimens, *A*
and *C/W*, respectively, refer to exposure at ambient and cold/wet conditions. Open
holes or filled holes respectively refer to tension or compression loading. Taken from
Ref. 8.**

repair is proportional to the load carried by that ply, which is in turn assumed to
be proportional to the relative stiffness of the ply. An analysis on this basis should
give an upper bound (i.e., an overestimate) for the variation of adhesive shear
stress along the scarf.

The average shear stress τ_{av} is given by:

$$\tau_{av} = \frac{[n_0\,\tau_0 + n_{45^\circ}\tau_{45} + n_{90}\,\tau_{90}]}{n_{total}} \tag{10.13}$$

where τ_{0°, τ_{45°, and τ_{90° represent the shear stress in the adhesive adjacent to 0°,
45°, and 90° plies, respectively, and n is the number of plies.

The ratio of the laminate stiffnesses is 1 (0°), 0.23 (45°), 0.07 (90°), and
therefore the equation can be rewritten as

$$\tau_{av} = \frac{[n_0\,\tau_0 + 0.23n_{45}\,\tau_0 + 0.07n_{90}\,\tau_0]}{n_{total}} \tag{10.14}$$

Inserting $\tau_{av} = 19$ MPa from above and solving for τ_{0° gives $1.74 \times \tau_{av} = 33.5$
MPa, with $\tau_{45^\circ} = 0.23 \times \tau_{0^\circ} = 7.7$ MPa and $\tau_{90^\circ} = 0.07 \times \tau_{0^\circ} = 2.3$ MPa.

The peak shear stress value of 33.5 MPa for τ_{0° is well above the hot/wet yield
allowable for FM300 of 13 MPa, and, from this very simple analysis, the scarf
may be expected to yield locally before a strain of 5200 $\mu\varepsilon$ is reached in the skin.

Although local yielding in the adhesive does not necessarily lead to immediate failure, it could lead to failure through creep. Thus it was conjectured[9] that final failure in the joint specimen under hot/wet conditions was initiated by strain build-up in the outer doublers as the scarf region experienced creep deformation in the adhesive layer. The outer doublers would be anchored against creep by the elastic trough in the adhesive layer.

The scarf specimens differ significantly from repairs in that they represent a single load path situation. Thus creep deformation in a repair will be much more limited and should result simply in load redistribution—not failure of the joint. Failure of the component would result only if the strain at the edges of the repaired hole exceeded the critical value due to the increased compliance. Thus the scarf results can be considered a conservative estimate of repair performance.

The shear stress distribution in the bondline for the ply-by-ply model, estimated using a finite-element model (elastic adhesive) is shown plotted in Figure 10.9. Results are included for both room temperature and hot/wet adhesive properties and for reference a similar aluminum-skinned beam. The shear stress in the composite-skinned beam is observed to vary with position along the bondline, with the maximum stress occurring adjacent to the ends of $0°$ plies, as expected from the simple model previously outlined. The magnitude of the variation in shear stress along the bondline is, however, much less than that predicted by the simple analysis.

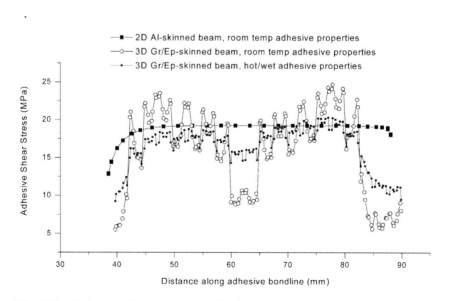

Fig. 10.9 Estimated shear stress distribution along the scarf for *FE* models of aluminum and carbon/epoxy scarf repair beam specimen. Taken from Ref. 8.

10.8 Materials Engineering Aspects

10.8.1 Bonded Patch System Options

The options for external patches for carbon/epoxy components are 1) carbon/epoxy, based on cocured or precured prepreg materials; 2) carbon/epoxy, based on wet lay-up with carbon cloth and resin; and 3) titanium alloy, based on laminated sheet. For scarf repairs, the main materials options are carbon/epoxy pre-preg, co-cured or pre-cured or, for lower stress requirements, wet lay-up.

Titanium foil can be used to produce a patch with good mechanical properties. In this case, layers of foil interleaved with adhesive film are bonded to the parent laminate. This approach appears to work well for repairs to fairly flat thin-skinned regions. To obtain strong durable repairs with titanium alloy patches, it is essential that the foil be correctly surface-treated and primed and that it not be contaminated during handling.

Where pre-preg materials or titanium foil cannot be used because of storage or forming problems, the wet-lay-up approach, using carbon fiber cloth and liquid-epoxy resin, is the best option. The manufacturing flexibility of wet lay-up procedures makes it well suited to the repair of complex stiffened internal structure, provided access is available. With suitable resins, wet lay-up is also highly suited for rapid field repairs, such as the repair of battle damage.

The advantages of the wet lay-up approach include:

● Long-time ambient-temperature shelf life for the resin because hardener and resin are stored separately
● High patch formability—patch can be formed over complex contours
● No separate adhesive required—the resin forms the matrix and the adhesive layer
● Processable even without vacuum bagging, although properties are markedly improved if bagging is used.

10.8.2 Patch Materials and Adhesives

The storage and processing properties of the repair adhesives and matrices (for cocured composite patches) strongly influence composite supportability.[10]

As well as having mechanical properties matching the parent structure, an ideal adhesive or matrix resin will be storable for long periods at ambient temperature, curable in short times at modest temperatures, and processable under simple vacuum bag conditions. As may be anticipated, no available materials meet all these requirements, and various compromises must be made.

Structural film adhesives provide excellent mechanical properties and durability in repair joints, provided they are processable under repair conditions. Film adhesives are also very convenient and reliable to use because, unlike with paste adhesives, there is no requirement for weighing and mixing of resin and hardener.

Film adhesives may be used for repair work in a partially precured condition; this is called B-staged or (when even more advanced) C-staged. The aims of staging the adhesive are to:

- Reduce the amount of flow during the cure, avoiding the danger of excessively thin bond lines
- Minimize voiding—high resin viscosity results in high hydrostatic pressure during the cure, discouraging void formation
- Improve storage life—a C-staged film adhesive may be storable at ambient temperature for several months with minimal property change

To provide an easy exit route for entrapped air and volatiles during cure, the film adhesive may be embossed by using a honeycomb panel as a caul plate for the staging.

Unfortunately, structural film adhesives suitable for repairs to carbon/epoxy (such as FM300, usable up to 110°C) have the major disadvantage of limited storage life, even under deep-freeze conditions, nominally 6–12 months at −20°C. A related problem with film adhesives is high cost and the large minimum order quantity. Furthermore, lead time for reordering some adhesives can be over 3 months. To maximize life, refrigeration (usually in dry ice) is essential, even during transportation. More recently, film adhesives specially developed for repair applications with long ambient-temperature storage capability have become available (FM275 is an example), which could greatly aid use of these materials for repairs.

In contrast, two-part paste adhesives have considerable advantages for long-term storage because the reactive components can be kept separate until required. The pressure requirements to cure paste adhesives is much lower than for film adhesives so that vacuum bag pressure is sufficient. Generally, low (not full) vacuum is used because this minimizes void formation in low-pressure regions. Special systems have been developed suitable for repair applications (such as Hysol EA 9391) with properties comparable with structural film adhesives (e.g., FM300) and good processing qualities.

A major disadvantage with paste adhesives (or resins) is the need to weigh the components accurately and to mix them thoroughly. The problem can be substantially reduced with the use of suitable packaging. Each pack contains the two components, preweighed for a single application and separated by a breakable seal; the seal is broken and the components mixed while contained in the outer envelope. The mixed adhesive is then ejected after cutting the envelope. Although most components of two-part systems have a long storage life under ambient conditions, refrigeration significantly increases life.

The repair approach that provides the best combination of formability and mechanical properties is to cocure the patch in pre-preg form with an appropriate structural film adhesive. However, the highest mechanical properties are obtained by precuring the patch in an autoclave under optimized processing conditions and then bonding in a separate operation. This is sometimes called the hard patch approach, and can also be used with scarf repairs.[11]

Pre-preg materials similar to those used in the manufacture of the composite component provide optimum properties, provided that they can be processed under repair conditions. Generally, however, the pressure requirements to process standard pre-preg are higher than can be achieved by vacuum bag processing. The result is a relatively high void content and low fiber/volume fraction. Often the patch is so porous that attenuation is too great for the use of ultrasonic NDI. However, using a combined pre-consolidation and de-gassing approach known as double-vacuum processing,[12] it is possible to reduce voids to less than 3% and markedly increase fiber/volume fraction. This procedure, which reduces the pressure required during patch application and minimizes porosity, involves placing the patch lay-up with the vacuum bag inside a sealed box to which a vacuum can be applied. First, the vacuum is applied under the bag and to the box, which allows the lay-up to degas under no external pressure, maximizing the removal of trapped air and volatiles. The vacuum in the box is then vented and normal vacuum allowed to consolidate the patch lay-up.

The double-bag technique can also be used to pre-process wet lay-up patches resulting in a marked reduction of voids and improved fiber/volume fraction.[13]

10.8.3 Repair Joint Preparation

The damaged region is first outlined as a geometrical shape that allows the accurate preparation and installation of a patch. Usually, the shape will be elliptical and will encompass the area of damage, as determined by NDI and visual inspection, but will include as little as possible of the sound material.

Carbon/epoxy is best cut with tungsten-carbide-tipped tools; conventional high-speed tools can be used, but their life is short. Most forming operations for repair purposes can be performed with an end-mill cutter or router mounted on an air motor on a portable base. Air-driven tools are preferred because carbon fibers are known to short-circuit electrical motors. A template may be used to control the outline of the shape of the cut and shims used to control its depth. Taper cuts may be made, using shims to allow cuts of one ply at a time. Alternatively, a sanding drum (alumina or silicon carbide grit) may be used to cut a smooth taper. In this case, the tool may be hand-guided (controlled by the operator's observation of the ply exposure) or, preferably, template-guided (robotic machines for cutting tapers are under development). The taper may extend fully through the thickness of the laminate in the repair of penetration damage, or only part-way through in the repair of delamination damage.

For scarf repairs, a taper angle of approximately $3°$ provides acceptable levels of shear stress in the adhesive. If ground with a reasonable surface finish, the ply sequence in the repair region is clearly visible.

Instead of a cutting or grinding operation, it is possible to form the taper using a peeling procedure. This involves using a sharp knife to cut through the composite, one ply at a time, and then using grips to peel each ply back to the cut. By this approach, a step-lap joint is produced.

10.8.4 Pre-Bonding Surface Preparation

It is vitally important for the success of bonded repairs that all bonded surfaces be correctly prepared. Surface treatment is required for precured composite patches, metallic patches, and the parent material.

The first step in preparing a component for repair is to remove paint and major surface contaminants. This is generally done by a solvent degrease with MEK and then removal of the original surface material with abrasive pads. To improve environmental health and safety, the aim is now to avoid volatile organic solvents (VOCs) by using water-based solvents.

For thermosetting-matrix composites, the most effective surface-treatment for strong, durable bonding is to grit-blast with alumina or silicon carbide particles. When done correctly, this process provides a clean, uniform, high-energy surface without removing too much of the original surface resin.

Thorough abrasion of the surfaces with silicon carbide paper is a reasonable alternative, but is less satisfactory because minor depressions in the surface are left untreated unless a considerable amount of surface material is removed. This results in a weaker joint because little surface resin remains and surface fibers are exposed and damaged.

10.8.5 Moisture Problems

Moisture can cause serious problems if it is not removed by an initial heat-treatment, especially with composites based on high-temperature matrices, such as bismaleimides, because repair cure temperatures will exceed 200°C. During patch application, the moisture may vaporize, split the laminate in the voided regions, and form voids in the adhesive and in the matrix of the repair laminate (if being cocured). Damage in the matrix can be severe if heat-treatment is performed above its T_g, when its strength is quite low. During cure of the adhesive or patch, moisture that has diffused in from the parent laminate will produce voids[14] if the partial pressure of the moisture exceeds the applied (hydraulic) pressure during cure. In all cases, the result may be a severe degradation in mechanical properties. The problem of moisture removal is much more difficult in a thick laminate (50 plies or more) because many days of heating may be required. However, it is not necessary to remove all the moisture; only the surface moisture causes problems in curing the patch and adhesive.

Thin laminates (16 plies or less) can be dried out fairly rapidly. However, if the laminate forms the face of a honeycomb panel, care must be taken because high internal pressure can develop[15] that can easily exceed the strength of the skin-to-core bond. The internal pressure developed in the core during cure is made up of the partial pressure of the air and the partial pressure of moisture desorbed from the skin. Typically, at a cure temperature of 175°C, pressures well over 0.5 MPa can develop, which, depending on the adhesive, can exceed the hot/wet adhesive strength, resulting in skin/core separation.

With precured patches, precured bonded plies, or titanium foil patches, the patches do not suffer moisture problems. However, the problem of adhesive porosity is even more severe because the patch is unable to absorb any of the evolved moisture.

Contrary to expectation, application of the vacuum during drying of the skin does not significantly increase the drying rate. This is because drying is controlled by the rate of moisture diffusion through the laminate. However, a vacuum is used to aid in the removal of entrapped moisture from honeycomb panels.

There are several methods for quantitatively assessing moisture behavior during drying of the laminate and subsequent cure of the patch system. However, a simple but useful method for estimating drying requirements is based on the concept[16] of drying depth. As discussed in Chapter 9, the drying time t for which moisture concentration in the composite at depth x is reduced to half its original value is given by $t = x^2/D$, where D is the diffusion coefficient.

As an example, consider a moist carbon fiber/epoxy laminate on which an external patch will be bonded at 120°C for 1 h. Taking $D = 2 \times 10^{-6}$ mm^2 s^{-1} (typical value) gives a value of x of 0.085 mm. To be safe, it is suggested that the composite should be initially dried to give a value of x of twice this value. For drying to be undertaken at 105°C (where $D = 3 \times 10^{-7}$ mm^2 s^{-1}), the time for x to reach 2×0.085 mm is found to be 26 h.

If moisture is present in the core of a honeycomb panel, and particularly if cure is at high temperature, an elaborate drying cycle is required. The procedure used is to apply an external supporting pressure using a vacuum bag and then to place the component in an oven at about 90°C for about 30 h, allowing the moisture to escape by the route it entered the component. The temperature is then raised to just above 100°C and held for several hours. The gases drawn out of the vacuum bag are checked for moisture and the process is continued until no trace is found.

10.9   Application Technology: In Situ Repairs

Heat and pressure are required to cure the adhesive and obtain a uniform nonporous adhesive layer. Cure pressure requirements are most simply satisfied using a vacuum bag, [1] that provides a pressure of around 1 atm. This pressure is adequate if the patch mates well with the parent material (by pre-forming the patch on a mold made on the parent structure) or is cocured with the adhesive on the surface of the parent material.

Heat may be applied internally by encasing a heater blanket under the vacuum bag (usually an electrical resistance wire embedded in silicone rubber). Alternatively, a reusable combined vacuum bag and heater blanket may be used, consisting of silicone rubber with built-in heater wires. Silicone rubber heater blankets can be unreliable because they are prone to burn-out during a repair, particularly if used for large heat inputs or for high-temperature cures.

Figure 10.10 illustrates the vacuum bag assembly for an external patch, and Figure 10.11 illustrates the assembly for a flush or scarf patch. The illustration for the scarf patch shows its use to repair part-through damage.

The simple vacuum bag procedure has several major drawbacks, most of which are associated with the low pressure that may be created in some regions inside the bag. These include:

- Entrapped air and volatile materials in the resin matrix and adhesive expand, leaving large voids in the cured resin
- Moisture absorbed in the carbon fiber/epoxy parent laminate enters the adhesive, producing voids (and possibly interfering with the cure mechanism)
- Air that, is drawn into the bond region due to porosity in the parent material produces voids in the patch system
- Reduced pressure produced inside a honeycomb panel can subsequently cause the panel to collapse.

Thus, although the vacuum bag procedure generally works well, its use has dangers. A safer alternative is to use pneumatic or mechanical pressure. The problem here is to work out how to react out the resulting loads. If they cannot be reacted out by the surrounding structure, vacuum pads or adhesively bonded anchor points can be used.

10.10 Bolted Repairs

Bolted repairs of composites are based on well-established procedures for the repair of metallic aircraft components. They are suitable for field repair of thick

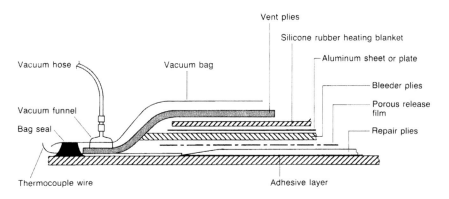

Fig. 10.10   Vacuum bag and patch arrangement to bond an external patch repair.

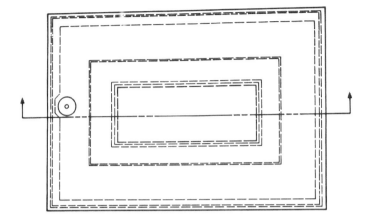

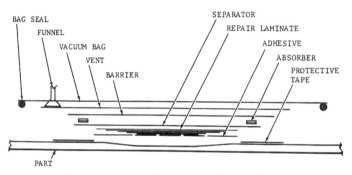

Fig. 10.11   Plan and section views of a vacuum bag and patch arrangement for application of a scarf repair.

laminates (over 3 mm) where the stressing requirement for external patch repairs exceeds the capability of adhesives. They are also suitable for depot-level repairs where the complexity of repair implementation and requirement for extensive material removal preclude the use of scarf repairs. Bolted repairs have the important advantage that no drying of the damaged component is required.

Bolted patches are generally external (sometimes called scab or boiler-plate patches) but they can also be flush, with the patch on the inside surface and the damage hole filled with some resin filler. External bolted repairs are particularly well-suited to the rapid repair of battle damage because they are easy to apply and require minimal facilities.

The stress concentrations associated with bearing loads in a bolted repair are not a serious disadvantage in a composite structure already mechanically fastened—for example, a composite wing skin bolted to a metal or composite substructure. A major advantage of bolted repairs is that the bolts provide a transverse reinforcement (with clamping pressure), which can be effective in preventing the spread of pre-existing delaminations.

An alternative option is the bonded/bolted approach. As discussed in Chapter 9, although it is not generally possible to obtain satisfactory load-sharing between the mechanical fasteners and the adhesive, there are several advantages in this approach for repairs:

- Bolts can provide an alternate (fail-safe) load path in the event of bond failure. Thus, bonding and bolting can be used in some situations where the bond quality may be questionable due, for example, to moisture problems or in thick structure where failure of the bond is the likely failure mode in an overload situation.
- Bolts can stabilize delaminations (as previously discussed), thereby minimizing or even avoiding the need to remove the damaged region before a bonded repair.
- Bolts can be used as jigs to locate and pressurize a bonded repair during the cure cycle.

10.10.1 Bolted Patch Repairs: Design Approaches

A bolted patch repair is usually modelled as a single-lap bolted joint. If backing structure is provided such that the loads in the damaged material can be shared equally between the patch and the backing structure, double-shear conditions can be assumed. In the case of a single-lap joint, the patch is assumed to be supported against secondary bending resulting from loading eccentricity.

The design procedure described in Ref. 17 is based on a compliance approach that assumes compatible deformation of a metallic patch plate and composite skin and allows for fastener flexibility and hole fit. A recent and more detailed analysis is provided in Ref. 18, based on similar principles.

The software developed in Ref. 17 is called BREPAIR and is used to estimate 1) the strain at the edge of the hole and 2) the load distribution in the bolt holes.

Three failure modes are considered: 1) net-tension at the repaired hole, 2) laminate bearing and tension interaction, and 3) fastener shear failure. The allowables for each of these modes were obtained from coupon tests on the composite system under consideration (AS/3501–6).

The net-tension allowable was simply obtained from tests on coupons with open holes of various sizes and measuring the peak strain at the edge of each hole. Failure strains fell below the required far field 4000 microstrain only for holes larger than 25 mm, suggesting that repairs are not required for smaller holes.

The tension/bearing interaction allowables were based on test results on repaired specimens and the fastener shear allowables obtained from manufacturers' data. The analysis proceeds as follows:

The maximum load carried by the repair joint is estimated from:

$$P = eE_s t_s D \qquad (10.15)$$

were D is the hole diameter, E_s and t_s are, respectively, the modulus and thickness of the skin, and e the allowable strain, 4000 microstrain in this case.

A first approximation to the number of fasteners n required to carry the load is the greater of:

$$n = \frac{P}{V_{al}} \text{ based on fastener shear allowable } V_{al} \quad (10.16)$$

and

$$n = \frac{P}{(\sigma_{bu}dt_s)} \text{ based on bearing allowable } \sigma_{bu} \quad (10.17)$$

For the given P and n, the program is used to estimate actual faster loads, laminate bearing stress, and laminate strain at the ends of the hole. These are compared with the allowables and the analysis continued until a sufficient margin of safety is achieved, for example, by increasing the number of fasteners or changing the hole pattern. Figure 10.12 shows a typical bolted repair designed using the foregoing procedure and indicates the loads in the critical fastener holes and at the edge of the circular cut-out. An edge distance of $4d$ and fastener separation of $2d$ are used.

10.11   Materials Engineering Aspects

10.11.1   Patch Materials

Titanium alloy is generally used for the metal patch because (unlike aluminum alloy) it does not suffer from galvanic corrosion when in contact with carbon/epoxy. However, aluminum alloy patches can be used if precautions are taken to avoid corrosion by insulating the repair from the carbon/epoxy structure. Aluminum alloy is significantly easier to drill than titanium and therefore better suited to rapid repair of damage where facilities are limited.

Carbon/epoxy is an alternative to titanium alloy for the patch and can be formed by wet lay-up from woven carbon cloth. However, such patches are limited to low-load applications because they have low bearing strength. Composite patches formed from pre-preg provide significantly higher bearing strengths.

Unless the patch is attached to the inner surface to form a flush repair, the holes in the patch must be countersunk and the patches chamfered on their edges to maintain aerodynamic smoothness; generally, the patch must not protrude more than about 4 mm. Countersinking limits the bearing strength because most of the bearing loads are transmitted by the non-countersunk region. To avoid bearing failure caused by insufficient shank in countersunk holes, it is important that the patch be sufficiently thick. The requirement for countersinking is a particular problem for composite patches, therefore these are best used for internal patches where countersinking is not required.

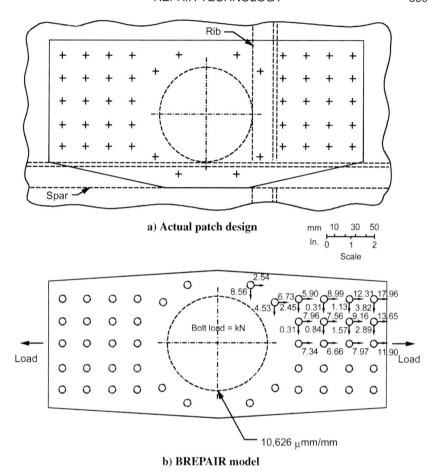

a) Actual patch design

b) BREPAIR model

Fig. 10.12 Schematic illustration of *a*) bolted repair near a spar and rib to a thick laminate, and *b*) predictions of loading at the edge of the repair cut-out and in some of the bolt holes made using the BREPAIR program. Taken from Ref. 17.

10.11.2 Patch Installation

Titanium alloy fasteners are generally used for permanent repairs, although corrosion-resistant steel is a suitable alternative. Blind fasteners (applied from only one side) are the most critical because these are subjected to single-shear loading.

The patch is first drilled with the appropriate hole pattern and then used as a template to drill the composite skin. Aluminum alloy patches are initially drilled undersized and then drilled out to the full size when drilling the composite. Because it is much harder than aluminum, titanium is usually initially drilled to final size. Where possible, existing fastener holes are included as part of the hole pattern. To improve the bearing strength of these holes, the countersink can be filled with a metal washer.

Patches are generally wet-installed (sealant at all interfaces), particularly if the repaired structure is a fuel tank. This is a particularly important requirement if an aluminum alloy patch is used to electrically isolate the patch from the composite.

Because access is generally from only one side, blind fasteners are used wherever possible; special blind fasteners have been developed for composite applications. These provide good filling of the bolthole without developing excessive pressure that could split the composite. They are particularly effective if used with a soft-metal sleeve.

Load-transfer efficiency with single-shear fasteners is limited because the fasteners tend to rotate under load, causing edge-bearing failure in the composite skin. Thus, for improved load-transfer efficiency in highly loaded joints, it is usually necessary to use a backing plate to load the fasteners in double shear.

If the bolted patch is attached to the inner surface for a flush repair, the patch plates must be inserted through the hole. This can be a difficult operation and involves using special tools to hold the patch in position on the underside of the component while the blind bolts are inserted.

Hole-drilling in composites can be a problem, even when access is possible from both sides and a backup plate can be used. When a backup plate cannot be used, it is very easy to produce an oversized hole or, when using excessive pressure (generally with a blunt drill), to cause severe delaminations or back-face splintering. Special drill presses have been developed for hand-use that control drill pressure and speed to avoid these problems.

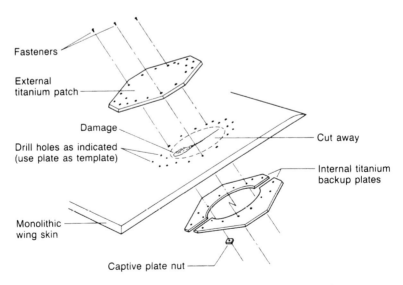

Fig. 10.13   Bolted titanium external patch repair for thick carbon/epoxy laminates, as used for the skins of an aircraft wing.

A typical bolted patch configuration is shown in Figure 10.13. The patch has a chamfered edge to minimize any disturbance of the airflow. The backup plate consists of two sections to allow blind insertion.

References

[1] Baker, A. A., "Repair Techniques for Composite Structures" *Composite Materials in Aircraft Structure*, edited by D. H. Middleton, Longman Scientific and Technical Publishers, 1990, Chap. 13.

[2] Baker, A. A., "Joining and Repair of Aircraft Composite Structures," Chapter 14 in *Composites Engineering Handbook*, edited by P. K. Mallick, Marcel Dekker, 1997.

[3] Saunders, D. S., Clark, G., van Blaricum, and T. J., Preuss, T. E., "Carbon/epoxy Laminate Testing Coupon Program" *Theoretical and Applied Fracture Mechanics*, Vol. 13, 1990, pp. 105–124.

[4] Russell, A. J., and Bowers, C. P., "Resin Requirements for Successful Repair of Delaminations," *Proceedings of 36th National SAMPE Symposium*, 1991, pp. 2279–2289.

[5] Russell, A. J., Bowers, C. P., and Moss, A. J., "Repair of Delaminations and Impact Damage in Composite Aircraft Structures," *Composite Structures*, Vol. 19, Elsevier Applied Science Publisher, 1991, pp. 145–149.

[6] Rodgers, B. A., and Mallon, P. J., "Post-Impact Repair of Thermoplastic Composite Materials Using Induction Heating," *Proceedings of the 14th European SAMPE*, 1993, pp. 250–270.

[7] Rose, L. F. R., "Theoretical Analysis of Crack Patching," *Bonded Repair of Aircraft Structures*, edited by A. A. Baker and R., Jones, Martinus-Nijhoff, 1988.

[8] Baker, A. A., Chester, R. J., Hugo, G. R., and Radtke, T. C., "Scarf Repairs to Carbon/ Epoxy Composites," *Composite Repairs of Military Aircraft Structures*, Paper 19, AGARD-CP-550, 1995.

[9] Baker, A. A., Chester, R. J., Hugo, G. R., and Radtke, T. C., "Scarf Repairs to Highly Strained Carbon/Epoxy Structure," *International Journal of Adhesion*, 1999, Vol. 19, pp 16–171.

[10] Armstrong, K., and Barrett, R. T., *Care and Repair of Advanced Composites*, SAE International, New York, 1998.

[11] Bauer, J., and Maier, A. E., "On Aircraft Repair Verification of a Fighter A/C Integrally Stiffened Fuselage Skin," *Composite Repairs of Military Aircraft Structures*, Paper 11, AGARD-CP-550, 1995.

[12] Diberardino, M. F., Cochran, R. C., Donnellan, T. M., and Trabocco, R. E., *Materials for Composite Damage Repair*, Proceedings of the 5th Australian Aeronautical Conference, The Institution of Engineers, Australia, 1993.

[13] Cochran, R. C., Trabocco, R. E., Mehrkam, P., and Diberardino, M. F., "Field Repair for Naval Aircraft," *Composite Repairs of Military Aircraft Structures*, Paper 10, Spain, AGARD-CP-550, 1994.

[14] Augl, J. N., "Moisture Transport in Composites During Repair Work" *Proceedings 28th National SAMPE Symposium*, 1983, pp. 273–286.

[15] Garrett, R. A., Bohlmann, R. E., and Derby, E. A., "Analysis and Test of Carbon/ Epoxy Sandwich Panels Subjected to Internal Pressures Resulting from Absorbed Moisture," edited by J. R. Vinson, ASTM, 1978, pp. 234–253.

[16]Trabocco, R. E., Donnellan, T. M., and Williams, G. J., "Repair of Composite Aircraft," *Bonded Repair of Aircraft Structures*, edited by A. A. Baker, R. Jones, Martinus-Nijhoff, 1988, Chap. 7.

[17]Bohlmann, R. E., Renieri, G. D., and Libeskind, M., "Bolted Field Repair of Carbon/Epoxy Wing Skin Laminates" *Joining of Composite Materials*, edited by K. T. Kedward, STP 749, American Society for Materials, 1981, pp. 97–116.

[18]Kradinov, V., Hanauska, J., Barut, A., Madenci, E., and Ambar, D. R., "Bolted Patch Repair of Composite Panels With a Cutout," *Composite Structures*, Vol. 56, 2002, pp. 423–424.

11
Quality Assurance

11.1 Introduction

Quality control for composites is often seen simply as validation of the physical and mechanical properties of the cured laminate. However, thorough control begins long before the part is completed and is more correctly termed *process control*—overseeing its application is the task of quality assurance. Quality control involves control of the incoming material, control of the process, and finally, inspection for defects.[1,2]

Section 11.2 presents an overview of the quality control of composites. Control of the cure process is especially important and is discussed in Section 11.3, where some of the current direct measurement methods of control are discussed.

Non-destructive inspection (NDI) is the final quality check on the finished part, and this is discussed in Section 11.4. This section also covers inspection of service defects.

Most aerospace composite parts are manufactured by autoclave curing of pre-preg, and the following discussion refers specifically to this fabrication route. Many of the quality requirements are, however, common to all fabrication processes.

11.2 Quality Control

11.2.1 Raw Materials

The raw material for producing aerospace composites is usually obtained as pre-impregnated yarn, unidirectional tape, or fabric (frequently abbreviated to *pre-preg*) but quality control starts with the component materials of the pre-preg, namely the fibers and the resin.

11.2.1.1 Fibers. Fiber testing is performed principally by the fiber manufacturer, although pre-preg manufacturers may also test incoming material to verify the manufacturer's data and to check for damage during shipping and handling. Tests may also be done to monitor the fiber properties during the fabrication process. The most common fiber properties used for composite control are longitudinal tensile strength, elastic modulus, elongation, yield, density, twist, and sizing content.[3] These properties may be tested on single fibers, multifilament yarns, or impregnated strands. In many cases, the incoming material contains a textile fabric rather than a simple yarn, and fabric testing, such as measurement of aerial weight, may additionally be required. Standard tests for tensile testing of fibers, yarns, strands, and fabrics are available as ASTM standards.[4] An example is given in Table 11.1. Additionally, chemical assay tests are conducted by the fiber manufacturers to check the chemical composition of the fibers while surface analysis techniques, such as X-ray photoelectron spectroscopy (XPS) and electron spectroscopy for chemical analysis (ESCA), are used for determining the surface characteristics of the fibers.[5]

11.2.1.2 Resins.   Testing is performed by the resin manufacturers during formulation of the resin. The tests involve physical, chemical, and spectrographic techniques. The tests are typically performed on the individual component materials, on mixtures of several ingredients, and on the blend in its final composition. Typical tests are gel time, viscosity, chromatography, and infrared spectroscopy. Gel-time tests measure the time for the resin to undergo gelation (gel) at a predetermined temperature. The simplest method involves probing the heated resin until gel is reached. *Gel* is defined as the point at which the resin strings break sharply when probed and strung. Chromatography and infrared spectroscopy[1,6] provide a "fingerprint" of the resin chemistry.

11.2.1.3 Pre-Preg.   Both the pre-preg manufacturer and the composite fabricator perform tests on the uncured pre-preg. The latter is either recommended or specified because further curing may have occurred during transport to the fabricator. These tests are a mixture of physical and chemical tests and are intended principally to ensure that the component materials are

Table 11.1   ASTM Standards for Tensile Testing of Fibers, Yarns, Strands, and Fabrics

Standard	Title
D 3379	Standard Test Method for Tensile Strength and Young's Modulus for High-Modulus Single-Filament Materials
D 2256	Standard Test Method for Tensile Properties of Yarns by the Single-Strand Method
D 4018	Standard Test Methods for Tensile Properties of Continuous Filament Carbon and Carbon Fiber Tows
D 5034	Standard Test Method for Breaking Strength and Elongation of Textile Fabrics

present in the correct proportions and to confirm the processability of the pre-preg. The requirements for these tests are usually given in the user's specification and may vary somewhat from user to user.

Physical tests typically include resin content, areal fiber weight, resin flow, volatile content, tack, and, sometimes, drape.[6]

Resin content is the weight fraction of active resin/hardener/catalyst. Areal or dry fiber weight is the weight of reinforcing fiber in the pre-preg per unit area. This test is usually measured on the same sample as used for resin content. Subjecting samples to heat and pressure tests the degree of resin flow. The resin lost through either lateral or perpendicular flow under these conditions is measured. The test may not be appropriate for controlled-flow resins because values are typically near zero. Volatile percentage is determined by heating either a single ply or a ply stack at the curing temperature and recording the mass loss. This is an important test because trapped volatiles in a component can result in excessive surface pores and internal voids.

Tack and drape are both more subjective tests. Tack is an assessment of the stickiness of the pre-preg. Drape is the ability of a pre-preg to be formed around defined radii and to remain tacked for a specified period of time.

The most widely used tack test involves "tacking" a ply of pre-preg to a tool and then tacking a further ply of pre-preg to the first. The test requires that the second ply be capable of being removed and repositioned without either excessive distortion or removal of the underlying ply.[6] However, even a material of low tack can pass this test but still prove to have poor drape. A superior test is to measure the adherence strength of two plies rolled together under controlled conditions. The plies are then pulled apart in the form of a "T" peel test and the force recorded.

Chemical tests performed on the pre-preg by both the material supplier and the composites manufacturer include gel time, high-pressure liquid chromatography (which provides a good fingerprint of the resin components), and differential scanning calorimetry [which measures the degree of resin cure and can also provide a crude measure of the glass-transition temperature (T_g) of the resin]. Infrared spectroscopy is usually carried out by both the pre-preg manufacturer and the fabricator to ensure that no major changes have occurred in the resin during impregnation or B-staging of the pre-preg (partial cure by pre-preg manufacturer) or during its subsequent transport.

In addition to the tests done on the uncured pre-preg, tests are also performed on cured laminates. Physical and mechanical tests are performed to ensure that the material is closely similar to that originally qualified to the specification from which engineering design properties were measured and calculated. Many of these tests are covered by ASTM[4] and Suppliers of Advanced Composite Materials Association SACMA[7] standards. Physical tests typically include fiber and resin volume fractions, void content, cured ply thickness and T_g. Mechanical tests are selected to cover critical material properties. Typical tests are 90° or 0°

tensile strength and modulus, 90° or 0° compression strength, and short beam shear strength or $\pm 45°$ tension strength. Short beam shear strength testing is of limited value because the failure mode is frequently by compression, but it is useful as a monitor of the degree of cure in process control panels. The $\pm 45°$ tension strength test is, however, preferable because it is more sensitive to resin-dominated properties and it is easier to perform with simpler specimens and test jigs. Compression and $\pm 45°$ tension strength testing is sometimes performed at the maximum design temperature, after conditioning at the maximum humidity/temperature, as well as at room temperature, to ensure the material's temperature capability.[1] Mechanical property measurement is discussed in Chapter 7.

The ultimate user needs to define the suite of tests to be used on incoming material, the frequency of testing, and the criteria for retesting if the material fails some or all of the specified tests. Also necessary are appropriate tests when the normal storage life expires; these tests should be resin-dominated ones. These requirements are normally documented in the user's specification for the material. As use and confidence increase, the test frequency is often reduced.

11.2.2 Process Verification

It is necessary to verify that the fabrication process is performed in accordance with the engineering requirements. These are normally specified in an engineering process specification.

11.2.2.1 Material Control.   Before fabricating a component, the material to be used must first be identified as the correct material ordered; must have been tested to the correct material specification by the manufacturer, and met its requirements; and must have satisfied the specified receipt inspection testing requirements by the user/fabricator. Perishable materials such as pre-pregs and adhesives must also be within their allowable storage life and below the maximum specified storage temperature at the time of removal from storage. During this period, materials should be stored and packaged in a manner that precludes contamination or damage, for example, horizontally in sealed polyethene (polyethylene) bags. Once removed from storage, pre-pregs and adhesives must be within their working life (able to be draped, laid, and tacky) and within their allowed mold life (able to flow and gel) at the time of cure. To avoid contamination by condensed moisture, it is important to allow refrigerated materials to reach ambient temperature before removal from the package. The accumulated time at temperature may be recorded for the remaining unused material to assess remaining life.

It is necessary to control both the composite work area environment and the equipment used for composite fabrication. These requirements are normally embodied in the engineering process specification. Particulate or chemical matter that could affect the manufacturing process must be prohibited from the work area, and lay-up and clean rooms should be pressurized to a slight positive pressure. Because epoxies degrade with excessive temperature and humidity, clean rooms need to be air-conditioned. Typical conditions are $20-30°C$, 60% relative humidity maximum, with a filtered air supply.

Lay-up tools need to be thermally profiled to check conformance with the heating rates required in the engineering process specification and thermocouples subsequently attached to the areas of the part or tool that show the fastest and slowest heating rates. Calibration requirements must be specified for autoclaves and ovens as well as the requirements for temperature uniformity. The latter is best performed with a dummy load so as to better simulate gas flows, rather than test an empty autoclave or oven.

11.2.2.3 Process Control. Processing of composites involves both laying the material and its subsequent cure. During the laying process, it is necessary to ensure that all plies are laid in the correct orientation; that they are positioned in the correct sequence in the stack; that they are laid in the correct position, and that the number of plies used is correct. The cure cycle must then be monitored to ensure that the heating rate, time at temperature, and cooling rate all comply with the engineering requirements. Pressure, vacuum, and temperature must be maintained within the prescribed tolerances and sequence.

Some manufacturers require physical and mechanical tests to validate the processing. The requirement for test specimens can also depend on the class of part being fabricated. Parts that are non-critical or secondary structure may not require any test specimens.[1] Test pieces may be from special panels laid and cured with the production parts, from material trimmed from the parts themselves (trim sections), or from coupons attached to the part and subsequently removed. If test specimens are absolutely necessary (there are many arguments to the contrary if proper process control has occurred), then the two latter specimen types are the best. Typical tests conducted are flexural strength and modulus, short beam shear strength, fiber volume fraction, void content, T_g, and degree of cure.

11.2.3 Final Inspection

After fabrication, the parts must be inspected for conformance with dimensional and workmanship requirements (i.e., visually inspected) and, depending on part criticality, inspected non-destructively for possible processing-induced defects. Some destructive testing may also be required; this is described below, and non-destructive testing is discussed separately in Section 11.4.

When part integrity cannot be ensured simply by dimensional, visual, and non-destructive testing, destructive testing may be required. Destructive tests may be done by dissection of an actual part or by examination of trim sections taken from the part. The type and frequency of destructive testing depends on both the part type and the experience of the user or fabricator. Tests can range from simple tests such as fiber volume fraction and porosity to full-scale, proof tests. Although the use of trim sections is clearly preferable, full dissection is frequently required for the first article (a production part subjected to a series of destructive tests to verify the production process) of a complex, critical part, even when manufactured by an experienced fabricator. Periodic, full dissection, with increasing intervals, may be more appropriate when experience is low.

11.3   Cure Monitoring

Cure procedures for thermosetting composite materials often follow a rigid recipe of temperature, vacuum, and pressure provided by the material manufacturer. Such an approach does not take account of material batch variations, material age, and deviations from the recommended cure cycle due to the presence of thermally massive tooling or exothermic chemical reactions within thick sections of the curing part causing excessive temperatures. Also, it does not allow the cure cycle to be optimized for a particular part under manufacture. Knowing when a part is fully cured can save production time and costs.

The use of cure monitoring systems[8,9] can be effectively applied to both traditional autoclave curing procedures as well as to resin-transfer molding (RTM) manufacture, where information such as pressure, resin viscosity, and the gel point can be critical in optimizing manufacturing processes. An ideal cure-monitoring system would be able to show basic information such as the degree of compaction, pressure, and temperature as well as information specific to the resin itself either through physical and chemo-rheological properties such as the resin viscosity, gel point, and the degree of cure.

The use of a sensor to directly monitor some critical property or properties of the cure process is required to give confidence in the manufacturing process and component quality. Such sensors may also be used in a feedback loop to drive the application of temperature, pressure, and vacuum. The use of a suitable cure-monitoring sensor will usually lead to the production of high-quality parts on a consistent basis.

11.3.1   Sensor Placement

The placement of sensors in a cure monitoring system is of primary importance. Many sensors can only provide detail about a small area within the component. This is a limitation of the most popular type of cure sensor, the thermocouple. In production, thermocouples are placed at numerous locations over the composite tooling and part. The same approach may not be feasible for expensive or complex sensors.

For this reason, the placement of sensors should be made to examine problem areas on a component or those regions that are likely to have the lowest or highest values of interest. For example, the placement of thermocouples at the hottest and coldest part of a tool would meet this requirement. Such regions of interest often involve those that are most likely to undergo a runaway exotherm reaction (thick sections) or regions that are likely to be under-cured (cold parts of the tool). These areas may be chosen on the basis of part thickness, thermal mass behind the curing part, and other important process variables.

There are many techniques and sensors that have been used to measure the extent of cure in thermoset-resin-based composite materials. A complete description of all these techniques is beyond the scope of this book. Sensors[8] can measure the extent of cure directly or indirectly through calibration or modelling of the process. An example of a direct measure could be determining the chemical spectroscopic makeup of the resin at any time. An indirect measure could be to determine temperature.

The suitability of a sensor for embedding into a laminate for the purposes of cure monitoring of composite structure (or repairs) needs to be considered carefully before implementation in production. These criteria should include the effectiveness of the sensor in assessing the state of cure, its suitability for embedding into a composite component, size, weight, complexity, cost, and applicability to a wide variety of components as well as its capability for multi-parameter sensing. The last criterion is important in that it is desirable to keep the overall number of sensors as low as possible. For example, combined dielectric and temperature sensors can reduce the number of sensors and provide a much more detailed picture of the curing process.

The techniques currently developed for cure monitoring can be broadly classified into five areas that base the sensing system on electrical, acoustic, optical, thermal, and indirect or other properties.

11.3.2 Electrical Measurements

Electrical measurements include capacitance, conductance, dielectric constant, and dielectric loss tangent. Dielectrometry has created much interest in cure monitoring but has not been used extensively in production environments. Electrical techniques are subject to electrical interference in a processing environment and need to be carefully shielded when used with conductive fibers such as carbon fibers.

11.3.2.1 Dielectrometry. Dielectric monitoring has been used for some time in cure monitoring systems. Essentially the technique depends on the measurement of the mobility of polymer molecules in an oscillating electric field.

Dipoles arise in the polymer molecules due to electronic asymmetries in their structure.[10] Thus, if an electric field with varying polarity is applied to a liquid polymer, the molecules attempt to rotate into alignment. The rate of rotation in an oscillating electric field depends on the resin viscosity and thus on the temperature and on the degree of cross-linking. The mobility decreases rapidly as the resin viscosity increases and ceases once gelation is complete.

Heating the resin thus results in a reduction in polarization and permittivity as cure occurs, which is measured as the loss factor ε. This parameter can be correlated[11] with the degree of cure, as a shown in Figure 11.1.

The dielectric technique has several shortcomings.[12] The main concern is that the degree of cure and viscosity are not easily deduced from resulting capacitance and dielectric loss tangent curves. However, dielectric sensing units and sensors are available commercially and have found their way into some production processes.

11.3.2.2 Electrical Conductivity. This technique is based on a measurement of electrical conduction as a function of the degree of cross-linking. Conductivity in a polymer melt arises from the impurity ions that may be present in the polymer and arise from the solvent and catalyst. When the

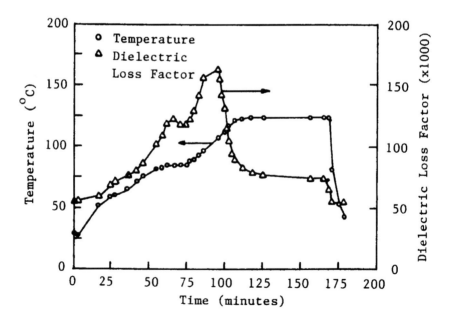

Fig. 11.1   Plot of changes in dielectric loss factor and cure temperature versus time for a glass epoxy pre-preg. Taken from Ref. 11.

resin is in a liquid state, the ions can migrate rapidly in a polarized electric field, therefore the conductivity is high. As the viscosity increases, the conductivity falls off with increasing rapidity as gelation is approached. Conductivity is considered to have a clearer functional relationship with the degree of cure. For example,[11] it is shown that the ionic conductivity is maximum at approximately the same time as the resin viscosity reaches a minimum, as shown in Figure 11.2, and that the conductivity falls to zero as the rate of change of conductivity reaches zero.

Dielectrometry and conductivity techniques require the user to either embed a sensor within the composite lay-up or attach it to its surface. In either case, to use the sensor in the presence of electrically conducting fibers such as carbon, the sensor must have a cavity that excludes fibers and fills with resin as the part cures. The shortcoming of placing the sensor on top of the part is that the resin must be in a very liquid state before the sensing cavity fills with resin. This negates the advantage of knowing the early changes in viscosity that is critical for correct timing of the application of pressure.

11.3.3 Other Methods

11.3.3.1 Acoustic Methods. These techniques involve the use of both ultrasonic wave propagation techniques as well as acoustic emission. Ultrasonic measurements may be correlated with parameters such as degree of cure, porosity, viscosity, delaminations, and fiber volume fraction. Acoustic emission also allows the cooling phase of a cure cycle to be monitored to determine

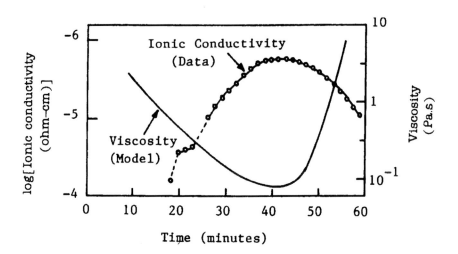

Fig. 11.2 Plot of variation in ionic conductivity and resin viscosity with time during cure of an epoxy resin. Taken from Ref. 11.

whether thermal stresses are cracking the composite. Problems can arise when a number of these parameters are changing simultaneously because it may not be possible to distinguish between them. So far, these techniques have not found their way into mainstream cure monitoring.

11.3.3.2 Optical Methods.   Spectroscopic sensors provide information on the chemical changes that are occurring in the resin. The degree of cure may be related directly to the amount of unreacted resin. Sensors of this type tend to utilize optic fibers, which need to be embedded carefully into the part during lay-up. Optic fibers have been used to measure strains within composites.[13] It may be possible for the same optic fiber to be used for this purpose after it has been used as a cure sensor. The apparatus required to run these types of sensors is usually both costly and bulky.

Techniques that measure the infrared spectrum of the curing resin are perhaps the most useful because actual chemical information is being gained. Such techniques can also require special fibers (e.g., chalcogenide) that transmit light in the infrared region.[14] These fibers are expensive and can be used only once. Other types of infrared spectroscopy include Raman spectroscopy, which has a low sensitivity and requires costly instrumentation.

The fluorescence of chemical species in the UV/visible region can used for cure monitoring. Probe molecules that have a strong fluorescence in the UV/visible region but do not take part in the curing process may be used if the signal from the neat resin itself is insufficient. The necessity of adding such probe molecules to the resin may make it unsuitable for use with commercial pre-pregs. In many cases, the UV/visible spectra derived from these probe molecules can depend on other parameters such as resin viscosity rather than the actual degree of cure. Such techniques have not been widely used.

The refractive index technique works based on the fact that the refractive index of the resin changes as the cure proceeds. The correlation between refractive index and extent of cure was first established[15,16] using differential scanning calorimetry (DSC) as a more direct measure of cure. Techniques such as refractive index sensing are available to measure this property directly and accurately, but they are expensive and may only be used once.

11.3.3.3 Thermal Properties.   The use of thermocouples is perhaps the simplest method of cure monitoring. They ensure that the part reaches the temperature required and that the cure cycle specified is achieved. Their worth as a cure sensor is very limited except for the fact that an exothermic reaction can be detected.

The use of heat flux sensors is a method similar to that of a DSC, which measures heat flux versus time under a controlled temperature program. The heat released during cure (the reaction exotherm) can be monitored[17] and related to the extent of cure. DSC data are used widely in chemorheological models of the resin curing process. No commercially available units are available at present, and the use of heat flux sensors is not widespread in the cure monitoring area.

11.3.3.4 Pressure and Compaction Sensors. Displacement transducers are useful for monitoring the compaction of a part during cure. If pressure application is to be optimized, this type of sensor may be essential.

Pressure sensors provide information on the pressure in a localized area. The sensors operate using a capacitive effect, which directly correlates to pressure after appropriate signal conditioning. The pressures measured by these sensors may differ to autoclave pressure in areas where the part is contoured. This type of information is useful if accurate determination of part compaction is required. Furthermore, the sensor can alert the autoclave operator of failure in the vacuum-bagging material during the vacuum cycle. Dual-function pressure/temperature transducers are available and can form a very functional sensor combination.[18]

11.3.4 Conclusions on Cure Monitoring

Table 11.2 lists the techniques and their performance against the selection criteria listed. This Table shows that the techniques that show the most promise are dielectrometry, ionic conductivity, spectroscopic techniques, and measurement of refractive index. The refractive index technique is quite new and relatively unexplored for in-field or commercial use.

Table 11.2 **Summary of Performance of Various Techniques for Embedding and Cure Monitoring of Composite Components**

Technique	Cure sensing ability	Size, complexity	Cost	Multi-parameter sensing	Embed into Composites
Dielectric	High	Low	Med	No/Yes	Yes
Conductivity	High	Low	Med	Yes	Yes
Acoustic	Medium	Low	Med	Yes	Yes
Spectroscopic	Excellent	Med-High	High	No	Yes
Refractive Index	Good	Low	Low	Yes	Yes
Thermocouple	Low	Low	Low	No	Yes
Heat Flux	Good	Med	Med	No	Yes
Pressure Sensor	Low	Low	Med	No	Yes
Displacement Transducer	Low	Low	Low	No	No

11.4 Non-destructive Inspection of Advanced Composite Aerospace Structures

The processes of advanced composite manufacture, described in Chapter 5, are inherently prone to errors, particularly human errors, that can lead to the formation of defects or anomalies in the structure. Many defects cause a reduction in the mechanical properties of a composite structure and in some cases can lower the properties below the design allowables, hence the importance of detecting defects in composite aircraft structures before service. The strict quality assurance policy of the aviation industry enforces components to be inspected for defects using non-destructive technologies. In some cases where the composite component forms part of the primary structure, 100% inspection is required, which is a major cost penalty.

During service, aircraft structures are prone to many mechanical and environmental conditions that can cause damage to composite structures in the form of delamination, fiber breakage, and matrix cracking. The most well known example is impact damage caused by severe mechanical contact. Monitoring the level and type of damage to a composite structure is vital to determining the component's structural integrity and preventing the failure of the structure during flight. Thus, in-service inspection is also important.

In contrast to glass-fiber composites, which are translucent, carbon-fiber composite components are opaque, preventing the visual detection of internal defects. In service, both glass and carbon composite aircraft components are typically painted. Thus, some form of non-visual inspection using various physical techniques is used to detect defects in nearly all composite structures. This section provides an overview of defects commonly found in fabricated composite structures and presents the current and emerging technologies for NDI.

11.4.1 Requirements for Quality Assurance

The knowledge of the size and location of defects is critical to assessing the flight-worthiness of aerospace components. The main function assigned to NDI is the reliable and repeatable detection of defects of a specified size in a component. In commercial aviation, the minimum allowable size of a defect for composites is typically 12.5 mm (0.5 in). For military aircraft, which operate at higher stress levels than civil aircraft, the minimum allowable defect size is generally smaller, depending on the role of the structure and the method of design. In limited cases, the design of some structures allows for typical damage so has no mandatory requirement for NDI. Table 11.3 lists typical manufacturing defects, whereas Table 11.4 lists typical defects that can develop in service.

Table 11.3   Common Defects Found in Fabricated Advanced Composite Structures

Defect	Description
Delaminations	An area of separation between fabric layers in the laminate structure.
Unbond	An area in which two adherends or pre-preg layers failed to bond together.
Disbond	An area in which two adherends have separated at the bondline.
Porosity	The entrapment of pockets of air or gas(es) within a solid material.
Crack	A fracture of material in the laminate that typically extends through the thickness.
Core crush	Damage of the honeycomb core due to impact or excessive pressure during cure.
Foreign object	An inclusion of a foreign substance, such as peel ply, during the manufacturing process.

Often, a sampling plan is used for the inspection routine for an advanced composite component as part of manufacturing quality control. In some cases, the first 50 shipsets of a component are all inspected to form the first sample. A statistical analysis is conducted on this sample to determine the proportion of components that need to be inspected to maintain a reliable and repeatable NDI routine. A new sample plan is usually formulated when there is a change in job structure, when the installation of new processing equipment occurs, or after a period of work shutdown.

Table 11.4   Common In-service Defects Found in Advanced Composite Aircraft Structures

Defect	Description
Impact damage	Internal damage of composite caused by collision with an external body during flight or docking, typically marked by delaminations, fiber breaking, and matrix cracking.
Delaminations	Separation within the composite has occurred generally due to unexpected out-of-plane stresses.
Lightning burns	An area of the composite that has been subjected to high temperatures causing decomposition and degradation in properties of the matrix.
Disbonding	Interfacial separation in composite/composite or composite/ metal bonded joints due to out-of-plane stresses or, in the case of metallic joints, to environmental degradation.
Core, degradation	Areas in honeycomb sandwich panels with cores where water has penetrated leading, in the case of metallic cores, to disbonding and corrosion.

Table 11.5   NDI Techniques to Detect Defects in Advanced Composite Structure

Technique	Operating Principles	Applications in Industry	Defect Detection Capabilities	Related Emerging Technologies
Ultrasonic	An ultrasonic pulse is transmitted through a sample and is scattered or reflected by regions with differing acoustic impedance, such as defects. Defect information is measured from A- or C-scan images.	Hand-held probes—used for inspection of small components, and complex regions of structures, relies on use of small probes and A-scan images. Automation C-scan—used for inspection of large structures, such as rudder skins.	Planar cracks, delaminations, large voids, high porosity, and some foreign object materials can be detected. Identifying through-thickness defect location reliant on pulse echo technique.	Non-contact (non-couplant) ultrasonics, including laser induced, electromagnetic acoustics, air couplant probe miniaturization
Radiography	X-rays are differentially absorbed when passed through a material, where rates of absorption are dependent on material physical density.	Film radiography—used for inspection of structures with large regions of honeycomb and material variations, such as landing gear doors.	Bond lines, core-crush, foreign object, through-thickness cracks, and voids can be detected.	Filmless radiography

Method	Description	Application	Detects	Technique
Thermography	Dissipation of temperature from a material subjected to an initial heat source is measured using infrared equipment, where anomalies lead to different rates of heat release.	Being developed for rapid area inspection of structures, with possible applications for skins, spars, ribs, and control surfaces.	Delaminations, large voids, and some foreign objects can be detected, depending of thickness of structure.	Pulse thermography
Holography/ Shearography	Surface strains are measured as fringe patterns caused by the application of a load to the structure, where submerged defects affect surface strain continuity.	Being developed for rapid area inspection of large structures.	Bond lines, core crush, and delaminations.	Digital shearography
Acoustic Sensing	Elastic waves are used to induce natural frequency response from structure.	Bond-tester used to inspect bonding flaws. AE being developed for real-time inspection of in-service damage to aircraft structures, AU and AI being developed for rapid field inspection of complex structures.	Impact detection, bonding flaws.	Acoustic emission, acoustic impact, and acoustic ultrasonics

11.4.2 Current Technologies

There are a number of NDI techniques used in the aerospace industry. Some of these techniques are better suited to particular types of materials, geometries and defect types. The traditional methods of inspection for defects in fabricated laminate structures are ultrasonics and radiography. Table 11.5 lists the operational principles, capabilities and industry applications of the current NDI technologies used in the production line.[19] Table 11.5 also lists promising techniques not yet readily used in production or service, such as thermography, holography, and acoustic sensing, which have been developed to the extent that they could shortly be introduced in industry. From this Table it is seen that no single NDI technique provides all the information necessary to detect all types of defects. Often it is the geometry of the structure that limits the type of inspection technique that can be used.

Compared with the inspections of parts before service, in-service inspection is typically conducted with the structure attached to the aircraft. Damage monitoring is most usually conducted when the aircraft is undergoing routine maintenance. Restriction of access to areas of the structure requiring attention is a problem. The inspection of assembled structures is a much more difficult task than the inspection of detail parts on the production lines.

There are, however, synergies between the NDI technologies used for the inspection of fabricated and in-service defects in composite aircraft structures. As with the inspection of fabricated defects, ultrasonic inspection is the most common NDI method used to inspect and locate service defects in composite aircraft components. The development of new technologies is focused on increasing the efficiency of NDI that can be applied to the inspection of fabricated and in-service defects. These technologies include real-time radiography, thermography, and mobile automated ultrasonics.

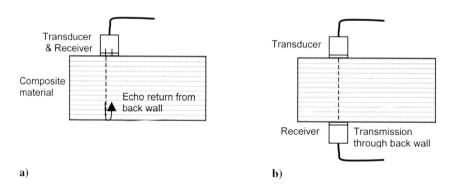

a)   b)

Fig. 11.3   Schematic representation of *a*) **pulse-echo ultrasonic inspection and** *b*) **through-transmission ultrasonic inspection.**

11.4.2.1 Ultrasonic Inspection. The basis of ultrasonic inspection is the propagation and measurement of a sound pulse through the composite specimen. The sound pulse is emitted from a transducer into the composite material and is recorded by a receiver. A certain percentage of the sound wave will reflect from the back surface and is recorded as a "pulse-echo" by a sensor typically located with the emitting transducer, as shown in Figure 11.3a. Another percentage will be transmitted through the back surface and can be recorded as a "through-transmission" signal by a sensor located at the opposite surface, as shown in Figure 11.3b.

The ultrasonic wave will be reflected or scattered by any defect that differs significantly from the acoustic impedance (product of the acoustic velocity and material density) of the composite material, as shown in Figure 11.4. The measured difference in the emitted signal energy compared with that received provides information on the presence of defects in the composite material. Defects such as delaminations, large voids, and cracks that are planar to the surface, or normal to the propagated pulse, will cause a loss or attenuation in the transmitted sound.

The two common methods of data presentation for ultrasonic inspection are A-scan and C-scan. An A-scan presentation displays the distance-amplitude of the transmitted sound through the thickness of the component at a single point. An A-scan image is typically displayed on an oscilloscope screen, as shown in Figure 11.5. C-scan presentations provide a plan view of a composite material, where the information of the movement of the transducer across the composite surface is combined with the distance-amplitude information and is displayed as a video image. A color scheme is used to represent different levels of sound transmission based on a calibration.

Figure 11.6 shows a C-scan image from a through-transmission ultrasonic test of a rib-stiffened box structure, with defects highlighted visually by contrast differences compared with the surrounding material. In this C-scan image, a defect at the rib-to-skin junction is shown as an area of high dB loss, identified by black pixels. Tab markers placed on the structure before inspection are placed as an aid to location and scale of defects and are evident here as darker shaded

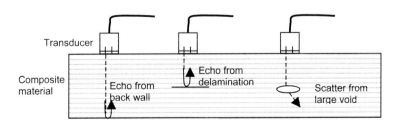

Fig. 11.4   Schematic representation of sound wave response to the presence of defects in a composite material in ultrasonic inspection.

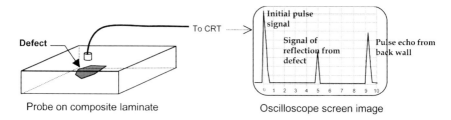

Probe on composite laminate   Oscilloscope screen image

Fig. 11.5   A-scan presentation of amplitude-distance signal recording from pulse-echo inspection showing detection of defect on CRT screen.

rectangles in Figure 11.6. Thickness variations in the structure lead to differences in the greyscale. Many systems display in color, making the images easier to interpret.

The amplitude or degree of attenuation of the signal can be used as a measure of the nature and size of porosity or voiding, provided a calibration of the attenuation in material of varying porosity contents is first determined. It may be

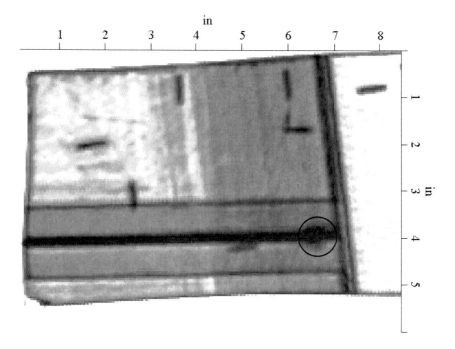

Fig. 11.6   The dark area ringed is a defect in the rib-to-skin junction. More information, such as dB loss, is indicated in the scan image by color changes (not shown here).

possible to estimate properties such as interlaminar shear (ILS) from attenuation data, provided that porosity is the only determining variable.

The transmission of sound from the probe to the structure is reliant on a couplant such as water or a suitable gel. High loss of the sound occurs when passed through air. The acoustic impedance of air is significantly lower than that of both the piezoelectric transducer and the composite material, causing loss of most of the sound energy. A medium such as water provides more efficient transmission and reception of the sound pulse to and from the component and probes. Water baths or squirter systems are commonly used in automated ultrasonic scanning of composite structures.

In industry, relatively complex composite structures that are accessible from both sides, are usually inspected using automated ultrasonic through-transmission scanning (AUSS).

The control of the probes on a gantry system allows for a more reliable and repeatable method for continuous inspection of a series of parts. Transmission of the sound is typically achieved through the application of a water jet from the probe to the surface of the part. Submersion of the part in a water bath is a technique applied to box-type structures. Here, water completely fills the box, allowing the transmission of sound from one side of the box to the other.

Hand-held ultrasonic scanning with direct contact of a probe is common in the inspection of aircraft structures, typically in localized complex areas such as radii and flanges. The development of cavity probes and mobile automated ultrasonic scanning has focused on replacing the labor-intensive hand-held ultrasonic scanning method for production inspections.

The traditional ultrasonic methods for in-service inspection involve the use of a small probe. This approach is time consuming when scanning large areas and is subject to access difficulties for particular structures on the aircraft. This has led to the development of systems better suited to rapid, large area scanning. The use

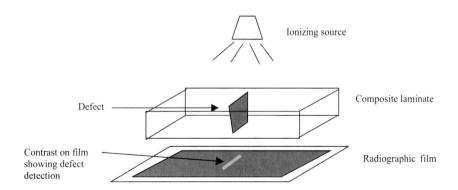

Fig. 11.7   Schematic diagram of application of X-ray to composite laminate as an NDI method.

of robotics in conjunction with ultrasonics has led to the development of equipment such as the mobile automated ultrasonics system (MAUS) that permits rapid collection of data into a C-scan image.

11.4.2.2 Radiography.   X-rays, when passed through a structure, will be absorbed where the level of absorption is dependent on the physical density of the material. The differential absorption of materials allows the use of radiography for the inspection of particular defects in composite structures. The method of X-ray radiography as a NDI technique uses ionizing radiation through a structure (Fig. 11.7) where the level of absorption of the radiation is recorded by film on the opposing side of the structure. The level of contrast on the recording film is dependent on the level of radiation that has passed through the structure. The presence of varying local physical densities in the composite structure will show as a differential contrast on the film. Defects, which include foreign objects or debonds that have different physical densities to the resin and fiber of the composite, will be detected on film when oriented in the same plane as the transmitted beam. Defects such as delaminations and planar cracks are difficult to detect using radiography.

Penetrants are often used to enhance the contrast in the detection of planar defects. Penetrants used include zinc iodide, silver nitrate, trichloromethane, and diiodomethane. Choice of the penetrant is determined by the ease with which it can penetrate the delaminations and also with which it can be subsequently removed. Diiodomethane has the advantages of high opacity, ease of penetration, and ease of removal because it evaporates fairly quickly. However, it can cause skin burns.

The dangers of radiography have generally limited its use to inspection of parts removed from the aircraft. The development of real-time radiography using a localized computer controlled X-ray source and point detector has led to the wider use of the technique for in situ inspection.

11.4.3 Emerging Technologies

The development of alternative technologies for NDI of advanced composite structures has been driven by the need to dramatically reduce inspection times and increase the capability of detection for complex component design concepts. There are parallel efforts in NDI technologies for detection of defects of fabricated and in-service structures. The development of rapid and more efficient inspection technologies is being led by work in the fields of non-contact ultrasonics, real-time radiography, pulse thermography, digital shearography, and acoustic emission technologies.[20] Work in these fields focuses on improving conventional NDI techniques, such as the replacement of the expensive and time-consuming development of film in X-ray radiography using real-time imaging. The integration of the emerging NDI technologies with existing technologies using data fusion software to form an efficient multi-purpose NDI system for families of composite structures is the focus of current major research. A possible future direction of research in NDI will be toward the establishment of a technology that can be used during and immediately after cure of the component as well as during the in-service life of the structure. This could be achieved using smart structure technology with embedded sensors, such as optical fibers, in the structures.[21]

11.4.3.1 Non-contact Ultrasonics. The problems with using a liquid couplant between the probe and component, particularly in terms of access to areas of a component, has led to developments in non-contact ultrasonics. Moreover, the application of NDI as an on-line inspection routine for some composite fabrication processes, such as tape laying, has fuelled the development of these techniques. There are several techniques available for non-contact ultrasonics including air-coupled detectors and laser-induced detectors.[22]

Air-coupled ultrasonic systems focus on transmitting high-frequency sound waves using high gain and low noise amplification. The development of a transducer that allows for a more focused transmission of sound has led to the use of air-coupled probes to characterize carbon/epoxy pre-preg materials.[23] Figure 11.8 shows the use of QMI Inc. through-transmission air-coupled probes

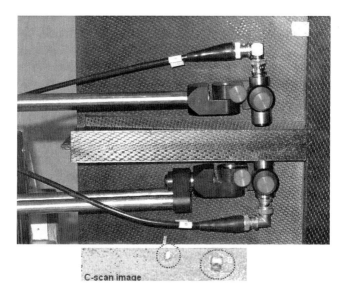

Fig. 11.8   Air-coupled non-contact ultrasonics image from QMI Inc. of web region of rib of composite box structure showing foreign object detection.

for inspection of a rib-stiffened composite box structure. Foreign object detection is shown from the inspection in the C-scan image.

Laser beam ultrasound is applicable to both electrically conducting and nonconducting materials with less disturbance in detection as a function of distance from part surface compared with the other non-contact techniques. Laser beam ultrasonics provides access in geometrically difficult-to-reach locations. In this method, short pulses are induced that cause rapid heating and expansion of the component surface. Laser detection of the reflected signals from the excited component is performed using an interferometer system. Fiedler et al.[24] have shown the capability to generate a three-dimensional C-scan image of a curved part with discontinuities at various depths using laser ultrasonics. The main limiting factor of laser ultrasonics is the cost of the hardware. Buynak et al.[25] inform of work that has demonstrated the relative ease for introducing perpendicular sound pulses on round surfaces using laser-based ultrasonic (LBU) technology, a task that is said by the same authors to be difficult to achieve with the traditional water jet systems.

A hybrid system that uses lasers to induce ultrasonic signals and electromagnetic acoustic transducers (EMAT) to measure the signals is reported.[26] This system overcomes the shortfalls of EMAT to induce ultrasonic signals when used alone.

11.4.3.2 Real-Time Radiography.   Recent developments in real-time imaging technology have raised interest for expanding radiographic testing. Advances have been achieved in the areas of reverse geometry X-ray and microfocus X-ray microscopy.

Real-time reverse X-ray systems that allow for portable and filmless inspection have been successfully used to detect in-service defects.[27] In the reverse X-ray technique, a component is placed adjacent to the large scanning source and a point detector. A computer controls the X-ray tube and image construction. This technology is demonstrated for inspection of water entrapment and core crush in honeycomb core composite sandwich structures. The development of an integrated robotic X-ray system, as shown in Figure 11.9 demonstrates the potential implementation of an automated system for inspection in a production line and in the field for aerospace structures.

11.4.3.3 Thermography.   In thermography, heat-sensing devices are used to measure temperature variations caused by differences in heat capacity or thermal conductivity in a structure. Thermography is well suited to detecting disbonds and delaminations.

The advantages of thermography are based on its non-contact application and high scanning rates. Passive thermography has been able to provide qualitative assessment of sub-surface defects, but has failed to match the quantitative capabilities of ultrasonics. This technique relies on heat diffusion driven by

Fig. 11.9   Robotic Digital X-ray probe. Courtesy Digiray Corporation.

ambient or process-related temperature fluctuations as the basis for detecting hidden structural flaws.

Developments in the field of pulse thermography have largely bridged the gap between the capabilities of ultrasonics and thermography. In pulsed thermography, the surface of the sample is irradiated by a pulse of heat from a high-powered light source and monitored using an infrared sensor. Ideally, the heating should be highly uniform; however, it is often very difficult to achieve uniform heating (this being dependent on the shape and complexity of the component). The relative time and amplitude of the measured signal provides information about the depth and size of sub-surface defects. Areas located near defects will cool (heat diffuses away) at a different rate compared to defect-free areas. Figure 11.10 shows the basic set-up of the thermography NDI method, where the application of a flash lamp heats the composite component and an infrared camera measures the temperature distribution in the component over time. The thermal image shows defective areas as lighter regions compared to dark for the surrounding material.

Limitations on thermography include optical reflectivity, infrared emissivity and thermal diffusivity of the material. Thermography is most suited to large planar structures, or curved components with large radii of curvature. It is generally found that parts thicker than 12 mm are not practical for thermographic inspection. The low infrared emissivity, or high reflectance, of unprepared metal

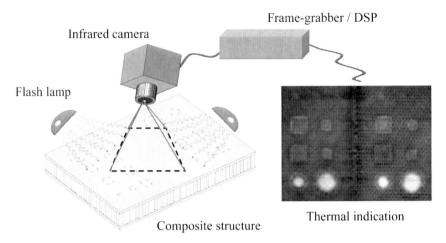

Fig. 11.10   Schematic of pulse thermography NDI method, courtesy of DSTO.

surfaces can present a problem in allowing stray infrared emissions to potentially contaminate a thermogram. This can be overcome with the application of paint. Developments in pulse thermography have focused on advanced signal processing and synthetic imaging that considers the behaviour of each pixel over the entire cooling sequence.

A comparison, has been undertaken of results for detection of Teflon inserts in a carbon/epoxy 5 ply laminate with aluminium honeycomb core using flash thermography and through transmission ultrasonics. A high level of defects was found using thermography; however the resolution of data images from the use of ultrasonics were superior to those obtained by thermography. These findings suggest a need for work on advanced signal processing and synthetic imaging.

Thermographic imaging successfully detected disbonds between an 11 ply carbon/epoxy skin and a titanium spar in a rudder leading edge, adhesive voids in boron patch repairs, water incursion in composite radomes, and interstitial voids at the skin to rib junction in a co-cured carbon/epoxy flap structure, as shown in Figure 11.11.

An alternative thermographic technique is to detect heat directly generated by the defects themselves In this approach, called vibrothermography, low-amplitude mechanical excitations induce local heating by friction when relative motion of the flaw surface occurs. Figure 11.12 shows thermal images at various delays after excitation of an impact damaged composite laminate sample with a photographic flash lamp. The defect indication is observed to develop gradually over time, consistent with a diffusion governed process that this technique is suited to the detection of delaminations and matrix cracking.

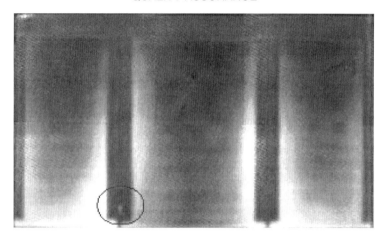

Fig. 11.11   Digital image from EchoTherm (thermal wave imaging) showing detection of interstitial void at skin to rib junction of a carbon/epoxy flap.

11.4.3.4 Optical Methods, Shearography, and Holography. In shearography a load is applied to a laminated structure that causes submerged defects to create surface strain discontinuities that are visually shown in a fringe pattern. The strain levels in the structure are measured by a digital interferometry system before and after a load is applied. Digital mapping of the component using image acquisition equipment generates fringe patterns permitting real-time inspection.

The basis of forming a shearographic fringe pattern is the application of a load to the structure. This is achieved through thermal and surface vacuum techniques. Davis[28] demonstrated the capabilities of inspecting large areas of composite materials using thermal-stress shearography, whilst Bar-Cohen[20] demonstrated the use of thermal shearography on an aircraft. Figure 11.13 details the detection of a void at the junction of a rib to skin for a rib stiffened carbon/epoxy box structure. This image was generated by Steinbichler with the stationary Shearography System by using thermal excitation with an 8-mm objective.

Environmental disturbances, such as thermal currents and room vibrations are overcome in shearography by integrating the use of a common path optical arrangement and surface strain measurement. This system overcomes the problem of conventional holography. This technique can also detect very small defects through the formation of fringe patterns under stress. However, it is more sensitive to the mechanical stability of the structure.

11.4.3.5 Acoustic Excitation and Sensing. The use of low frequency acoustic waves to excite a natural frequency response from a structure is the basic principle of the tap testing method. The tap test is the simple technique of using a

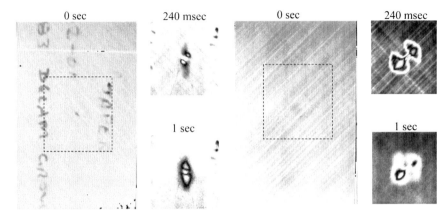

Fig. 11.12   Flash thermographs of an impact damaged 50 ply carbon/epoxy composites at three stages in the cooling process. Taken from impact surface left and opposite surface right, courtesy of DSTO.

coin or light hammer to tap a structure, where the resulting natural frequency response at a sub-surface defect will give a hollow sound. The methods of exciting a structure and recording the vibrational response have led to the development of instruments such as the digital bond-tester and techniques such as acoustic-ultrasonics and acoustic impact. These methods being developed using sensing of acoustic waves are applicable to non real-time inspection. The real-time monitoring of acoustic waves caused by an impact to a structure during service is a technique under development. The following describes these developing acoustic excitation and sensing technologies.

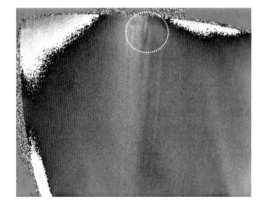

Fig. 11.13   Shearography image at 8-mm objective of rib to skin junction of composite box structure showing detection of a void. Courtesy of Steinbichler Optotechnik GmbH.

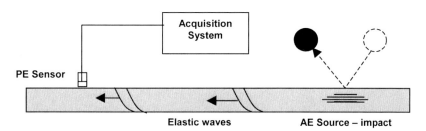

Fig. 11.14   Schematic of acoustic emission method.

11.4.3.6 Acoustic Emission. Acoustic emission (AE) is defined as the generation of a transient elastic wave caused by the rapid release of energy from a localised source within a structure. AE may be used to detect crack initiation and growth, impact damage and to determine the location of damage. In AE, piezoelectric sensors are used to detect elastic waves generated within the structure, as shown in Figure 11.14. The generation of elastic waves within a composite structure is attributed to failure mechanisms, such as fiber fracture, matrix cracking or delamination. A good analogy for the AE source location is the detection of the epicenter of an earthquake. Hamstad et al.[29] have investigated a correlation between the recorded emission signal and the location of the defect in composite structures. The progress of this work is focused on complex analysis of the emission signal using fixed threshold techniques. A more primitive method of identifying the general location of the impact is reliant on detecting the first of an array of AE sensors across a structure hit by an emitted signal, known as the "first hit" method.[30] The need to use sensors on the structure carries concerns of extra weight and possible failure sites. The development of wireless technology and electronic miniaturisation will assist in the viability of this technology to be applied as a NDI method.

The technique is found to be of limited use for NDI purposes. However, it may find some value for proof testing where it could be used to detect serious hidden defects.

11.4.3.7 Acousto-Ultrasonics. In contrast to placing two transducers in line of sight of each other, a technique known as acousto-ultrasonics (AU) uses two transducers on the same side of a structure, one to transmit the signal, the other to receive the signal after the wave has propagated along the material. This is shown schematically in Figure 11.15. The method is reliant on the use of a transmitting piezoelectric transducer where issued acoustic waves are propagated through the structure, and the responding emitted wave components are received by at least one remotely located transducer.[31] The initial development of this method[32] focused on correlation between the mechanical strength of the structure with a stress wave factor. An investigation[33] on the application of AU as a

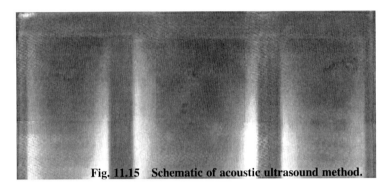

Fig. 11.15   Schematic of acoustic ultrasound method.

quality control mechanism for thick radial ply composite shows the capability of applying this technology to detecting defects in composite structures. The application of AU to aircraft structures is reliant on using multiple sensor configurations, a technology that requires further analysis of wave propagation with transducer and receiver pairing.

11.4.3.8 Acoustic Impact.   The impact of a structure with an acoustic wave is a method used to excite natural frequencies in a structure.[34] Changes in structure, such as sub-surface defects, will locally affect the natural frequency response. Recording of the relaxation frequencies across the surface of a structure using a scanning laser Doppler vibrometer can detect sub-surface defects. Figure 11.15 shows how the generation of a pressure wave at distance from the structure leads to an impact by an acoustic wave.

11.5   Conclusion

Non-destructive inspection for advanced composite aerospace structures plays a significant role in the assurance of forming high quality composite components

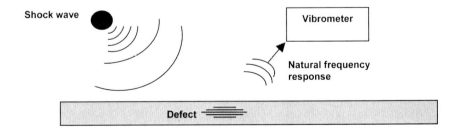

Fig. 11.16   Schematic of acoustic impact method.

that meet the stringent product quality demands of the aerospace industry. The current NDI technologies used in industry employ a combination of automation and hand-held labor. In many instances these technologies are slow, and contribute significant cost to the final product. The continual development of a lower cost, simple and reliable system for detection of defects in all current and future families of advanced composite structures is a main driver in research and development activities in the aerospace industry.

References

[1] "Polymer Matrix Composites", *Military Handbook*, MIL-HDBK-17-ID, U.S. Department of Defense, 1994.

[2] *Quality Control for the Manufacture of Composite Structures*—FAA Advisory Circular, AC 21–26, 1989.

[3] "Composites," *Engineered Materials Handbook*, Vol. 1, ASM International, Materials Park, OH, 1987.

[4] *Annual Book of ASTM Standards*, American Society for Testing and Materials.

[5] Strong, A. B., *Fundamentals of Composites Manufacturing*, SME, Dearborn, MI, 1989.

[6] "Polymer Matrix Composites", *Military Handbook*, MIL-HDBK-17-ID, U.S. Department of Defense, 1994..

[7] *SACMA Recommended Methods (SRM)*, Suppliers of Advanced Composite Materials Association, Arlington VA, 1994.

[8] *Assessment of the State-of-the-Art for Process Monitoring Sensors for Polymer Composites*, U.S. Department of Commerce, NISTIR 4514, 1 June 1991.

[9] Kent, R., "Process Control for Composite Materials," *Comprehensive Composite Materials*, Vol. 2, edited by A. Kelly, C. Zweben, R. Talreja, J. Anders, and E. Manson, Elsevier, 2000.

[10] Mallick, P. K., "Non-Destructive Tests" *Composite Engineering Handbook*, edited by P. K. Mallick, Marcel Dekker, 1997.

[11] Ungarish, R., Joseph, R., Vittoser, J., and Kenig, S., "Cure Cycle Optimization by Dielectric Measurments," *Composites*, Vol. 21, 1990, p. 481.

[12] Ciriscioli, P. R., and Springer, G., "Dielectric Cure Monitoring: A Critical Review," *SAMPE Journal*, Vol. 25, No. 3, May/June 1989, pp. 35–42.

[13] Turner, R. D., Valis, T., Dayle Hogg, W., and Measures, R. M., "Fiber-Optic Strain Sensors for Smart Structures," *Journal of Intelligent Material Systems and Structures*, Vol. 1, 1990, pp. 26–49.

[14] Young, M. A., Druy, W. A., Stevenson, W. A., and Compton, D. A. C., "In-situ Composite Cure Monitoring Using Infrared Transmitting Optical Fibres," *SAMPE Journal*, Vol. 25, No. 2, 1989, pp. 11–15.

[15] Lam, K.-Y., and Afromowitz, M. A., *Applied Optics*, Vol. 34, No. 25, 1995, pp. 5635–5638.

[16] Lam K.-Y., and Afromowitz, M. A., *Applied Optics*, Vol. 34, No. 25, 1995, pp. 5639–5644.

[17]Perry M. J., and Lee, L., "On-Line Cure Monitoring of Epoxy/Carbon Composites Using a Scaling Analysis and a Dual Heat Flux Sensor," *Journal of Composite Materials*, Vol. 26, No. 2, 1992, pp. 274–292.

[18]Fanucci, J. P., Nicolet, S. C., Koppernaes, C., Chou, H.-N., *Thin Disposable Pressure Sensors for Composite Material Process Monitoring*, 35th International SAMPE Symposium, pp. 1205–1219, Apr. 1990.

[19]Hoskin, B. C., and Baker, A. A., *Composite Materials for Aircraft Structures*, AIAA Education Series, AIAA, New York, 1986.

[20]Bar-Cohen, Y., "Emerging NDT Technologies and Challenges at the Beginning of the Third Millennium," Part 1, *Materials Evaluation*, Jan. 2000, pp. 17–30.

[21]Bar-Cohen, Y., "Emerging NDT Technologies and Challenges at the Beginning of the Third Millennium," Part 2, *Materials Evaluation*, Feb. 2000, pp. 141–150.

[22]Green, R. E., "Emerging Technologies for NDE of Aging Aircraft Structures," *Proceedings of the Workshop on Intelligent NDE Sciences for Aging and Futuristic Aircraft*, C. Ferregut, R. Osegueda, and A. Nunez, (Eds.), Univ. of Texas at El Paso, 1997, pp. 267–278.

[23]Grandia, W. A., and Fortunko, C. M., "NDE Applications of Air-coupled Ultrasonic Transducers," *Proceedings of the 1995 IEEE Ultrasonic Symposium*, Vol. 1, 1995, pp. 697–709.

[24]Fiedler, C. J., Ducharme, T., and Kwan, J., "The Laser Ultrasonic Inspection System (LUIS) at the Sacramento Air Logistic Center," *Review of Progress in Quantitative NDE*, Vol. 16, Plenum Press, New York, 1997, pp. 515–522.

[25]Buynak, C., Cordell, T., Golis, M., "Air Force Research Laboratory Program for Nondestructive Testing of Composite Materials," *43rd International SAMPE Symposium*, 1998, pp. 1724–1729.

[26]Oursler, J. D., and Wagner, J. W., "Narrow-Band Hybrid Pulsed Laser/EMAT System for Non-contact Ultrasonic Inspection Using Angled Shear Waves," *Materials Evaluation*, Vol. 53, 1995, pp. 593–559.

[27]Albert, R., Pember, W., Garrison, J., and Reyna, D., "Aircraft Inspection with a Portable, Filmless X-ray System using Reverse Geometry," *Materials Evaluation*, May 2000, pp. 643–645.

[28]Davis, C. K., "Shearographic and Thermographic Non Destructive Evaluation of the Space Shuttle Structure and Thermal Protection Systems (TPS)," *Nondestructive Evaluation of Aging Aircraft, Airports, and Aerospace Hardware, SPIE Proceedings*, edited by R. D. Rempt and A. L. Broz, Vol. 2945, Scottsdale, AZ, 1996, pp. 36–47.

[29]Hamstad, M. A., and Downs, K. S., "On Characterisation and Location of Acoustic Emission Sources in Real Size Composite Structures: A Wavefrom Study," *Journal of Acoustic Emission*, Vol. 13, Nos. 1–2, Jan–Jun 1995, pp. 31–41.

[30]Hamstad, M. A., Whitaker, J. W., and Brosey, W. D., "Correlation of Residual Strength with Acoustic Emission from Impact-Damaged Composite Structures Under Constant Biaxial Load," *Journal of Composite Materials*, Vol. 26, No. 15, 1992, pp. 2307–2328.

[31]Vary, A., "The Acousto-Ultrasonic Approach," *Acousto-Ultrasonics, Theory and Applications*, edited by J. C. Duke, Jr., Plenum Press, 1988.

[32]Vary, A., and Bowles, K. J., "Ultrasonic Evaluation of the Strength of Uni-directional Carbon-Polyimide Composite," NASA TM X–73646, 1979.

[33] Gill, T. J., and Bartos, A. L., "An Acoustic-Ultrasonic Platform for the Quality Assessment of Thick Radial Ply Composite Structures," *Nondestructive Characterisation of Materials VI*, edited by R. E. Green, Jr., K. J. Kozaczek, and C. O. Rudd, Plenum Press, 1994.

[34] Webster, J. M., "Method and Apparatus for Non-Destructive Inspection of Composite Materials and Semi-Monocoque Structures," US Patent No. 505,090, 1996.

12
Aircraft Applications and Design Issues

12.1 Overview

This chapter deals with the application of the technologies and materials described in preceding chapters. Its purpose is to highlight the interpretation of the strengths and limitations of polymer composites and to provide some examples of generally accepted design rules and guidelines. Although a vast amount of research has been undertaken on composite materials and structures, much of this has been done by the major aircraft manufacturers and is proprietary. Consequently, design rules vary somewhat from organization to organization, reflecting the different experiences within each. The rules of thumb given here are therefore rudimentary and should be checked with the relevant design authorities before being applied to any particular project.

The chapter also includes some examples of the applications of mainly carbon/epoxy composite structures, and it is hoped that this will show the evolution of their use, which is an inference of the experiences gained by manufacturers. More details on applications can be found in Refs. 1 and 2.

Initially, mention is made of applications with glass-fiber-reinforced polymer laminates, which were the first composite materials used in aircraft structures.

12.2 Applications of Glass-Fiber Composites

Glass-fiber composites were first used during World War II, which was about 20 years before carbon- and boron-fiber composites were used in aircraft structures. The earliest composites were made of E-type glass fabric and polyester resin, and these were used in a few niche components not subject to high loads, such as fuselage-lifting surface attachments or wing and empennage tips. At the time, the aircraft industry was reluctant to use glass-fiber composites more widely because of the low stiffness of glass-fibers and the poor strength and toughness of polyester resins, particularly at elevated temperature. The development of stronger, tougher, and more durable resins, such as epoxies, led to the increased use of E-glass laminates in some aircraft. For example, virtually the entire airframe, wings, and fuselage of modern gliders are built of glass/epoxy.

In the 1960s the development of S2-type glass, which has greater stiffness and strength than E-glass, allowed a greater variety of aircraft structures and components to be made. S-glass composites are often used as the face skins to ultra-light sandwich honeycomb panels, and typical applications in commercial aircraft are wing-fuselage fairings, rudder and elevator surfaces, and the leading and trailing edges of wing panels. Glass/epoxy honeycomb sandwich panels are also used in a variety of components on modern military aircraft, such as the fixed trailing edge on the B-2 bomber. Another common use of composites with E-glass or quartz fiber reinforcement is in radomes on commercial and fighter aircraft, in bay- and wing-mounted radomes on supersonic aircraft and missiles, and in the large radar domes on Airborne Early Warning and Control (AEW&C) military aircraft. This is because of the excellent transparency of glass to radar signals. Glass/epoxy is widely used in helicopter components, such as in the spars to the main and tail rotor blades, fuselage body panels, and flooring. Glass fibers are also used in combination with carbon and Kevlar fibers in hybrid composites for a wide variety of aircraft components, such as wing-body fairings, engine pylon fairings, and engine cowlings. Polyesters have been used in composites for cabin interiors; however, in this application, phenolics are now preferred due to their excellent flame resistance.

12.3   Current Applications

12.3.1   Fixed Wing Civil Applications

As mentioned in Chapter 1, the adoption of composite materials for aircraft structures has been slower than originally foreseen, despite the weight-saving and corrosion and fatigue immunity offered by these materials. The reasons for the restrained use include the high cost of certification and higher materials and production costs for composite components. Composite structures must not be significantly more costly to acquire[3] than those made of aluminum alloy and, to maintain the advantage of weight saving, maintenance costs also, must not be greater.

Sensitivity to impact damage and low through-thickness strength are also inhibiting factors. Other issues are the poor reliability in estimating development costs and difficulty in accurately predicting structural failure.[4]

Although a few inroads have been made in terms of reducing certification costs, recently there has been the development of more cost-efficient manufacturing methods, such as resin-transfer molding and pultrusion, and improved resin and fiber systems that provide increased toughness are making composites very strong candidates for new designs. Another important benefit is the reduction of airframe assembly costs, as composites lend themselves to the manufacture of large unitized structures.

After some years of stagnation, the use of composite materials in large aircraft structures has increased over the past half-decade as manufacturers take advantage of the unique properties of these materials and find solutions to lower the cost of production of composite structures.

As an example, Airbus Industrie has continued to increase applications of composite materials into its new aircraft programs, and in the A380 structure, composite applications amount to approximately 16% of the total airframe weight. Theoretically, this is equivalent to the replacement of about 20% of conventional aluminum structure by composites. Large commercial transport aircraft designs had, in the past, tended to limit the use of composite materials to secondary structures—ailerons, flaps, elevators and rudders—although Boeing has used the material on the tailplane and floor beams of the B777 and Airbus on the empennages of most of its fleet. More recently, several commercial airliner manufacturers have been considering and choosing composite materials for other primary structures.

The Airbus A380 will employ carbon-fiber-reinforced plastic composite materials in the massive (7 × 8 × 2.4 m) wing carry-through structure; inside the cabin the upper floor beams are pultruded 7-m long, 0.3-m deep sections. Resin infusion is used to form the rear pressure bulkhead and several of the wing panels. Leading edges will be thermoplastic to obtain improved impact resistance.

The upper fuselage skin panels (over 400 m^2) will be manufactured from a hybrid metal and fiberglass laminate, Glare; this material is discussed briefly in Chapter 1. Figure 12.1 illustrates the material used on the A380 as projected in the advanced development stage of the project. The carry-through structure represents probably the largest, most complex, and critical aerospace composite structure yet attempted in civil aircraft applications.

As technologies in both composite structures and aluminum structures advance, and with service experience, preferred options will change over time.

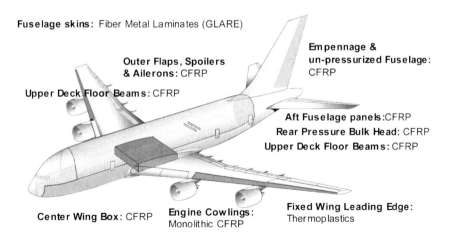

Fig. 12.1   Advanced composite materials selected for the A380. Courtesy of Airbus Industries.

Figure 12.2 shows the fluctuations of structural design selection for a number of Airbus products.

Of the smaller transport and general category aircraft, the Beechcraft Starship was the first all-composite aircraft certificated to FAR 25. Later, Raytheon products, the Premier 1 and the Horizon corporate jets, have reverted to metal wings for cost reasons; however, the fuselages remain as composite structures. In addition, new, automated methods of production are employable on surfaces of revolution. Figure 12.3 shows the Premier 1 fuselage being produced using a tow-placement process.

An attraction for the smaller fabricators is the ability to produce aerodynamically smooth surfaces with relatively low tooling costs, and many high-performance homebuilt aircraft use composite materials almost exclusively. With the drive toward lower-cost carbon fiber, promoted, in part, by the interest in the automotive industry, the use of these materials is sure to expand further.

12.3.2 Fixed-Wing Military Applications

Up to 70% of the airframe weights of some modern military airframes are manufactured from composite materials. This is due in part to the pursuit of ultimate performance, with less emphasis on cost, but also to the low radar signature obtainable through use of these materials. Perhaps the most ambitious example of the use of composites is the USAF B-2 bomber,[4] which is an almost all-composite structure. The wing, which is almost as large as that of a B-747, is

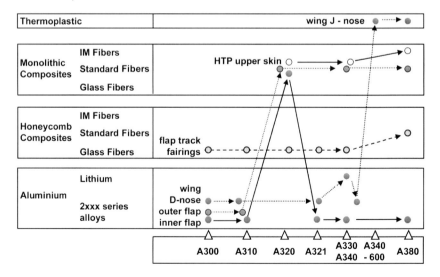

Fig. 12.2   Evolution of Airbus materials selections. Courtesy of Airbus Industries.

Fig. 12.3   Premier 1 composite fuselage. Courtesy of the Raytheon Corporation.

mostly made of carbon/epoxy, with honeycomb skins and internal structure. The fuselage makes extensive use of composites. However, this form of construction is very costly and more recently, affordability is considered to be as important as performance and is now a major design parameter.

The need for high stiffness to minimize the depth of wings and tail in high-performance military aircraft both for aeroelastic and stealth reasons ensures that all future aircraft will have composite wing and empennage skins. The requirement for stealth as well as minimum weight also ensures that most of the fuselage skin will be composite. For radar absorption, leading edges will be made of honeycomb structure with outer composite skins based on non-conducting fibers such as quartz rather than carbon in the rest of the structure. This skin material allows the radar waves to penetrate into the honeycomb core coated with radar-absorbing material, rather than being reflected back to the receiver.

Despite the structural advantages of honeycomb construction, there is a trend to replace this form of construction with stiffened cocured composite panels, because these are much less prone to damage and to water entrapment. Honeycomb is still used in some regions for stealthy structure as discussed previously and where structurally advantageous, for example, in control surfaces.

Some military aircraft such as the Harrier, have much of the internal structure of the wing made of carbon fiber reinforced plastic composite, in addition to wing skins, some in the form of sine wave spars (see Figure 12.4). However, in more recent fighter aircraft there is a trend back to metals for much of the wing substructure. This is because of the relatively high cost of composite substructure, compared to high-speed machined aluminum and the limited tolerance of composites to ballistic impact. Often titanium alloy is used for the main load-bearing spar because of its superior resistance to ballistic impact and its excellent fatigue properties.

The airframe of the F-22, as an example,[4] is made of 39% Ti 64 titanium, 16% aluminum alloy, 6% steel, 24% thermoset composite – carbon/epoxy and carbon/BMI and 1% thermoplastic. The structure is given as follows.

- Forward Fuselage:
  - skins and chine – composite laminates
  - bulkhead/frames resin transfer moulded composite and aluminium
  - fuel tank frames and walls- RTM composite
  - side array doors and avionics – formed thermoplastic
- Mid Fuselage:
  - skins – composite and titanium
  - bulkhead and frames – titanium aluminum and composite
  - weapon-bay doors -skin thermoplastic, hat stiffeners, RTM composite
- Aft Fuselage:
  - forward boom- welded titanium
  - bulkhead and frames- titanium
  - keel web-composite
- Wings:
  - skins composite
  - spars - front titanium, intermediate and rear- RTM composite and titanium
  - side of body fitting HIP cast titanium
- Empennage:
  - skin composite
  - core – aluminium
  - spars and ribs-RTM composite
- Duct Skins:
  - Composite
- Landing Gear
  - steel

Some general details of the construction of some current fighter are provided in Figure 1.2 for the F/18EF and in Figure 12.5 for the Joint Strike Fighter. In the JSF extensive use was planned (at the time of writing) of the lightweight aluminum lithium alloy for the wing and other substructure.

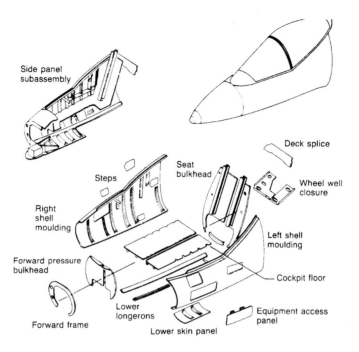

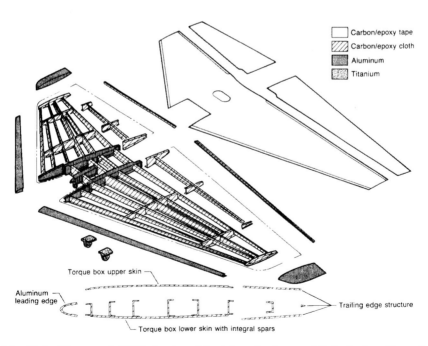

Fig. 12.4   Diagram of AV8B showing of (*top*) **front fuselage and** (*below*) **wing skin and substructure all made largely of carbon-fiber-reinforced plastic composite. From Ref. 2.**

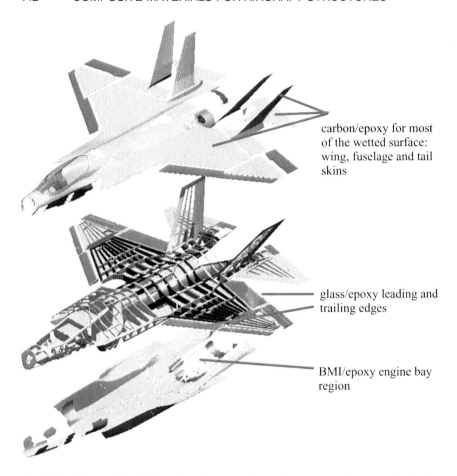

carbon/epoxy for most
of the wetted surface:
wing, fuselage and tail
skins

glass/epoxy leading and
trailing edges

BMI/epoxy engine bay
region

Fig. 12.5   Joint strike fighter showing extensive planned use of composite in the skins of the aircraft but use of aluminum alloy for much of the substructure.

Many future fighter and attack aircraft will be unmanned. Here the emphasis is on very high g manoeuvres to evade missiles in high-threat regions, two or three times the 7–9 g allowed in manned aircraft. Only all-composite construction could be considered for the structure in such situations and design will be based on very high strain allowables.

Both manned and unmanned aircraft will in future aircraft be continuously monitored using embedded sensors (see Smart Materials Chapter 15). These sensors will provide information on the stress, strain, temperature and any damage experienced by the structure and may also provide an indication of absorbed moisture.

12.3.3 Rotorcraft Applications

The early applications for composite materials in helicopters were in rotor blades and drive shafts. The attraction for rotor blades is the ability to produce complex aerofoil shapes and high-quality surface contours using simple construction methods. Fiberglass has often been used because the stiffness of the blades is not usually a design problem, the predominant load being tension caused by centrifugal forces. Use of composites in drive shafts is attractive but the opposite reason applies and here, torsional stiffness is an imperative and carbon fiber reinforced plastic composites offer a significant weight saving. Filament winding is an attractive manufacturing process for these components particularly for drive shafts where there is a need for ply orientations at $+/-45°$ for maximum torsional efficiency.

Composite materials are now used for flex-beams in the design of 'bearingless rotor hubs' that are now becoming universally adopted. Composites allow flexural stiffnesses to be tailored into the otherwise rigid beam allowing the necessary blade flapping action arising from forward flight. Pitch cases, that transmit the pitch angle to the blade, have similar requirements to drive shafts and are also being constructed from carbon fiber reinforced plastic composite.

Over recent years, the use of carbon fiber shell structures for fuselages and tailbooms has also been spreading. The MD Explorer employs carbon fiber reinforced plastic composite for almost 100% of the non-transparent external structure (see Figure 12.6). The US ACAPS helicopter crashworthiness assessment program run in the 1980s showed the advantages of using composites in the tub structures for energy absorption under crash-landing conditions. Composite structures when designed properly have a significantly better specific energy absorbing capacity than aluminum alloy structures under crushing conditions.

The V-22 tiltrotor is an excellent example of the beneficial use of carbon/epoxy composite construction.[4] Use of composites is credited with saving 13% structural weight and reducing costs by 22%. However, to save cost, even in this highly weight-sensitive application, some of the internal fuselage structure, originally planned to be made of composite, is now made of aluminum alloy.

12.3.4 Common Configurations

Table 5.1 lists the various types of composite construction used in aircraft structure. Early composite designs tended to be of sandwich construction, featuring honeycomb cores. This construction is highly efficient structurally and, provided the core is relatively shallow, also quite cheap to manufacture. Unfortunately there have been many examples of disbonding in service. This problem in honeycomb structure is common to both metallic- and composite-skinned construction and mostly results from the ingress of moisture into the core

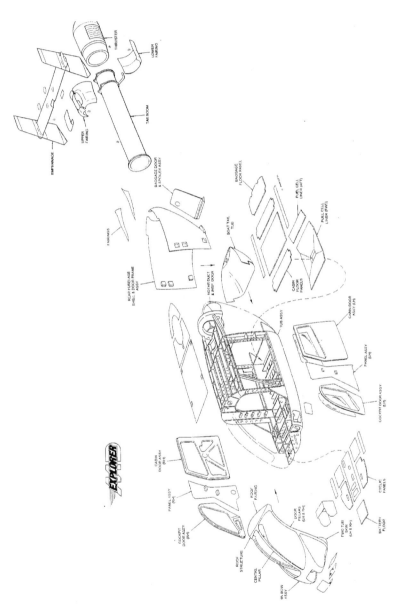

Fig. 12.6   Composite components on the MD Explorer fuselage. Courtesy of Hawker de Havilland Ltd.

through poorly sealed ends during ground-to-air pressure changes. It can also be a problem with thin composite skins, which can allow moisture to penetrate through microcracks. However, transport of moisture through the composite skins by diffusion does not seem to be a problem. Moisture penetration is particularly serious when the core is made of aluminum alloy because corrosion and bond separation result. Ingress of moisture can also cause de-bonding of the skins caused by expansion of entrapped moisture on freezing when operating at altitude.

A good design practice with honeycomb panels is to envelop the sandwich in a thermoplastic film such as Tedlar, which acts as a moisture barrier, that can be cobonded with the laminate. Cuts and darts in this film should be avoided, otherwise moisture can penetrate to the composite surfaces where it can then be absorbed into the substrate. Skin thicknesses should also not be less than 0.6 mm for the same reason. The use of an appropriate sealant must be applied to all cut edges.

Honeycomb-sandwich structures are also more prone to impact damage, and for these reasons, although accepted for secondary structures, some aircraft companies will not sanction the use of sandwich construction in primary structures. Closed-cell rigid foam cores are possible substitutes; however, the low melting temperature of PVC foams restrict its use to lower-temperature-curing (and hence lower-performing) systems. Higher-temperature-curing foams such as PEI may overcome this problem; however, some observations of the material cracking under cyclic strains have been reported, and care must be taken to ensure that the foam is completely dried before processing.

The alternative is a stiffened monolithic construction, and here the main issue is the means of attachment of the stiffeners. Some alternatives for attaching stiffeners are shown in Figure 12.7.

Although honeycomb construction is generally lighter than stiffened structure, this situation is reversed if the structure is allowed to buckle at limit-load. Compared with unbuckled stiffened structure, honeycomb saves approximately 20% weight, but post-buckled structure[5] can save approximately 30%.

From a structural point of view, the integral cocured design is the most effective solution, particularly if the stiffeners must endure buckling of the skins without disbonding; however, lay-up costs are higher. To some extent, this cost may be offset by the reduction in parts count. With bonded discrete stiffeners (although cheaper to manufacture), care needs to be taken in matching the stiffness of the panel with the attaching flange, and avoiding excessive through-thickness stresses to avoid the possibility of peel failures. Thorough surface preparation is also essential to ensure a good bond.

Conventional mechanical fastening can be used with bonding as a conservative solution to improve through-thickness strength. Alternatively, z-pinning (Chapter 14) is a novel method in which small-diameter composite pins are inserted through the thickness of the laminate for the same purpose.

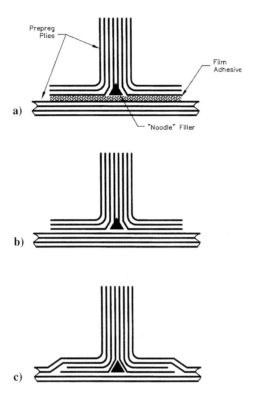

Fig. 12.7 *a*) **Secondary bonded blade stiffener;** *b*) **cobonded blade stiffener;** *c*) **integrally cured blade stiffener.**

A major NASA initiative in recent years has been to develop a cost-effective stitched stiffener wing plank using dry preforms and a resin film infusion process[6] (see also Chapter 14).

The design of composite details has to be made with a clear view of the proposed assembly procedure. A major advantage of using composite materials is the possibility of reducing parts count by making very large components (and hence subsequent joining assembly costs and problems). "Single-shot" structures, such as has been achieved on the Boeing/NASA wing plank, in which components that would previously have been individually manufactured and assembled are molded in a single operation, are becoming the goal for many designers. Although this approach brings assembly savings, the additional complexities in NDI also needs to be considered.

Another key attraction of designing with composite materials is the opportunity to tailor the design through orientation of the fiber in the direction of the load. Although it is possible to optimize structural performance through fiber alignment and by providing ply buildups at load concentration points, the value of these measures must always be considered against the increased manufacturing and certification costs. Many designs have reverted to quasi isotropic lay-ups with the aim of reducing costs. The advantages of near quasi isotropic lay-ups for optimizing strength in mechanically fastened components are discussed in Chapter 9.

12.4 Design Considerations

12.4.1 Choice of Materials

There are wide ranges of choice for both the reinforcement and the resin materials of the composite. This subject is covered more fully in Chapter 8. A summary is provided here. The most common combination for aerospace applications is an epoxy resin with carbon-fiber tape or fabric reinforcement, although BMI resins are used for high-temperature applications. In addition to these two thermosetting resins, there have been some successful applications of thermoplastic matrices such as PEEK, PEI, and PPS. Parts manufactured from thermoplastics are usually used in the smaller details due to the high forming pressures required that limit the size of part that can be formed in a conventional press. These can then be welded together to form larger components, a process not possible with thermosetting details. Thermoplastic resins were seen as attractive in the past due to their higher toughness and consequent improved resistance to impact damage. However, this advantage has been eroded somewhat by later-generation toughened epoxies. In addition, some thermoplastic resin matrices lose some toughness under some in-service conditions. PEI, in particular, has been shown to embrittle when exposed to prolonged high temperatures and furthermore is susceptible to attack from various chemicals occurring in standard aircraft fluids.

The costs of high-temperature thermoplastic materials are also considerably greater than those of competing thermosetting materials, as are the processing costs. As a result, thermoplastic systems have not been widely adopted in aerospace structures at this point.

Composite materials are usually supplied with the reinforcement pre-impregnated with resin (pre-pregs) or, less frequently, separately. In the latter case, the resin is introduced after the dry reinforcement has been placed into a mold using some form of liquid-molding process. Details of these processes are covered in Chapter 5.

Because of the high cost of material qualification, aerospace companies are typically conservative when choosing materials and tend to select early-generation materials rather than those with improved properties to avoid additional material qualification costs. Unfortunately, there are no common materials data shared between users and, in many cases, a single material is qualified to similar requirements for several different customers. An attempt is currently being made through MIL-HDBK 17 to deliver sets of properties for standard materials; however, this is as yet not comprehensive.

Carbon fiber is by far the most commonly used reinforcement material for aerospace composites. Boron fiber continues to be used for some older applications, particularly in the United States (e.g., the F-15); however, its high cost and the difficulty of processing into convenient reinforcement forms (e.g., woven and braided fabrics) and the difficulty of drilling or machining has very severely limited its application. Kevlar aramid fiber from DuPont had found some early applications, however, the limited compression strength of Kevlar composites and its tendency to absorb high proportions of moisture have led to a declining interest. It is now only mainly used for applications in which high-energy impact containment is required. The properties of composites based on these fibers are discussed in Chapter 8.

Reinforcements can be provided in a variety of woven or braid styles as well as in unidirectional plies. The latter provide the highest in-plane mechanical performance (stiffness and strength) due to the straightness and uniformity of the tows. Most weaves and all braids have "crimped" tows that reduce in-plane properties. This is particularly the case for compression strength that is very sensitive to fiber straightness. Nevertheless, braids provide a more convenient form for parts to be laid-up by hand.

Non-crimp weaves in which layers are stitched together into a carpet give properties somewhere between unidirectional and woven reinforcement, because the fibers are not held as straight as unidirectional tows. Non-crimps are highly drapeable and provide considerable advantage by reducing the number of individual plies to be laid. Currently they are not available as a pre-preg material and must be processed using liquid-molding techniques. Chapter 14 describes these forms in more detail.

12.4.2 General Guidelines

Composite structural design should not be attempted without a good working knowledge of the manufacturing limitations applying to composite materials. Generally, concurrent engineering is practiced whereby designers and manufacturing engineers work toward solutions that satisfy both design intent and production needs.

When specifying lay-ups (laminate ply stacks) and design details, some basic guidelines should be followed:

- Use balanced laminates to avoid warping
- Use manufacturing techniques that produce a minimum fiber content of 55% by volume;
- Use a minimum of 10% of plies in each of the principal directions ($0°$, $90°$, $\pm 45°$) to provide a minimum acceptable strength in all directions
- Use a maximum of four adjacent plies in any one direction to avoid splitting on contraction from cure temperature or under load

- Place $\pm\,45°$ plies on the outside surfaces of shear panels to increase resistance to buckling
- Avoid highly directional laminates in regions around holes or notches because stress concentration factors are significantly higher in this ply lay-up
- Add ply of woven fiberglass barrier between carbon and aluminum alloy for galvanic protection
- Drop plies where required progressively in steps with at least 6 mm (0.25 in) landing to improve load redistribution
- Where possible, cover ply drops with a continuous ply to prevent end-of-ply delamination
- Maintain minimum edge distance equal to three times hole diameter (edge distance measured from center of hole to edge of part) and minimum pitch for mechanical fasteners equal to four times fastener diameter
- Where feasible, avoid honeycomb in favor of stiffened construction, because honeycomb is prone to moisture intrusion and is easily damaged
- Avoid manufacturing techniques that result in poor fiber alignment, because wavy fibers results in reduced stiffness and compression strength
- Minimize the number of joints by designing large components or sections because joints reduce strength and increase weight and cost
- Allow for impact type damage (see later discussion); this may vary with risk (e.g., upper horizontal surfaces are at greatest risk).
- Exploit the non-isotropic properties of the material, where feasible.
- Ensure that the design reflects the limitations of the manufacturing processes to be used.
- Predict the failure loads and modes for comparison with test data
- Minimize or exclude the features that expose the notch-sensitivity of the material.
- Allow for degradation due to the environment.
- Provide for ready inspection of production defects.
- Allow for repair in the design.
- Predict and minimize, by design, out-of-plane loading.
- Include consideration of residual stresses in the cured laminate when calculating strength.

12.5   Design of Carbon-Fiber–Based Components

12.5.1   Static Strength

Carbon/epoxy in conventional ply configurations generally has significantly higher static strength than aluminum alloys. However, because of the brittle nature of the fibers, the composites are essentially elastic materials with very limited ability to redistribute loads at structural features such as fastener holes.[7] The result is that they are quite notch-sensitive under static loading. As may be expected, the higher the fiber modulus, the higher the notch-sensitivity, because the stiffer fibers have a reduced ability to accommodate high local strains. By contrast, aluminum alloys (and other structural metals) can redistribute stresses at mild stress concentrators by local yielding, so strength loss is often simply due to the reduction in net section.

The performance of laminates in the vicinity of holes and joints is highly affected by the lay-up.[8]

Figure 12.8 shows the variation in stress concentration at the edge of a circular hole with ply lay-up. This shows that the estimated stress concentration factor increases with the proportion of fibers oriented in the load direction (e.g., if there are no $\pm 45°$ fibers and 100% 0° fibers, $K_t = 8$). Composites also have relatively low bearing strengths and quasi isotropic laminates are preferred in the area of bolted joints to ensure that there is at least some 0° fibers support the bearing loads regardless of load direction.

For these reasons, bonded joints are a better structural solution for composites; however, there are issues of maintenance and assurance of adequate bonded joint quality that must be taken into consideration. Also, bonded joints in thick section composites are complex and costly to manufacture. Joints are an extremely important design consideration, and Chapter 9 is devoted to this topic.

It is important to note that prior cyclic loading markedly reduces notch sensitivity of the composites by the formation of microcracks in the matrix and micro-delaminations between plies in regions of high initial stress concentration.

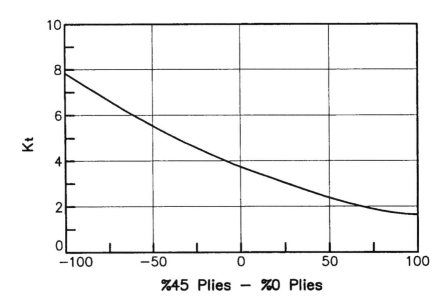

Fig. 12.8 Stress concentration factors in laminates with varying proportions of on- and off-axis plies. Based on Ref. 8.

However, this reduction may not be allowed for in assessment of static strength for certification purposes.

12.5.2 Through-Thickness Strength

The foregoing comments refer to in-plane strength properties for typical two-dimensional reinforcement. Through-thickness (or z-direction) strength is about an order of magnitude lower than that of metals (Fig. 12.9), limiting application of laminated composites to two-dimensional loading situations. It should be realized that even two-dimensional loading can result in through-thickness or peel stresses at ply drop-offs, stiffener run-outs, or edges.

Particular care is required when designing curved sections as interlaminar tension stresses that arise will often result in unexpected failure. Some examples of these situations[9] are shown in Figure 12.10.

The following simple equation may be used for approximating the through-thickness stresses in curved sections under bending.

Maximum radial (interlaminar tension) stress:

$$\sigma_r(\max) = 3M/2t(R_iR_o)^{1/2} \qquad (12.1)$$

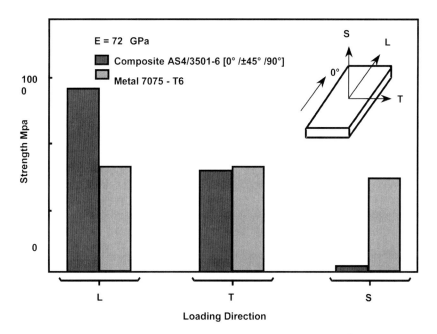

Fig. 12.9   Comparisons of strength of aluminum alloy and carbon/epoxy laminates in various loading directions. Note the very low through-thickness strength of the composite. Adapted from Ref. 7.

In addition, a temperature change in a cured curved laminate such as the drop from cure temperature to room temperature will result in the following distortion and residual radial stress:

$$\gamma = (\alpha_\theta - \alpha_r)\Delta T \pi/2 \tag{12.2}$$

and

$$\sigma_r(\text{max}) \sim (t/R_m)^2(\alpha_\theta - \alpha_r)\Delta T\ E_\theta/R_m \tag{12.3}$$

where:

$M =$ applied moment
$R_i =$ inner radius
$R_o =$ outer radius
$R_m =$ mean radius
$t =$ thickness
$\gamma =$ springback in degrees
$\alpha_\theta =$ circumferential coefficient of thermal expansion
$\alpha_r =$ radial coefficient of thermal expansion
$\Delta T =$ temperature change
$E_\theta =$ circumferential modulus of elasticity

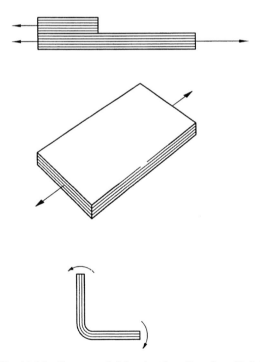

Fig. 12.10   Sources of delamination. Based on Ref. 9.

More accurate results can be obtained from finite element analyses; however, whichever method is used to calculate induced stresses, the actual failure stresses need to be established through a calibrated test.

Joints, tapers, and ply drop-offs also give rise to significant through-thickness or peel stresses that can result in the formation of delaminations. The development of unexpected or higher than expected through-thickness stresses are major reasons for the formation of delaminations in large components. In many cases, these problems only arise when full-scale or large components are tested, or even in service, because they are often not detected at the coupon or structural element scale.

Detailed two-dimensional or three-dimensional finite-element analysis is used to determine the state of stress in complex full-scale components. However, modelling at the ply level can be prohibitively time-consuming and in any case may not correctly represent the "as fabricated" component.

12.5.3   Manufacturing Defects

The mechanical properties of composite structures are influenced by the presence of defects in the material arising from inconsistencies in manufacturing processes and controls. Typical defects include resin-rich or resin-dry areas, fiber misalignment, porosity, delaminations, and the inclusion of foreign materials, such as peel ply.

Most aircraft parts are inspected using automated equipment, set to scan the work at a discrete interval. A defect smaller than the interval may not be detected. On large parts, the interval is often set at approximately 6 mm, consequently defects smaller than 6 mm diameter may be missed on successive passes.

Other forms of defect can be inadvertently introduced at the assembly stage. Exit-side fiber damage and delamination can occur on drilled holes, for example, particularly if insufficient support is provided. The extensive use of composite materials in recent years and the development of drill bit technology has minimized these effects; however, it is important to ensure that test specimens used to obtain design allowables are representative of the accepted production practice. Handling damage and damage due to excessive force fit are also possible during the assembly stage.

Typical manufacturing defects must be allowed for in design, but allowance for impact damage as described in the next section will usually cover this requirement.

12.5.4   Impact Damage

Impact damage in composite airframe components is usually the main preoccupation of designers and airworthiness regulators. This is in part due to the extreme sensitivity of these materials to quite modest levels of impact, even when the damage is almost visually undetectable. Chapter 8 describes the mechanisms involved in impact damage and also provides more background on the influence of mechanical damage on residual strength.

Horizontal, upwardly facing surfaces are obviously the most prone to hail damage and should be designed to be at least resistant to impacts of around 1.7 J. The value represents the energy level generally accepted to represent extreme value in (1% probability of being exceeded) hail conditions.[10]

Surfaces exposed to maintenance work are generally designed to be tolerant to impacts resulting from tool drops.[11] Figure 12.11 provides impact energy levels for a variety of different tool-drops, and Figure 12.12 indicates that monolithic laminates are more damage resistant than honeycomb structures. This is due to their increased compliance. However, if the impact occurs over a hard point such as above a stiffener or frame, the damage may be more severe, and if the joint is bonded, the formation of a disbond is possible.

12.5.4.1 BVID, VID, and Energy Cut-off Levels.
The authorities have generally divided impact damage into two categories. The categories are

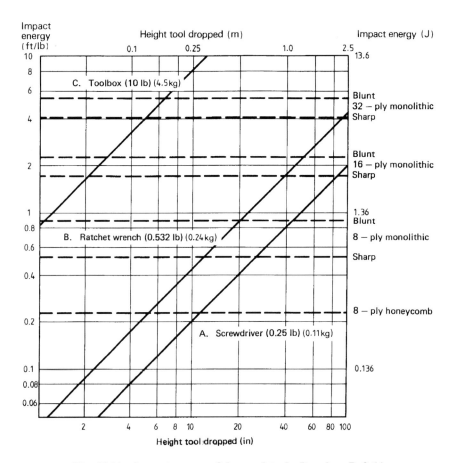

Fig. 12.11   Impact energy of dropped tools. Based on Ref. 11.

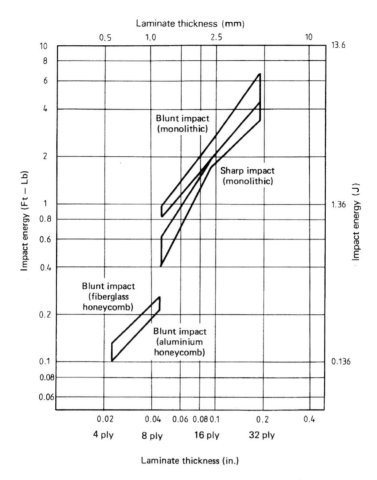

Fig. 12.12   Impact energy for incipient damage to carbon/epoxy laminates.

delineated by the ease of visibility (by the naked eye) of the damage rather than the energy of the impact: barely visible impact damage (BVID) and visible impact damage (VID). The definition of visibility is difficult to quantify because it depends on access, light conditions, and differences in human capability. Damage to an external surface could be expected to be more readily detectable; however, because it can be masked by paint. Quite often, backside damage fiber-break is more apparent than the corresponding impression on the impacted face. For airworthiness certification, the structure is expected to demonstrate an acceptable strength margin with BVID because this may not be detected for some time. It is not usually the surface condition that promotes a subsequent static failure, but more the associated underlying delaminations.

There is no current universally accepted definition of the term *barely visible*. Some authorities accept surface indentations of 1 mm; others give more qualitative requirements, for example, that an indication be observable from a given distance (say, 1 m). It is invariably agreed that structures must be able to sustain ultimate load with this level of impact damage present in the structure and that it be able to withstand limit-load with damage that is clearly visible.

The USAF has accepted an upper threshold of impact energy of 100 ft lbs (around 135 J) as equal to a dropped tool box—a once-in-a-lifetime expected event. Consequently, if the structure is capable of withstanding this without reduction in strength below an acceptable margin, the above criteria are not imposed. Figure 12.13 illustrates the situation. Other authorities such as the Joint Airworthiness Authority (JAA) have nominated 50 J as the energy cut-off.

12.5.5 Residual Strength

As noted, the compression strength of a composite laminate is substantially reduced subsequent to an impact event causing visible or even non-visible damage. For example, with laminates less than 3 mm thick, typical of control surface structures, compression strength can be reduced by more than 50% with BVID (Fig. 12.14). These reduction factors are often established at the coupon level through a standard compression-after-impact test, as discussed in Chapter 7. These tests generally involve impacting the test coupon with a specified energy level rather than specifying a degree of damage and were initially devised to provide a means by which different materials could be compared. They have, however, been widely adopted to establish allowable values for design.

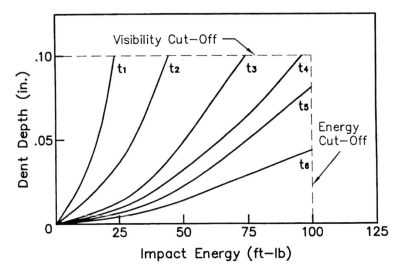

Fig. 12.13   Impact damage assumptions. The symbols t₁, t₂, etc. indicate increasing laminate thickness. Adapted from Ref. 7.

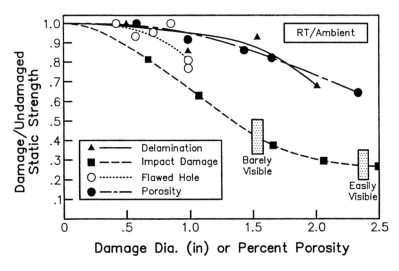

Fig. 12.14   Strength loss associated with impact damage.

In contrast, the residual strength after impact damage under tension is not usually considered as significant as other geometric characteristics, for example, fastener holes and notches, which are more critical. The case of the pressurized fuselage is an exception in which fail safety must be demonstrated in the presence of significant damage.[11] In such cases, the nature and size of damage is prescribed often following similar patterns to those known to occur in metal structures. Residual strength is usually then demonstrated by tests on full-scale subcomponents rather than by predictions from coupon data.

Horton et al.[13] provide more information on the subject of damage tolerance of composite laminates.

As discussed in Chapter 8, modelling tools for post-impact strength[14] are not sufficiently mature to be relied on, and certification is usually based on demonstrating (by test) that strain levels are sufficiently low and that failure will not occur even if damage is present. Thus residual strength tests, after impact (and other representative damage) are often performed at the various scale levels,[15] including full scale after conclusion of the fatigue test program. Residual strength testing may follow some further representative cyclic loading to check for damage growth.

When quantifying residual strength after impact, it is preferable to work in terms of strain, because the stiffness of the laminate does not then need to be considered. The allowable ultimate compressive strain with BVID is not much less than the ultimate strength of an undamaged laminate in the region of a 6-mm hole, and this latter allowable is sometimes used to cover both circumstances.

12.5.6   Damage Growth Prediction

As noted in Chapter 8, prediction of damage growth in composite laminates under cyclic loading is not straightforward. Consequently, design is generally based on a safe life with BVID damage assumed; in other words, there is no damage growth allowed under cyclic loading. Inspection intervals are set based on a demonstrated safe or no-growth life, suitably factored to allow for statistical variability.

12.5.7   Bird Strikes

Bird strikes are special cases, for example, in composite fan blades and leading edges, where it must be demonstrated that in the event of such an impact, safe continued flight and landing will not be impaired. As with metal structures (that must meet the same requirements) the issue is as much one of protection of systems behind the impact zone as of structural damage.

12.5.8   Damage Tolerance Improvements

Various methods can be considered to enhance the damage tolerance of composite materials. Some of these methods are discussed in the following paragraphs.

The ability of the composite structures to tolerate impact damage is largely dependent on the fiber and matrix properties. The increase in matrix material fracture toughness greatly enhances the damage tolerance of the composites. Published data[13] indicates that the residual compressive strength of composites after impact is directly proportional to the mode 1 strain energy release rate, G_{IC}. In tests on the same reinforcement with different resins, a matrix (resin) with twice the value of G_{IC} showed a 50% improvement in residual strength after impact when compared with the base system.

The use of a tougher resin system or thermoplastic significantly improves damage tolerance. For example, G_{IC} of a typical thermoplastic material is approximately 1050 J m^{-2} compared with 180 J m^{-2} for an un-toughened epoxy material.

There are two distinctly different issues in relation to the influence of matrix toughness on impact damage: resistance to damage and residual strength in the presence of damage. Generally, composites with tough matrices are resistant to delamination damage, as measured by delamination size for given impact conditions. However, for a given area of impact damage, both brittle and tough composites suffer about the same degradation in residual strength.

Fiber properties significantly influence damage tolerance: the stiffer the fiber, the less damage tolerant it will be. Composites with hybrid fiber construction [that is, where some percentage of the carbon fibers are replaced by fibers with higher elongation-to-failure ratios, such as E-glass or aramid (Kevlar)] have been shown to have improved compression and tension strengths after impact. However, their basic undamaged properties, that is, strength and stiffness, are usually reduced.

Impacted laminates with higher percentages of plies oriented in the loading direction typically fail at lower strains than laminates with more off-axis plies. This is demonstrated in the case of open-hole strengths (Fig. 12.15). This shows typically how laminate strain-to-failure varies with lay-up and load orientation. Open-hole compression (OHC) and filled-hole tension (FHT) values are plotted against the percentages of bias plies in laminates. Similar data would be obtained from residual strength testing. This presentation is popular among several U.S. aerospace company design groups and is referred to as the angle-minus-loaded (AML) ply curve. It allows the establishment of relationships between lay-up and strength and enables projections and interpolations to be made, thus minimizing the testing that would otherwise be necessary. The horizontal axis is the percentage of bias ($\pm$ 45° plies) minus the percentage of on-axis (0° plies).

The designer needs to perform trade-off studies to optimize the lay-up; however, increasing percentages of softer plies in the load direction may improve the failure strain but reduce the load-carrying capability of the laminate. Even if failure occurs at a lower strain in a stiffer laminate, the higher modulus may result in higher stress-to-failure and thus higher load.

As noted earlier, laminated composites suffer from relatively poor through-thickness strength and stiffness. One of the more novel attempts to improve this is by through-thickness stitching of the fabric. Stitching is performed on a dry preform that is subsequently impregnated with resin using a liquid molding or RTM process (see Chapter 5). Stitching has been found to improve the

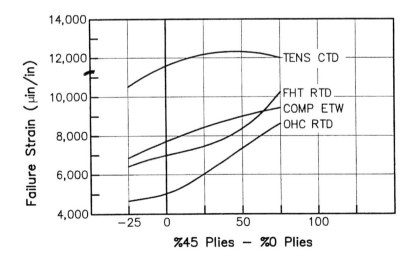

Fig. 12.15   Effect of lay-up on failure strain.

delamination fracture toughness[16] and in some cases, also improves the impact resistance and tolerance. Some studies[17] have shown little improvement in damage resistance (measurement of damage after impact) of composites (laminates 1–3.5 mm thick) made from stitched carbon woven fabrics compared with non-stitched fabric laminates. Stitching was shown to improve impact damage tolerance; however, this was offset by the reduction of undamaged compressive strength of the stitched laminate. The investigation of failure modes has revealed that stitching may offer benefits where unstitched damaged material fails by sub-laminate buckling. Where the failure mode is predominantly transverse, stitching does not provide any benefit.

Other textile preforming techniques such as knitting, braiding, and three-dimensional weaving also improve residual strength, however, again, their in-plane properties degrade appreciably. Composites with three dimensional reinforcement are discussed in Chapter 14.

12.5.9 Elevated Temperature and Moisture Exposure

Probably the most critical environmental exposure condition for composite materials is the effect of elevated temperature. This is particularly the case for composites with thermoset matrices because these polymers absorb moisture when exposed to hot-humid conditions, further reducing elevated temperature properties. Chapter 8 covers more fully the mechanics of property degradation under elevated temperatures and moisture absorption. Thermoplastic matrices, by contrast, absorb little moisture; however, they soften at elevated temperatures and are often vulnerable to chemical attack (see again Chapter 8).

Exposure extremes vary depending on the intended operation conditions, but typically chosen values for subsonic aircraft are 70 °C and 85% relative humidity. Under these conditions, thermoset composites will absorb up to 1% by weight of water over time with a corresponding reduction of glass-transition temperature, T_g, of around 25 °C. The moisture plasticises the matrix-reducing stiffness at elevated temperatures.

The effect of the matrix softening on the composite is a reduction in matrix-dominated properties, such as shear or compression strength. Figure 12.16 shows a comparison of the marked effect of temperature on compression strength for a typical thermoset composite and for comparison an aluminum alloy, where the loss in strength is seen to be minimal.

Because of the dramatic reduction in properties above T_g, the certification authorities specify a separation K between T_g and a maximum operating temperature of 25 °C (JAA) or 50° F MIL-HDBK 17 Figure 12.17.

It is normally required that property knockdowns for design are established after the material has become moisture saturated under the extreme operating conditions. Because of the slow absorption rate, particularly noticeable in thick specimens, conditioning can take many months. Recent efforts are investigating the possibility of testing a dry specimen under a higher temperature to

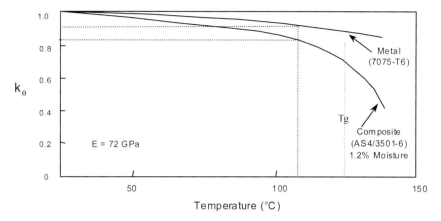

Fig. 12.16   Influence of temperature on compression strength of carbon/epoxy laminate. Adapted from Ref. 7.

compensate for the lack of moisture, however the validity of such an approach has not yet been proven.

Fiber-dominated properties, for example, tension strength, are not adversely affected by resin plasticization. In fact, the tensile properties of woven (crimped) materials are increased. However, fiber-dominated properties are adversely affected by embrittlement arising from exposure to very low temperatures. A typical tensile strength reduction for a carbon-fiber-reinforced plastic material exposed to temperatures existing at very high attitude is around 20–25%.

12.5.10   Lightning Effects

Carbon-fiber reinforced plastic composites are conducting materials, but because they have a significantly lower conductivity than aluminum alloys, the effect of direct lightning strikes is an issue of concern to airworthiness authorities. The severity of the electrical charge profiles[18,19] depend on whether the structure is in a zone of direct initial attachment, a "swept" zone of repeated attachments or in an area through which the current is being conducted. Survivability of structures in the direct attachment or swept zones will require some form of protection. The most effective methods involve the incorporation of a metal, bronze, copper, or aluminum, mesh, or foil co-bonded on the outer skin of the laminate. This mesh must make direct contact with the carbon-fiber material to be effective. Particular attention must be paid to the electrical bonding (connectivity) of the panel to the adjacent structure. Current will gravitate to points of high conductivity such as mechanical fasteners, and good electrical contact between the fastener, protective mesh, and subsequent electrical

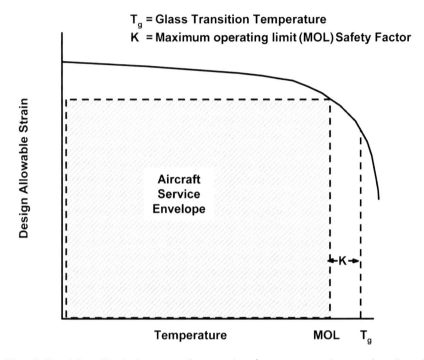

Fig. 12.17   Allowable design range for a carbon/epoxy composite as a function of strain and temperature. Adapted from Ref. 7.

path must be ensured. Severe burning around the fasteners will otherwise occur.

Composite panels with a suitable protective conducting coating in many cases out-perform thin-gauge aluminum alloy panels in terms of resistance to puncture by lightning.

12.6   Design Methodologies

The term *design* in relation to the design of composite structures refers to the process of establishing an appropriate laminate configuration (e.g., ply lay-up, built-up regions, etc.) to perform the given function. Functional requirements are usually given in terms of strength or stiffness. In the latter case, elastic properties can be reduced from coupon tests and laminate theory or the approximations thereto presented in Chapters 6 and 7. These properties can then be used to calculate strains, deflections and/or frequencies of vibration by standard techniques. Where it is necessary to base the design on a prescribed minimum strength, there are a number of analysis methods that can be used, each involving a different set of assumptions; these are discussed in Chapter 6. The choice of method will dictate the details of the laminate and qualification testing that will subsequently be required to validate or show that the various assumptions that have been made are adequately conservative.

A common assumption when analyzing rods and beams is that plane sections remain plane. In this case, for the condition of "no bending," strain is constant through the thickness, whereas stress varies from ply to ply depending on the modulus and orientation of each ply. For convenience, this leads to the use of strain analyses rather than stress analyses. Similarly, it is assumed that strains vary linearly through the thickness of plates in bending, an assumption that is reasonable, particularly for thin-shell aircraft structures. It enables the laminate to be treated as a homogeneous material and for the strains in the 1-1, 2-2, and 1-2 directions to be calculated (see Chapter 6). The simplest method of the subsequent strength prediction then introduces the assumption that the strength of any laminate is limited to a value pertaining when the strain in any one ply in the laminate exceeds a prescribed value. This is known as the first-ply failure method. Some variations of this method set the limiting value as a principal strain or maximum directional strain, whereas others base the ply failure on more complex relationships of bi-axial strain—see for example the Tsai-Hill criterion (also see Chapter 6). There has, long been debate over which of these criteria provide the best estimates of strength, however, this is likely to depend on the particular materials under consideration, the relative strains-to-failure of the reinforcement and matrix systems, and the loading. For many laminates, the maximum directional strain criterion is often used. Failure strain values are established from coupon tests on standard laminates in which the plies are orientated in the direction of the (uniaxial) load.

The more rigorous approach recognizes that the laminate strength is influenced by lay-up and stacking sequence. These influences are not altogether well understood. Some credit is given to differences in residual stresses remaining in the laminate after cure; however, predictions of residual stress and subsequent laminate strength do not always provide improved estimates. As it stands currently (if these effects are to be included) laminate capacities have to be established by tests on individual laminates. The difficulty with this approach is that there are often many different laminates in a single structure, and there may be several different load vectors applied. This means that each laminate may need to be tested under each loading combination, and to satisfy issues of variability, a number of coupons are required to establish each data point, leading to hundreds, and in some cases thousands, of tests. The larger companies have established such databases over long periods of time, and this explains the reluctance of many to change systems even when improved or cheaper materials become available.

The integration of testing into the overall design process is illustrated in Figure 12.18. (Note here the emphasis on trade-off studies that will establish an appropriate balance between cost and weight. These are essential if cost-effective design solutions are to result.)

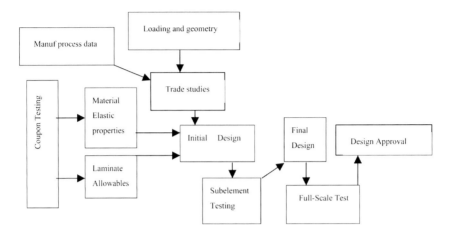

Fig. 12.18   An outline of the design process.

12.6.1   Use of Knockdown Factors

Figures 12.16, 12.19 to 12.21 illustrate property reductions of a typical composite material as compared with metal. As shown in the various figures, the knockdown factors used are:

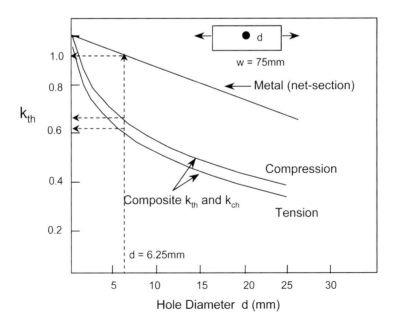

Fig. 12.19   Open-hole knockdown factors for quasi isotropic carbon/epoxy laminates compared with aluminum alloy. Adapted from Ref. 7.

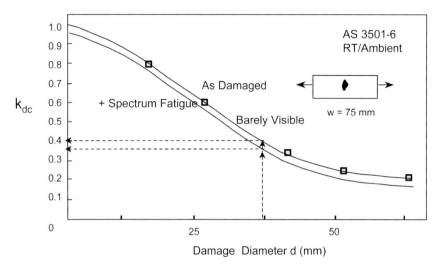

Fig. 12.20   Knockdown factor compression residual strength for impact damaged carbon/epoxy laminate after spectrum loading. Adapted from Ref. 7.

k_θ: *temperature;* k_{th}, k_{ch}: *open-hole tension and compression, respectively;* k_{dc}, k_{dt}: *impact damage tension and compression, respectively.*

The values to be attributed to these knockdowns will vary with material and lay-up, and the values provided in these figures are only a guide.

It is a common practice to multiply these factors to obtain combined affects. For example, in the case of a combined factor for a specimen with a 6.25 mm open hole, the compression allowable under hot/wet conditions would be:

$$k_{ch\theta} = k_{ch} \times k_\theta = 0.65 \times 0.85 = 0.55$$

Combining these factors in this manner tends to be highly conservative and for this reason is generally acceptable to airworthiness authorities.

Typical maximum strain values used in design are between 4000–5000 microstrain (strain $\times 10^6$) in tension and 3000–4000 microstrain compression. These values take into account combinations of environmental conditioning and impact damage or other stress concentrations.

In addition to point strain, other potential failure modes such as local and general instability (buckling), interlaminar strain, and bearing require consideration. Local instabilities by themselves may not be limits to load capacity; however, their presence will elevate point strains due to local bending and ultimately the maximum allowable ply strains may be exceeded. Non-linear finite element analyses are required for investigation of these conditions. Chapters 6 and 16 provide further information on this topic.

In the case of carbon/epoxy laminates, if the static strength has been established with due account for knockdown effects and the usual ultimate/limit load factor, it is not usually necessary to consider fatigue because the design limit

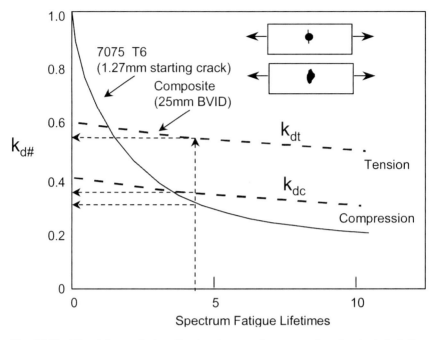

Fig. 12.21   Knockdown factor for tension- and compression-dominated fatigue spectrum loading following BVID for a carbon/epoxy laminate compared with an aluminum alloy with cracked fastener hole. Adapted from Ref. 7.

stresses will be below the fatigue limit of the laminate. This is not, however, the case for glass-fiber-reinforced composites. A discussion on fatigue properties of composite materials and structures is given in Chapter 8.

12.7   A Value Engineering Approach to the Use of Composite Materials

The demands of today's marketplace for new aircraft are significantly different from the past, where the pressure was to improve performance to deliver operational benefits. What both commercial and military aircraft operators now seek is a significant reduction in the initial purchase price of aircraft. Additionally, the ability to rapidly evolve an aircraft variant to meet an emerging niche application or opportunity is highly desirable. The latter has implications for material selection and new product development times.

The aircraft industry is going through a global rationalization of suppliers while product variety is increasing in a similar way to the automotive industry, and most large aircraft manufacturers are modelling their approach to the market and their suppliers on the automotive industry. With regard to composite materials, this means (for a given application) providing a comparable or better performance at a reduced cost in a shorter time.

12.7.1 Cost/Performance Trade-Offs

Composite structures have clearly been cost-effective in enhancing aircraft performance because their weight fraction in aircraft has steadily increased with time. But compared with standard aluminum alloys, they are relatively expensive, therefore there is continued price competition from metal com-ponents, particularly those produced by improved manufacturing methods. Further, it is believed that current design approaches do not fully utilize the potential of the unique material properties of these composites.

Table 12.1 provides cost and other property data for typical competing aircraft materials. This data has been obtained from several sources and is only accurate to the first order. The k terms are the knockdown factors described in Section 12.6.1.

C_r and C are the raw material cost and finished component cost (neglecting scrap), respectively. Note that these values have been obtained from one aircraft manufacturing company at one point in time and are reproduced here only as a guide to the approach that should be taken to material trade-studies.

Both the underlying material price and how efficiently material is processed are issues. Many metal components in modern aircraft are produced in high-speed machining centers where material removal can be achieved very rapidly. This has the effect of encouraging large amounts of scrap, for example, when a wing rib is hogged out of an aluminum alloy billet. Typically up to 90% of the material is removed, and consequently, the real cost per kilogram of the fly-away material is 10 times the raw material cost. In examples such as these, composite materials can be very cost-effective provided that the subsequent processing costs can be minimized. In other cases, the raw material costs can still rule out the composite materials option.

The following is an example of a typical approach to evaluating the effectiveness of a material choice for a given application.

A list of typical aircraft components is listed in Table 12.2 together with each component's design failure modes and the percentage of its weight contribution to the overall structure. Note that a fighter aircraft has been chosen in this example. For transport or other aircraft categories, the failure modes will be much the same, however, the weight percentages will be somewhat different.

12.7.1.1 Weight-Saving as a Function of Failure Mode. The starting point of this analysis is Table 12.1, based on the analysis developed in Eckvall et al.[21] for comparing two materials 1 and 2 for weight-saving. Material 1 is the benchmark and is taken here to be aluminum alloy 2024 T3. Material 2 is any of the other referenced materials.

The thickness, and therefore the weight, of each component of the airframe is determined by the primary loading it is required to support and the design failure modes. No alternative failure mode under these loads can be any weaker; if it is, then the thickness (and therefore the weight) must be based on this alternative mode.

Table 12.1   Properties Assumed for Candidate Airframe Materials

Material Type	Code	C_R $/Kg	C $/Kg	ρ Kgm^{-3}	E GPa	σ_e MPa	k_{ht}	k_{hc}	k_{dt}	k_{dc}	k_θ
Al Alloy	2024T3	10	229	2800	72	325	0.94	0.94	0.31	0.94	0.90
Al Alloy	7075 T76	10	229	2796	72	483	0.94	0.94	0.29	0.94	0.90
Al Alloy	A357	5	58	2800	72	276	0.94	0.94	0.30	0.94	0.90
Al/Li Alloy	8090 T3X	50	329	2530	80	329	0.94	0.94	0.39	0.94	0.90
Ti Alloy	Ti6Al4V	300	398	4436	110	902	0.94	0.94	0.20	0.94	1.00
Al Laminate	GLARE 1	100	550	2520	65	545	0.94	0.94	0.69	0.90	0.85
Carbon/epoxy	3501/6	160	788	1600	67	736	0.61	0.65	0.55	0.38	0.83
Carbon/epoxy	3501/6	160	788	1600	80	880	0.55	0.62	0.55	0.38	0.83

Table 12.2 Typical Fighter Aircraft Structural Breakdown (Based on Ref. 20)

Category	Component	% Of Structure	Design Failure Mode
1	Lower wing skin, wing-attachment lugs, longerons	18.6	Tensile strength
2	Upper wing skin	3.5	Compressive strength
3	Spar caps, rib caps	19.5	Crippling
4	Wing upper surface	9.7	Column and crippling (compression surface)
5	Horizontal tail torsion box	18.1	Buckling (compression or shear)
6	Fin torsion box, aft fuselage	11.6	Aeroelastic stiffness
7	Fin box	19.0	Durability and damage tolerance

The equations used for each failure mode are based on the equations provided in Ref. 20, but expressed in terms of the knockdown factors. The terms S_1 and S_2 represent any of the mechanical properties, and ρ_1 and ρ_2 represent their respective densities.

Using the data from Table 12.2 with the equations in Table 12.3, the weight ratio W_1/W_2 for each of the failure modes can be estimated. These data are provided in Table 12.4, where the lowest value is the most desirable. It is seen that the carbon-fiber-reinforced plastic composites are generally the optimum choice. This is particularly true for optimally designed orthotropic laminates (O), however this remains generally the case even for the less-than-optimum quasi isotropic (QI) ply configuration. The exception is for damage tolerance in compression where the carbon-fiber composite is similar to the standard aluminum alloy.

12.7.2 Cost Value Analysis of Weight-Saving

Unfortunately, it is not sufficient to choose a material based on weight-saving alone; the cost must also be considered. The value of saving a kilogram of weight will depend on the actual application, and for the relative comparison made here, the values provided in Table 1.2 in are used.

The analysis of the value of weight-saving is made as follows. For material 2, let the required thickness per unit area,

$$t_2 = t_1 \left(\frac{S_1}{S_2}\right)^n$$

[Note: For tensile, compressive strength and aeroelastic stiffness $n = 1$, whereas for buckling, $n = 1/3$.]

Table 12.3   Weight Ratio Equations for Various Failure Categories (Based on Ref. 20)

Category	Failure Mode	Weight Ratio (W_2/W_1)
1	Tensile strength	$\dfrac{\rho_2}{\rho_1}\dfrac{\sigma_{e_1}}{\sigma_{e_2}}\left[\dfrac{k_{th1}}{k_{th2}}\dfrac{k_{\theta1}}{k_{\theta2}}\right]$
2	Compressive strength	$\dfrac{\rho_2}{\rho_1}\dfrac{\sigma_{e_1}}{\sigma_{e_2}}\left[\dfrac{k_{ch1}}{k_{ch2}}\dfrac{k_{\theta1}}{k_{\theta2}}\right]$
3	Crippling	$\dfrac{\rho_2}{\rho_1}\left[\dfrac{E_{s_1}\sigma_{e_1}}{E_{s_2}\sigma_{e_2}}\right]^{0.25}$
4	Compression surface column and crippling	$\dfrac{\rho_2}{\rho_1}\left[\dfrac{E_{s_1}E_{t_1}\sigma_{e_1}}{E_{s_2}E_{t_2}\sigma_{e_2}}\right]^{0.2}$
5	Buckling compression and shear	$\dfrac{\rho_2}{\rho_1}\left[\dfrac{E_1}{E_2}\right]^{\frac{1}{3}}$
6	Aeroelastic stiffness	$\dfrac{\rho_2}{\rho_1}\dfrac{E_1}{E_2}$
7	Durability and damage tolerance	$\dfrac{\rho_2}{\rho_1}\dfrac{\sigma_{e_1}}{\sigma_{e_2}}\left[\dfrac{k_{d1}k_{\theta1}}{k_{d2}k_{\theta2}}\right]$

Then, the weight change per unit area

$$\Delta W = W_1 - W_2 = t_1\rho_1 - t_2\rho_2$$

Substituting for t_2,

$$\Delta W = t_1\left(\rho_1 - \left(\frac{S_1}{S_2}\right)^n \rho_2\right)$$

The cost change per unit area

$$\Delta C = t_1\rho_1 C_1 - t_2\rho_2 C_2$$

where C_1 or C_2 is cost per unit weight and ΔC is cost change per unit area. Substituting again for t_2,

$$\Delta C = t_1\left(\rho_1 C_1 - \left(\frac{S_1}{S_2}\right)^n \rho_2 C_2\right)$$

Thus, the cost per unit weight change is

$$\frac{\Delta C}{\Delta W} = \frac{\left(\rho_1 C_1 - \left(\frac{S_1}{S_2}\right)^n \rho_2 C_2\right)}{\left(\rho_1 - \left(\frac{S_1}{S_2}\right)^n \rho_2\right)} = C_W$$

Table 12.4 Weight Ratios for Candidate Airframe Materials for the Various Failure Categories

Material Type	Code	Weight Ratio $(S_1/S_2)^n(\rho_2/\rho_1)$						
		Cat 1	Cat 2	Cat 3	Cat 5	Cat 6	Cat 7a	Cat 7b
Aluminum alloy	2024T3	1.0	1.0	1.0	1.0	1.0	1.0	1.0
Aluminum alloy	7075 T76	0.7	0.7	0.9	0.9	1.0	0.7	0.7
Aluminum alloy	A357	1.2	1.2	1.0	1.1	1.0	1.2	1.2
Aluminum lithium	8090 T3X	0.9	0.9	0.9	0.9	0.8	0.7	0.9
Titanium alloy	Ti6Al4V	0.5	0.5	1.1	1.0	1.0	0.8	0.5
Aluminum laminate	GLARE 1	0.6	0.6	0.8	0.8	1.0	0.3	0.6
Carbon/epoxy	3501/6 QI	0.4	0.4	0.5	0.4	0.6	0.2	0.7
Carbon/epoxy	3501/6 O	0.4	0.3	0.4	0.4	0.5	0.1	0.6

Let the value of unit weight saved be C_V using the data provided in Table 1.1 in units of \$/kg.

[Note: Compared with C_1 and C_2, the values for C_V, are taken as negative. All costs are in \$/kg.]

Thus, to break even: $C_W = -C_V$

Then

$$-C_V = \frac{\left(\rho_1 C_1 - \left(\dfrac{S_1}{S_2} \right)^n \rho_2 C_2 \right)}{\left(\rho_1 - \left(\dfrac{S_1}{S_2} \right)^n \rho_2 \right)}$$

This leads to

$$\frac{W_2}{W_1} = \frac{\rho_2}{\rho_1} \left(\frac{S_1}{S_2} \right)^n = \left(\frac{C_1 + C_V}{C_2 + C_V} \right)$$

Thus, the difference between cost ratio and weight ratio is an index of value. The difference is zero for break even, positive for better than break even, and negative for worse than break even, with the magnitude giving an indication of the degree in each of the non-zero cases.

Finally, Table 12.5 presents the results of these calculations for the fighter aircraft applications chosen here as an example.

Although the above analysis indicates the trade-off between acquisition cost and structural performance, it should also be noted that through-life support costs will also have a bearing on the final selection. As previously indicated, well-designed composite structures can be expected to be more durable than metal structures; however, conversely, they can be more costly to repair.

Further material adoption might be approached from two perspectives:

(1) As operational experience builds confidence in non-aerospace materials, these materials, or the processes used to make them, may be adapted for aerospace use.

(2) As an aerospace material becomes more widely used, volume factors may help reduce the price.

In addition to reducing material cost, it is also necessary to minimize material usage for a given application. Composite materials have finite shelf lives and purchasing and production must be managed to ensure that all stock is consumed in a timely fashion. This becomes an issue in providing support for low-volume production or out-of-production items. The other factor related to consumption is the minimization of scrap, both in production components and in off-cuts and process-related consumable materials (e.g., bagging film). Here again, pursuing closer associations with customers and suppliers to optimize the formulation of composite materials within the specification and to deliver configurations that help optimize utilization is appropriate.

Table 12.5 Value Indices for a Typical Fighter Aircraft

Material type	Code				(Cost Ratio–Weight Ratio) Fighter			
		Cat 1	Cat 2	Cat 3	Cat 5	Cat 6	Cat 7a	Cat 7b
Aluminum alloy	2024T3	0.0	0.0	0.0	0.0	0.0	0.0	0.0
Aluminum alloy	7075 T76	0.3	0.3	0.1	0.1	0.0	0.3	0.3
Aluminum alloy	A357	0.2	0.2	0.4	0.4	0.4	0.2	0.2
Aluminum lithium	8090 T3X	0.0	0.0	0.0	0.0	0.0	0.1	0.0
Titanium alloy	Ti6Al4V	0.3	0.3	-0.3	-0.2	-0.3	0.0	0.3
Aluminum laminate	GLARE 1	0.1	0.1	-0.2	-0.1	-0.4	0.4	0.0
Carbon/Epoxy	3501/6 Q	0.1	0.1	0.0	0.1	-0.1	0.4	-0.2
Carbon/Epoxy	3501/6 O	0.1	0.2	0.1	0.1	0.0	0.4	-0.1

There is also an issue in relation to the disposal of composite material waste. Metal waste has some residual sale value and can be recycled. This is not currently the position with most composite materials.

12.8   Conclusion

There is an increasing amount of applications for composite materials in aircraft structures; however, their very different properties from traditional metallic materials need to be thoroughly understood to produce a satisfactory design. The increasing scrutiny of costs means that careful consideration must be given to the total cost of ownership before deciding on a particular application.

In the aerospace industry, companies do not have full freedom to choose the materials to be used in a particular design. The costs of testing and analysis needed to qualify a new material are high, and this can lead to an impasse, even where lower-cost or higher-performance possibilities emerge.

As indicated, material costs typical for airframe alloys can be significantly lower than for composite materials. Further, metal products can be produced by automated processes with minimal quality assurance testing required, thus reducing the labor cost of manufacture. Many composites manufacturing processes remain labor intensive and require extensive non-destructive testing, therefore process cost issues are also critical to broader composite structure applications and usage.

References

[1]Niu, M. C., *Composite Airframe Structures*, Comilit Press Ltd, Hong Kong, 1992.

[2]Middleton, D. H., (ed), *Composite Materials in Aircraft Structures*, Longmans, UK, 1990.

[3]Ilcewitcz, L. B., Hoffman, D. J., and Fawcett, A. J., "Composite Applications in Commercial Airframe Structures Section 6.07," *Comprehensive Composite Materials*, edited by A. Kelly and C. Zweben, Elsevier, 2000.

[4]Harris, C. H., Starnes, J. H., Jr., and Shuart, M. J., "Design and Manufacture of Aerospace Composite Structures, State-of-the-Art Assessment," *Journal of Aircraft*, Vol. 39, 2002, pp. 545–560.

[5]Mills, A. R., "Manufacturing Technology for Aerospace Composite Structures," *The Aeronautical Journal*, Vol. 100, 1996, pp. 539–545.

[6]Dexter, H. B., *Innovative Textile Reinforced Composite Materials for Aircraft Structures*, 28th International SAMPE Technical Conference, Nov. 1996.

[7]Whitehead, R. S., *Certification of Primary Composite Aircraft Structures*, 14th Symposium of the International Conference on Aeronautical Fatigue (ICAF), June 1987.

[8]Humphreys, E. A., and Rosen, B. W., "Engineering Materials Handbook," Vol. 1, *Composites*, ASM International.

[9]Kedward, K., "Generic Approaches and Issues for Structural Design and Application," *Comprehensive Composite Materials*, edited by A. Kelly and C. Zweben, Elsevier, 2000, Sec. 6:15.

[10]MIL-STD-210C.

[11]Naval Air Engineering Center, NAEC Report 92–136.

[12]Rouse, Amber, Bodine, Dopke, *Evaluation of a Sandwich Fuselage Side Panel with Damage and Subjected to Internal Pressure*, Feb. 1997, NASA TM 110309.

[13]Horton, R. E., and McCartney, J. E., "Damage Tolerance of Composites," *Composite Materials Analysis and Design*, 1984, pp. 260–267.

[14]Khan, H. P. "Enhanced Reliability Prediction Methodology for Impact Damaged Structures," DOT/FAA/AR-97-79, Oct. 1998.

[15]Ilcewitcz, L. B., "Composites Technology Development for Commercial Airframe Structures," *Comprehensive Composite Materials*, edited by A. Kelly and C. Zweben Elsevier, 2000, Sec. 6:08.

[16]Jain, G., and Mai, Y. W., "Mode 1 Delamination Toughness of Laminated Composites with Through-Thickness Reinforcement," *Applied Composite Materials*, Vol. 1, 1994.

[17]Herszberg, I., Bannister, M. K., Leong, K. H., and Falzon, P. J., "Research in Textile Composites at the CRC-ACS Ltd.," *Journal of the Textile Institute*, Vol. 88, Part 3, 1997.

[18]"Lightning Qualification Test Technique for Aerospace Vehicles and Hardware." MIL-STD-1757A.

[19]"Lightning Test Waveforms and Technique for Aerospace Vehicles and Hardware," SAE AE4L, 20 June 1978.

[20]Eckvall, J. C., Rhodes, J. E., and Wald, G. G., "Methodology for Evaluating Weight Savings from Basic Materials Properties," *Design of Fatigue and Fracture Resistant Structures*, edited by P. R. Abelkis and C. M. Hudson, ASTM STP 761, 1982.

13
Airworthiness Considerations For Airframe Structures

13.1 Overview

Airworthiness is often thought to mean little more than how safe an aircraft is to fly, rather than a more appropriate and specific definition such as: "safe to meet the operational needs of the ... user."[1] Attaining satisfactory airworthiness requires that conflicting design characteristics be balanced to enhance the level of safety inherent in an aircraft type and is a key factor in design. In the past, aircraft development tended to focus only on developing adequate aerodynamic performance and structural strength, with the by-product hopefully being a "safe" aircraft. Contemporary design practices, however, place airworthiness considerations alongside performance, operational effectiveness, reliability, maintainability, and economy—all are important in determining the success of an in-service product.[2]

One of the earliest examples of airworthiness regulation was the 1916 publication of a pamphlet detailing design requirements for military aircraft during World War I by the Royal Aircraft Factory. And although this publication was little more than a list of strength requirements for early aircraft, it became the forerunner of the first British airworthiness regulations. In February 1940, the British Air Ministry formed the Joint Airworthiness Committee to collect all technical design instructions (including the derivations of the original 1916 document) into a single publication. This new document, rather than being prescriptive in its requirements, was to provide an unambiguous statement of the aim of each regulation rather than the detail of how the aim should be achieved. This approach of providing airworthiness regulations that state a required outcome, rather than the method by which the outcome is to be achieved, remains in practice today in both military[3,4] and commercial airworthiness authorities.[5]

Preceding chapters have addressed the technical concerns raised by the use of composite materials in aircraft structures. The critical step between these concerns and delivery of the final product is the demonstration of an acceptable safety performance. This issue has, in the case of metallic structures, been addressed by certification procedures developed as much by experience as science. An example of the combination of science and experience in the development of airworthiness regulation can be found in the derivation of the safety factor applied to full-scale fatigue test results by the U.S. Navy (USN).[6]

A purely analytical approach to the problem of reducing test-demonstrated-lives to in-service-lives with an acceptable low likelihood of failure would lead to a factor approaching three. But through examination of decades of aircraft usage data and a measure of engineering judgement, the USN rationalized the use, to a factor of two. Because advanced composite structures are relatively new to the aviation industry, the development of certification procedures must necessarily rely less on experience and more on the mechanics of the composite.

Initial attempts to certify composite structures simply adopted those requirements already existing for metals without recognizing the inherent differences between the two materials, even though these differences can significantly affect airworthiness considerations. For example, under static loading, composites typically exhibit linear elastic behavior to failure and are extremely sensitive to stress concentrations. In contrast, metals, with a few rare exceptions, exhibit plastic behavior above a yield stress and are not notch sensitive under static conditions. Another example of where significant differences exist between composite and metallic structures is in their damage tolerance under compressive loading. Advanced composite structures are much more sensitive to damage, and for this reason there has been an increased requirement on toughness in newly developed composite systems. Typically, certification guidelines deal with the issue of damage-tolerance in composites by requiring new designs to be based on the assumption that damage at the inspection threshold is initially present in the material.

Yet another critical difference includes damage growth due to fatigue. This often represents a critical design condition in metals, whereas composites typically show excellent resistance to such loading. The stress levels associated with design critical load cases in composite materials, such as compression in the presence of impact damage, have traditionally been low enough to ensure that the damage does not grow due to fatigue. Thus, designs in composite materials have typically been determined by static considerations rather than by fatigue.[2] As designers strive to fully use the specific strength and stiffness advantages of composites, the stress levels within components will increase, and fatigue issues must necessarily be given greater consideration in the airworthiness of future aircraft.

Perhaps the most critical difference between composites and metals is in their varying performance under different operational environments. The degradation of composite structures under certain environmental conditions has led to a number of standard certification approaches.[7] Essentially, it is necessary to establish the critical material properties after exposure to the extreme thermal and moisture environments to which the structure will be subjected. In addition, it must be demonstrated that there would be no degradation after exposure to chemicals that can be present (e.g., hydraulic fluid, fuel, and de-icing fluids).

Composites based on thermosetting matrices generally demonstrate significant sensitivity to absorbed moisture (the level of which in a thermosetting resin is proportional to atmospheric humidity) and temperature. Most engineering composites (typically epoxy based) can absorb up to one percent by weight of moisture in a normal aircraft-operational environment. The moisture softens the matrix resin, reducing those composite properties dependent on the resin, such as shear and compression stiffness and strength. This effect is particularly apparent at elevated temperatures, when the matrix is additionally softened. The simultaneous inclusion of environmental effects with structural testing of full-scale components has been demonstrated previously,[8] although such testing has generally been seen as prohibitively expensive. An alternative technique to account for the decreased performance of composites at elevated temperature and humidity is to increase the applied loads in structural tests conducted at room temperature and humidity. Unfortunately, this often leads to additional problems and typically prevents the clearance of hybrid metallic and composite constructions because the stress factoring necessary to evaluate the composite structure increases the risk of premature and unrepresentative failure in the metallic components.[9,10]

The U.S. Federal Aviation Authority (FAA) has developed a document, FAA AC 20-107A[7] that describes an acceptable means of demonstrating compliance to the FAA airworthiness certification requirements for composite structures. The document describes the additional considerations that must be given specifically to the certification of composite structures and includes topics such as:

- Effects of the operational environment on material properties and fabrication techniques
- Static strength with consideration of operational environments, repeated loading, impact damage, and material variability
- Fatigue (safe-life) and damage tolerance (fail-safe) evaluation

There are also several additional considerations including flutter, flammability, lightning protection, quality control, maintenance, and repair.

In AC 20-107A, the crucial issue of adequately considering environmental effects is addressed by allowing either full-scale testing under environmental conditions or testing through a "building-block" approach. The latter method is by far the most commonly used, because of its lower cost, but still involves extensive design development testing to 1) establish environmental and scatter knockdown (or load enhancement) factors for strength-critical failure modes, and 2) validate critical design features.

Full-scale testing will also be required, but under ambient temperature/dry conditions.

The major issues affecting the airworthiness of composite structures, are the static and fatigue strengths, effect of environmental exposure, damage tolerance, and flammability.

In this chapter, typical certification procedures for metallic airframe structures are briefly outlined. This is followed by a consideration of the significant differences between metals and composites for aircraft applications and the resulting requirement for the modified procedures. Methods of extracting design allowables from test data are then discussed and procedures for certificating composite structures are outlined.

13.2   Certification of Airframe Structures

The following fundamental requirements have been developed around the experiences of metallic airframes and remain the basis for the certification of composite airframe structures. These require that the structure (by test and/or analysis) demonstrate the following capabilities:

- **Static strength:**
  - Design limit load (DLL), no failure or unacceptable deformations. DLL is normally the maximum load anticipated to be placed on the structure in its lifetime.
  - Design ultimate load (DUL), no failure, although limited permanent deformation is acceptable; DUL = DLL × 1.5 (generally).
- **Fatigue strength:**
  - *Safe life approach:* No significant cracking that could lead to failure should occur in the life of the airframe. This approach was used in design of most of the metallic structure in the older fighter aircraft, and is still used for USN fighter aircraft, such as the F-18, and generally in helicopters.
    or
  - *Fail-safe approaches:*
    > *A. Alternate load path:* The structure is damage tolerant in that cracking may occur but will not reduce strength below an acceptable level before being detected. This requirement is generally met by multi-load-path design where, should one load path fail, the remaining load paths can continue to provide the required level of residual strength until the damage is detected. This approach is generally used in the structure of large military transport and civil aircraft.
    or
    > *B. Slow crack growth approach:* The structure is damage tolerant in that cracking may occur, but cracks will grow slowly and will not cause failure for the full life of the structure *or* will not cause failure before detection by planned inspection (safety by inspection). This approach can be applied to single-load-path structure, where failure would be catastrophic. Damage-tolerant design for single-load-path structure is based on the assumed presence of flaws at critical locations. This is the design approach adopted for modern U.S. Air Force fighter aircraft, such as F-16.
- **Damage tolerance general requirement:**
  - The strength will not fall below an acceptable level (typically 1.2 × DLL) due to representative damage to the structure (e.g., caused by fatigue cracking, corrosion, or accidental mechanical contact) before being detected. Critical damage must be of a size that can be detected with a high degree of probability.
- **Durability/economic requirement:**
  - For the life of the airframe, damage requiring costly repairs will not occur, for example, due to fatigue or corrosion. Note that this is not a regulated

airworthiness requirement mandated by the airworthiness authority; however, it is often prescribed by the customer of military aircraft and is an important consideration in the choice of fleet by a civil airline.

Although composite structures are required to demonstrate the same level of safety as a metallic structure, the means of compliance has to take into account the differences in material behavior discussed in preceding chapters.

Design of the airframe for static strength first involves a detailed structural analysis, usually using a structural finite-element (F-E) model, and second involves a test program on specimens of increasing complexity, from simple coupons to structural elements and full-scale structures, as illustrated in Figure 13.1. Coupon and structural element tests are used to obtain material and structural allowables for design and must therefore interrogate all critical loading

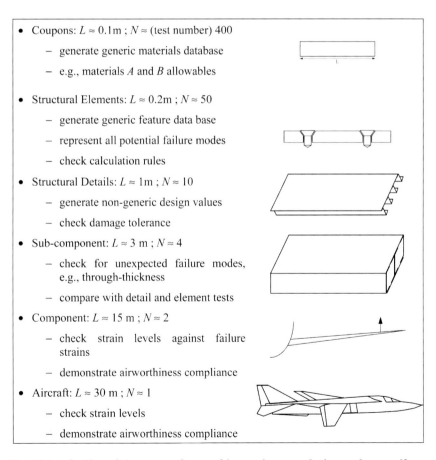

- Coupons: $L \approx 0.1$m ; $N \approx$ (test number) 400

    - generate generic materials database

    - e.g., materials A and B allowables

- Structural Elements: $L \approx 0.2$m ; $N \approx 50$

    - generate generic feature data base

    - represent all potential failure modes

    - check calculation rules

- Structural Details: $L \approx 1$m ; $N \approx 10$

    - generate non-generic design values

    - check damage tolerance

- Sub-component: $L \approx 3$ m ; $N \approx 4$

    - check for unexpected failure modes, e.g., through-thickness

    - compare with detail and element tests

- Component: $L \approx 15$ m ; $N \approx 2$

    - check strain levels against failure strains

    - demonstrate airworthiness compliance

- Aircraft: $L \approx 30$ m ; $N \approx 1$

    - check strain levels

    - demonstrate airworthiness compliance

Fig. 13.1.   Outline of the range of tests of increasing complexity used to certify an airframe structure made predominantly from composite material.

conditions and potential failure modes; the other tests are essentially for proof of structure. These tests are outlined in the following sections.

13.3   The Development of Design Allowables

Design allowables have to be established at the most critical environmental conditions. "Hot/wet" and "cold/dry" extremes are the most critical. Because coupons and structural details are generally small, there are no major difficulties in moisture-conditioning them. To ensure conservativeness, airworthiness authorities generally require full moisture-saturation at the highest anticipated operating temperature (typically of the order of a 1% weight increase). Special attention must be given to matrix-dominated failure modes, because these are most prone to degradation.

Sufficient coupon tests are conducted on the main laminate patterns to establish the allowable values for the critical temperature/moisture combinations in addition to the room temperature values. As well as establishing design allowables, these tests also provide knockdown factors (i.e., reduction factors). A comparison of, say, the room temperature/dry value and the hot/wet value of an allowable provides an environmental knockdown factor. Similarly, comparison of any mean value with its associated allowable value provides a variability knockdown factor.

A limited number of structural detail tests are made to confirm these allowables at the worst environmental conditions. These tests generally include open- and filled-hole tension and compression and bolt-bearing, including load bypass. Tests should also include details representative of areas of out-of-plane loading, such as stiffener run-outs.

The development of design allowables from coupons and structural details is a very important and costly component of the design and certification process. This is particularly the case for composites because of the high scatter in most mechanical properties.

13.3.1   Static Strength Allowables

Airframe static strength design is based on coupon and structural detail data that allows for statistical variation or scatter in strength. Two statistical levels of allowable values are possible:

- **A-allowable**—value achieved by 99% of the population at the 99% confidence level
- **B-allowable**—value achieved by 90% of the population at the 95% confidence level

To determine these allowables, the statistical model that best fits the property distribution is first determined. For metals, the distribution is generally normal or (for fatigue) log-normal. When dealing with composites, the first model evaluated is usually the two-parameter Weibull distribution (because it is a more physically realistic model for brittle materials) followed by the normal and then the log-normal.

An important economic aspect in testing is the estimation[11] of the minimum number of specimens that need to be tested to obtain acceptable allowables. This depends on the statistical parameters. Testing can be reduced significantly if the distribution parameters are already known.

The choice of which allowable to work with depends on the particular application. For materials with a low scatter, such as airframe alloys, the A-allowable strength is often used because this obviously offers the greatest margin of safety, but in cases in which scatter is large, this may impose too great a penalty on useable strength. The B-allowable strength is also appropriate for fail-safe or multiple-load-path design. For composites, the B-allowable is generally used because of the relatively high scatter on strength.

If service requirements can lead to a further reduction in static strength, the allowable static strength may be reduced by multiplying by knockdown factors. A similar procedure can be used to obtain allowables for structural details. As discussed in Chapter 8, several knockdown factors may be applied to coupon data to obtain the final design allowables.

This approach, inherently conservative, avoids exhaustive testing that would be needed to develop allowables for all conceivable conditions and designs. It is generally assumed that the scatter is unchanged from that obtained when deriving the allowables.

13.3.2 Fatigue Allowables

For development of the fatigue or durability allowables, composite coupons and structural elements are tested under constant amplitude and also under spectrum loading representative of expected service conditions. To simulate the most environmentally degraded condition, some testing will be conducted at elevated temperatures with the coupons appropriately moisturized.

The fatigue tests at constant amplitude cycling provide basic data for assessment of spectrum loading behavior and establish load discrimination levels—the load levels that can be neglected in the test spectrum. In addition, constant amplitude testing provides information on environmental effects.

The main feature of fatigue is that scatter is significantly greater than for most other mechanical properties, so many more of these time-consuming tests are required to obtain the allowable values. Fiber composites have a very flat S-N curve (stress versus number of cycles to failure) compared with metals because they are highly resistant to fatigue (see Chapter 8).

Significant damage growth generally occurs only at strain levels above 60% of the static strength. However, once growth commences, its progression is generally rapid, often catastrophic. Thus unlike metals, the slow growth option for composites is not considered possible, therefore damage growth data are rarely obtained.

A similar situation holds for bonded joints for which the rate of damage growth can also be rapid, and tests are generally made to establish the threshold for damage growth (see Chapter 9).

It is generally found that when the various knockdown factors are applied to the static strength obtained from the coupon data, the resulting design allowables are sufficient to provide an adequate margin for in-plane strength degradation under cyclic loading. However, this may not be sufficient to allow for strength degradation in some types of joint.

13.3.3   Influence of Damage on Allowables

For damage-tolerant design, the reduction in the strength allowables caused by impact damage, over the range of likely energy levels, must be quantified. As discussed in Chapter 8, the most severe loss in static strength occurs under compression loading; Chapter 7 describes the testing approach used for simple coupons.

Cyclic loading at representative strain levels can cause further loss in allowable static compression strength as well as limited damage growth and therefore will also require evaluation.

It is important in the setting of design allowables to assess the influence of impact damage on structural details such as ply run-outs and panels with stiffeners because the location of the damage is very important. When impact damage is located between stiffeners, failure can occur in two stages if the damage exceeds a threshold,[12] the first being rapid growth of the damage to the stiffener, followed somewhat later by failure of the stiffeners. Damage inflicted at a stiffener run-out can result in early loss of the stiffener.

13.4   Demonstration of Static Strength

The same broad program for a metal structure is generally followed for a composite structure. Attention has to be paid to the significant differences, as discussed in the preceding sections. A large number of coupon and element tests are performed, as previously discussed, to provide generic design data and to assess the effect of the operational environment and damage on the materials and details used in the complete structure. They are also used to check safe strain levels in sub-components, components, and the full-scale test.

Fewer sub-component level tests (see Fig. 13.1), are used to refine the predictions made for the complete structure from the results of the element and coupon testing and to validate critical design features. Certification usually culminates in one or two room-temperature ambient, full-scale static and fatigue tests. Environmental effects are accounted for in either the testing or the analysis of the test results.[13] This building-block approach to composite certifi-cation is commonly used for both military[14] and commercial aircraft and helicopters.[10,12,15–17]

13.4.1   Structural Detail and Sub-component Tests

Structural detail tests and sub-component tests are made to develop non-generic data related to the specific design. The structural details, elements, and sub-components selected for test will initially be based on the predictions of the finite element model. They are then statistically tested to failure under the most severe environmental conditions and the failure strain measured. These tests establish the mean values of ultimate strains in the environmentally degraded condition. (Because of the size constraints of sub-components, these are usually tested at ambient conditions and knockdown factors applied from coupon tests.) It is also important to note the region and nature of the failure and to ensure that the structural detail tests relevant to the region demonstrate the same failure mode. If this is not the case, then such tests must be repeated with appropriate adjustments to the loading or constraints. Then, assuming that the scatter in the structural element and sub-component tests are the same as those in the detail tests, application of the variability knockdown factor to the mean values determined gives allowable values for the full-scale structure in the environmentally degraded condition.

An important economic issue is the time required to develop a representative moisture distribution. Depending on the thickness of the composite structure, this may take from several weeks to several months.

13.4.2   Full-Scale Tests

The full-scale test is very important, as any secondary stresses (for example, from out-of-plane loading) will be correctly represented. Such loads arise from eccentricities, stiffness changes, discontinuities, and local buckling, which may not be fully predicted or eliminated in design nor represented by the structural detail specimen. In addition, it is also important to validate the F-E model to ensure that internal loading of the structure occurs as predicted.

The full-scale article, which may be a wing, fuselage, or full aircraft, is generally tested in the room-temperature/dry condition. The main difference between this test on a composite and a metal aircraft is that, for the composite, the structure is much more extensively strain-gauged. This test largely serves to validate the finite element model. If the strain gauge results show regions of high strain in areas where no sub-components were tested, then it is necessary that such testing be performed. Then, concentrating on the ultimate load test, the measured strains at 150% DLL are compared with the knocked down design allowables as established by the coupon and structural element tests. If the measured strain exceeds the allowable value, failure is deemed to have occurred, and some redesign is necessary. Although there are uncertainties at various stages in the above test, the general approach seems reasonable. It can be seen that, for composite aircraft, virtually all development testing (on small and large specimens) becomes an integral part of the airworthiness certification.

However, it should be pointed out that the above is not the only approach to demonstrating static strength. One alternative sometimes proposed is to carry out the test of the full-scale article under ambient conditions (as above), but with the applied loads increased to allow for environmental effects. (The amount of the load increase is determined from specimen tests, much as already described.) Another alternative, of course, is to accept the need for a full-scale environmental test.

13.4.3 Proof Tests

In the past, because of certification or non-destructive inspection (NDI) concerns, some airworthiness authorities have required that every production composite component be given a proof test, generally to a load slightly in excess of the design limit load. In such cases, the components are given a thorough NDI both before and after test to check for damage that may be caused by the proof test. Because confidence in the material properties and analysis methods has improved, this approach is no longer usually insisted upon.

13.5 Demonstration of Fatigue Strength

The situation with regard to demonstrating a satisfactory fatigue performance for composite aircraft structure is far from clear. However, at least one requirement is to check for through-thickness failure modes, caused, for example, by unexpected through-thickness stresses.

The full-scale fatigue tests that have been carried out on current aircraft containing composites have generally been the same as would have been used for an all-metal aircraft, in other words, a test to N lifetimes (where N may be 2, 4, etc.) in a normal environment. (Of course, such aircraft are mainly metal.) Again, the prospect of doing a fatigue test on a full-scale aircraft with the moisture/temperature environment fully represented is daunting. One method for wings with integral fuel tanks is to fill the tanks with continually heated water; however, this convenience is not available for most other structures. Also, sufficient data are not available on the state of fatigue of large composite structures to provide any real basis for selecting a scatter factor. The full-scale test in a normal environment will certainly continue to be performed to verify the metal structure, and it may sometimes also serve to reveal unsuspected problems with the composite structures. However, it seems that the main verification of the fatigue performance of the composite structure will be based on structural detail and sub-component and possibly component testing in an appropriately humid environment, with the temperature cycling (especially the thermal spikes) accurately represented.

The apparent large scatter in composite fatigue life would suggest the need for testing composite structures for excessively long periods (e.g., 30 or more lifetimes) to satisfactorily account for the variability knockdown factor. The main approach to reduce excessive testing periods is load enhancement as described in Ref. 18. By suitable elevation of loads, it is possible to allow the test to be conducted for only one lifetime. If this is too severe on other parts of the structure, the application of somewhat reduced loads can allow the tests to be conducted to only two or three lifetimes. An important issue in mixed composite and metal structure is that the metal components may need to be strengthened (beyond that required in the actual airframe) to allow adequate testing of the composite components under enhanced loads.

It should not, however, be inferred from the above, that the fatigue of composites is necessarily a cause for major concern; it is more a matter of there being difficulties in establishing a convenient test demonstration. A more detailed discussion of the fatigue issue is given in Chapter 8.

13.6   Demonstration of Damage Tolerance

Damage tolerance is generally evaluated at all levels from the coupon to the full-scale article. Damage can be deliberately inflicted, for example, using a portable impact tester in critical regions, such as over fasteners. Damage can also include saw cuts and, in the case of sub-components, disbonds and delamination incurred during manufacture.

Demonstration of damage tolerance on full-scale articles involves residual strength checks usually conducted after several lifetimes of fatigue cycling have been performed on an undamaged article. Damage as described above is then inflicted on the article in the critical areas and limit-load-testing performed. Often, at this stage, the fatigue testing is continued for one or more further lifetimes of fatigue cycling to observe any damage growth. Provided that failure has not occurred, the next step is to repair the damage and continue fatigue cycling for a further one or two lifetimes. Finally, the article is tested to failure. A satisfactory, if quite conservative, result would be to achieve ultimate load in this test.

13.7   Assessment of the Impact Damage Threat

For damage tolerance design and evaluation, it is important to assess the threat of impact damage in relation to the airframe structure. Clearly, vertical surfaces and surfaces that are high on the aircraft are less prone to damage than horizontal surfaces. The top horizontal surface will be more prone to damage from dropped tools and hailstones, whereas the bottom surface will be more prone to damage from runway stones and burst tires.

Ref. 12 describes a comprehensive statistical study to assess impact threat. The data used are based on measurement of impact dents in U.S. military aircraft, including F-4, F-111, A-1, and F-18. The measured dent depth is converted, through calibration, into the equivalent impact energy. The threat is then quantified in terms of Weibull distribution, predicting the probability of occurrence of impacts over the range of energy levels. This information could be used to plan the level and location of damage on a test article.

It is of interest to note that this approach can be used, independent of the test, to assess the probable residual strength ("structural reliability") for the various zones in the aircraft. The structural reliability is obtained by integrating the product of $P(E)$, probability of occurrence of energy level E with $p(e)$, the probability of survival of the structure at strain e at that energy level.

References

[1] Meekoms, K. J., *The Origin and Evolution of the Design Requirements for British Military Aircraft*, RAE publication, June 1983.

[2] Cardrick, A. W., and Curtis, P. T., *Certification of Composite Structures for Military Aircraft*, D/RAE(F)M&S/5/15/1, 13 Oct 1991, presented at Aerotech '92 at the NEC, 14–17 January 1992.

[3] U.K. Ministry of Defence, *Design and Airworthiness Requirements for Service Aircraft, Vol. 1: Aeroplanes*, DEF STAN 00-970, Directorate of Standardisation, U.K., May 1988, pp. 2512.

[4] U.S. Department of Defense, *Aircraft Structures; General Specifications For AFGS-87221A*, 8 June 1990.

[5] Federal Aviation Administration, *Federal Aviation Regulations, Part 25, Airworthiness Standards: Transport Category Airplanes*, U.S. Department of Transportation, Oct., 1994.

[6] Elby, D., Hoffman, P., Hoffman, M., and Polakovics, D., *Managing Safety: The Mathematical Basis and Origins of the Navy's Factor of Safety*, Naval Aviation Structural Integrity and Aging Aircraft Conference, 3–5 Feb. 1998.

[7] Federal Aviation Administration, *Composite Aircraft Structure*, Advisory Circular AC 20-107A, 25 April 1984 and companion document by the JAA, ACJ 25.603, *Composite Aircraft Structure Acceptable Means of Compliance*, 1986.

[8] Ripley, E. L., and Cardrick, A. W., *The UK Approach to the Certification of Composite Components for Military Aeroplanes and Helicopters*, AGARD Report No. 660, April 1977.

[9] Perry, F. S., "Harrier II: A Comparison of U.S. and U.K. Approaches to Fatigue Clearance," AGARD Meeting on An Assessment of Fatigue Damage and Crack Growth Prediction Techniques, Sept., 1993.

[10] Dutton, S. E., and Lofland, R. A., "Certification of Structural Composite Components Used on the MD900 Helicopter," *Proceedings of ICCM-11*, 14–18 July 1997.

[11] Park, W. J., "On Estimating Sample Size for Testing Composite Materials," *Journal of Composite Materials*, Vol. 13, 1979, pp 219–212.

[12] Khan, H. P., Cordero, R., and Whitehead, R. S., *Advanced Certification Methodology for Composite Structures*, DOT/FAA/AR-96/111, Federal Aviation Administration, 1997.

[13]Whitehead, R. S., Kan, H. P., Cordero, R., and Saether, E. S., *Certification Testing Methodology for Composite Structure: Vol. II: Methodology Development*, NADC-87042–60, Naval Air Development Center, Oct., 1986.

[14]Weinberger, R. A., Somoroff, A. R., and Riley, B. L., *U.S. Navy Certification of Composite Wings for the F-18 and the Advanced Harrier Aircraft*, AGARD Report No. 660, April 1977.

[15]McCarty, J. E., Johnson, R. W., and Wilson, D. R., "737 Graphite-Epoxy Horizontal Stabilizer Certification," AIAA 82-0745, 1982.

[16]Fawcett, A., Trostle, J., and Ward, S., "777 Empennage Certification Approach," *Proceedings of ICCM-11*, 14–18 July 1997.

[17]Whitehead, R. S., *Certification of Primary Composite Aircraft Structures*, 14th Symposium of the International Conference on Aeronautical Fatigue (ICAF), June 1987.

[18]Lameris, J., *The Use of Load Enhancement Factors in the Certification of Composite Aircraft Structures*, NLR TP 90068U, National Aerospace Laboratory, 1990.

14
Three-Dimensionally Reinforced Preforms and Composites

14.1 Introduction

Conventional fiber-reinforced polymer (FRP) laminates have a layered two-dimensional construction. The lack of reinforcement in the through-thickness or z-direction results in the laminates having low interlaminar strength and fracture resistance.

Laminated two-dimensional composites are not suitable for applications where through-thickness stresses may exceed the (low) tensile strength of the matrix (or matrix/fiber bond) and in addition, to provide sufficient residual strength after anticipated impact events, two-dimensional laminates must be made thicker than required for meeting strength requirements. The resulting penalties of increased cost and structural weight provide impetus for the development of more damage-resistant and tolerant composite materials and structures.

Considerable improvements in damage resistance can be achieved by using tougher thermoset or thermoplastic matrices together with optimized fiber/matrix bond strength. However, this approach can involve significant costs, and the improvements that can be obtained are limited. There are also limits to the acceptable fiber/matrix bond strength because high bond strength can lead to increased notch-sensitivity.

An alternative and potentially more effective means of increasing damage resistance and through-thickness strength is to develop a fiber architecture in which a proportion of fibers in the composite are oriented in the z-direction. This fiber architecture can be obtained, for example, by three-dimensional weaving or three-dimensional braiding. A much simpler approach is to apply z-direction reinforcement to a conventional two-dimensional fiber configuration by stitching; however, this does not provide all of the benefits of a full three-dimensional architecture.

In all of these approaches, a three-dimensional preform is first produced and is converted into a composite by one of the liquid resin molding techniques described in Chapter 5.

Even without the benefits of three-dimensional reinforcement, the preform approach has the important advantage that it is a comparatively low-cost method of manufacturing composite components compared with conventional laminating procedures based on pre-preg. Indeed, preforms for resin-transfer molding (RTM) and other liquid molding techniques are often produced from a two-dimensional fiber configuration by stitching or knitting.

A summary of the main aspects of these and other approaches to three-dimensional reinforcement and preform manufacture is given in Table 14.1. Most of these are discussed in this chapter, which also includes a discussion on the relatively new topic of z-pinning.

14.2 Stitching

Stitching is best applied using an industrial-grade sewing machine where two separate yarns are used. For stitching composites, the yarns are generally aramid

Table 14.1   Description of Three-Dimensional Textile Manufacturing Techniques

Textile Process	Preform Style	Fiber Orientation	Productivity/ Setup
Stitching	Complex preforms possible by combining several structures	Dependent on basic preforms	High productivity; short set-up time
Embroidery	Additional fibers incorporated onto basic fabric	Complex fiber orientations possible (e.g., maximum stress direction)	Moderate productivity; short set-up time
Three-Dimensional Weaving	Flat fabrics, integral stiffeners, integral sandwich structure and simple profiles	Wide range of through-thickness architectures possible but in-plane fibers generally limited to $0°/90°$ directions (except with advanced looms)	High productivity, long set-up time
Three-Dimensional Braiding	Open and closed profiles (I, L, Z, O, U, etc.) and flat fabrics	$0°$ fibers; braiding fibers between $0–80°$ and $90°$ fibers possible	Medium productivity; long set-up time
Knitting	Flat fabrics and very complex performs	Highly looped fibers in mesh-like structure	Medium productivity; short set-up time
Non-crimp	Flat fabrics and integral sandwich structures	Multi-axial in-plane orientation $0°/90°/\pm45°$, up to 8 layers possible	High productivity; long set-up time

(Kevlar), although other yarns such as glass, carbon, and nylon have also been used. A needle is used to perforate a pre-preg stack or fabric preform, enabling the insertion of a high-tensile-strength yarn in the thickness direction, as shown in Figure 14.1. The yarn, normally referred to as the needle yarn, is inserted from the top of the stack/preform, which is held in place using a presser foot. When the yarn reaches the bottom of the stack/preform it is caught by another yarn, called the bobbin yarn, before it re-enters the stack/preform as the needle is withdrawn from the stack/preform, thus forming a full stitch. The stack/preform is then advanced a certain distance between the presser foot and a roller mechanism before the needle is used to effect the next stitch. This process is repeated to form a row of stitches. Figure 14.2 shows the various types of stitches commonly used to effect z-direction reinforcement. Among the three stitches, the modified lock stitch, in which the crossover knot between the bobbin and needle threads is positioned at either laminate surface to minimize in-plane fiber distortion, is most preferred.

Apart from improving z-direction properties, stitching serves as an effective means of assembling preforms of dry two-dimensional tape or cloth, for example, attaching stiffeners to skin preforms, that are then consolidated using processes such as liquid molding.

14.2.1 Mechanical Properties

14.2.1.1 Out-of-Plane Properties.
The most significant improvement resulting from stitching is the increase in the interlaminar delamination resistance of FRP laminates under mode I and, to a lesser degree, mode II loadings. To achieve this, the stitches need to remain intact for a short distance behind the crack front and restrict any effort to extend the delamination crack. As expected (with the enhanced fracture toughness), stitched FRP composites have a better resistance to delamination cracking under low energy, high energy, and ballistic impacts as well as under dynamic loading by explosive blasts. They also possess higher post-impact residual mechanical properties than do their unstitched counterparts,[1] as illustrated in Figure 14.3. It has been shown that the

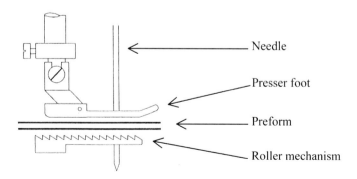

Fig. 14.1   Schematic diagram of the stitching configuration.

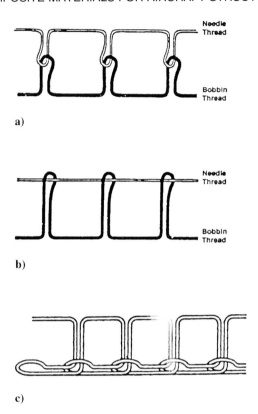

Fig. 14.2   Schematic diagrams of three commonly used stitches for z-reinforcement of two-dimensional composites: *a*) lock stitch; *b*) modified lock stitch; *c*) chain stitch.

effectiveness of stitching for improving residual strength is dependent on factors such as the stitch density, stitch type, and stitch thread. However, only in relatively thick laminates are significant improvements in compression-after-impact strength evident. Although it is noted that a toughened matrix could also provide similar improvement in residual strength[2] (Fig. 14.4), it is two or three times more expensive than stitching.

There have been, however, conflicting results that report that stitching does little (if anything) to improve either impact damage resistance or tolerance. In the cases considered, this is normally attributed to two factors: 1) the stitching yarns were insufficiently strong (both in terms of breaking strength and providing traction) to afford the necessary resistance to delamination growth; and 2) the bridging zone (of between 20–30 mm) needed for stitches to be effective, was not fully realized.

Undisputed, however, is the advantage of stitching for improved shear lap joint strength under both static and cyclic loading, largely due to reduced peel stresses. Stitches can delay the initiation of disbonds and provide load transfer even after failure of the bond line. Therefore, stiffeners stitched onto a panel are

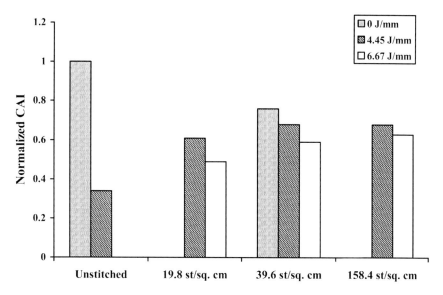

Fig. 14.3   Compression after impact (CAI) strength for stitched and unstitched laminates normalized with respect to undamaged compression strength.

more resistant to disbonding; improvements in load-carrying capability of approximately 15% have been observed. There is also evidence that stitching is effective in suppressing delamination due to free-edge effects.

14.2.1.2 In-Plane Properties.   While attempting to improve the out-of-plane properties, the introduction of stitches into a two-dimensional composite laminate can also affect the in-plane performance of the stitched composite. This is due to induced defects in the final laminate introduced during needle insertion or as a result of the presence of the stitch yarn in the laminate. These defects may occur in various forms including broken fibers, resin-rich regions, and fine-scale resin cracking. Fiber misalignment, however, appears to have the greatest detrimental effect on mechanical properties, particularly under tensile and compressive loading.

To keep defects in stitched laminates to a minimum, careful selection and control of the stitching parameters (including yarn diameter, tension, material, stitch density, etc.) are necessary. Analysis of the effects of stitching on the basic mechanical properties of two-dimensional composite laminates in general have yielded contradictory results.[3] These show that stiffness and strength of the composites under tensile as well as compressive loadings can be degraded, unchanged, or improved with stitching, depending on the type of composite, the stitching parameter, and the loading condition. The improvements in tensile and compressive stiffness are believed to be due to an increase in fiber/volume fraction that results from a compaction of in-plane fibers by the stitching. Any enhancement in compressive strength is attributed to the suppression of

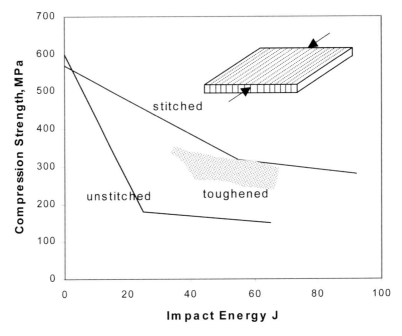

Fig. 14.4   NASA results for compression after impact for 48-ply quasi isotropic AS4/3506 laminates, either stitched or unstitched, and an unstitched laminate of similar configuration with a highly toughened matrix. Stitch pitch and spacing around 3 mm. Based on data provided in Ref. 2.

delaminations. The stiffness in tension and compression is mainly degraded when in-plane fibers are misaligned by the presence of the stitching yarn in their path.

Premature compressive failure can be triggered if stitches are too taut, which in turn can cause excessive crimping of the in-plane fibers. Conversely, insufficient tension of the stitching yarn can cause the stitches to buckle under consolidation pressures and render them ineffective as a reinforcement in the thickness direction, the purpose for which they were originally intended. Tensile strength, on the other hand, is normally degraded due to fiber fractures arising from damage by the stitching needle. Enhancement of tensile strength, which has been observed, is attributed to an increase in fiber/volume fraction resulting from compaction of in-plane fibers by the stitching.

It is also considered that the inferior fatigue performance observed for stitched composites under tension and compression loadings is due to the same failure mechanisms that are responsible for deterioration in their corresponding static properties.

Finally, it appears that the flexural and interlaminar shear strengths of two-dimensional laminates may also be degraded, unchanged, or even improved with stitching. In general, the conflicting effects of stitching, in increasing fiber content and suppressing delamination, on the one hand, and introducing misalignment and damage to in-plane fibers, on the other, are possibly responsible for the reported behaviors.

14.2.2 Applications of Stitching: The Stitched Wing

To date, by far the most ambitious development of stitched composite structures is a NASA sponsored demonstrator program to develop a cost-effective damage-tolerant composite wing. A 28-m-long sewing machine,[4] shown in Figure 14.5 was developed by Boeing to manufacture preforms with enhanced impact tolerance for the production of composite aircraft wing covers. The machine is able to stitch layers of carbon fabric of over 25 mm in thickness at a rate of over 3000 stitches a minute. In addition to stitching the skin preform, the blade stiffener flanges are also stitched to the skin. The stiffeners are formed by stacking tubular braided fabrics and partially stitching them together, leaving an unstitched region that is folded out to form the flanges before they are stitched to the skin.

After stitching, the flexible wing preform is placed on an outer mold-line tool pre-covered by film of partially cured resin; thereafter, the assembly is bagged and placed in an autoclave. Under heat and pressure, the resin melts and flows through the skin and stiffeners before curing. This process is known as resin film infusion (RFI) and is covered in Chapter 5. The resulting panel is claimed to be 25% lighter and 20% cheaper than an equivalent aluminum part.

Fig. 14.5   Boeing sewing machine for stitched wings.

14.2.3 Modified Stitching—Technical Embroidery

A version of stitching that can be used to provide localized in-plane reinforcement together with through-thickness reinforcement is technical embroidery. In this process, a reinforcement yarn is fed into the path of the stitching head and is thus stitched onto the surface of the preform (Fig. 14.6). With current computer-controlled embroidery heads, it is possible to place this in-plane yarn with high accuracy in quite complex paths, which allows high-stress regions of a component to be reinforced by fibers laid in the maximum stress direction. Improvements of 55% in specific bearing strength have been achieved through the use of this local reinforcement technique.[5]

14.3 Z-Pinning

Z-pinning is a simple method of applying three-dimensional reinforcement with several benefits over stitching. However, unlike stitching, z-pinning cannot

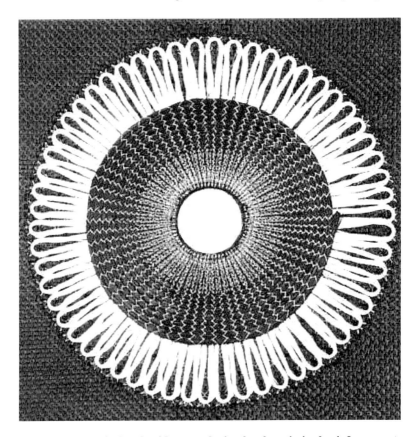

Fig. 14.6   Technical embroidery producing local, optimized reinforcement.

be used to make preforms. In the z-pinning process,[6,7] thin rods are inserted at right angles into a two-dimensional carbon/epoxy composite stack either before or during consolidation. The z-rods can be metallic, usually titanium, or composite, usually carbon/epoxy. The composite rods are typically 0.25 mm and 0.5 mm in diameter, although slightly smaller or larger sizes are also available.

The rods are held with the required pattern and density in a collapsible foam block that provides lateral support.[8] This technique prevents the rods from buckling during insertion and allows a large number of pins to be inserted in a single pressing operation. The rods are typically driven into the two-dimensional composite in one of two ways. The first technique (See Fig. 14.7) involves placing the rod-laden foam on top of an uncured pre-preg and autoclave curing. During the cure, the combination of heat and pressure compacts the collapsible foam layer, driving the rods orthogonally into the composite. When curing is completed, the residual foam preform is then removed and discarded, and rods sitting proud of the surface of the cured laminate are sheared away using a sharp knife.

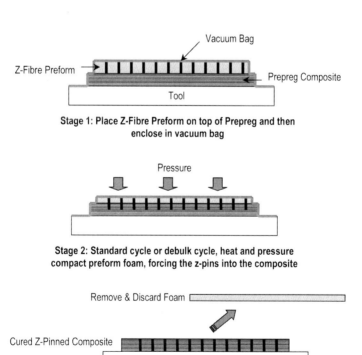

Fig. 14.7   Foam method of applying z-pins. Adapted from Ref. 6.

The second technique uses a purpose-built ultrasonic insertion gun to drive the rods into the two-dimensional composite. As shown schematically in Figure 14.8, this is a two-stage process whereby during the first stage the preform is only partially compacted using the ultrasonic horn, and hence the rods are not fully inserted. The residual foam is removed afterward and a second insertion stage is then carried out, also with the ultrasonic gun, to complete the insertion of the rods. If the rods are not flush with the part surface, the excess is sheared away. In principle, the part to be z-pinned could take on any shape provided there is an

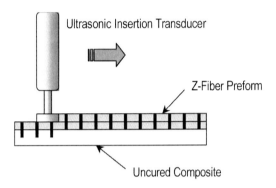

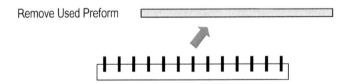

a) Primary insertion stage and residual preform removal

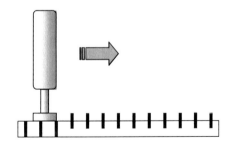

b) Secondary insertion stage

Fig. 14.8   Ultrasonic vibrator method of applying z-pins Adapted from Ref. 6.

appropriate ultrasonic horn. It is claimed that the ultrasonic insertion technique can be used to insert metallic pins into cured composites, a capability that could be used in the repair of delaminations in composites, although considerable damage to the parent material would result.

Between the two pin insertion methods, the vacuum bag route is perhaps more suitable when a large or relatively unobstructed area is to be z-pinned. On the other hand, localized z-pinning or difficult-to-access areas are more efficiently achieved using the ultrasonic process by configuring and shaping an appropriate ultrasonic horn.

14.3.1 Mechanical Properties

Relatively little work has been published on the mechanical properties of z-pinned composites. Based on available data,[7] it can be deduced that significant improvements in both mode I and mode II fracture toughness are achievable through z-pinning, which in turn translate to superior damage resistance and tolerance,[8] and improved skin-stiffener pull-out properties.[9] There is evidence[9] that these improvements in out-of-plane properties are achievable without much, if any, sacrifice to in-plane properties. Other work,[10] however, shows that the pins can introduce excessive waviness to the in-plane fibers, causing compressive properties to be severely degraded. Clearly, in much the same way as in the case of stitching, the degree to which the in-plane properties are detrimentally affected, and the out-of-plane properties are improved, is dependent on the pinning parameters, such as density and configuration.[9]

14.3.2 Stitching Versus Z-Pinning

Research into the effects of z-direction reinforcement in traditional two-dimensional laminates on mechanical properties has been particularly extensive over the past decade or so. The impetus for this research is derived from the potential of stitching, and more recently, z-pinning to fulfil the need for a simple and cost-effective remedy for the poor out-of-plane properties of conventional two-dimensional FRP composites. The amount of z-direction reinforcement required to provide a substantial amount of out-of-plane improvement is small, typically no more than 5%.

The improvements in fracture toughness afforded by the two techniques mean that higher design allowables could be used in the designs of composite structures. In other words, stitched and z-pinned composites can be more readily considered as candidate materials for structures where impact damage (e.g., due to dropped tools), high peel stresses (e.g., in joints and at hard points), and cut-outs (e.g., edges and holes) are difficult to avoid. Stitching and z-pinning also provide the opportunity for parts integration to be incorporated into the production of composite components, thus improving the ease of handling, the potential for process automation, and the overall cost-effectiveness of the manufacturing process. Further, when used in conjunction with a liquid molding technique, stitching can provide some pre-compaction of the preform and this can reduce mold clamping pressures required while ensuring a high fiber/volume fraction in the finished product.

A potential benefit of these reinforcement techniques is that post–catastrophic failure, they can hold fragments together—although stitches, compared with z-pinning rods, would be more effective in this respect. This benefit would be especially important in applications such as fan blades in aero engines, where fragments from a fractured blade, if unrestrained, could be swept into the engine and cause further damage. In fact, carbon/epoxy pins are already used in operational General Electric (GE90) fan blades to reinforce areas that require higher strength, and there are plans to increase the level of pinning in the growth version of these blades.[11] Z-pinning has also been used to produce high-performance sandwich structures. This is achieved by integrally connecting the skins through a foam core. It is claimed that, compared with traditional aluminum honeycomb sandwich structures, Z-pinned cores have three times the crush strength as well as superior damage tolerance. Although z-pinning is still inferior to mechanical fasteners in terms of pull-out failure load, it has good potential as an alternative shear attachment technique because its use would result in lighter-weight structures at a lower cost.

Stitching is inferior to z-pinning in three major ways. First, there are practical restrictions on the size and shape of the component that can be stitched, which usually can only be overcome with purpose-built stitching machines that demand large capital costs. Further, z-pinning is more appropriate than stitching for reinforcing regions with small radii of curvature. Second, the wrapping effect of the stitching yarn means that careful tension control has to be exercized so that in-plane fibers are not excessively crimped in the thickness direction. Each z-pin is independent of the others and hence does not pose this problem. Finally, to ensure minimal breakage, a limited number of fiber materials can be used as the stitching yarn. Alternatively, z-pins can be manufactured from a much wider range of materials, which can have large aspect ratios (l/d) to ensure good traction between the z-direction reinforcement and the base material.

14.4   Three-Dimensional Weaving

14.4.1   Process

Woven fabrics are made of warp (longitudinal) and weft (transverse) yarns interlaced in a regular order on mechanical looms. The process of weaving is already used extensively within the composite industry to produce the vast majority of the single-layer, broadcloth fabric that is currently used as a reinforcement. With minimal modification, the same standard industry mac-

hines can be used to manufacture flat, three-dimensional fabrics in a wide variety
of yarn architectures.

Three-dimensional fabrics can be woven using almost any type of yarn,
including carbon, glass, aramid, and ceramic fibers or combinations of these
yarns. In addition, the proportions of the yarns in the x, y, and z directions can
be controlled to tailor the properties of the composite for specific applications.
Idealized examples of weave architectures that can be manufactured are
illustrated in Fig. 14.9. In reality, the three-dimensional architectures that can be
produced are significantly different from these idealized forms because tension in
the binder yarns causes bunching up or crimping of in-plane yarns, as shown in
Fig. 14.10 and Fig. 14.11. The path that the binder yarn follows as it traverses
through the thickness of the woven preform plays an important part in controlling
the final three-dimensional architecture and thus the resultant mechanical
properties.

The main function of the z-direction yarns is to provide the composite with
its improved impact performance. However, these yarns also bind the layers

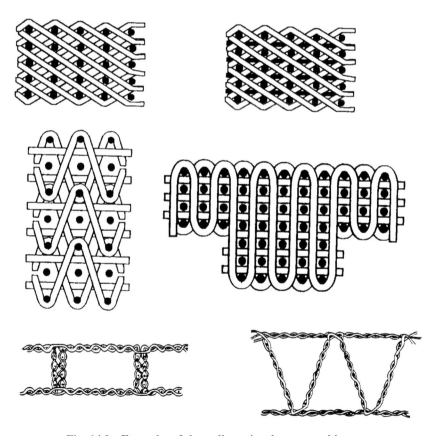

Fig. 14.9   Examples of three-dimensional weave architectures.

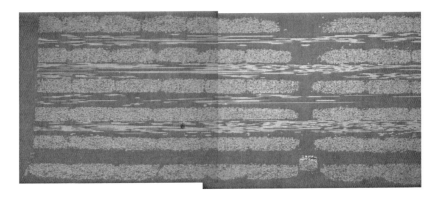

Fig. 14.10   E-Glass/vinyl ester three-dimensional orthogonal weave with warp yarns normal to the page. Courtesy of the CRC-ACS Ltd, Melbourne, Australia.

together to produce a net-shape preform that can be easily handled, reducing the manufacturing time associated with the lay-up of individual fabric layers. Importantly, three-dimensional woven preforms can also be designed to fold out into more complex shapes, for example, integrally woven blade-stiffened panels or I-beams, an ability that can help reduce costs in preform assembly.[7]

The main disadvantage of three-dimensional weaving is that standard looms cannot produce a fabric that contains in-plane yarns at angles other than 0° and 90°. This results in structures having very low shear and torsion properties, thereby making them unsuitable for use in most aircraft structures where high shear strength and stiffness are generally required. However, more specialized

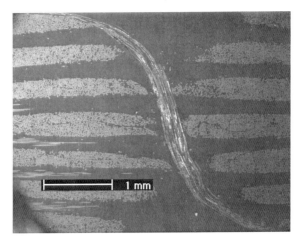

Fig. 14.11   E-Glass/vinyl ester weave (Fig. 14.10) with weft yarns normal to the page. Illustrates collimation of weft yarns by a binder yarn travelling in warp direction. Coutesy CRC-ACS Ltd, Melbourne, Australia.

looms have been in use since the early 1970s when the first was developed to produce three-dimensional woven carbon–carbon preforms for aircraft brakes.[12] These looms allow complex-shaped structures to be woven in the final shape without the need for folding operations and can produce fabric with yarns at angles such as $\pm 45°$. Structures of such complexity are often difficult to manufacture using normal pre-preg technology, therefore the use of weaving technology can result in substantial cost savings in the production of complex composite structures.

14.4.2 Mechanical Properties

14.4.2.1 In-Plane Properties.
The tensile and compressive properties of 3-D woven composites have been studied since the 1980s, but a clear picture of their in-plane performance and how it is affected by variables such as the weave architecture is still developing.[7] Many of the studies on the performance of three-dimensional woven composites have been conducted with comparison to two-dimensional laminates manufactured with similar, but not always the same, parameters (fiber content, lay-up, etc.), and often these differences have prevented conclusive comparisons of performance being made.

Numerous investigations of the tensile properties of three-dimensional woven composites have led to conflicting results. Some researchers have reported the tensile modulus of three-dimensional woven composites to be reduced in comparison to similar two-dimensional laminates, whereas other researchers have reported an increase. However, in spite of this conflict in the reported results, it has been observed that (in the majority of cases) the tensile modulus of a three-dimensional woven composite is within 20% of the modulus of the comparable two-dimensional laminate. The studies have also shown that the modulus of the three-dimensional woven composite is not significantly influenced by the content of the z-direction reinforcement or the weave architecture. The explanation for the higher tensile modulus of some three-dimensional material is thought to be due to a slightly higher fiber content than the comparable two-dimensional laminate. The lower modulus in other cases is generally considered to be due to the increased waviness of the in-plane yarns caused by the presence of the z-direction reinforcement.

There is also no conclusive evaluation of the tensile strength of three-dimensional woven composites. The failure strength of three-dimensional woven composites has been found to be the same or (more often) less than the strength of a comparable two-dimensional laminate, but the difference is rarely more than 20%. As with tensile modulus, the strength of 3-D woven composites does not appear to be significantly affected by the z-direction reinforcement content or weave structure. The reduction in the tensile strength of three-dimensional woven composites is considered to be primarily due to the increased waviness of the in-plane yarns.

With regard to the compressive properties of three-dimensional woven composites, the modulus is generally reduced due to the z-direction yarns causing an increased waviness and local crimping of the in-plane yarns. A comparison of the compression strength of three-dimensional woven composites relative to similar two-dimensional laminates is more complex, and so far the findings have not been conclusive with both improvements and reductions in strength being observed. The compressive strength appears to be independent of weave architecture or the proportion of z-direction fiber. Degradation of the compressive strength is believed to be due to the kinking or microbuckling of the load-bearing yarns, which in turn is attributed to local waviness or crimping of the yarns as a result of the z-direction reinforcement. The occasional observed improvement in strength could be attributed to the initiation of delamination being suppressed by the z-direction yarn.

14.4.2.2 Out-of-Plane Properties. The most significant difference between the performance of three-dimensional and two-dimensional woven composites is apparent when examining their interlaminar fracture properties (delamination resistance) and their impact properties.[7]

Most interlaminar fracture studies have been performed in mode I, or tensile crack opening, conditions. The delamination resistance increases with the volume content, elastic modulus, tensile strength, and pull-out resistance of the z-direction yarn, but even a relatively modest amount of z-direction reinforcement can provide a large improvement to the delamination resistance. As with the other forms of z-direction reinforcement (stitching, z-pinning, etc.), the improvement in the delamination resistance occurs by the formation of a bridge of z-direction fibers spanning the crack faces behind the advancing crack tip, which restricts the further growth of the delamination.

The enhanced interlaminar fracture properties translate into improved impact properties. Impact performance has been extensively studied, and it has been found that in comparison with two-dimensional laminates, the improved delamination resistance of the three-dimensional woven composite results in a reduced area of impact damage over a range of impact energies. This superior impact damage resistance usually results in higher post-impact mechanical properties than that obtained from two-dimensional laminates, Fig. 14.12.

14.4.3 Applications

Three dimensional woven composites were used in the Beech Starship.[12] Woven H-joint connectors were used for joining honeycomb-sandwich wing panels together. The use of this woven connector was reported to be critical to the cost-effective manufacture of the wing and improved stress transfer at the joint, thus reducing peel stresses.

Three dimensional woven composites are used by Lockheed Martin for the air inlet duct in the F35 military fighter jet. In this example, the stiffeners are

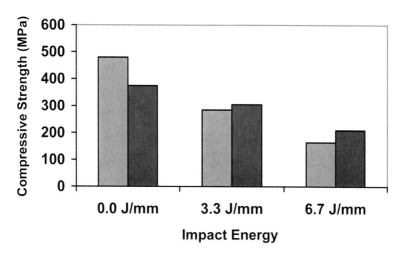

Fig. 14.12   Effect of impact energy on the compressive strength of two-dimensional and three-dimensional woven carbon/epoxy composites

integrally woven with the duct shell, reducing the need for secondary fastening. Ninety-five percent of the fasteners through the duct are eliminated, thereby improving aerodynamic and signature performance, minimizing the risk of fasteners being injested by the engine, and simplifying manufacturing assembly.[13]

Other, three-dimensional for woven composites have been investigated in a number of demonstration structures for aircraft including thrust reversers, rotor blades, engine mounts, T-section fuselage frames, stiffener gap fillers, and multi-blade stiffened panels.[12]

In more advanced applications, three-dimensional woven sandwich composites are also being used in prototype Scramjet engines capable of speeds[14] up to Mach 8. The material is a ceramic-based composite consisting of three-dimensional woven carbon fibers in a silicon carbide matrix and is used in the combustion chamber. A key benefit of using a three-dimensional woven composite in this application is the ability to manufacture the chamber as a single piece and the consequent reduction in connection issues and leakage problems associated with conventional fabrication methods.

14.5   Braiding

Braiding is basically a textile process that enables the interweaving of two or more systems of yarn in the bias and longitudinal direction to form an integrated structure referred to as the preform. Due to the interweaving of the yarns, braided preforms have conformability, torsional stability, and structural integrity as well as some degree of three-dimensional reinforcement (depending on the process), making them easy to handle and work with. The braiding process is capable of producing preforms of intricate shape; however, the size and length of the preform is generally limited to the size of the machine and yarn supply, respectively.

The adaptation of braiding to the composites industry has meant extensive research and development of the basic braiding process. This has focused on the hardware, production, and the geometric analysis of the braids, with the ultimate goal of complete automation and integration of machining and composite processing incorporating CAD/CAM (computer-aided design/manufacture) in aerospace factories.

Braided preform architectures can effectively be classified into two categories: two-dimensional and three-dimensional. Two-dimensional braiding has become well established over the past 15 years in the composites industry with a steadily growing database of knowledge and expertise. In contrast, three-dimensional braiding is still in its infancy.

14.5.1 Two-Dimensional Braiding Process

The traditional two-dimensional braiding process can be used to produce preforms of complex tubular shapes or in collapsed form, flat panels. The process of two-dimensional braiding can perhaps be best visualized by relating it to a maypole dance, in which the yarns are braided over a mandrel by yarn carriers that move in an interlinking rotational fashion around the mandrel. The simplicity makes it an efficient and cost-effective process compared with some other textile processes.

The braiding machine, shown schematically in Figure 14.13a, consists of three primary components: 1) yarn or fiber tow carriers, 2) interlinking mechanism and 3) take-up mechanism. The machine set-up involves placing the braiding fiber tow onto spools that are then loaded onto the carriers. The carriers (Fig. 14.13b) comprise a track follower, spool shaft, tensioning mechanism (weights or springs), and let-off mechanism (via hooks, loops, or wheels).

The carriers are connected to the braiding machine through "horndogs" and "horngears," which propel the carriers into their interlinking rotational path as shown in Figure 14.13c. The usual yarn structure resulting from two-dimensional braiding is a simple regular biaxial braid where each yarn or tow in the two bias directions pass over and under two yarns in a repeat. The orientation (or braid angle, Figure 14.14) of these bias yarns typically range between 15° and 85°. By modifying the horngears on the braiding machine, different braid patterns can be achieved. Hollow horngears also allow the introduction of axial yarns in the braid that add to the stiffness of the preform. Two-dimensional braids, which contain longitudinal yarns, are referred to as triaxial braids (Fig. 14.14).

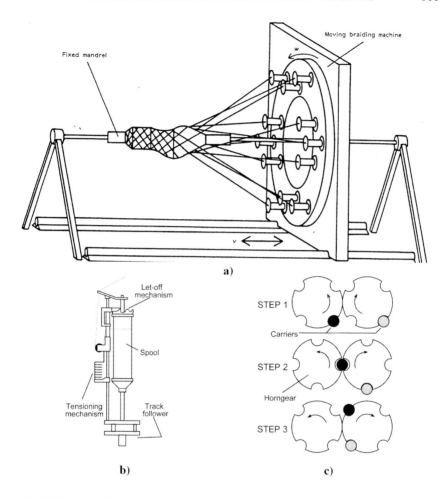

Fig. 14.13 *a*) **Schematic diagram of a typical braiding machine;** *b*) **typical yarn carrier;** *c*) **horngear movement.**

To form a continuous preform, a mechanism is also required to pull the fabric as it is formed. This is the take-up mechanism. Although there are several different types of take-up mechanisms, there are basically two systems that are applicable for braids intended for use in the aerospace industry. The first system involves a mandrel mounted on a gantry, allowing the mandrel to move back and forth while the braid is formed as shown in Figure 14.13a. The other system involves fixing the mandrel and allowing the braiding machine to move back and forth.

Research and development into the two-dimensional braiding process has focused on reducing the cost of the process and investigating its limitations and applications. Attempts at reducing the cost have resulted in the development of high-speed automated braiding machines that can braid intricate shapes rapidly. The use of this type of machinery has been further assisted by the development of kinematic equations relating the machine parameters to the braid architecture that can be extended for use in CAD/CAM.[15]

14.5.2 Manufacturing Issues

There are a number of issues that must be considered when manufacturing braided preforms. A balance must be met between the design and manufacturing requirements. Although a particular braid angle may be required to obtain optimal structural performance, this angle may need to be modified to meet manufacturing requirements. That is, depending on the number of carriers, the size of the part to be braided, and the size of the tows, a particular fiber orientation may be unachievable. The reason for this is that either there will be jamming of the fiber tows, or at the other extreme, poor fiber coverage over the mandrel.

The mechanical properties are not only affected by the braid angle but also by the amount of crimp in the yarn. Fiber crimp, which occurs in the braider tows as they pass over and under other braider and axial tows, causes a reduction to the in-plane mechanical properties. This can be controlled to a degree by using smaller axial tow sizes and changing the braid pattern. A regular braid pattern has less crimp than a diamond braid (Fig. 14.14).

Issues related to the manufacture of two-dimensional braided preforms include preform quality, fiber orientation and coverage, fiber crimp, and mandrel design. The braided preform quality is highly dependent on the type of fiber being used. In the braiding process, the fibers are inevitably bent and twisted as they move from one machine surface to another. As the fibers are converted to the fabric structure, the process introduces stresses resulting from the interlacing and intertwining of the tows. This can cause damage to the fibers, degrading their properties. The amount of damage that takes place is dependent on the fiber stiffness, brittleness, diameter, coating (sizing), tow structure, and processing

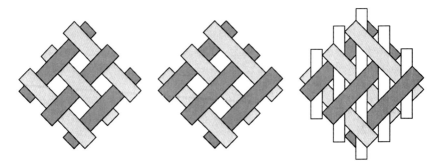

Fig. 14.14   Different braid patterns produced by two-dimensional braiding.

speeds. Carbon fibers have shown to be more susceptible to damage than aramid or glass fibers.

The mandrel forms an integral part in the fabrication of two-dimensional braided structural preforms. It not only provides the shape of the preform, but can also be used in the consolidation process and may also provide structural benefits. Mandrels may be rigid or flexible and are made from a number of materials such as metals (steel/aluminum), structural foams, and water- soluble or fusible casting compounds.

14.5.3   Design of Braided Composites

The design of braided composites needs to take into account the structural requirements of the part in question as well as the manufacturing issues outlined above and the limitations of the braiding process. Techniques used to design the braided preform may involve models that relate the geometric features of the braid architecture to the process parameters. Using such models enables the designer to accurately specify a braided preform with the desired fiber orientations. There is a range of analytical tools that can be used to predict the mechanical performance of the braided composite. Conventional techniques such as classical laminate theory and stiffness averaging have shown to work well in predicting stiffness. However, strength prediction is somewhat more difficult, as is the case for all composite structures. Traditional laminate failure theories do not work because they do not take into account the different failure mechanisms of these materials. Specialized methods that model these mechanisms should be used.

14.5.4   Mechanical Properties

Although the mechanical property database of two-dimensional braided composites is not as large as that for unidirectional tape or two-dimensional woven pre-preg, testing of these materials has shown that their properties compare favorably with other forms of composites. Two-dimensional braided composites have been shown to have similar stiffness and strength values compared with two-dimensional woven composites of similar lay-up. When compared with unidirectional tape, braids have also shown similar elastic properties; however, their strength values are reduced by as much as 25%. This discrepancy in strength is mainly attributed to the difference in fiber architecture e.g., fiber waviness that causes changes in failure mechanisms, particularly in compression.

With regard to damage resistance and tolerance, two-dimensional braids have been shown superior to both unidirectional and two-dimensional woven composites. Low-energy impacting followed by compression testing has revealed that braided composites can be significantly more resistant and tolerant to

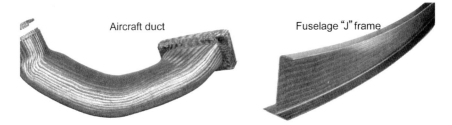

Aircraft duct   Fuselage "J" frame

Fig. 14.15   Examples of parts fabricated using two-dimensional braiding. Courtesy Fiber Innovations Inc.

damage. This is a result of the slightly three-dimensional nature of the reinforcement architecture that acts to contain damage growth in the laminate.

14.5.5 Applications

By braiding over a diverse range of mandrels and increasing the size of the two dimensional braiding machine, it is possible to produce intricate tubular preform shapes of various sizes. There have been a number of low- and high-technology items manufactured this way that have been cited in open literature. Some examples, two of which are shown in Figure 14.15, include cellular stiffened panels, pressure vessels and drive shafts, aircraft propellers, truss joints, a monocoque racing car chassis, rocket launchers, aircraft fuselage frames, helicopter rotor blade spars. Metallic end fittings have also been attached to tooling mandrels and then braided over to produce an integrated preform.[16] The braiding process not only makes it possible to manufacture these structures, but what is most important is that it is also able to provide the desired fiber reinforcement. When required, axial yarns are used to provide the tensile and compressive strength and stiffness, whereas the bias yarns supply adequate reinforcement for torsional or shear loads.

Braided preforms have generally been consolidated using liquid molding processes such as RTM and RFI; however, there have been cases where other infusion methods have been used. Preforms braided with commingled yarns (combination of fiber with thermoplastic) have been consolidated using compression molding techniques. There has also been the marriage of braiding with pultrusion, which enables the automated and continuous production of composite parts.

14.5.6 Three-Dimensional Braiding Process

With two-dimensional braiding, thick-walled structures are made by repeatedly braiding over the mandrel resulting in a multi-layer preform without significant through-thickness reinforcement. Some attempts have been made to

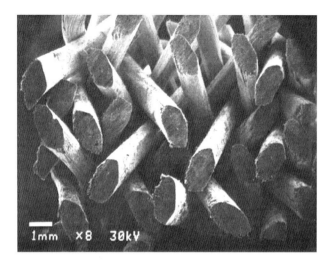

Fig. 14.16 Three-dimensional braid architecture. Courtesy Atlantic Research Corporation, Gainesville, VA.

overcome the lack of through-thickness reinforcement with multi-layer two-dimensional braids by interlocking the multi-layers with binding yarns. This has led to the development of three-dimensional braiding techniques that have provided new possibilities in the development of near net-shape preforms with added through-thickness reinforcement.

The first serious development of three-dimensional braiding, which occurred in the 1960s, was referred to as *four-step* (or row-and-column) braiding, a term given because of the four distinct operations in the braiding process. Since then other variations have been developed, along with some new techniques yielding three major styles of three-dimensional braiding: four-step braiding, two-step braiding, and multi-layer interlock braiding. Figure 14.16 provides an example of the type of construction that can be achieved with three-dimensional braiding.

Despite its advantages, the use of three-dimensional braiding has been limited. The maximum size of the preform is determined by the braiding machine size, and most industrial machines are only able to braid preforms with small cross-sections (less than 100 mm). Extremely large and expensive machines are required to produce preforms large enough for typical aircraft structures. Three-dimensional braiding machines are still at the research and development stage, and only a few machines are currently producing commercial preforms.

Three-dimensional braiding was developed in the late 1960s to produce three-dimensional carbon/carbon composites (Chapter 1) to replace high-temperature metal alloys in rocket motor components.[7] These components achieved weight savings of 30–50% and demonstrated the ability of braiding to produce composite components of complex shape. The various styles of three-dimensional braiding can be tailored for specific structural applications and can all be accomplished with a range of fiber materials: glass, carbon, aramid, ceramic, and metal. With three-dimensional braiding, it is possible to braid inserts or holes into the structure that have a greater stability than holes that have been machined. The braid pattern can be varied during operation so that a change in cross-sectional shape is possible, including introducing a taper to the preform. Thick-walled tubular structures can also be made by suitable arrangement of the braiding architecture and flat preforms can be made from these tubular structures by braiding splits into the preform then cutting and opening it out to the required shape.[17] A bend is also possible as well as a bifurcation, which will allow junctions to be produced and these processes even allow $90°$ yarns to be laid into the preform during manufacture. This wide range of possible preform shapes makes three-dimensional braiding one of the most potentially versatile ways of producing a three-dimensional fiber reinforced preform.

14.5.7 Mechanical Properties Three-Dimensional Braided Composites

14.5.7.1 In-Plane Properties. The mechanical properties of three-dimensional braided composites have been studied since the 1980s, but in spite of this, the extent of the published literature only constitutes a small part of the information necessary to fully characterize this class of composite material. The current lack of detailed test data and an inadequate understanding of their mechanical behavior is limiting the use of three-dimensional braided composites in aircraft structures.

The most influential factor on the in-plane properties is the angle that the braided yarns (including the axial yarns if present) make with the loading direction. The braiding angle is set by the pattern to which the preform is being braided, and a closer orientation of the yarn to the load direction increases the mechanical properties in this axis but lowers the properties transverse to this direction. A similar result is obtained when some of the braiding yarns are kept fixed in the axial position or extra axial fibers are inserted. Because the braided yarns all travel to the specimen surface in the common three-dimensional braiding processes, any machining of the surfaces will result in the braiding yarns becoming discontinuous along the specimen length, with a resultant drop in performance.

Other aspects of the braided preform such as tow size and the type of three-dimensional braiding process used to manufacture the preform have also been seen to influence the in-plane properties.[7] When compared with two-dimensional laminates with similar lay-ups and fiber contents, it has generally been observed that three-dimensional braided composites have inferior in-plane properties. This is because, as mentioned previously, the braiding process tends to crimp the yarns, lowering their performance relative to tape laminates.

14.5.7.2 Out-of-Plane Properties.   There is, equally, a lack of published data on the impact performance of three-dimensional braids. A limited amount of work is published in the open literature. The results tend to indicate that, compared with conventional laminates, three-dimensional braided specimens suffer a much reduced damage area. Futher, the residual compression strength after impact is also higher in the three-dimensional braided specimen than in the two-dimensional laminated material. However, the impact performance of two-dimensional braids is approximately the same as three-dimensional braids. This result is explained on the basis that even with an absence of z-direction yarns, the architecture of a two-dimensional braid is undulated with the layers significantly nesting with each other. This makes it very difficult for impact damage to propagate extensively within the composite when compared with the relatively straight crack paths available in tape laminates.

14.5.8 Applications

A variety of demonstrator parts have been made that clearly illustrate the versatility of the three-dimensional braiding process. C-, J-, and T-section panels, I-beams, bifurcated beams, connecting rods, airframe spars, F-section fuselage frames, fuselage barrels, and rocket engine nozzles have all been produced using this process, and examples of such products are shown in Figure 14.17. However, in spite of these successful manufacturing demonstrations, there is currently no reported aerospace use of a component manufactured using a three-dimensional braided reinforcement.

14.6   Knitting

Knitting refers to a technique for producing textile fabrics and preforms by intermeshing loops of yarns using knitting needles. A continuous series of

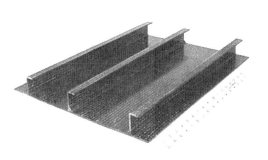

Fig. 14.17   Examples of parts that were fabricated using three-dimensional braiding. Courtesy Atlantic Research Corporation.

knitting stitches or intermeshed loops is formed by the needle, which, catching the yarn and drawing it through a previously formed loop, forms a new loop. In a knit structure, rows, known as *courses*, run across the width of the fabric, and columns, known as *wales*, run along the length of the fabric. The loops in the courses and wales are supported by and interconnected with each other to form the final fabric. Depending on the direction in which the loops are formed, knitting can be broadly categorized into one of two types—*weft knitting* and *warp knitting* (Fig. 14.18). Weft knitting is characterized by loops forming through the feeding of the weft yarn at right angles to the direction in which the fabric is produced. Warp knitting, on the other hand, is characterized by loops forming through the feeding of the warp yarns, usually from warp beams, parallel to the direction in which the fabric is produced. These basic knit architectures can be modified through the use of tuck and float loops to achieve specific macroscopic properties in the fabric. In general, the former makes a knitted fabric wider, thicker, and slightly less extensible, and the latter creates the opposite effect, as well as increases the proportion of straight yarns in the structure, which is an important consideration for many composites applications.

Since fibers are required to bend over sharp radii and maneuver sharp corners to form the knitted loops of the structure, knitting may not at first appear to be a manufacturing technique that would be suitable for use in the production of aerospace components. However, the knitted carbon and glass fabric that can be produced on current, standard industrial knitting machines has particular properties that potentially make it very suitable for certain aerospace composite components. Current machinery is also capable of producing preforms with up to four interconnected layers of knitted fabric. Therefore, although the process is not yet able to manufacture preforms with thickness dimensions as large as weaving or braiding, it is still able to produce three-dimensional fiber architectures.

Knit architectures result in a fabric of relatively low strength and stiffness compared with tape or woven cloth, but the knitted fabric is highly conformable

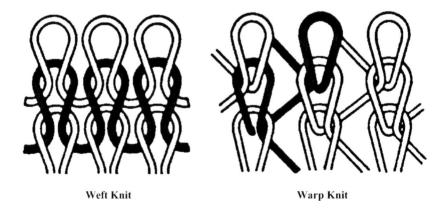

Weft Knit   Warp Knit

Fig. 14.18   Schematic diagram illustrating weft and warp knitting.

and is therefore ideally suited to manufacture non-structural components of complex shape. Layers of knitted fabric can be stretched to cover a relatively complex tool surface without the need to cut and overlap sections. This reduces material wastage and helps decrease the costs of manufacturing complex shape components such as fairings (Fig. 14.19).

More advanced industrial knitting machines are now capable of producing very complex, net-shaped structures at high production rates with little material wastage. Through careful knit loop control, structures that are very difficult to produce using conventional fabrics can be knitted to net shape, thereby further reducing manufacturing costs. These preforms can also incorporate oriented fibers in selected areas to improve the mechanical performance of the finished component.[18]

14.6.1 Mechanical Properties

14.6.1.1 In-Plane Properties. The in-plane mechanical properties of knitted composites are usually anisotropic. This is due to a difference in the relative proportion of fibers oriented in the knitted fabric, and is therefore a function of the knit structure as well as knitting parameters, such as stitch density. The knit structure is not only controlled by the choice of knit architecture but also by the amount and manner to which the fabric is deformed, thereby modifying the relative fiber orientation prior to consolidation. Similarly, knitted composite properties are also controlled by manipulating parameters such as loop lengths or

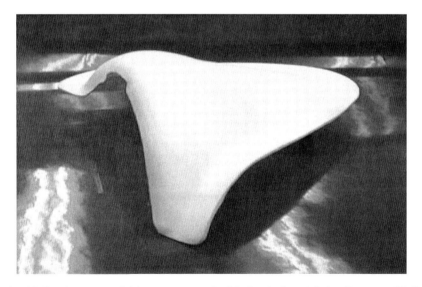

Fig. 14.19   Aerospace fairing constructed of knitted glass fabric. Courtesy CRC-ACS Ltd, Melbourne, Australia.

stitch density of a particular knit architecture. Nevertheless, the strength of knitted composites in compression is dominated by the properties of the resin.

The strength and stiffness of knitted composites are inferior to woven, braided and unidirectional materials having an equivalent proportion of in-plane fibers. This is due to the limited utilisation of fiber stiffness and strength resulting from the severely bent fibers in knit structures. Similarly, knitted composites are expected to have in-plane properties that are close to those of random fiber mats composites (Table. 14. 2).

Failure of knitted composites is a complex process with the yarn crossover points and the curved side legs of the knit loops being critical points at which failure occurs. Substantial microcracking from yarn-matrix debonding at these positions within the knitted fabric is also observed during failure.

14.6.1.2 Out-of-Plane Properties. The three-dimensional nature of knitted fabrics is effective in promoting fiber bridging to enhance Mode I fracture toughness where improvements over more conventional composites of up to 10-fold have been observed. These superior Mode I fracture toughness values are reflected in the energy absorption capabilities and impact penetration resistance of knitted composites. As illustrated in Fig. 14.20, under impact conditions, knitted composite materials are found to retain far higher proportions of their undamaged strength when compared with conventional two-dimensional composite reinforcements[19].

14.6.2 Applications

The highly looped fiber architecture ensures that knitted fabrics are able to easily undergo significant amounts of deformation when subjected to an external force. Their formability raises the potential of knitted fabric for cost-effective composite fabrication of complex and intricate shapes. This advantage extends to permitting holes in a composite to be formed or knitted in, instead of drilled. As continuous fibers diffuse stresses away from the hole, the strength in the knitted/formed hole region is increased leading to notch strength and bearing properties

Table 14.2   Typical Mechanical Properties of E-Glass/Vinyl Ester Knitted Composites Vf ~ 55% Courtesy of the CRC-ACS Ltd.

	Plain knit	Rib knit	Milano knit
Tensile strength (MPa)	165	114	135
Tensile modulus (Gpa)	13.6	14.3	14.8
Tensile failure strain (%)	2.7	1.7	2.3
Compressive strength (MPa)	138	169	168
Compressive modulus (GPa)	11.6	11.2	11.2
Compressive failure strain (%)	1.9	2.0	1.9

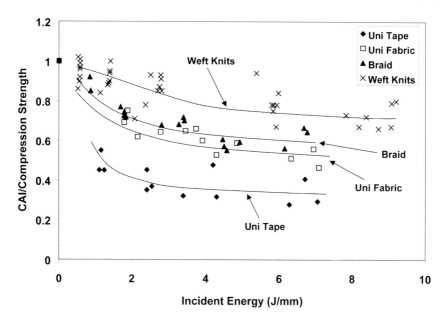

Fig. 14.20   Comparison of normalized retained compression strength after drop weight impact of various E-Glass reinforcements. Vf ~ 55%.

that are relatively a higher proportion of un-notched strength than is the case for composites with a drilled hole. Generally, knitted composites are generally notch-insensitive.

In general, flat knit and shape knit products have so far been used primarily as a demonstration of the ability of the knitting process to manufacture complex shaped components. Jet engine vanes, T-shaped connectors, car wheel wells and aerospace fairings have all been successfully manufactured,[7] however the low mechanical performance of the knitted fabric is a deterrent to its wider use.

14.7   Non-crimp Fabrics

One application of knitting is the subject of intense interest within the aerospace industry. Using warp-knitting techniques in conjunction with fiber placement concepts, multiaxial, multilayer warp-knit fabrics, more commonly known as non-crimp fabrics, can be produced with in-plane fibers that are relatively straight. These in-plane fibers are held in place by a stitched or knitted thermoplastic polymer (typically nylon or dacron) fiber or a flexible high performance fiber such as glass or aramid. The material is not crimped as in the case of woven material, and as such the fibers are arranged in a more optimal fashion (Fig. 14.21). The availability of heavy multi-layered fabric with the

a)

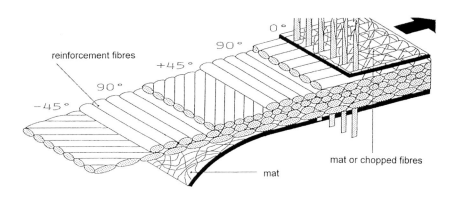

b)

Fig. 14.21 *a)* **Non-crimp fabric being produced;** *b)* **typical non-crimp fabric. Courtesy of LIBA-Maschinenfabrik GmbH, Naila, Germany.**

desired fiber orientations also has significant economic benefits in production because the reduced ply count required means that lay-up rates are much higher than for conventional lighter fabrics.

A reasonably wide variety of these non-crimp broadcloth fabrics are currently commercially available in glass and carbon yarn. They have three main advantages. First, unlike multilayer woven preforms, the material affords cost-effective off-axis reinforcement. Second, like other multilayer textile preforms, this material has the potential to greatly reduce production cost through reducing the time taken to lay-up the composite component. Finally, this material has the potential to outperform traditional two-dimensional pre-preg tape laminates because it too contains nominally straight fibers but with the added advantage of having through-thickness reinforcement for improved out-of-plane properties. Although stitched two-dimensional laminates can also offer the same attributes, stitching is nevertheless a secondary operation, and there appears to be a general component size and cost restriction with this technique.

14.7.1 In-Plane Properties

In general, three-dimensional warp-knit non-crimp composites have slightly inferior in-plane properties when compared with unidirectional pre-preg tape laminates of similar lay-up[20] (Table 14.3). The tension control of the through-thickness component is of paramount importance to minimize any out-of-plane crimping (waviness) of the in-plane fiber yarns while maintaining good controllability of the preform. Similarly, the yarn size and stitch density will determine the degree of in-plane crimping and fiber damage in the load-carrying fiber yarns. The presence of any such crimping could render the non-crimp composites inferior under tensile, compressive, and flexural conditions, compared with two-dimensional woven composites. On the other hand, insufficient tension in the through-thickness yarns will cause them to buckle under cure pressure and hence, be ineffective at providing a crack closure force.

It should be noted that the in-plane properties could be degraded by the impalement of the non-crimp layers by the knitting needles. This impalement causes fiber distortion and damage, a phenomenon not dissimilar to that observed for stitched composites. A way to eradicate this is to ensure knitting needles are

Table 14.3   **Comparison of in-plane mechanical properties for carbon/epoxy tri-axial layups manufactured from two-dimensional unidirectional pre-preg tape and 2 layers of tri-axial non-crimp fabric**

	2-D Unidirectional Pre-preg Tape $[45_2, -45_2, 0_6, -45_2, 45_2]_s$		Non-crimp $[\{45, -45,0\}, \{0, -45,45\}]_s$	
Test orientation	$0°$	$90°$	$0°$	$90°$
Tensile modulus (GPa)	64.8	21.4	60.8	17.2
Tensile strength (MPa)	951	123	621	159
Compressive modulus (GPa)	59.9	19.6	54.7	16.5
Compressive strength (MPa)	852	215	574	236

inserted between tows of in-plane fibers. However, the gaps that are formed between the tows by doing this are potential resin-rich sites that are considered detrimental to some properties.

Microscopic analysis has shown that the knit structure in the non-crimp composite appears effective in constraining the delaminations and longitudinal splitting that are normally associated with unidirectional pre-preg tape laminate. Other than that, it seems that non-crimp and unidirectional pre-preg tape laminates have very similar failure mechanisms, essentially, multiple cracking in off-axis plies and delamination at $\pm 45^\circ$ interfaces.

14.7.2 Out-of-Plane Properties

The interlaminar fracture toughness of non-crimp composites is superior to that of unidirectional pre-preg tapes due to the knitting yarn acting to bridge the crack and restrict its further growth when subjected to out-of-plane loads. In spite of this, little improvement is observed in the suppression of delamination damage due to impact. The damage tolerance of non-crimp and unidirectional pre-preg tape composites is similar, although the former exhibits superior compression-after-impact strengths with increasing impact energy level.

The damage generated in non-crimp composites by low-energy impact is more complex than that in unidirectional pre-preg tape laminates. Instead of a collection of shear cracks linking delamination planes, which is normally observed in unidirectional pre-preg laminates, the impact damage created within non-crimp composites consists of an intricate array of cracks not dissimilar to that observed in more conventional knitted composites. This highly branched cracking links planes of delamination which also contain parallel matrix cracks that appear to coincide with the inter-fiber tow resin-rich regions. The presence of the z-direction reinforcement yarns in the non-crimp fabric should be very effective in reducing the amount of back face spalling compared with unidirectional pre-preg tape laminates. The level of performance improvement in this area would be linked to the mechanical properties of the z-direction yarns.

14.7.3 Applications

There are significant cost incentives to be gained with non-crimp fabric in comparison with unidirectional pre-preg tape composites. These include reduced wastage and labor, adaptability to automation, and virtually unlimited shelf life without the need for refrigeration. Limitations arise from issues such as relatively higher raw material cost, impracticality in terms of ply drop-offs, and restrictions on the number of fabric types available commercially. The overall cost implication is, therefore, an important consideration when deciding between the more traditional unidirectional pre-preg tapes and non-crimp composites. In spite of these issues, a great deal of effort is being devoted within the aerospace industry to develop these fabrics for use within secondary and primary structures and components that have been demonstrated include wing stringers and wing panels. It is anticipated that a number of significant components on the Airbus A380 will be manufactured from non-crimp fabrics.

14.8   Conclusion

Stitching and z-pinning are applicable to current two-dimensional composites and provide improved damage tolerance and strength to bonded joints. They are also beneficial as manufacturing aids and may reduce the need for mechanical fasteners in some cases. The main issues are the increased costs and the need for specialised equipment. The reduction of some in-plane properties may also be an important issue.

Three-dimensional textile manufacturing processes are an emerging field and they offer similar advantages to two-dimensional processes, albeit not without their restrictions. Design or manufacturing criteria that favor the use of a particular textile process for one application may not necessarily be relevant for another. It is also possible that for some structures it may be necessary to combine a number of the textile processes to achieve a cost-effective product with the required performance. Of particular importance is the intimate connection between the textile manufacturing process, the required preform design, the cost, and the performance of the resultant composite. A large range of possible preform architectures can now be produced, each with its own mechanical performance and associated cost. It is, therefore, critical that in the design of any component, early consideration is given to the method of manufacture because only seemingly slight, relatively unimportant changes to component shape or required performance may result in significant changes to the cost of manufacturing a preform.

In spite of the relative youth of these manufacturing techniques, advanced textile preforms are beginning to be used in the manufacture of aerospace components. The potential savings in cost and improvements in performance that can be realized through the use of these processes are sufficiently attractive that extensive efforts are being put into further developing these processes. It is not yet clear how far these developments will go, but as designers and manufacturers become more familiar, and hence confident, with the advanced textile composites on offer, the use of these techniques will become more commonplace.

References

[1]Dow, M. B., and Smith, D. L., "Damage Tolerant Composite Materials Produced by Stitching Carbon Fabrics," *Proceedings of the 21st International SAMPE Technical Conference*, Sept. 1989, pp. 595–605.

[2]Poe, Jr, C. C., Dexter, H. B., and Raju, I. S., "Review of the NASA Textile Composites Research," *Journal of Aircraft*, Vol. 36, 1999, pp. 876–884.

[3] Mouritz, A. P., and Cox, B. N., "A Mechanistic Approach to the Properties of Stitched Laminates," *Composites Part A*, Vol. 31A, No. 1, 1999, pp. 1–27.

[4] Beckwith, S., and Hyland, C., "Resin Transfer Molding: A Decade of Technology Advances," *SAMPE Journal*, Vol. 34, No. 6, 1998, pp. 7–19.

[5] Crothers, P., Drechsler, K., Feltin, D., Herszberg, I., and Kruckenberg, T., "Tailored Fibre Placement to Minimise Stress Concentrations," *Composites Part A*, Vol. 28A, 1997, pp. 619–625.

[6] Freitas, G., Fusco, T., Campbell, T., Harris, J., and Rosenberg, S., "Z-fiber Technology and Products for Enhancing Composite Design," *Proceedings of the 83rd Meeting of the AGARD Structures and Materials Panel on Bolted/Bonded Joints in Polymeric Composites*, Sept. 1996, pp. 17–11 - 17–18.

[7] Tong, L., Mouritz, A. P., and Bannister, M. K., *3D Fibre Reinforced Polymer Composites*, Elsevier Science, Oxford, UK, 2002.

[8] Freitas, G., Magee, C., Dardzinski, P., and Fusco, T., "Fiber Insertion Process for Improved Damage Tolerance in Aircraft Laminates," *Journal of Advanced Materials*, July 1994, pp. 36–43.

[9] Renze, S. P., Carnegie, S. W., and Sandow, F., "Experimental Evaluation of Survivable Composite Structural Concepts," *Proceedings of the 37th AIAA/ASME/ASCE/AHS/ASC, Structures, Structural Dynamics, and Materials Conference and Exhibition*, April 1996, pp. 39–46.

[10] Steeves, C., and Fleck, N., "Z-pinned Composites: Knockdown in Compressive Strength," *Proceedings of the Fifth Conference on Deformation and Fracture of Composites*, 18–19 March 1999, pp. 60–68.

[11] Kandebo, S. W., "Upcoming Blade Tests Aimed at Growth GE90," *Aviation Week and Space Technology*, 1999, pp. 40–41.

[12] Mouritz, A. P., Bannister, M. K., Falzon, P. J., and Leong, K. H., "Review of Applications for Advanced Three-dimensional Fibre Textile Composites," *Composites: Part A*, Vol. 30, 1999, pp. 1445–1461.

[13] Black, S., "Preforms Get Lean and Mean," *High Performance Composites*, March 2002, pp. 42–47.

[14] Kandero, S. W., "France, Russia to Join in Scramjet Flight Tests," *Aviation Week and Space Technology*, 26 March 2001, pp. 60–62.

[15] Yang, G., Pastore, C. M., Tsai, Y. J., Soebroto, H. B., and Ko, F. K., "CAD/CAM of Braided Preforms for Advanced Composites," *Proceedings Advanced Composites III—Expanding the Technology*, ASM International, Materials Park, OH, 1987, pp. 103–107.

[16] Hess, J. P., "Braided Composite Structures," *Composite Applications: The Future is Now*, 1st ed, SME, 1989, pp. 375–381.

[17] Brown, R. and Crow, E., "Automated Through-the-Thickness Braiding," *Proceedings of the 37th National SAMPE Symposium*, 9–12 March 1992, pp. 832–841.

[18] Van Vuure, A., Ko, F. K., and Balonis, R. J., "Textile Preforming for Complex Shape Structural Composites," *Proceedings of the 44th International SAMPE Symposium*, 23–27 May 1999, pp. 293–302.

[19] Khondker, O. A., Leong, K. H., Bannister, M., and Herszberg, I., "Performance of Weft-knitted Glass Fibre Fabric Composites with Respect to Impact Damage Resistance and Tolerance," *Proceedings of the 32nd International SAMPE Technical Conference*, 5–9 November 2000.

[20] Bibo, G. A., Hogg, P. J., and Kemp, M., "Mechanical Characterisation of Glass- and Carbon-fibre Reinforced Composites Made with Non-crimp Fabrics," *Composites Science and Technology*, Vol. 57, 1997, pp. 1221.

15
Smart Structures

15.1 Introduction

Through evolution, biological structures have become highly optimized both in their mechanical properties (e.g., strength, stiffness, and toughness), and in their ability to sense and respond to the environment—to sense threats, heal damage, and respond to external demands (e.g., adaptive shape and other functions such as stealth).

The active/sensory "smart" behavior of these materials involves the following systems:

- **Sensor**
  - nerve: develops signals from external stimuli: senses overstress, physical damage, temperature, chemical attack
- **Actuator**
  - muscle: provides response to a signal; provides force for movement or shape change
- **Processor**
  - brain: monitors sensor, processes data, provides signal to actuator

Smart behavior of biological structures includes:

- Adaptive shape
  - e.g., for aerodynamic control
- Adaptive stiffness
  - to optimize for loading conditions
- Adaptive strengthening
  - reinforcement deposition to optimize strength and stiffness
- Health monitoring
  - indication of damage or overstress
- Self repair
  - heals damage by local deposition of material
  - re-grows damaged component
- Reversible adhesion
  - ability to form and break strong adhesive bonds at will
- Stealth
  - change in form, colour, and/or pattern

Fiber composites simulate natural materials, such as wood and bone, in forming lightweight, stiff, tough structures. Now there is a rapidly growing interest in simulating selected aspects of this intelligent or "smart" behavior, particularly in aerospace composite structures.

15.2 Engineering Approaches

Based on the discussion of the proceding section, smart structures can be defined as structures that are "aware" of their state and have the ability to respond to changes in the operating environment or to other stimuli in an intelligent way. This ability may be achieved by processing information from sensors and driving actuators or more simply from a built-in response mechanism. The terminology adopted here has been taken from Gandhi and Thompson,[1] and is illustrated in the flow diagram in Figure 15.1. This Figure shows the various sub-systems in a so-called active smart structure that consists of structural health monitoring systems

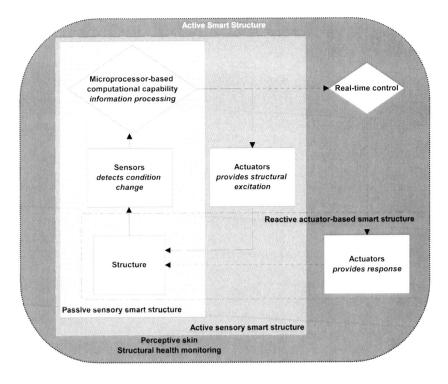

Fig. 15.1 Schematic diagram showing components of an active smart structure—different sensory schemes are indicated.

and the reactive actuator-based smart structure, in other words, systems without an adaptive feedback loop. Systems that incorporate adaptive feedback loops are referred to as active smart structures.

Currently, smart structures are made up of individual sensors and actuators embedded in the material or bonded to its surface, as well as microprocessor and possibly a power source. In the future, these components may be integrated, possibly at the molecular level.

The engineering analogies for the basic smart functions of biological materials are:

- **Sensor**
  - strain: optical fibers, electrical-resistance strain gauges, surface acoustic wave sensors, piezoelectric transducers (ceramic and polymer)
    * interrogated electrically or optically in the case of passive elements, or by generated charge in the case of piezoelectric transducers
  - chemical: optical fibers, surface acoustic wave sensors, and various ceramics
- **Actuator**
  - piezoelectric ceramic transducers, shape memory alloys and ceramics, magnetostrictive materials, electrorheological fluids, and carbon nanotubes
    * actuated by electric, magnetic, or thermal (electric current) energy to change shape or produce a force from a power source, generally an amplifier
- **Processor**
  - microcomputer or a built-in response that may simply be included in the sensor or actuator

Appendix A provides a brief description of some current sensor and actuator systems. These elements (not including the power source) may be integrated into free-standing microscopic devices called micro-electromechanical systems (MEMS) or micro-systems. These systems can sense, control, and actuate at the micro scale and function individually or in arrays to generate effects on the macro scale. Micro-systems may also include optical components for sensing and processing; these systems are referred to as micro-electro-opto-mechanical systems (MEOMS).

Polymer-matrix composites lend themselves well to the embedded approach because these elements can be incorporated during manufacture of the component and the mechanical properties of the composite tailored to provide the desired mechanical response for the actuators. Thus, composites are well suited to the formation of adaptive structures (for example, structures able to change geometry). Embedding is possible because the relatively low temperatures and pressures required to produce the materials will not damage the sensors or actuators. However, for existing composite structures and metallic structures (where embedding is not possible), the elements can be attached to the surface of the component. Although this approach is much less robust than the embedded approach, it will be effective for some applications.

In the medium term, it is hoped that the life-cycle costs of airframe structures can be reduced by the application of smart structure technologies for structural health and usage-monitoring and even to extend life. Long-term aims are to develop structures with adaptive shape and other morphological capabilities.

Some of the potential applications of smart structure technologies are as follows:

Health and usage monitoring

- Damage detection
  - sensors to measure stress, strain, temperature or life consumption
  - sensors indicating damage size and severity and location over the whole structure
- Environmental degradation (bonded joints)
  - embedded chemical sensors to detect incipient bond degradation
- Internal environment
  - environmental sensors to detect moisture content

Life extension

- Smart repairs
  - bonded patches or reinforcements with damage sensors to detect disbonding of the patch or growth of the repaired damage
- Self-healing materials
  - encapsulated adhesive systems (separate resin and hardener) in composite structures that activate on local damage and react to re-bond the damaged zone)
  - Memory alloys contract on activation to close up the damaged region
- Vibration suppression
  - bonded on sensor/controller/actuator system
    * providing out-of-phase force to increase damping
  - electrorheological fluids to enhance damping

Improved operations

- Signature reduction (acoustic, infrared, radar, visual)
  - active paints—thermochromatic, photochromatic, electrochromatic
    * change color and/or infrared emissivity when stimulated
  - active coatings with embedded MEMS to send out false signal
- Integrated antenna airframe structure
  - embed antenna into composite skins
    * reduce drag, observables, etc.
- Adaptive structures
  - embedded sensor/controller actuator system to modify shape of component
    * wings, helicopter blades, etc.

- Adaptive surfaces
  - use of MEMS to modify surface contour
    * may eliminate need for large hinged control surfaces
- Active noise suppression
  - sensor/controller/actuator system
    * generate a disturbance to cancel out noise (if narrow band)
    * change model shape

15.2.1 Structural Health Monitoring

Figure 15.1 illustrates that structural health-monitoring systems can be classed as two types of systems: passive and active sensory smart structures. The passive sensory smart structure contains only sensors and electronics, with a communication mechanism and potentially some storage and processing capability, which is capable of processing the sensor data in such a way that will provide the operator with structural condition information. These systems are passive to the extent that the sensors are using the structural in-flight loads to detect/monitor structural damage. Active sensory systems contain both sensors and actuators. In this case, the actuators provide a well-defined (known) excitation and the response is monitored by the sensors. This sensing system can be used on demand by the operator, for example, at the beginning or end of each flight.

Current approaches to ensure aircraft integrity for metallic components rely simply on measuring fatigue consumption, achievable through the use of usage monitoring techniques. However, when this approach is combined with continuous damage detection it is called a health and usage monitoring system (HUMS) or structural health monitoring (SHM).

This approach can eliminate or drastically reduce the need for inspection. The ability to detect damage is particularly important for composite structures that are susceptible to impact damage and disbond damage in secondary bonded joints. Here, SHM systems will enable the detection and characterization of this type of insidious damage. The introduction of SHM-based structures may allow less stringent certification requirements, thus reducing the cost of certification of composite structures and possibly reducing certification concerns with secondary bonded structures.

Using smart sensor concepts, damage and damage growth in the airframe and other structural life-related problems would be continuously monitored on-board the aircraft to provide real-time damage assessment. This technology could permit a reduction in inspection and regular maintenance costs with substantial impact on the through-life costs.

The overall goal is for the structural health monitoring system to form a sub-system of a total integrated vehicle health monitoring system (IVHMS).[2] To achieve this goal, significant progress needs to be achieved in the areas of structural health monitoring sensors, data/information processing, diagnostic and prognostic algorithm development, and data dissemination and storage. Current SHM programs are concentrating on the demonstration of various sensor systems, such as optical fiber and piezotransducer systems, through civil flight-testing and the development of design guidelines for incorporation of sensors into composite manufacturing processes.

15.2.2   Improved Aircraft Operations and Extended Airframe Life

Figure 15.1 illustrates that the next category of smart structure (beyond the perceptive structures/structural health monitoring systems) is the reactive actuator-based smart structure that is devoid of sensors and contains only actuators. One example would be a shape memory alloy, actuated temperature fuse. Finally, the fully active smart structure is one that contains sensors, actuators, information processors, and a real-time control capability (i.e., with feedback).

Smart materials and structures technologies can be used in various ways to improve operations or extend life, for example, by:

- Reducing dynamic instabilities, vibrations, and noise by using active vibration and noise control
- Improving aircraft/rotorcraft handling, manipulating lift, or reducing drag by the application of adaptive structures and aerodynamic flow control
- Incorporating conformal antennas to improve aerodynamics and low observable characteristics, as well as reducing fabrication costs by developing multi-functional structures integrated electronics and devices

Excessive vibration and noise may affect the fatigue life of the structure and electrical components and crew/passenger effectiveness/comfort. A number of applications have been identified in which smart structure technologies have the potential to improve structural life and operational performance[:3] tail buffet wing/store flutter, isolation of electronics from forced vibration, helicopter blade/vortex interaction, and blade tracking.

By incorporating actuators within the composite structure to make the structure bend and flex, the concept of shape control or morphing can be applied.[4] The actuators may induce wing warp, camber shaping and/or control surface deformation; they may also produce structures with variable stiffness. Lift/drag of a control surface may also be controlled/improved by changing the flow conditions over the lifting surface. The expected benefits from such concepts are: reduced drag over a broad range of flight conditions, increased payload, greater range, improved aerodynamic performance, and improved low-observability characteristics.

Composite structures allow for fabrication of smart skins that incorporate radiofrequency (RF) antennas, signal processors, and various other types of sensors and devices. One example is conformal antennas, that is, load-bearing structures that incorporate embedded controllable and reconfigurable antennas. Typical military aircraft have a large number of antennas; for example, the

F/A-18 has approximately 70 antenna apertures for radar and communication functions.

Conventional antennas require structural cut-outs, and with their associated structural reinforcements, protrude from the airframe thus degrading aerodynamic performance; weight consequently increases, further adding to operation costs. It has been estimated that up to 50% of an aircraft's surface, if composite, could be used to incorporate RF antenna functions. Potential benefits of conformal antennas include reduced weight and volume, lower observability, reduced power requirements, greater radar and communication range, reduced manufacture and maintenance costs, and improved aerodynamic performance.

15.3 Selected Applications and Demonstrators

To illustrate smart structure applications to composite components, a few examples are discussed below.

15.3.1 Structural Health (and Usage) Monitoring Systems

15.3.1.1 Smart Patch. The application of bonded composite patches to repair or reinforce defective metallic or composite structures is a very effective and versatile procedure.[5] However, airworthiness authorities are often reluctant to certify bonded composite repairs to primary structures because of concerns with the reliability and durability of adhesive bonds.[6] The smart patch approach is being developed to alleviate these concerns and thus facilitate the application of composite bonded repairs to primary structure.

The smart patch concept consists of a bonded composite repair with the ability to monitor its own health,[7] thus enabling a continuous safety-by-inspection approach to be applied. This approach will allow timely decisions on preventative and scheduled maintenance before failure of the repair or repaired structure.

The specific objectives of the smart patch are:

- To detect disbond growth in the safe-life zone of the patch (Fig. 15.2a), which is unacceptable because damage can grow very quickly
- To monitor damage growth in the damage-tolerant zone, where damage growth is stable and slow

Damage in the damage-tolerant zone may consist of either cracks or delaminations in the parent metallic or composite structure and also disbonds in the adhesive or delaminations in the patch system. Current research[7] is focused on the assessment of new sensing techniques and sensors, which may be incorporated in bonded repair systems, to detect and monitor disbonds in the adhesive layer, delamination in the patch system, quality of the bond, and crack growth rates in the underlying metallic substrate.

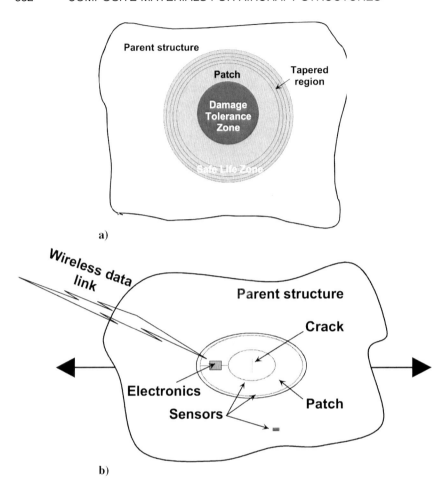

Fig. 15.2   Schematic diagram of *a*) **a generic external bonded repair showing safe-life zone (no disbonding allowed in this zone) and damage-tolerant zone (stable disbonding growth allowed in this zone) and** *b*) **the smart patch concept.**

The most direct approach to assess the health of the patch system is to measure the level of load transfer in the safe-life zone (See Fig 15.2a). The concept is to monitor the ratio: (patch strains)/(strain in the component) during service life. Any decrease in this patch health ratio is an indication of disbonding of the patch in this critical end region. There is no requirement to measure the actual loading; disbonding is indicated by the reduction in relative strain. The strain sensors are continually monitored by an on-board miniaturized system that processes and stores patch health information and then transmits these data to an external computer by an infrared link when required, as shown conceptually in Figure 15.2b.

An alternative approach for monitoring the patch is to measure damage directly, as described later.

15.3.1.2 Optical Fiber Sensors: Loads and Damage Monitoring.

For embedded optical fiber systems, the interaction between the optical fiber and the host composite needs to be considered from the point of view of structural integrity and also in understanding the response of the sensor due to its embedding. Considerable effort has been directed toward characterizing the effects of embedded optical fiber sensors on the polymer fiber composite.[8] Figure 15.3 is a micrograph of cross-sectioned carbon/epoxy laminates with embedded 150-μm polyimide buffered optical fibers, showing that the introduction of the optical fiber is relatively unobtrusive in terms of fiber and resin distribution in these laminates when the optical fiber is collinear with the reinforcing fiber. Because of the better thermal stability of the polyimide-coated fibers compared with acrylic, these fibers give superior interfacial mechanical properties. In general, as long as the optical fibers are collinear with the reinforcing fibers, and the percentage of the optical fibers is significantly lower than that of the reinforcing fibers, the mechanical properties are not compromised. Numerous static and fatigue studies of carbon/epoxy laminates with embedded optical fibers (when the fibers are collinear with the reinforcing fibers) have indicated no significant variation in the mechanical properties for room temperature/dry and hot/wet environmental conditions.[9,10] From the point of view of understanding the performance of the sensor due to embedding, the

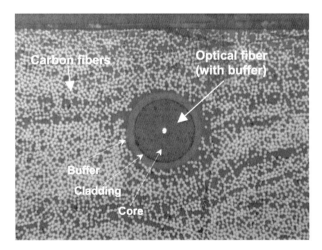

Fig. 15.3   Micrograph of cross-sectional laminates illustrating a polyimide coated fiber in carbon/epoxy laminate. The carbon fibers have typical fiber diameters of 7 μm, the optical fibers have typical core and cladding diameters of 10 μm and 125 μm, respectively, and the polyimide coating is typically about 12 μm thick.

fiber is considered as an elastic inclusion within the host, and therefore the interaction between this inclusion and the host needs to be considered when interpreting data from the sensor. For example, a significant difference has been observed between the sensitivity of embedded and surface mounted metal-coated optical fibers.[11]

Rugged and non-intrusive connection systems for optical fiber sensors are required for these systems to be accepted. Therefore, either embedded optical fiber connectors and/or (embedded) wireless communication systems will need to be installed, allowing robust connection on demand without interfering with the measurand.

One of the earliest uses of optical fiber systems was to detect impact damage and monitor damage growth in aramid fiber/epoxy in the leading edge of the DASH-8 aircraft.[12] In this case, special sensitized optical fibers were embedded within the composite leading edge that was fractured after an impact event that exceeded a certain threshold value. The fibers only fractured within the immediate vicinity of the impact site. Thus, when HeNe laser light was transmitted through the fiber, light was emitted from the fiber-fractured ends. Thus, the impact sites were observed visually by significant leakage of laser radiation at these sites. Without treatment, these silica optical fibers can withstand significant shear and in-plane stresses sustained during impact damage without breaking; these fibers break at much higher strains ($\sim 5\%$) than do most structural materials. Therefore, the most difficult aspect of this technique is in the application of surface treatments that sensitize the fiber to break at a given consistent strain level.

Fiber Bragg grating sensors (see Appendix A) provide a quasi distributed, non intrusive, accurate, and reliable measurement of temperature, strain, and pressure. A fiber Bragg grating system was used on the DC-XA prototype[13] (Delta Clipper experimental advanced re-usable rocket program) to monitor loads on ground tests and during takeoff of several highly stressed components. The system enabled the ground personnel to achieve readily understood (in graphical format) load and temperature distributions of the advanced structural components in the vehicle.

A successful application of the fiber Bragg grating system has been applied to yacht composite masts[14] where 60 optical fiber strain sensors were embedded in 12 separate optical fibers at various locations throughout the rig. Figure 15.4 shows the optical fiber Bragg grating sensors being embedded in the carbon/ epoxy masts during fabrication. A total of 43 sensors were monitored in real time, at a rate of about 500 times per second, with most sensors measuring strains within the range of 3500 $\mu\varepsilon$ and some sensors measured extreme strains ($\pm 15,000$ $\mu\varepsilon$). The system was constructed using several optical fibers and a demodulation system with several channels in parallel, which were multiplexed electronically (Fig. 15.5). These systems have been successfully used to monitor loads in the mast for design information (allowing reduced weight, size, and cost) and to enable optimal safe performance during race conditions.

Fig. 15.4   Fiber Bragg grating sensors being embedded in carbon/epoxy composite yacht mast during construction.[10]

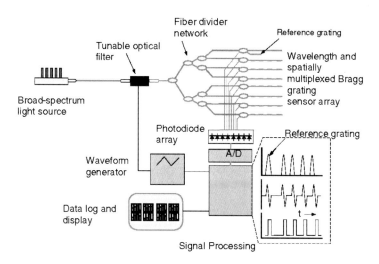

Fig. 15.5   Fiber Bragg grating strain sensor interrogation system architecture used to monitor the fiber Bragg gratings embedded in the carbon/epoxy yacht mast. [10,14]

15.3.1.3 Piezotransducers: Damage Detection/Monitoring. Low-profile piezotransducer elements for sensing and actuation offer an encouraging alternative in situ structural health monitoring (i.e., an active sensory smart structure) system for composite structures. Generally piezoelectric ceramic PZT wafers (See Appendix A) are used for actuation because these materials offer excellent force transfer to the structure, and either piezoelectric film or ceramic transducers can be used for sensing. These materials are preferred over conventional electrical resistance-foil strain gauges because they do not require an external power source; instead, they generate charge when a strain is applied, whereas conventional strain gauges require external power to operate.

The piezotransducers can be either embedded or surface-mounted. These elements offer at least three modes of interrogation: electro-mechanical impedance, transfer function, and stress-wave (or acousto-ultrasonic) technique modes. To date, the stress-wave technique offers the most promising approach as a wide-area damage detection and monitoring system. The excitation of elastic stress waves is relatively straightforward given the broadband frequency response characteristic of piezoelectric ceramic materials. The elastic stress waves travelling through the structure will be reflected/diffracted and subject to wave mode conversions by material and structural discontinuities (such as disbonds, delaminations, etc.) as shown schematically in Figure 15.6. The system can then detect and possibly characterize the damage by monitoring and analyzing the change in the reflected or transmitted signals.

One of the inherent advantages of the stress-wave arrangement over the strain-based load transfer approaches, just discussed, is that it does not require a priori

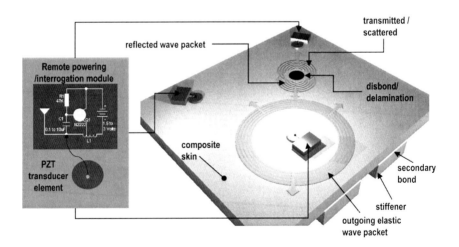

Fig. 15.6 Schematic diagram illustrating the stress-wave concept where piezotransducers are used to generate elastic stress waves that enable global structural health monitoring with low sensor density.

knowledge of the likely location of damage initiation and should therefore allow for a lower sensor density where large structures are considered. The broader sensitivity range also provides a better basis for the quantitative assessment of disbond growth. Some examples on the application of the stress-wave technique are given in the following.

Studies on composite bonded repairs have shown the excellent sensitivity of the stress wave technique to detect disbonds in secondary bonded joints.[7] In this study, the approach was to excite elastic stress waves in the host by applying a short voltage pulse to a piezoelement, SP1, surface-mounted to the metal substrate some distance from the patch edge as shown in Figure 15.7a. Part of the elastic energy is transmitted through the bond-line into the patch and received at the two piezoelectric sensor locations (SP2, located on step 3 of the patch, and SP3, located on the far-field region of the patch). Damage in composite bonded repairs was assessed by monitoring the transmitted sensor power (P) within a prescribed time window. The response at sensor SP2, as shown in Figure 15.7b, reflects a high level of sensitivity to disbond growth and correlates well with the strain gauge results.

Significant progress has been achieved in the development of the Stanford Multi Actuator Receiver Transduction (SMART) layer that consists of an array of piezoelectric ceramic wafers encapsulated within two layers of Kapton sheets,[15] as shown in Figure 15.8. The Kapton layers incorporate the copper tracks for the electrical connectivity. These SMART layers can be embedded or surfacemounted on the composite component for process control and/or damage detection. One piezotransducer (actuator) generates controlled repeatable diagnostic (acousto-ultrasonic) signals, and the resulting response is detected by the neighboring piezotransducers. By analyzing the resulting response, an indication of the state of cure (for process control) and size and location of damage sites (for structural health monitoring) can be ascertained. The SMART layer has been incorporated in composite bonded repairs and successfully used to detect and monitor crack growth in the metallic substructure.[16] Alternatively, this SMART layer can be used passively to detect noise from impacts that might occur to alert the operator to impact damage.

Novel acousto-ultrasonic (elastic stress wave) generation and detection techniques were developed to generate 2D maps of damage and failure in composite structures.[17] Phase-delayed multi-element low-profile piezoelectric ceramic actuators were designed and fabricated to generate selected ultrasonic Lamb waves, within carbon/epoxy and glass/epoxy fiber epoxy laminates. The detection of the ultrasonic response was achieved using surface-mounted interferometric optical fiber sensors. Advanced signal processing was then used to detect defects and achieve enhanced images of the defect. A multivariate outlier analysis was used to detect changes the signal that corresponded to damage, that is, generated the damage index. A visual representation of impact damage was then achieved using a mapping technique. This study also showed that the passive listening mode is also an effective technique to detect impact damage in composite laminates.

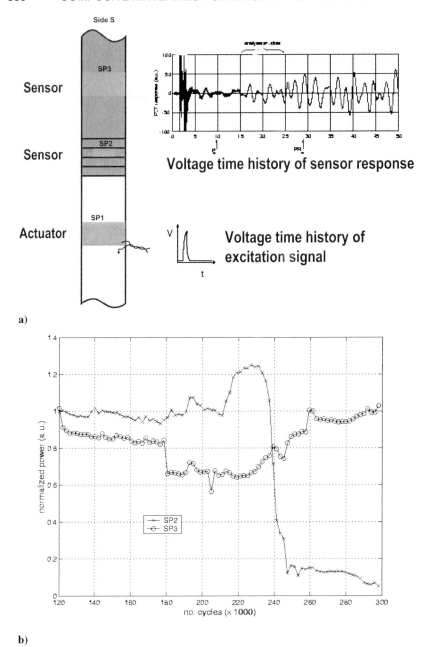

a)

b)

Fig. 15.7   *a*) Schematic diagram of skin-doubler specimen (Chapter 9), representing the termination of a repair patch, showing typical time varying voltage signals to the actuator and from the sensor; *b*) signal power versus number of cycles for piezoelectric ceramic sensor SP2 and SP3.

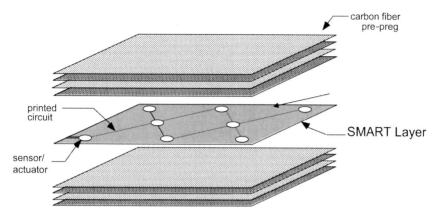

Fig. 15.8   Schematic diagram illustrating the piezoelectric sensor network, or SMART (Stanford Multi-Actuator Receiver Transduction) layer, embedded in a carbon/epoxy laminate. Taken from Ref. 15.

15.3.2   Active Smart Structures

15.3.2.1 Vibration Suppression.
High-performance aircraft, especially those with twin vertical tails such as the F/A-18, are commonly subject to an aeroelastic phenomenon called buffeting when the aircraft flies at high angles of attack. These high-performance aircraft are often required to undergo maneuvers involving high angles of attack, and under these conditions unsteady vortices emanating from the wing and the fuselage impinge on the twin fins, causing substantial buffet loads. These loads result in oscillatory stresses, which may cause significant fatigue damage that may restrict the capabilities and availability of the aircraft.

Design of aircraft to accommodate these buffet loads is a difficult task. Therefore, the use of piezoelectric ceramic actuators in conjunction with active structural control to alleviate damaging buffet induced strain (and therefore increase the fatigue life of vertical tails) is a possible solution to this important design issue.

To demonstrate this technology, a full-scale test was conducted on the vertical tail of an F/A-18. Piezoelectric ceramic actuators were attached to the composite skin of the starboard fin,[18] as shown in Figure 15.9. The fin was tested in a rig, which generates representative static and dynamic flight loads on the airframe, as well as maneuver loads. In this study, it was demonstrated that at maximum control gains, the active buffet load alleviation system was able to reduce the overall root mean square (rms) strain level over the control bandwidth from 0 to 100 Hz. The tests were carried out at a number of different flight conditions where, at the nominal flight condition, the critical strain was reduced by 51%, whereas at the penultimate severe flight condition, the reduction was 15%.

Fig. 15.9   This photograph shows the piezoelectric ceramic actuators, bonded to the carbon/epoxy composite skin of an F/A-18 fin to reduce vibration response of the fin due to buffet loading.

Figure 15.10 shows a comparison of strain density as a function of frequency between the open-loop and closed-loop configurations at the nominal flight condition. From these results, it is estimated (taking into account usage rates) that if the current active buffet load alleviation system were installed on an F/A-18, the increase in life would be approximately 70% or, in other words, 4000 hours could be added to the life of the tail.

15.3.2.2 Damage Mitigation.   Shape memory alloy (SMA) wire (See Appendix A) actuators embedded in a hybrid composite system have been demonstrated to provide active damage control.[19] In this case, the SMA wires were embedded in a composite material, making the SMA wire an integral part of the overall system. The basic approach was to elongate inelastically the SMA fibers before being embedded (the SMA fibers are constrained from reverting to their original length during the curing process). Upon heating the wires beyond their transition temperature (by passing an electric current through them), the wires were activated, causing them to revert to their original length thus changing the stress and strain fields in the specimen. The aim here is to change the stress field around areas of high stress concentration to reduce the effective stress intensity factor and reduce crack growth. This concept was experimentally demonstrated by embedding elongated SMA (nickel-titanium alloy, NiTi) fibers in a photoelastic epoxy material. When the SMA fibers, which were located about 0.5 mm ahead of a crack, were activated, a reduction of 24% in the stress intensity factor was measured.[19] Similar studies were conducted with NiTi fiber/epoxy

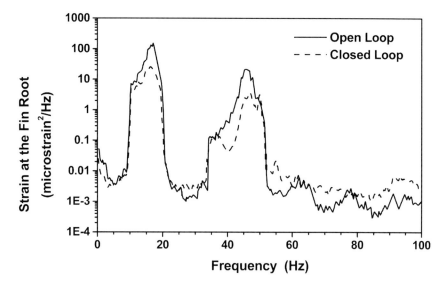

Fig. 15.10   Comparison of open-loop and closed-loop strain response at the root of the vertical fin.

specimens with the SMA fiber located at various distances ahead of the crack.[20] Four different pre-strain levels were studied (0%, 1%, 2%, and 5%) at various crack lengths. Experimental results showed the drastic reduction in stress intensity factor when the SMA wires were activated. The degree of reduction in stress intensity factor depended on the level of pre-strain and the compressive stress domain size between the crack tip and the fiber. Reductions of up to 50% were measured, using photoelastic techniques, when the fiber was 0.2 mm ahead of the crack and with the 5% pre-strained fibers. Figure 15.11 shows the fringe pattern before and after the SMA fiber is activated with the fiber about 2 mm ahead of the crack tip. In this case, a reduction in the number of fringes of about 1–1.5 can be observed, and because the stress intensity factor for crack opening mode I is proportional to the number of fringes,[20] this represents a reduction of about 25–33% in the stress intensity factor. Embedded pre-strained SMA fibers have been used to provide restoration forces to enhance the post-buckling behavior of composite plate structures.[21] Experimental studies showed that quite low volume fractions of SMA fibers significantly reduced the out-of-plane displacements in composite panels. This study concluded that many buckling critical aerospace structures could benefit from such adaptive SMA-based control systems, particularly when mechanically loaded structures are exposed to elevated temperatures—for example,the next generation of supersonic aircraft.

15.3.2.3 Shape Adaptive Structures and Flow Control.   A recent Defense Advanced Research Projects Agency (DARPA)–sponsored Smart

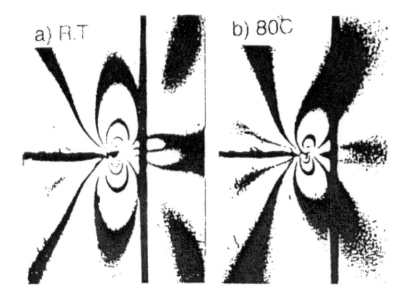

Fig. 15.11 Photoelastic fringe patterns observed at a side notch in a NiTi wire/ epoxy resin specimen loaded at 300 N, at room temperature and 80°C (i.e., with the NiTi wires activated).

Wing Program investigated incorporating integrated actuation mechanisms, based on SMA and piezoelectric-based actuators, to replace conventional hinged control surfaces to provide variable optimized aerodynamic shapes for a variety of flight conditions.[4,22] The concept is shown in Figure 15.12.

Initial activities focused on the development of a SMA torque tube in a 1/6 scale F/A-18 wing to achieve twist within the wing and also SMA wire tendons to actuate the trailing edge. Optical fiber pressure and strain sensors were included in this demonstrator. The demonstrators focused on two variations of the smart wing on a scaled unmanned air combat vehicle, the first incorporating SMA-actuated leading edge and trailing edge control surfaces and the second using an ultrasonic piezoelectric motor to drive a control arm to manipulate the trailing edge. A 30% scale model of an unmanned air combat vehicle was fabricated with one wing using conventional control technologies and the other with smart control surfaces.

The unmanned air combat vehicle consisted of aluminum spars, bulkheads, ribs, and longerons, with glass/epoxy skins. The SMA-based hingeless control surface system used SMA tendons, demonstrated the benefits of this technology compared with conventional designs. However, because of the slow response of the SMA (in seconds), only quasi static conditions could be achieved. In maneuver situations where higher responses are required (i.e., typically require about 60° of deflection per second), an actuator with higher bandwidth is

Conventional "hinged" control surface

"Hingeless" control surface

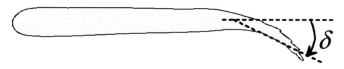

Fig. 15.12 Schematic diagram of conventional "hinged" control surface and "hingeless" control surface (i.e., morphing structure).

required. To this end, various actuators were investigated, including actively cooled SMA, electro-active polymers, piezo-hydraulic pumps, and ultrasonic piezoelectric motors. The final design used an ultrasonic piezoelectric motor to achieve a hingeless control surface with a response of up to $80°$ deflection a second and deflections up to $\pm 20°$.

Another method of achieving aerodynamic control (without the use of hinged control surfaces) is by manipulating the aerodynamic boundary layer over the wing using MEMS technology.[23] The concept of active conformable surfaces is illustrated in Figure 15.13. The concept is to wrap the flexible smart skin, with distributed micro-sensors, micro-actuators, and micro-electronics (referred to as the M^3 system), around the three dimensional leading edge of a delta wing. Shear-stress sensors detect the location of separation of the leading-edge vortices and then (through the built-in micro-electronic circuitry) the micro-actuators manipulate the thin boundary layer around the leading edge to control the aerodynamic forces and reduce drag on the delta wing. Figure 15.3 shows two types of actuators that are under investigation, viz. flap and bubble actuator.[24] Current activities involve the trials of the MEMS shear stress sensors on the NASA Dryden F-15 and on a delta wing unmanned aerial vehicles.[23]

15.3.3 Multi-functional Structures

Composite materials allow the integration of RF antennas into load-bearing aircraft structures. Recently, a multi-disciplinary program has involved the development and ground testing of a conformal load-bearing antenna structure[25] to improved aircraft operational effectiveness (increased stealth, reduce weight,

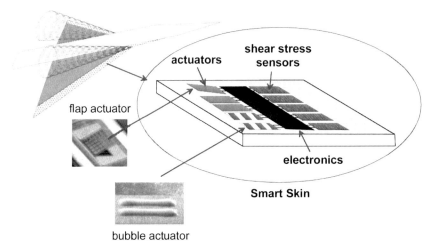

Fig. 15.13   Schematic diagram showing planned use of MEMS (combined sensors and actuators) to control leading edge vortices. Taken from Ref. 24.

drag, radar signature, communication range, and electronic warfare capability). One antenna can now undertake multifunctional roles, whereas before several antennas would have been required. Various sites around the aircraft may be used (e.g., wings, tails, empennage). Testing has shown significant (orders of magnitude) improvements in operational performance of antennas over conventional antennas' configurations (e.g., improved range from 40 to 200 miles). Structural issues like buffets mean that antennas must be robust. Also, high-frequency antennas need to be compensated for spatial deformation, therefore structural vibration effects can be significant. Another key issue for such structures is the durability and repair. Testing to date has shown that structures with embedded antennas can withstand static strains up to 4700 $\mu\varepsilon$.

15.4   Key Technology Needs

To be practicable, smart applications must be rugged and unobtrusive; they must not increase the burden on an aircraft's monitoring system nor on the pilot and ground staff. They must be able to withstand severe operating conditions for prolonged periods and be able to operate under temperatures ranging from $-50°C$ to over $100°C$. Some surface-mounted systems will be exposed on the outside of the aircraft and will need to withstand aerodynamic stresses, sunlight, moisture, other aircraft fluids and erosion.

The key technologies for the development of many of the smart applications lie in the elements: sensors, actuators, and control and power systems.

Current sensors and actuators are much too large and generally too fragile, particularly in the case of piezoelectric actuators, which are prone to cracking and burn-out when used to produce large forces. The current generation of piezoelectric systems lack the force required to make shape changes or to develop sufficient loads in many practical situations.[26] Magnetostrictive transducers allow higher forces than the piezoelectric materials and should prove to be more robust; however, they are heavy and have significantly high power requirements. Clearly, further technological breakthroughs are required for these elements.

There is also the necessity for rugged miniaturized microprocessors (and associated instrumentation) that can be embedded in the component or bonded to its surface (or nearby) and, where data transfer are required, for low-power, long-life, robust, wireless systems. Small power units that can be mounted in, on, or close to the smart structure are a major requirement for applications involving actuators—mini fuel cells are a possibility.

For low-power requirements such as structural health monitoring, it is highly desirable for the system to be self-powering, thus avoiding the complications and the increasing problems associated with the use of batteries. One promising approach[7] is to use piezoelectric materials to harvest power from energy sources (e.g., dynamic straining) in the parent structure, as is being developed for the smart patch described earlier. To avoid the need for battery power in the smart patch, a self-powered (piezoelectric film-based) patch health-monitoring system was developed.[7] This system operates by using the electrical power generated by the straining of the structure. The piezoelectric transducers convert the dynamic strain to electrical energy to power the electronics, which interrogate the piezoelectric film sensors, and process and store the patch health data on a non-volatile memory.

Large-scale use of sensors (for example, extensive use of optical fibers with Bragg gratings) for health monitoring brings with it problems of data presentation.[26] The need will be to present the information to ground staff as pictorial maps, ideally indicating changes from the original state.

References

[1] Gandhi, M. V., and Thompson, B. S., *Smart Materials and Structures*, Chapman and Hall, New York, 1992.

[2] Ikegami, R., "Structural Health Monitoring: Assessment of Aircraft Customer Needs Structural Health Monitoring," *Proceedings of the 2nd International Workshop on Structural Health Monitoring*, 10 Sept 1999.

[3] Crow, C. R., and Slater, J. M., *Smart Aircraft Structures*, AGARD-CP-600, Vol. 2, Paper 10, AGARD Conference on Future Aerospace Technologies in the Service of the Alliance, 14–17 April 1997.

[4] McGowan, A. R., Washburn, A. E., Horta, L. G., Bryant, R. G., Cox, D. E., Siochi, E. J., Padula, S. L., and Holloway, N. M., "Recent Results from NASA's Morphing Project,"

Proceedings of SPIE—The International Society for Optical Engineering's 9th Annual International Symposium on Smart Structures and Materials, Vol. 4698, 2002, pp. 97–111.

[5]Baker, A. A., Rose, L. R. F., and Jones R., (eds), *Advances in the Bonded Composite Repair of Metallic Airframe Structures*, Elsevier, 2002.

[6]Baker, A. A., *Advances in the Bonded Composite Repair of Metallic Airframe Structures*, edited by A. A., Baker, L. R. F. Rose, and R. Jones, Elsevier, 2002, Chap. 22, pp. 643–656.

[7]Galea, S. C., *Advances in the Bonded Composite Repair of Metallic Airframe Structures*, edited by A. A. Baker, L. R. F. Rose, and R. Jones, Elsevier, 2002, Chap. 22, pp. 571–612.

[8]Udd, E., *Fibre Optic Smart Structures*, John Wiley and Sons, New York, 1995.

[9]Skontorp, A., "Structural Integrity of Quasi-isotropic Composite Laminates with Embedded Optical Fibres," *Journal of Reinforced Plastics and Composites*, Vol. 19, 1998, pp. 1056–1077.

[10]Roberts, D. R., Everall, L. A., and Howlett, I. C., "Fibre Optic Strain Sensing for Composite Structural Lifetime Health Monitoring," *Proceedings of the International Conference on Lightweight Construction—Latest Developments*, Paper 5, 24–25 Feb. 2000.

[11]Sirkis, J. S., and Grande, R., "Non-linear Analysis of Ductile Metal Coated Optical Fiber Sensors Embedded in a Unidirectional Laminate," *Journal of Composite Materials*, Vol. 31, No. 10, 1997, pp. 1026–1045.

[12]Glossop, N. D., Dubois, S., Tsaw, W., LeBlanc, M., Measures, R. M., and Tennyson, R. C., "Optical Fibre Damage Detection for an Aircraft Composite Leading Edge," *Composites Journal*, Vol. 21, 1990, pp. 71–80.

[13]Baumann, E. W., Becker, R. S., Ellerbrock, P. J., and Jacobs, S. W., "DC-XA Structural Health Monitoring System," *Proceedings of SPIE—The International Society for Optical Engineering's Smart Structures and Materials Symposium: Industrial and Commercial Applications of Smart Structures Technologies Conference*, Vol. 3044, 1997, pp. 195–206.

[14]Everall, L. and Roberts, D., "Smart Composites for the Marine Industry," *Materials World*, Vol. 7, Issue 7, July 1999, pp. 406–408.

[15]Lin, M., and Chang, F., "The Manufacture of Composite Structures with a Built-in Network of Piezoceramics," *Composites Science and Technology*, Vol. 62, No. 7, 2002, pp. 919–939.

[16]Ikegami, R., "Structural Health Management for Aging Aircraft," *Proceedings of SPIE on Smart Structures and Material Systems, Industrial and Commercial Applications of Smart Structures Technologies Conference*, Paper 4332–8, March 2001, pp. 60–67.

[17]Pierce, S. G., Philp, W. R., Culshaw, B., Gachagan, A., McNab, A., Hayward, G., and Lecuyer, F., "Surface-Bonded Optical Fibre Sensors for the Inspection of CFRP Plates Using Ultrasonic Lamb Waves," *Smart Materials and Structures*, Vol. 6, No. 6, 1996, pp. 776–787.

[18]Hopkins, M., Henderson, D., Moses, R., Ryall, T., Zimcik, D., Spangler, R., "Active Vibration Suppression Systems Applied to Twin Tail Buffeting," *Proceedings of SPIE—The International Society for Optical Engineering's Smart Structures and Materials Symposium: Industrial and Commercial Applications of Smart Structures Technologies Conference*, Vol. 3326, 1998, pp. 27–33.

[19] Rogers, C. A., Liang, C., and Li, S., "Active Damage Control of Hybrid Material Systems Using Induced Strain Actuators," *Proceedings of AIAA/ASML/ASCE/AHS/ASC 32nd Structures, Structural Dynamics and Materials Conference*, AIAA-91-1145-CP, Part 2, 1991, pp. 1190–1203.

[20] Shimamoto, A., Azakami, T., and Oguchi, T., "Reduction of KI and KII by the Shape-memory Effect in a TiNi Shape-memory Fiber-reinforced Epoxy Matrix Composite," *Experimental Mechanics*, Vol. 43, No 1, 2003, pp. 77–82.

[21] Thompson, S. P., and Louglan, J., "Adaptive Post-buckling Response of Carbon Fibre Composite Plates Employing SMA Actuators," *Composite Structures*, Vol. 38, No. 1–4, 1997, pp. 667–678.

[22] Kudva, J. N., Sanders, B., Pinkerton-Florance, J., and Garcia, E., "Overview of the DARPA/AFRL/NASA Smart Wing Phase 2 Program," Smart Structures and Materials 2001: Industrial and Commercial Applications of Smart Structures Technologies, *Proceedings of SPIE 4332*, Vol. 4332, March 2001, pp. 223–233.

[23] Lee, G. B., Shih, C., Tai, Y. C., Tsao, T., Liu, C., and Huang Chih-Ming Ho, A., "Robust Vortex Control of a Delta Wing by Distributed Microelectromechanical-Systems Actuators," *Journal of Aircraft*, Vol. 37, July 2000, pp. 697–706.

[24] Haung, A., Folk, C., Ho, C. M., Liu, Z., Chu, W. W., Xu, W. W, Y., Tai, Y. C., "Gyphon M3 System: Integration of MEMS for Flight Control," *Proceedings of SPIE MEMS Components and Applications for Industry, Automobiles, Aerospace and Communications*, Vol. 4559, 22–23 Oct. 2001, pp. 85–94.

[25] Lockyer, A., Alt, K., Kudva, J., and Tuss, J., "Air Vehicle Integration Issues and Considerations for CLAS Successful Implementation Smart Structures and Materials 2001: Industrial and Commercial Applications of Smart Structures Technologies," *Proceedings of SPIE*, Vol. 4332, March 2001, pp. 48–59.

[26] Davies, G. A. O., "Aircraft Structures," *The Aeronautical Journal*, Vol. 100, 1996, pp. 523–529.

16
Knowledge-Based Engineering, Computer-Aided Design, and Finite Element Analysis

Computer-aided engineering (CAE) and knowledge-based engineering (KBE) are tools that are making a considerable impact on the design, manufacture, and through-life support of composite structures. Improvements in both the integrity of data and the accuracy of analysis have enabled engineering project teams to adopt CAE as a primary tool and reduce reliance on the manufacture of prototypes and experimental testing to prove design concepts. In composites manufacture, the applications of CAE include analysis and design using finite element analysis (FEA), design drafting, virtual prototyping, and the control of manufacturing processes, including control of robots and curing processes. KBE refers to processes that capture the intellectual property and core knowledge of the company. KBE applications include design rules that ensure compliance with best practice and tools to automate repetitive tasks.

16.1 Knowledge-Based Design Systems

In the context of this text, KBE is an engineering process in which knowledge about the product (e.g., the techniques used to design, analyze, and manufacture a product, and provide through-life support) is stored in the design system. The system captures the intellectual property of the company, including analysis experience, design rules, best practice, and advantages and limitations that define the best process to manufacture different components. It also provides tools to monitor the performance of the product so that operational experience can influence future design. The basis of the knowledge system is a database including a library of features, a list of rules, and checks on which the design can be based. These rules and checks are built into the design software and monitor the decision processes as the design evolves. By this means, the design process is controlled, and departures from recommended practice are immediately flagged. Applications in composite structures include the choice of manufacturing processes for a specific application, selection of materials, and preferred ply lay-ups. The design applications are also integrated into management software to support the decision-making process through accurate cost monitoring, support for marketing, and the evaluation of risk.

KBE can be applied at all stages of a project. The design parameters for the design of a riveted connection between a skin panel and supporting structure are shown in Figure 16.1. The dependence of the strength of the joint on fastener spacing and the distance to the edge of the panel is shown in Figure 9.24. If company policy selects bearing failure as the preferred failure mode, the minimum fastener spacing and fastener pitch can be defined. In addition, design practice may call for the edge distance to be based on the next larger fastener size. This allows for tolerance in drilling processes and allows the hole to be reamed and a new fastener inserted to execute a repair. This "best practice" can be implemented as rules and checks that are presented interactively to the design engineer using the system. Alternatively, they can be implemented in automated design software that is made available as a tool executed from the drafting system. Once data about the lay-up of the virgin panel and loads to be transferred by the joint are entered to the system, selection of the fastener to be used, fastener pitch, and edge distance can be automated.

KBE is not confined to structural details. Ribs (Fig. 16.2) are structural components that are repeated at regular intervals span-wise in an aircraft wing.

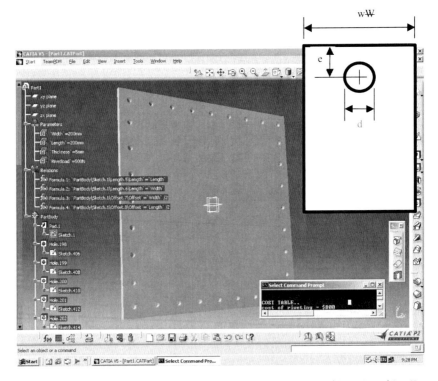

Fig. 16.1 Design detail in a riveted connection. Ratios e/d and w/d affect manufacture, repairability, and durability. Screen shows application of CATIA V5 (Ref. 1).

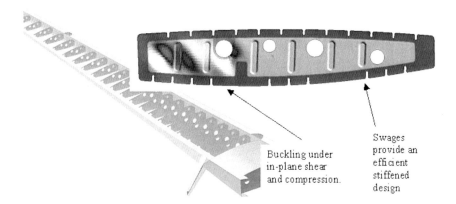

Buckling under
in-plane shear
and compression.

Swages
provide an
efficient
stiffened
design

Fig. 16.2   Design of a structural component.

If the wing tapers, each rib will have different dimensions, defined by the profile of the wing and spars, as well as varying loads. The design of these structures can be automated using a KBE system so that each rib is individually optimized. The materials, structural details, manufacturing methods, and parts list can all be defined from a knowledge database. This database could include knowledge about the company's manufacturing facilities, a preferred design strategy including goals of minimum cost or weight, and experience with design detail, for example, the design of swages to prevent panel buckling or lay-ups to improve damage tolerance. Issues related to tooling and definition of the manufacturing process can be embedded in the software and can incorporate the company intellectual property (IP) and specialized capabilities that define the position of the company in the market place.

Commercial Modelling Systems[1,2] provide a familiar framework for the design process. They can be used for the geometric modelling of structure, can provide virtual prototypes for assessing and marketing the design, and can be used to check operational functionality such as the ability to gain access for inspection and maintenance. An interface with a finite element program provides the geometry for meshing with finite elements, and an interface with a manufacturing system provides the tool paths for manufacture of molds and fittings. Cost and weight estimates are immediately available. These systems can also contain the knowledge base discussed in the preceding text. The knowledge may include a library of pre-designed and producible components allowing repeated items such as cleats, swages, and joint details to be inserted by a "paste" operation. Scaling to local geometry will ensure structural compatibility.

The aim of these systems is to reduce the time for a new product to be developed and to enter service. By capturing best practice about design and manufacture of composite products, the occurrence of mistakes and design errors is minimized.

16.2   Finite Element Modelling of Composite Structures

The validation of designs requires analysis of the structural performance under service loads. The analytical procedures described in Chapter 6 can be applied to simple components such as a plate or a beam. Once an effective modulus is defined, these classical analytical techniques can be implemented, and deflections and stresses can be predicted from standard formulae.[3] However, when the structure is more complex, the classical techniques become more difficult to apply and analysts resort to numerical methods to achieve the answers they need.

The finite element method is the computational tool most widely used to validate the performance of structures. It provides the analysis required for the design process. Typically it can be used to define the displacements, stresses, vibration, and buckling characteristics of a structure composed of metal or composite materials under a defined set of loads and displacement boundary conditions. It can either be applied at the macroscopic level to analyze the stiffness and strength of the complete structure, or it can be applied at the microscopic level to study the interface between fiber and resin. Finite element analysis procedures are either embedded inside the geometric modelling systems that carry the geometry database or are stand-alone packages capable of special analysis, such as post-buckling behavior or response to shock loading. The finite element analysis can be applied to assess structural performance, to form the geometric model to which an optimization algorithm is applied, or to provide simulations of molding processes and manufacturing strategies.

Here we will concentrate on the use of finite element analysis (FEA) to assess structural performance. A simple description of the finite element method in structural analysis[4] is that it involves dividing the structure into discrete elements as shown in Figure 16.3. Each panel becomes an assembly of non-overlapping plate or brick elements that are connected at discrete points called nodes. The behavior of each element is defined by a relation between force and displacement at the nodes that are usually located on the boundaries of the element. The elements are then assembled into a structure by satisfying the equilibrium of the forces. This process is equivalent to pinning the elements together at the nodes. Constraint of the deformation on the element ensures an appropriate level of continuity of displacement and slope is maintained on the element boundary. The result is a set of linear algebraic equations that are solved to determine the displacements of the nodes.

A more sophisticated description of the finite element method[4] regards it as a piecewise polynomial approximation defined in terms of nodal displacements. The best values at the nodes are defined by minimizing a physically meaningful global quantity such as the total potential energy. This minimization generates the set of linear equations that are solved for the displacements. This formal mathematical approach provides the vehicle for applying the method to an ever-increasing variety of problems in applied mechanics. The extension to heat transfer and flow modelling is based on these generalized theories.

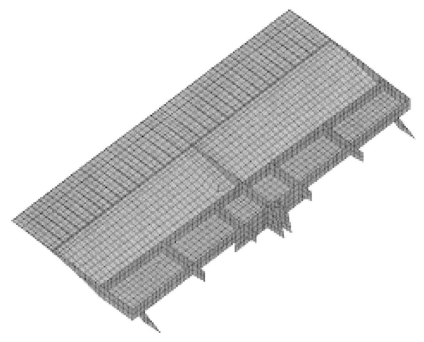

Fig. 16.3   Finite element model for a wing spoiler—top skin removed.

The finite element model, however, does not provide an exact match to experimental results. The theoretical processes are based on a numerical approximation related to the element size, the type of element used, the underlying theory, and the type of analysis performed. The modelling process involves approximations for geometry and may not reflect the true detail such as the change of the orientation of fibers during lay-up and cure. The stiffness of joints and imperfections such as the straightness of beams and flatness of panels can have considerable influence on the performance of actual structures.[5] The achievement of relevant and useful results relies on an understanding of the characteristics of the solution process and care when developing the numerical models.

16.3   Finite Element Solution Process

The finite element method provides the design team with information regarding the stiffness and strength of the structure. What confidence should the design team have in the results when analyzing composite structures? Unfortunately, the answer depends, in part, on how well the method is implemented. To indicate some of the features of the finite element method, the

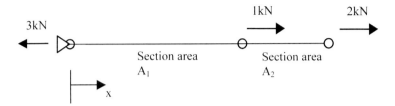

Fig. 16.4   A 1-D example to introduce FEA. A hollow tube of composite or metal is supported at its left-hand end and carries the loads shown.

one-dimensional problem shown in Figure 16.4 will be considered. The emphasis will be on explaining how the method works and how is it applied to composite materials.[6]

In all applications, as in this example, the development of the finite element model and completion of the analysis involves six basic steps:

Step 1. Select the type of analysis that will be executed. The selection of a full three-dimensional non-linear analysis is the most general but can lead to a model with a very large number of elements if the structure consists of thin panels. Finite elements need to be of moderate aspect ratio. The size of a three-dimensional brick element will therefore be governed by the minimum dimension (usually the thickness). As a result, engineers have developed beam, plate, and shell approximations to structural behavior. These approximations reduce the dimension of the problem. For example, in the classical laminate plate theory described in Chapter 6, the in-plane strains are assumed to be constant through the thickness in planar two-dimensional analysis, and linear through-the-thickness when the response includes bending. A finite element analysis based on plate elements will use these approximations to eliminate the thickness dimension. The finite elements are planar, and the size of each element is governed by the in-plane dimensions. The implications of assuming the behavior is linear will be discussed later.

The geometry considered here is that relevant to a hollow tube. The most detailed analysis could include accurate modelling of the tube wall in three dimensions with a layer of elements for each ply, modelling of the fixed support, modelling of the change in section, and how the load is applied. A simpler analysis would model the wall using plate or shell elements with the element lying in the plane of the wall, limiting the variation of strain through the thickness to a linear distribution and eliminating the modelling of more complex behavior.

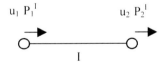

Fig. 16.5   The rod finite element used in the analysis.

Fig. 16.6   Load on an isolated element.

Here, the simplest rod element shown in Figure 16.5 will be chosen. The stress and strain will be assumed constant over the cross-section of the tube, and the behavior will be assumed linear. The change in cross-sectional area of the tube where the 1-kN load is applied will occur at the boundary between elements. The detail of how the cross-section changes, that is, how the number of plies is reduced, will not be included in the rod element model.

Step 2. Define the relation between force and displacement at the nodes of the rod element.

For the geometry shown in Figure 16.6 and small axial strain: $\sigma = E\varepsilon$.

For the simple tube: $\sigma = P/A$ and $\varepsilon = u/L$. Therefore

$$\frac{P}{A} = E\frac{u}{L} \quad \text{or} \quad \frac{AE}{L}u = P. \tag{16.1}$$

A value is required for the longitudinal stiffness $(AE)_{\text{effective}}$ for the composite tube. The effective modulus can be defined using equation (*6.19*) using the lay-up defined for the walls of the tube. The true crossectional area of the walls of the tube is the required A.

Step 3. Use the element load/displacement relations to define the element matrix equations between nodal force and nodal displacement.

On element I shown in Figure 16.7, we can assume a relation between forces and displacements at the nodes in matrix form:

$$\begin{bmatrix} k_{11} & k_{12} \\ k_{21} & k_{22} \end{bmatrix} \begin{Bmatrix} u_1 \\ u_2 \end{Bmatrix} = \begin{Bmatrix} P_1^I \\ P_2^I \end{Bmatrix}$$

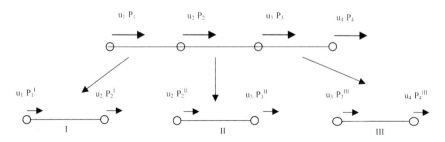

Fig. 16.7   Discretization into elements.

Set u_2 equal to 1 and u_1 equal to zero. Then, from equation (*16.1*),

$$P_1^I = -\frac{A_I E_I}{L_I} \quad \text{and} \quad P_2^I = \frac{A_I E_I}{L_I}$$

Substituting in the matrix equation:

$$\begin{bmatrix} k_{11} & k_{12} \\ k_{21} & k_{22} \end{bmatrix} \begin{Bmatrix} 0 \\ 1 \end{Bmatrix} = \begin{Bmatrix} -\dfrac{A_I E_I}{L_I} \\ \dfrac{A_I E_I}{L_I} \end{Bmatrix}$$

giving
$$k_{12} = -\frac{A_I E_I}{L_I} \quad \text{and} \quad k_{22} = \frac{A_I E_I}{L_I}$$

Defining a similar problem with u_1 equal to 1 and u_2 equal to zero identifies:

$$k_{11} = \frac{A_I E_I}{L_I} \quad \text{and} \quad k_{21} = -\frac{A_I E_I}{L_I}$$

Combining these results gives the matrix relation for element I.

$$\begin{bmatrix} \dfrac{A_I E_I}{L_I} & -\dfrac{A_I E_I}{L_I} \\ -\dfrac{A_I E_I}{L_I} & \dfrac{A_I E_I}{L_I} \end{bmatrix} \begin{Bmatrix} u_1 \\ u_2 \end{Bmatrix} = \begin{Bmatrix} P_1^I \\ P_2^I \end{Bmatrix} \qquad (16.2)$$

Step 4. Define the element mesh. In this step, the number of degrees of freedom in the model is set.

The elements are connected at nodes at which there are displacement degrees of freedom. The displacements on the element, and hence the stresses and strains, are uniquely defined by the displacements at the nodes on the element. The number of degrees of freedom in the model, and hence the accuracy of the approximation, is therefore linked directly to the number of elements.

Two factors that affect the accuracy of the finite element model have therefore been defined—the decision to base the model on a simple rod element and the design of the mesh. The size of the analysis model may be restricted by the memory available in the computer and may also be limited by the time a designer is prepared to wait for the solution once an analysis request is submitted.

Here a hand calculation is to be executed. Therefore the number of elements in the model will be restricted to, for example, three. The model shown in Figure 16.7 has four nodes with only four degrees of freedom. The degrees of freedom are the axial displacements u_I at each node.

The matrix relation in equation (*16.2*) is defined for each element.

On element I

$$\begin{bmatrix} \dfrac{A_I E_I}{L_I} & -\dfrac{A_I E_I}{L_I} \\[2ex] -\dfrac{A_I E_I}{L_I} & \dfrac{A_I E_I}{L_I} \end{bmatrix} \begin{Bmatrix} u_1 \\ u_2 \end{Bmatrix} = \begin{Bmatrix} P_1^I \\ P_2^I \end{Bmatrix}$$

On element II

$$\begin{bmatrix} \dfrac{A_{II} E_{II}}{L_{II}} & -\dfrac{A_{II} E_{II}}{L_{II}} \\[2ex] -\dfrac{A_{II} E_{II}}{L_{II}} & \dfrac{A_{II} E_{II}}{L_{II}} \end{bmatrix} \begin{Bmatrix} u_2 \\ u_3 \end{Bmatrix} = \begin{Bmatrix} P_2^{II} \\ P_3^{II} \end{Bmatrix}$$

On element III

$$\begin{bmatrix} \dfrac{A_{III} E_{III}}{L_{III}} & -\dfrac{A_{III} E_{III}}{L_{III}} \\[2ex] -\dfrac{A_{III} E_{III}}{L_{III}} & \dfrac{A_{III} E_{III}}{L_{III}} \end{bmatrix} \begin{Bmatrix} u_3 \\ u_4 \end{Bmatrix} = \begin{Bmatrix} P_3^{III} \\ P_4^{III} \end{Bmatrix}$$

where L_i, A_i and E_i are the length, cross-sectional area, and effective modulus of the *i*th element.

Step 5. Assemble the global equations by applying equilibrium of the forces at each node.

In this step, the global geometry is assembled from the smaller "finite" elements. Note that the fundamental principle of equilibrium is used. A second physical concept—that the structure must remain connected under load—is also enforced by the assumption that there is only one displacement at each node and that displacement is shared by both neighboring elements. Note the overlap of the displacements between the matrix relations defined in Step 4.

The forces on the nodes are identified in Figure 16.8. Note that the element forces defined in Figures 16.5 and 16.7 are forces applied to the element. The forces are reversed in Figure 16.8 because they are forces applied by the elements onto the nodes.

Applying equilibrium at node 1,

$$- P_1^I + P_1 = 0 \text{ or substituting for } P_1^I \text{ from the matrix relation}$$

$$\left(\frac{A_I E_I}{L_I} u_1 - \frac{A_I E_I}{L_I} u_2 \right) = P_1$$

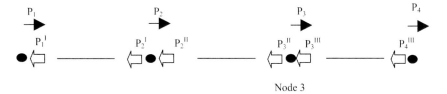

Node 3

Fig. 16.8   Applying equilibrium at the nodes.

At node 2,

$$- P_2^I - P_2^{II} + P_2 = 0 \text{ or substituting from the matrix relation}$$

$$\left(-\frac{A_I E_I}{L_I} u_1 + \left(\frac{A_I E_I}{L_I} + \frac{A_{II} E_{II}}{L_{II}} \right) u_2 - \frac{A_{II} E_{II}}{L_{II}} u_3 \right) = P_2$$

At node 3,

$$- P_3^{II} - P_3^{III} + P_3 = 0 \text{ or substituting from the matrix relation}$$

$$\left(-\frac{A_{II} E_{II}}{L_{II}} u_2 + \left(\frac{A_{II} E_{II}}{L_{II}} + \frac{A_{III} E_{II}}{L_{III}} \right) u_3 - \frac{A_{III} E_{III}}{L_{III}} u_4 \right) = P_3$$

At node 4,

$$- P_4^{III} + P_4 = 0 \text{ or substituting from the matrix relation}$$

$$\left(-\frac{A_{III} E_{III}}{L_{III}} u_3 + \frac{A_{III} E_{III}}{L_{III}} u_4 \right) = P_4$$

Assembling these equations into a matrix gives:

$$\begin{bmatrix} \dfrac{A_I E_I}{L_I} & -\dfrac{A_I E_I}{L_I} & 0 & 0 \\ -\dfrac{A_I E_I}{L_I} & \dfrac{A_I E_I}{L_I} + \dfrac{A_{II} E_{II}}{L_{II}} & -\dfrac{A_{II} E_{II}}{L_{II}} & 0 \\ 0 & -\dfrac{A_{II} E_{II}}{L_{II}} & \dfrac{A_{II} E_{II}}{L_{II}} + \dfrac{A_{III} E_{III}}{L_{III}} & -\dfrac{A_{III} E_{III}}{L_{III}} \\ 0 & 0 & -\dfrac{A_{III} E_{III}}{L_{III}} & \dfrac{A_{III} E_{III}}{L_{III}} \end{bmatrix} \begin{Bmatrix} u_1 \\ u_2 \\ u_3 \\ u_4 \end{Bmatrix} = \begin{Bmatrix} P_1 \\ P_2 \\ P_3 \\ P_4 \end{Bmatrix}$$

$$\text{or} \quad Ku = P \tag{16.3}$$

Step 6. Obtain the solution for displacements and stresses.

The loads and boundary conditions are now defined. For a unique solution, either the displacement or the load must be defined at each node, but not both. Application of this rule ensures that the number of unknowns in the matrix relation is equal to the number of equations. At fixed nodes a reaction will exist, but that reaction is determined after the solution for displacement. For the problem defined in Figure 16.4, the displacement u_1 is set to zero and the corresponding load becomes the reaction R_1. P_2 is set to zero because there is no external load at node 2. Solution for the unknown degrees of freedom u_2, u_3, u_4, and the unknown reaction R_1 proceeds by a standard matrix equation algorithm such as Gaus elimination.

The displacements at the nodes have now been defined. The stresses are determined by application of the element relations used in Step 2. A further subtle point arises. We note that the relations used in Step 2 depend on the deformation of the elements. This means that the set of equations contains no information about the absolute displacements—only the relative displacements. We must, therefore, ensure that the boundary conditions fix all rigid body motion, otherwise the solution process will fail. This failure manifests itself as a singular matrix K. In mathematical terms, this means the set of equations has no unique solution because the reference points relating deformation of the structure to absolute displacements have not been defined.

The material used in manufacturing the rods only enters the analysis in Step 2, where the relation between stress and strain is defined. Whether the rod is of circular, square, or more complicated cross-section is of no consequence to the following analysis. Only the cross-sectional area and the effective longitudinal modulus of the material are required. If the tube is manufactured from plies, the laminate analysis developed in Chapter 6 can be used directly. Most commercial finite element codes have laminate modellers included for this purpose. These modellers produce the coefficients A_{ij}, B_{ij}, and D_{ij} in equation (6.27) when defining the element matrices required for plate and shell analysis.

In addition, if different materials are mixed in the structure, this presents no difficulty to the analysis. One element could be made from carbon fiber and a neighboring element from glass fiber or metal. If materials are mixed within the element, the accuracy of the analysis will depend on the accuracy of the effective modulus defined in Step 2.

Often it is possible to model the material behavior as linear, especially when the response is dominated by stiff fibers. In linear analysis, the material properties are assumed constant, and deformation of the geometry under load is assumed to be small. Solution then follows by solving the matrix equation $Ku = P$ for the displacements. If however, the material properties depend on the strain in the material as indicated in Figure 16.9, or if deformations are large enough to

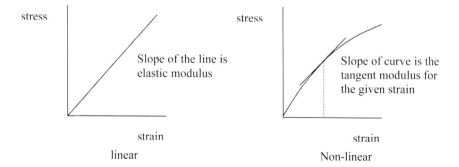

Fig. 16.9   Linear and non-linear material behavior.

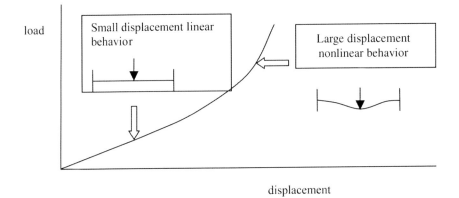

load

Small displacement linear behavior

Large displacement nonlinear behavior

displacement

Fig. 16.10   Linear and non-linear structural behavior. Note: an additional load path is introduced by the deformation of the structure.

cause geometry changes that modify the equilibrium relations as indicated in Figure 16.10, then a non-linear solution must be executed.

These non-linear solutions require iteration because the strain levels and deformation are not known in advance. Algorithms such as Newton-Raphson are used to execute the analysis. Typically, the load application is divided into a number of small steps and properties are defined from the current state of stress and strain in the structure (initially zero). After completion of an analysis, defined in Steps 4 and 5, an initial estimate of the stress and strain at the end of that load step is obtained. These stresses and strains allow the departure from the true behavior to be assessed, and the analysis is repeated until the updated properties converge.[4]

Commercial finite element systems can execute these more complicated analyses. However, the analyst must define the non-linear material properties and specify appropriate load levels and boundary conditions. All solutions are to some extent non-linear, but the iteration process can be expensive, and the definition of data to drive a non-linear analysis, such as a complete stress/strain curve for the material, can be difficult. Part of the skill required to execute an engineering analysis is in knowing when the linear approximation is adequate.

It is important to realize that the finite element solution is approximate. Equilibrium is satisfied at the nodes, but it is usually not satisfied on the elements or, in the two-dimensional and three-dimensional elements, across the boundary between elements. We expect the solution to converge as the element size is reduced. However, the solution will only converge to the mathematical solution of the theory implemented in the finite element formulation. For example, several assumptions are listed for the classical laminate theory described in Chapter 6 for linear analysis. Plate elements defined using this theory will converge to the solution afforded by laminate theory.

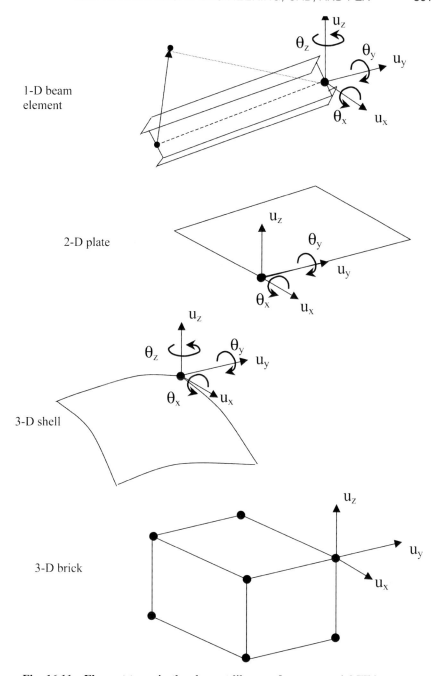

Fig. 16.11   Element types in the element library of a commercial FEA system.

The geometric model is also not exact. If the finite elements are based on an assumption that the fibers remain in their design orientation and are not realigned in the draping process, then the solution will converge to the exact solution for this configuration. The analysis described above using rod elements will also give no information about the detailed stresses at the point where the tube cross-section changes. A planar axi-symmetric or full three-dimensional analysis, which includes the geometry detail where the section changes, is required to generate these stresses.

At the end of Step 6, the analyst has information available to help make decisions about the accuracy of the modelling process. If a linear analysis was executed, the stress levels can be checked to determine whether the value of the stiffness modulus used in Step 3 was appropriate and the displacements can be checked to determine whether the predicted deformation of the structure is sufficient to introduce non-linear effects due to geometry change. If the answer to either question is "yes" then a non-linear analysis is required and the analysis returns to Step 3 with appropriate algorithms to update the solution and iterate towards the correct result.

16.4   Element Types

A finite element system contains a library of finite elements,[6] as indicated in Figure 16.11. The most general three-dimensional representation is given by brick elements. In a micro-mechanical model, these elements can be used to model individual fibers and resin to investigate, for example, stresses caused by thermal shrinkage of the resin relative to the fiber in the failure theories considered in Chapter 6.

For problems involving the behavior of structural components, such as the spoiler in Figure 16.3 models built with bricks can involve an unmanageable number of elements. A feature of digital computers is that the storage of numbers and performance of algebraic operations is not exact but is determined by the number of digits used to represent each number in the computer memory. If a brick element becomes long and thin, its stiffness in the shorter dimensions becomes much higher than its stiffness in the longer dimensions [see the dependence on $1/L$ in equation (16.1)]. Bending stiffness can vary with the cube of the length, and therefore only a moderate aspect ratio can be achieved before the terms in equation (16.3) will have vastly different magnitude and numerical instability becomes a problem.[4] The rule is that brick elements should be simple cubes, or at least should be of moderate aspect ratio. Therefore, if the cross-section of a structural beam or a thin plate was to be modelled with bricks, an extraordinary number of cube-like elements would have to be used.

To overcome these problems, finite element systems include elements that are based on beam, plate, and shell theory. These theories have been developed by engineers to analyze special structural configurations. The beam element is used for structural members for which the required stiffness and load paths can be represented by one-dimensional straight and curved elements. The calculations in the plane of the section are completed mathematically when the element is formed. The finite element model is then used to determine the response dependent on the axial stiffness, EA; the bending stiffness, EI; and the torsional stiffness, GJ. The difference in stiffness in the plane of the section compared with the longitudinal axis of the beam is then removed from the analysis.

The same is true for plates. The plan dimensions of a brick representing a plate are limited by the through-thickness dimension. Therefore, a large number of bricks are required to model a relatively simple plate. A brick model of the assembled set of plates that comprise a structure, such as that presented in Figure 16.3, is usually not feasible. However, if the limitations defined at the beginning of Chapter 6 are acceptable, the assumption that the strain varies linearly through the thickness can be used to integrate the through-thickness behavior as the elements are assembled, leaving the deformation defined by mid-plane strains and curvatures.

Plate elements are therefore two-dimensional and lie on the mid-plane of the surface they represent. The size of the elements is not linked to the thickness of the plate and the mesh requirement is that the elements be 'near-square' in plan view and small enough to capture the variation in stresses and strains caused by geometry features in the plane of the plate. A shell is similar to a plate, but the surface can be curved.

16.5   Finite Element Modelling of Composite Structures

Structural laminates can be modelled using the two-dimensional planar plate elements. Beams of various sections can also be assembled from plate elements if plate elements are used to represent the webs and flanges of the beam. In this approximation, the stresses acting through the thickness are not modelled. A pressure load applied to the plate can be approximated as varying linearly from the value equal to the applied pressure at the surface on which the pressure is applied, to zero, on the unloaded surface. Shear stresses with through-thickness components are defined in a post-processing process that applies plate theory.

If accurate through-thickness stresses are required, the model must be based on three-dimensional elements with, at least, one brick element in the through-thickness direction for each stack of plies with the same orientation.

The simplification of the model to one-dimensional rod and beam elements involves significant approximations and is only implemented when the beams are slender and simple axial deformation and bending theory is a good approximation to the structural response.

The steps taken in Section 16.3 are the same whether the structure is made from metal or composite. In the derivation of all types of finite elements, the modification required to allow the analysis of composite rather than a metal structure lies only in the definition of the material properties—the relationship between stress and strain—in Step 2.

16.5.1 *Plate and Shell Elements*

Plate and shell elements can be used to model structures composed of laminates such as the wing spoiler in Figure 16.3.

16.5.1.1 Plate and Shell Elements for Laminates Constructed from Orthotropic Ply Material.
For laminates constructed from orthotropic plies, the laminate theory of Chapter 6 is used to define the properties of the plate elements. Pre-processors in finite element systems allow the lay-up to be defined. First, a set of orthotropic properties is defined for the unidirectional or fabric plies to be used in the laminate. A tabular input is then used to define the orientation, thickness, and material for each ply. The properties required for the plate are then automatically calculated. As an added feature, the coefficients A_{ij}, B_{ij}, and D_{ij} defined in the laminate theory can be listed together with the effective orthotropic elastic constants E_{11}, E_{22}, etc.

16.5.1.2 Woven and Knitted Material (Unit Cell Approach).
Defining the elastic constants for a woven material is more complex, and a unit cell approach is often adopted.[7] In this approach, equivalent elastic constants are derived using a detailed finite element model of a representative unit cell. Actual fiber architectures are modelled using brick elements for the fiber tow and resin. Displacements are then applied to the cells to isolate the effective longitudinal, bending, and torsional components of deformation required to define the elastic matrices describing the laminate behavior. These constants are then available for subsequent analyses.

16.5.1.3 Brick Elements.
Brick elements can be used to model individual layers in a laminate, or a single element can be used to model several layers. When used to model layers, an "average" property for the combination of resin and fibers has to be defined. The stress-strain relationship for a general anisotropic material involves all 21 coefficients in the symmetric matrix $[G]$ defined below. The 21 coefficients are defined in terms of 12 elastic constants.

The three-dimensional stress-to-strain relationship for an orthotropic material representing a layer of fabric or unidirectional tape is simpler and is defined by:

$$\begin{Bmatrix} \sigma_x \\ \sigma_y \\ \sigma_z \\ \tau_{xy} \\ \tau_{yz} \\ \tau_{zx} \end{Bmatrix} = [G] \left[\begin{Bmatrix} \varepsilon_x \\ \varepsilon_y \\ \varepsilon_z \\ \gamma_{xy} \\ \gamma_{yz} \\ \gamma_{zx} \end{Bmatrix} - (T - T_{REF}) \begin{Bmatrix} \alpha_x \\ \alpha_y \\ \alpha_z \\ \alpha_4 \\ \alpha_5 \\ \alpha_6 \end{Bmatrix} \right]$$

where for an orthotropic material

$$[G] = \begin{bmatrix} G_{11} & & & & & \\ G_{12} & G_{22} & & \text{symmetric} & & \\ G_{13} & G_{23} & G_{33} & & & \\ 0 & 0 & 0 & G_{xy} & & \\ 0 & 0 & 0 & 0 & G_{yz} & \\ 0 & 0 & 0 & 0 & 0 & G_{zx} \end{bmatrix}$$

and

$$G_{11} = \frac{1 - \nu_{yz}\nu_{zy}}{E_y E_z \Delta} \quad G_{12} = \frac{\nu_{yz} + \nu_{zx}\nu_{yz}}{E_y E_z \Delta} \quad G_{13} = \frac{\nu_{zx} + \nu_{yx}\nu_{zy}}{E_y E_z \Delta}$$

$$G_{22} = \frac{1 - \nu_{xz}\nu_{zx}}{E_x E_z \Delta} \quad G_{23} = \frac{\nu_{zy} + \nu_{xy}\nu_{zx}}{E_x E_z \Delta} \quad G_{33} = \frac{1 - \nu_{xy}\nu_{yx}}{E_x E_y \Delta}$$

where ν_{ij} = Poisson ratios; E_x, E_y, E_z = Young's modulus in the x, y, and z directions; G_{xy}, G_{yz}, G_{zx} = Shear moduli; and

$$\Delta = \frac{1 - \nu_{xy}\nu_{yx} - \nu_{yz}\nu_{zy} - \nu_{xz}\nu_{zx} - 2\nu_{yx}\nu_{zy}\nu_{xz}}{E_x E_y E_z}$$

16.5.1.4 Rod and Beam Elements.   Rod and beam elements are seldom used in the analysis of composite components because the laminate theory lends itself to the definition of plate elements, and plate elements can usually be used effectively to model the webs and flanges of the standard beam sections. In Figure 16.12, plate and brick element models are defined for an I-beam. The plate model shown in Figure 16.12 can accurately represent the bending and torsional stiffness of the beam including (for more general sections) the

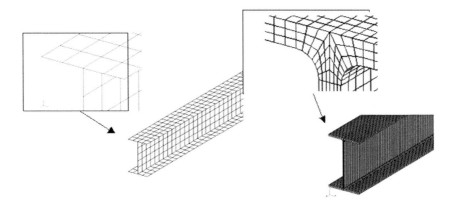

Fig. 16.12   Plate and brick models for an I-beam.

interaction between bending and torsion when the shear center is offset from the centroid of the section. In addition, local buckling modes involving the buckling of the flanges and web of the beam will be predicted, in addition to the global modes of Euler beam buckling when a buckling analysis is executed. However, the model cannot predict the detailed stress and strain distribution at the intersection of the web and flanges. If details of stress and strain are required at this intersection, a three-dimensional brick analysis is required, as indicated in the Figure.

If the structure is comprised of beams which are slender and transfer load by axial, bending and torsional components, then rod and beam elements can be used. The success of the analysis, summarized in Section 16.3 for the rod element, depends on the definition of the effective stiffness components.

16.6   Implementation

Once the details of how the composite material will be modelled have been resolved, the full power of the finite element analysis becomes available. The finite element method can be applied to structures of arbitrary shape and can include advanced applications including:

- Non-linear analysis for post-buckling behavior modes of failure, and ultimate collapse
- Static or dynamic solutions, including crash simulation
- Optimization.

16.6.1   Post-Buckling Performance and Stiffener Separation

Local failure of composite components has been discussed in Chapter 6. However, failure of structural assemblies was not considered. The analysis of these structures and the prediction of failure rely on finite element analysis.

For example, composite structures are often composed of assemblies of stiffened plates. Local buckling can be allowed to occur below the ultimate failure load in these stiffened structures so long as the residual strength of the structure is sufficient to carry the applied loads. Analysis is required to predict the post-buckling behavior as well as ensuring that buckling does not trigger separation of the stiffeners that would lead to a significant loss of strength. A geometric non-linear analysis is required to predict the post-buckling behavior of the panel shown in Figure 16.13b, and a fracture mechanics approach is used to predict growth of a disbond between the panel and the stiffener.[8] The initial disbond weakens the panel and is introduced into the analysis to prove its damage tolerance.

The analysis[8] is based on plate elements in a commercial finite element system.[9] The panel and stiffener have been modelled separately and connected by

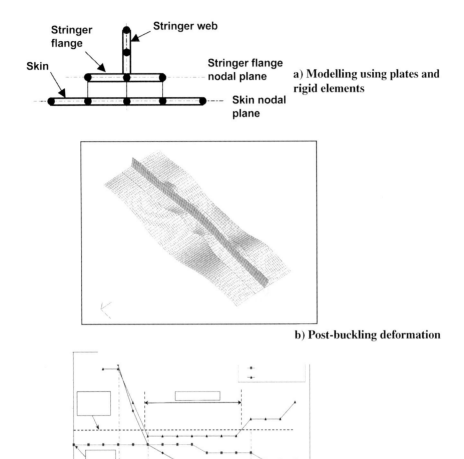

a) Modelling using plates and rigid elements

b) Post-buckling deformation

Fig. 16.13   Finite element analysis of stiffener separation.

rigid links. The rigid links are removed to model the area affected by the disbond. A virtual crack extension procedure is used to determine the energy release rate in modes I and II crack extension and predict growth of the disbond. Studies were completed to determine the buckling loads and the post-buckling behavior of a damaged panel in an empennage structure, the critical length of the disbond, and the residual strength of the damaged panel.

16.7   Design Optimization

The combination of knowledge-based systems and optimization algorithms allow an automated design process to include both performance and cost objectives in the design analysis. For example, the structure in Figure 16.3 was subject to an optimization process searching for a design that combined low weight and low manufacturing cost.[10] The structural performance under pressure loads is controlled by ply orientation in the laminate, by the thickness of the panels, and by the geometry, thickness, location, and shape of the stiffening members. All can be varied in a finite element model to satisfy strength, stiffness, and buckling requirements.

Procedures available in commercial finite element systems[11] include a topology optimization system,[12] to identify the principle structural members, and a parametric design algorithm that allows variables in the optimization algorithm to include dimensions such as the location of the stiffening members. Successful applications of these algorithms[10] do not necessarily require an automated process; rather, the algorithms can be used to guide the evolution of the design and help the design team to evaluate a number of different design options in a concurrent engineering approach. As the design evolves, so does understanding of the load paths in the structure and the redundancy that provides damage tolerance, often a primary design requirement.

16.7.1   Cost Estimates for Design Optimization

The design of weight-effective aerospace structures can no longer guarantee the success of the product. Manufacturers need to verify that their products are an optimal tradeoff between minimum weight, cost, and risk, all within a time frame that meets time-to-market needs. Costs here are taken to mean whole-of-life costs including manufacturing, operation, and maintenance costs. Optimization of these objectives must be carried out in the conceptual design phase because, once the design concept is fixed, up to 80% of the whole-of-life costs will also be fixed.[13] Further detail design alterations may not produce substantial reductions in manufacturing cost or reduce the requirements for through life support.

Implementation of CAE gives the designer the opportunity to enhance the understanding of the functionality of the design and to determine the primary drivers for cost and weight. Preliminary cost estimates for setting cost and weight targets can be based on $/kg and $/m^2 parameters, validated using data from completed projects. These estimates can be enhanced by identifying cost drivers that represent the complexity of the design, ensuring the cost estimate is not simply proportional to weight or size.[14]

As the design evolves, these cost estimates cannot reflect the effect of detailed design changes on cost. In the final stages of the design, the cost will rise as weight is removed from the structure. One approach to estimating cost is based on the Process Costing Analysis Database (1992–1997).[15] This approach separates a manufacturing process into discrete steps and identifies the parameters from which manufacturing time can be estimated. For example, the time required for a non-destructive inspection can be related to the length of a joint that is to be inspected for defects. Cost estimates follow by applying an appropriate hourly rate for the cost of labor.

Design and analysis of efficient composite structures is a complex process. Successful exploitation of these materials will depend on the efficient use of the latest CAE and KBE tools.

References

[1] CATIA Proprietary Software, Dassault Systems, www.catia.com.

[2] ICAD Proprietary Software, Knowledge Technologies International. www.ktiworld. com

[3] Young, W. C., *Roark's Formulas for Stress and Strain*, 7th ed., McGraw-Hill, 2000.

[4] Cook, R. D., *Finite Element Modeling for Stress Analysis*, Wiley, 1995.

[5] Adams, V., and Askenazi, A., *Building Better Products with Finite Element Analysis*, Onward Press, 1999.

[6] Matthews, F. L., Davies, G. A. O., Hitchings, D., and Soutis, C., *Finite Element Modeling of Composite Materials and Structures*, Woodhead Publishing, 2000.

[7] Tan, P., Tong, L., and Steven, G., "Micromechanics Models for the Elastic Constants and Failure Strengths of Plain Weave Composites," *Composite Structures*, Vol. 47, 1999, pp. 797–804.

[8] Yap, J., Scott, M., Thomson, R., and Hachenberg, D., *The Analysis of Skin-to-Stiffener Debonding in Composite Aerospace Structures, ICCS-11*, Monash Univ., Melbourne, Australia, Nov. 2001.

[9] MSC.NASTRAN Proprietary software of the MacNeal Schwendler Corporation, www.msc.com.

[10] Raju, J., "A Conceptual Design and Cost Optimization Methodology," *Proceedings of the 44th AIAA/ASME/ASCE/AHS Structures, Structural Dynamics and Materials Conference*, April 2003.

[11] ANSYS Proprietary software of Swanson Analysis Inc, www.ansys.com.

[12] Bendsoe, M., Diaz, A., and Kikuchi, N., "Topology and Generalised Layout Optimization of Elastic Structures" *Topology Design of Structures*, edited by M. P. Bendsoe and C. A. Mota Soares, Kluwer Academic Publishers, Netherlands, pp. 159–205.

[13] Wang, K., Kelly, D., Dutton, S., "Multi-objective Optimisation of Composite Aerospace Structures," *Composite Structures*, 2002, pp. 141–148.

[14] Hinrichsen, J., "A380—Flagship Aircraft for the New Century," *SAMPE Journal*, Vol. 38, No. 3, 2002, pp. 8–12.

[15] Gutowski, T. G., Neoh, E. T., and Polgar, K. C., *Adaptive Framework for Estimating Fabrication Time of Advanced Composite Manufacturing Processes*, Technical Report, Laboratory for Manufacturing and Productivity, Massachusetts Institute of Technology, Cambridge, MA, 1995.

Appendix
Overview of Some Sensors and Actuators Used for Smart Structure Applications

A.1 Piezoelectric Materials

Piezoelectric materials have the ability to generate charge when subjected to mechanical stress, and conversely can elongate or contract when subjected to an electrical field.[1] Typical piezoelectric materials are: quartz, barium titanate, cadmium sulphide, lead zirconium titanate (PZT) and piezoelectric polymers polyvinyldene fluoride (PVDF), polymer films, and polyvinyl chloride (PVC).

A.1.1 Ceramics

Piezoelectric ceramic materials such as lead zirconate titanate [$Pb(ZrTi)O_3$], known as PZT, exhibit the piezoelectric effect where the size of the deformation or voltage depends on crystal orientation. Properties of PZT are stable in the range $-22°C$ to $+155°C$. PZT can be manufactured in thin plates, strips, or fibers suitable for embedding or surface bonding.

Piezoelectric properties are established by applying at elevated temperature a high electrical field in a direction known as the polling direction to align all the ferroelectric domains within the ceramic (i.e., to achieve constant polarization direction). Conventional PZT wafers or plates are generally polarized normal to the plane of the sheet. When a voltage is applied to the conducting layers on the surface of the sheet, the sheet deforms or develops in-plane forces.

Conventional PZT sheets are quite brittle (low strain to failure), limiting in actuation capability, and are intrusive if embedded in composite laminates. A new concept for the actuation and sensing of structures using PZT fibers and interdigitated electrodes has been developed (Fig. A.1). This material incorporates unidirectional PZT fibers (typically about 130 μm in diameter) into a matrix, producing a highly conformable and directional actuator material. The interdigitated electrode pattern provides the electric field in the direction of the fibers, and therefore the primary piezoelectric effect is also in the direction of the fibers. Thus, these actuators are 2–3 times more effective then piezoceramic wafers when used to excite in-plane motion.

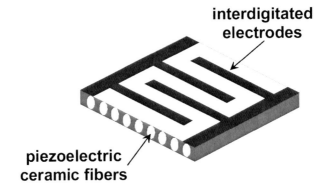

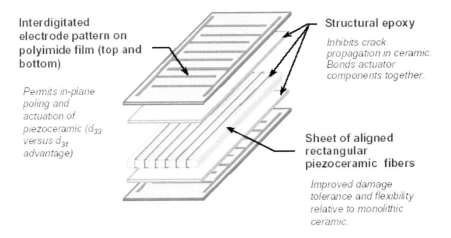

Fig. A.1   Schematic diagram of the MIT active fiber composite system and NASA Langley Research Centre Micro-Fiber Composite[TM] system.

A.1.2   Polymers

Piezoelectric properties can also be developed in light, flexible PVDF polymer films. These materials can develop much greater strains than PZT but require significantly higher electrical fields. These films have a high-voltage output when strained, making them suitable for very sensitive strain gauges.

A.2 Shape Memory Alloys

Nickel-titanium alloy (NiTiNOL) produces actuation forces through a solid-state phase transformation known as the shape memory alloy (SMA) effect.[2,3] SMAs can undergo one of two effects: the one-way effect or the two-way effect. Simply put, the one-way effect means that if plastically deformed in its martensitic form at low temperature, the material will return to its original shape when heated (for example, by an electric current) to form the high-temperature austenitic phase. That is, the SMA starts off in an austenitic phase in which the material possesses high molecular symmetry. Depending on the temperature, the SMA will undergo a martensitic transformation. The SMA starts off in an austenitic state above a temperature A_f (austenitic finish temperature). Once the austenite is cooled down to below the martensitic start temperature, M_s, the material starts to transform into a variation of martensite known as the R-phase. This transformation finishes once the temperature falls below the martensitic finish temperature, M_f. The material still has the same shape but is in a low symmetry phase and is much softer than austenite. It can be easily deformed at this stage via a twinning process. The martensite is able to accommodate the shape change in such a way that it is reversible. When the deformed martensite is heated, the material starts to transform to an austenitic static at the austenitic start temperature, A_s, and once the temperature reaches the austenitic temperature A_f, it returns to the austenite phase and its original shape because that is the only reverted structure possible. The one-way memory effect can be seen in Figure A.2.

The two-way effect uses the fact that the SMA can be trained to exhibit two-way shape memory effect. Strains of up to around 6–8% can be completely recovered or quite large tensile forces developed if an SMA wire is constrained by embedding in or bonding to a structure. The transformation temperature is in the range of 200–110°C, depending on the alloy composition. Because these materials are exited thermally their response depends on the rate of cooling. For thick actuators, high authority is possible, however, at a cost of slow response. Higher responses, but correspondingly at low authority, are possible by using thin film SMA systems.

When SMA fibers are embedded, the effects of the constraining matrix on the transformational temperatures and heats of the embedded SMA wires and the

One- way memory

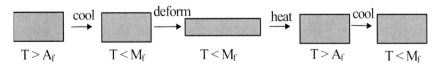

Fig. A.2   **Diagram showing the one-way shape memory effect.**[3]

generation of recovery stresses within the composites on heating have been shown to be related to the reversible martensitic transformation of the SMA wires.[4] Studies have shown that there is little change to the transformation temperatures of the constrained SMA wires with increasing pre-strain, but the measurable transformation heats decrease significantly with increasing pre-strain.

A.3 Optical Fiber Sensors

In an optical fiber, the light travels down a central core that is surrounded by a cladding and a buffer layer. The core and cladding are made from silica, however the core is "doped" to increase its reflective index to create the waveguide for the light. There are two major classifications of optical fibers: viz. Single- and multi-mode fibers. Single-mode fibers typically have a core diameter of 10 μm, whereas the multi-mode fibers have core diameters between 50 and 100 μm. External diameters of the fiber range from 80 to 250 μm, depending on whether the fiber is single- or multi-mode and depending on the type and thickness of the buffer layer.

The fibers are capable of withstanding strains up to 5%. However, any microcracks in the cladding greatly degrade the fiber strain to failure. Moisture also significantly degrades the mechanical performance of the fiber. The polymer or metallic buffer layer provides the fibers with mechanical strength and durability (allows handling without damaging the fiber), and protects the fiber from environmental damage. The suitability of the optical fiber for embedding applications in composites will depend on the buffer materials. Common telecommunications fibers consist of a 62.5- μm-thick ultraviolet (UV) cured acrylate layer. These coatings typically have an operational temperature range of -40°C to $+85^\circ$C. A range of commercially available buffer coatings with their operating temperature ranges[1] is tabulated in Table A.1. Therefore for embedding applications in the most common high performance carbon/epoxy composite materials (with curing temperatures ranging from $120-180^\circ$C), fiber with polyimide buffer coatings are required.

Optical fibers can be used as sensors to detect a wide range of physical parameters (e.g., pressure, strain, temperature, chemical species, vibration) or

Table A.1   Temperature Ranges for Typical Optical Fiber Buffer Coatings[1]

Buffer Coating Type	Minimum Temperature ($^\circ$C)	Maximum Temperature ($^\circ$C)
Acrylate	-40	85
Tefzel	-40	150
Polyimide	-190	300 (375 short term)
Aluminum	-269	400
Gold	-269	750

damage (e.g., inside composite structures or on the surface of metallic or composite structures). They have many advantages over conventional sensors including being light, small (intrusive when embedded in composites), low cost, very sensitive, and conformable. They have good spatial resolution, provide distributed or point sensing, have good fatigue/durability, are immune to electromagnetic interference, are safe in inflammable or explosive environments, operate over a wide temperature range, are capable of transmission over long distances, and are non-electrical and multifunctional. Sensing techniques may depend on modulation of the light in the fiber in amplitude, wavelength or frequency, phase, wavelength, polarization, optical backscatter, or modal distribution of the transmitted signal.[5-8]

The most common sensing technique used by many researchers incorporates the use of fiber Bragg grating sensors. A fiber Bragg grating sensor consists of a periodic modulation of the core refractive index of an optical fiber. Such a sensor is fabricated by forming defect sites in the glass matrix through exposure to intense UV light.[8] The effect of this periodic refractive index variation on propagating light is to reflect a narrow band of wavelengths back down the fiber, as is illustrated in Figure A.3. The peak wavelength of this reflected light is the Bragg wavelength of the grating (λ_B) and is given by equation (A.1):

$$\lambda_B = 2n\Lambda \tag{A.1}$$

where n is the effective core refractive index of the fiber and Λ is the period of the grating.

Temperature and strain both influence the Bragg wavelength because as they affect the physical properties of the fiber, resulting in changes to the refractive index and the period of the grating. The wavelength shift $\Delta\lambda_{BS}$, for an applied longitudinal strain $\Delta\varepsilon$ is given by:

$$\Delta\lambda_{BS} = \lambda_B(1 - p_\alpha)\,\Delta\varepsilon \tag{A.2}$$

where p_α is the photo elastic coefficient of the fiber and is given by:

$$p_\alpha = n^2/2\,[p_{12} - v\,(p_{11} - p_{12})] \tag{A.3}$$

where p_{11} and p_{12} are the components of the fiber optic strain tensor and v is Poisson ratio. Similarly, for a temperature change of ΔT, the corresponding wavelength shift is given by:

$$\Delta\lambda_{BT} = \lambda_B\,(1 + \xi)\,\Delta T \tag{A.4}$$

where ξ is the fiber thermo-optic coefficient. For silica fiber, the wavelength sensitivities of a fiber Bragg grating with λ_B of 1.55 μm have been measured as 1.15 μm/με and 13 μm/°C.[9] The various interrogation schemes are presented in Ref.A10

The reflected narrow spike central wavelength, λ_B, is linearly dependent on the grating period. Consequently, any external influences that act to alter the

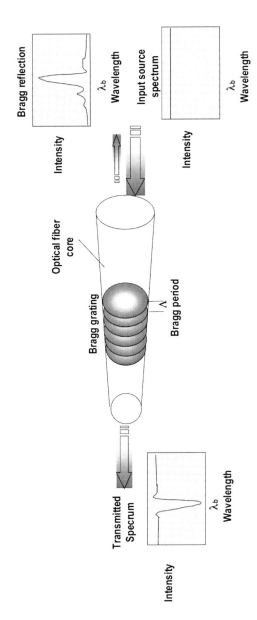

Fig. A.3   Schematic diagram of a fiber Bragg grating sensor.

grating characteristics, for example, strain and/or temperature, results in a shift in the reflected Bragg wavelength. The outer fiber diameter can vary between 80 and 250 µm, with gauge lengths from 1 mm to approximately 100 mm. The disadvantages with this approach at present are that costly and bulky instrumentation is needed to extract the information such as strain or temperature. However, the main advantage of these sensors is the potential of significant multiplexing, using wavelength division multiplexing (WDM), with the potential of hundreds of discrete sensing elements on the one optical fiber.

A.4 Electrorheological Fluids

In this system, microscopic hydrophilic non-conducting particles such as silica are suspended in a non-conducting hydrophobic carrier fluid. When a high voltage is applied to this suspension, the particles form a tight columnar arrangement. The viscosity of the fluid then increases dramatically to form a pseudo solid able to transmit forces.

Tubes or layers carrying these fluids could be used in smart structures, for example, to develop high damping properties.

A.5 Magnetostrictive Materials

Magnetostrictive materials develop large mechanical deformations when subjected to an external magnetic field. This phenomenon (as with normal magnetism) is attributed to the rotations of small magnetic domains that are randomly orientated when the material is not exposed to a magnetic field. The orientation of these small domains by the imposition of a magnetic field results in the development of a strain field. Terbium-iron alloys are typical magneto-strictive materials.

Magnetostrictive materials typically can develop strains an order of magnitude greater than the current generation of piezoelectric ceramic materials. Generally, magnetostrictive materials generate a greater force response than piezoelectric materials (when subjected to compressive loads) but have significantly greater power requirements.

A.6 Micro-Electro-Mechanical Systems

Micro-electro-mechanical systems (MEMS) are the integration of mechanical devices, such as sensors and actuators, and electronics on a common silicon substrate through microfabrication technology. MEMS fabrication technology is based on techniques developed by and used in the electronics industry. Whereas the electronics are fabricated using integrated circuit (IC) process sequences [e.g., complementary metal-oxide semiconductor (CMOS), Bipolar, or BICMOS processes], the micromechanical components are fabricated using compatible "micromachining" processes that selectively etch away parts of the silicon wafer or add new structural layers to form the mechanical and electromechanical devices, and can range in size from micrometers to millimetres.[11] The most common MEMS process is based on the use of masks (resists) and chemical etching techniques to produce three-dimensional and free-standing structures with integrated electronics. Because the fabrication process is currently limited to a few materials, with silicon predominating, the challenge is to design MEMS in more durable materials that can be fabricated as part of (or be compatible with) standard fabricating techniques for integrated circuits. Even though a significant number of MEMS fabrication processes have evolved from the lithography-based batch-fabricated world of microelectronics, some MEMS processes have evolved from other engineering activities and include microgrinding, electro-discharge machining (EDM), hot embossing, laser machining, and sol-gel techniques. These nonlithographic processes are extended to high-volume applications through their use is in creating master molds, for parts replication.

A.7 Comparison of Actuators

The preceding sections describe actuator systems that have been incorporated into composite structures for smart structure applications. A comparison of some

Table A.2 A Comparison of Smart Actuator Properties

Materials Properties	PZT G1195 Piezoelectric Ceramic	PVDF Piezoelectric Polymer	PMN-BA Electrostrictive	Terfenol Magnetostrictive	Nitinol SMA
Strain to failure (%)	0.13	300–400	0.13	>0.2	8.0
Elastic modulus (GPa)	63	2	121	48	83[a] 28–41[m]
Max. operating temperature (°C)	360	80–120	>500	380	−200–110°C
Linearity	good	Good	fair	fair	Poor
Hysteresis (%)	10	>10	1	2	5
Temperature sensitivity (%/°C)	0.05	0.8	0.9	high	
Bandwidth	high	high	high	moderate	Low

Sources: http://www.sma-inc.com/NiTiProperties.html; http://www.texloc.com/closet/cl_pvdf_properties.htm and Ref. 4.
a — austenitic phase   m — martensite phase   c — transformation temperatures

Table A.3   Comparison of the Capabilities of Various Smart Actuator Materials

	Stress (Mpa)	Strain	Efficiency (%)	Bandwith (Hz)	Work (J/cm^2)	Power (W^{-3})
Shape memory alloy	200	0.1	3	3	10	30
Electrostrictive	50	0.002	50	5000	0.05	250
Piezoelectric ceramic	35	0.002	50	5000	0.035	175
Magnetostrictive	35	0.002	80	2000	0.035	70
Single crystal (PZN:PT)	300	0.017	90	5800	2.55	15000

Source: Hollerback et al. "A Comparative Analysis of Actuator Technologies for Robotics."

mechanical and physical properties of various actuator materials is illustrated in Tables A.2 and A.3 The application of these actuators to dynamic applications for composite structures will depend on their relative weight, bandwidth, hysteresis, and environmental stability. The actuator performance is also an issue and is given by actuator authority, which is characterized by the maximum amount of work (stress strain product). Another significant parameter that needs to be considered is the robustness or damage tolerance of the actuator system.

References

[1]Tresler, J. F., "Piezoelectric Composite Sensors," *Comprehensive Composite Materials*, edited by A. Kelly and C. Zweben, Elsevier, 2000, Sec. 5.24.

[2]Roytburd, J., Slutsker, J., and Wuttig, M., "Smart Composites with Shape Memory Alloys," *Comprehensive Composite Materials*, edited by A. Kelly and C. Zweben, Elsevier, 2000, Sec. 5.23.

[3]Wayman, C. M., and Duerig, T. W., "Engineering Aspects of Shape Memory Alloys," *An Introduction to Martensite and Shape Memory*, Butterworth-Heinemann, Boston, 1990.

[4]Kelly Tsoi, A., Stalmans, R., and Schrooten, J., "Transformation Behaviour of Constrained Shape Memory Alloys," *Acta Materialia*, Vol. 50, Sept. 2002, pp. 3535–3544.

[5]Michie, C., "Optical Fibre Sensors for Advanced Composite Materials," *Comprehensive Composite Materials*, edited by A. Kelly and C. Zweben, Elsevier, 2000, Sec. 5.21.

[6]Rogers, A., "Distributed Optical-fibre Sensing," *Meas. Sci. Techno*, Vol. 10, 1999, pp. R75–R99.

[7]Mrad, N., "Optical Fiber Sensor Technology: Introduction and Evaluation and Application," *The Encyclopedia of Smart Materials*, Vol. 2, John Wiley and Sons, 2002, pp. 715–737.

[8]Hill, K. O., Fujii, F., Johnson, D. C., and Kawasaki, B., "Photosensitivity on Optical Fibre Waveguides: Applicatgion to Reflection Filter Fabrication" *Applied Physics Letters*, Vol. 32, 1978, pp. 647–649.

[9]Rao, Y. J., Ribeiro, A. B. L., Jackson, D. A., Zhang L., and Bennion, I., "Combined Spatial- and Time-division-multiplexing for Fibre Grating Sensors with Drift-compensated Phase-sensitive Detection," *Optics Letters*, 1995, pp. 2149–2151.

[10]Roa, Y. J., "In-fibre Bragg Grating Sensors," *Meas. Sci. Technol*, Vol. 8, 1997, pp. 355–375.

[11]Trimmer, W., *Micromechanics and MEMS*, IEEE Number PC4390, IEEE Press, New York, 1997.

Index

Supporting Materials

A complete listing of titles in the AIAA Education Series and other AIAA publications is available at http://www.aiaa.org.